A Textbook of General Botany

THE MACMILLAN COMPANY
NEW YORK · BOSTON · CHICAGO · DALLAS
ATLANTA · SAN FRANCISCO

MACMILLAN AND CO., LIMITED
LONDON · BOMBAY · CALCUTTA
MADRAS · MELBOURNE

THE MACMILLAN COMPANY
OF CANADA, LIMITED
TORONTO

Lichens of various types growing on rocks in Yellowstone Park. A lichen (see Chapter XXII) is formed by two very different plants, a fungus and an alga, living together in partnership.

A Textbook of General Botany

4th Edition

BY

Gilbert M. Smith

STANFORD UNIVERSITY

Edward M. Gilbert, Richard I. Evans

Benjamin M. Duggar, George S. Bryan

and Charles E. Allen

UNIVERSITY OF WISCONSIN

NEW YORK · The Macmillan Company · 1949

PRINTED IN THE UNITED STATES OF AMERICA

Published September, 1942

Reprinted November, 1944

Reprinted June, 1945

Reprinted March, 1946

Reprinted September, 1947

Reprinted June, 1948

Reprinted March, 1949

PREFACE TO THE FOURTH EDITION

In the preparation of the present edition, as the title-page indicates, changes have occurred for the first time in the list of authors. The lamented death of Professor Overton, who contributed greatly to the original writing and to the later revisions, necessitated one change; and Professor Denniston has found it necessary to withdraw from the task of authorship.

As was true in connection with previous editions, we have been greatly aided by suggestions and criticisms that have come from teachers of botany the country over. Many divergencies among the suggestions so offered were to be expected. It is a matter of course that what we have done will be subject to criticism, some to be expected because of inevitable differences in judgment as to organization and method, much of it doubtless deserved from any point of view.

While the general plan of the book has not been altered, several changes have been made in the arrangement of material, particularly of that covered by Chapters III to IX inclusive (corresponding to Chapters III to XI of the third edition). The chapter on Myxomycetes, omitted from the third edition, has been restored in response to numerous requests. New chapters have been added treating of plant diseases and fossil plants. The chapter of earlier editions dealing with the economic significance of plants is omitted, but its substance has been incorporated in other places. It is perhaps needless to add that an attempt has been made to bring the work down to date by changes and additions, in so far as new results can be incorporated in an elementary text.

A debt of gratitude is owing to all the members, past and present, of the Department of Botany of the University of Wisconsin who have helped in many ways in the preparation of the book; likewise to those of the Department of Plant Pathology for advice in the treatment of pathogenic fungi and plant diseases; to members of the Department of Agricultural Bacteriology, particularly Dean E. B. Fred, in connection with the discussion of bacteria; and to Dr. Eloise Gerry and Arthur Koehler, through whom we received the photographs credited to the U. S. Forest Products Laboratory.

Many of the drawings and photographs were made by the authors. Some photographs not specifically credited were taken by Dr. G. O. Cooper and Dr. D. F. McAlister. Certain of the drawings made for previous editions and retained in this were by Zona Briggs, Jane N. Gilbert, and the late W. S. Atkinson. Other drawings newly prepared for this edition are by Mrs. Carl F. Janish, Wilson N. Stewart, and Elliott R. Starks. Acknowledgments are due to many who have supplied photographs, and to the authors, editors, and publishers who have generously given permission to copy illustrations; we have attempted to give full credit in connection with individual figures. Especially should be mentioned Professor T. L. Lancaster of University College, Auckland, who sent photographs of tree ferns, and the McGraw-Hill Book Company who permitted the use of a number of drawings from Smith's *Cryptogamic Botany*.

The Authors

August, 1942

FROM THE PREFACE TO THE FIRST EDITION

This book is an outgrowth of the experience of the authors in the teaching of elementary botany at the University of Wisconsin. For the past three years the text, in successively revised form, has been used in our first-year courses.

In its preparation, we have been guided by the view that the subject of botany should be presented as a unit. The beginning student is not interested in, and should not be burdened with, distinctions between the artificially abstracted phases of the subject—morphology, physiology, ecology, and the like—distinctions which have their place in defining and limiting the scope of more advanced and special courses. Especially should the study of structure and that of function be intimately correlated in an elementary course.

It is hardly necessary, in the present state of development of the teaching of science, to point out that forms selected for study should, whenever possible, be such as are already known to the student, either because of their widespread occurrence in nature or in cultivation, or because of their economic importance; or that general conceptions should be illustrated by familiar facts. Particularly—in botany—should the beginning of the study be an observation of everyday plants. Considerations such as these have guided us in the choice of material to be used in an elementary course.

In a subject the teaching of which involves the introduction of the student to many new concepts, the use of a new terminology is unavoidable. However, the authors realize that each new term imposes an additional burden upon the student and correspondingly handicaps him in the mastery of the subject matter. We have attempted, therefore, to avoid technical terms except those which were found indispensable to a clear presentation.

Only such facts and conceptions have been introduced as our experience has shown can be successfully treated in the course of the beginning year. Necessarily the subject matter has been arranged in what seems to the authors a logical order, on the assumption of a continuous year's course. However, in many institutions, conditions necessitate the offering of a briefer elementary course in botany. We have tried to provide for the possibility of such a course by so treating various topics that, within reasonable limits, certain chapters and portions of chapters may be omitted without destroying the continuity of the course or impairing the utility of the later parts of the book.

The Authors

CONTENTS

A Textbook of General Botany

CHAPTER I

A FAMILIAR PLANT

The Plant and Its Parts. The plant kingdom includes more than 335,000 known kinds of living plants, ranging from relatively minute, simple forms which can best be observed and studied under a microscope to the highly developed, complex seed plants which constitute the conspicuous and dominant vegetation of the earth's surface.

In beginning the study of plants, it seems desirable first to consider one which is familiar and at the same time readily handled and easily observed. Such a plant is the sunflower. It may be noticed that this plant is composed of distinct parts, or *organs.* The organs that are present at almost any stage in the development of the plant are *leaves*, *stem*, and *roots.* Other organs may or may not be present; for example, *branches* are abundant in some varieties of sunflower but absent in other varieties. Still other organs, *flowers* and *fruits*, are present only when a plant approaches maturity.

The Development of a Plant. A sunflower plant originates from a seed (Fig. 1, *A*). What is generally thought of as a sunflower seed is in reality a fruit which contains a single seed. If this fruit is cut open lengthwise (Fig. 1, *B*), there may be found within it a new plant in an embryonic or undeveloped state—the *embryo.* The embryo is enclosed in a membranous *seed coat*, outside which is a thin, hard *fruit coat.*

Under favorable conditions of temperature and moisture the seed may *germinate.* The process of germination involves the growth and development of the various parts of the embryo (Fig. 1, *C–H*). However, the embryo is incapable of making its own food; hence its development depends upon the utilization of food stored within it or about it by the parent plant.

The greater part of the embryo of the sunflower consists of two "seed leaves," or *cotyledons*, in which most of the reserve food is stored. That much of this stored food is oil may be demonstrated by rubbing the cotyledons on a piece of paper and observing the resulting oil spot.

The two cotyledons are attached to a short axis. The sharply pointed part of the axis below the cotyledons is the *hypocotyl,* the end

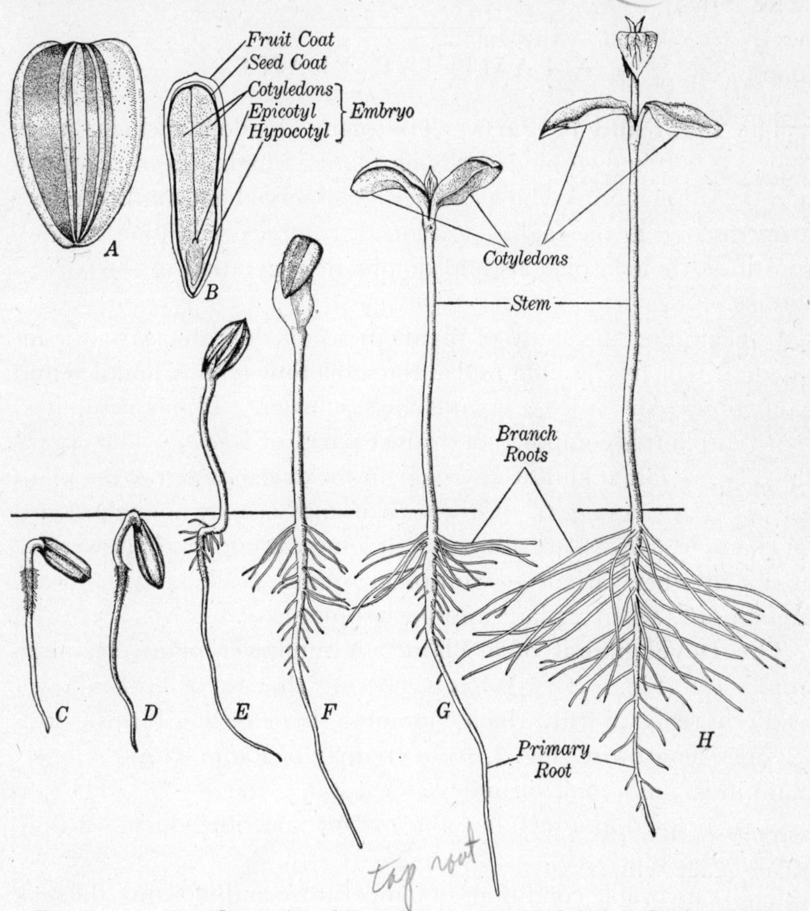

FIG. 1. *A*, a sunflower "seed," really a one-seeded fruit. *B*, the same cut in half lengthwise. *C–H*, stages in the development of a sunflower plant from a germinated "seed." The horizontal line indicates the ground level.

of which, as the seed germinates, grows into a *primary root.* From the primary root numerous branch roots may arise. The upper part of the axis, enclosed between the cotyledons, is the *epicotyl.* The epicotyl gives rise to the stem, from which the later green leaves develop. In the course of time, in the axils (angles between stem and leaves) branches may arise, which in turn bear more leaves. Finally, at the end of the main stem or of its branches flowers, and eventually fruits and new seeds, may be formed.

Organs of a Mature Plant: The Stem. The stem of a well-developed sunflower plant (Fig. 2) is composed of *nodes*, or joints, at which the leaves are borne; and *internodes*, the portions of the stem between successive nodes. The stem grows in length by the elongation of the internodes. At the top of the stem the nodes are crowded because the internodes have not as yet elongated. It thus becomes evident how it comes about that the leaves are close together at the apex of the stem but farther apart lower down.

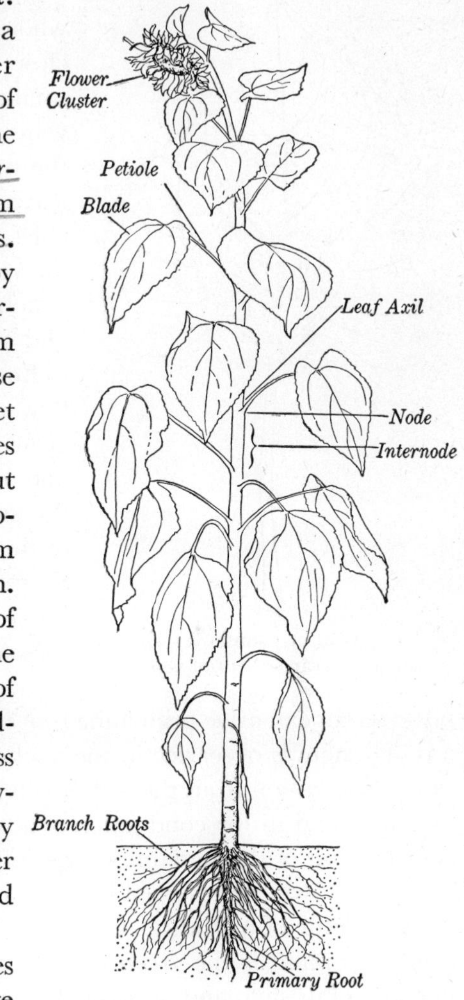

FIG. 2. A sunflower plant. Semi-diagrammatic.

Another characteristic of the sunflower plant is the capacity of the older parts of the stem or branches gradually to increase in thickness as long as the plant is growing. This type of growth by which an increase in diameter takes place will be described in Chapter IV.

The stem and its branches (if branches are present) serve for the production and support of leaves and flowers in positions favorable to the performance of their work and for the conduction of materials from roots to leaves and from leaves to roots.

Leaves. A mature sunflower leaf (Fig. 3) consists of two parts: a slender stalk, or *petiole*, and a broad *blade*. A blade held up to the light is seen to be marked by many light green lines, which are called *veins*. There is one large central vein (*midrib*), from both sides of which extend smaller branch veins; these latter in turn are joined together here and there, so that the whole blade is penetrated by a close network of veins, large and small. The positions of the larger veins are marked by ridges on the under side of the blade. The leaves, in most seed plants, are the chief food-manufacturing organs; the veins are the pathways through which substances are moved into and out of the blade.

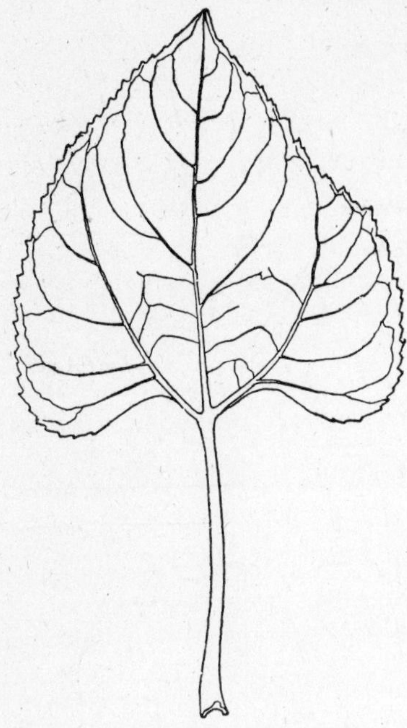

Fig. 3. Leaf of a sunflower, showing the arrangement of veins.

Roots (Fig. 2). In an older sunflower plant the primary root has grown to a considerable length and, especially in the region nearer the stem, has, like the older part of the stem, increased in diameter. From the primary root lateral branch roots have arisen, and these in turn may have branched. Hence, a mature sunflower plant possesses an extensive branching root system beneath the soil. Such a root system is of service in the anchorage of the plant in the soil, in the absorption from the soil of water and of substances dissolved in water, and in the conduction of absorbed substances to the stem. A discussion of the remaining organs of the mature plant—flowers and fruits—will be reserved for later chapters.

The Color of a Plant. One of the most notable features of the sunflower plant is the green color of its leaves and of the younger portions of its stem and branches. This color is due to the presence of certain green pigments (associated with some yellow pigments), spoken of together as *chlorophyll*. These green pigments absorb the energy which is received in the form of light waves from the sun. Some of this energy is used in manufacturing organic compounds (simple foods) out of carbon dioxide obtained from the air and water obtained from the soil. The energy thus stored in the manufactured food is utilized later not only in maintaining the existence of the green plant; it is basic also to the existence of non-green plants and of all animals. It is in the capture and storage of energy from the sun that green plants are unique among living things. Hence, all living organisms, except for a few microscopic forms (see Chapter XVI), are utterly dependent for their existence upon chlorophyll.

In addition to chlorophyll other pigments may occur in plants, such as the pigments which cause the diverse colors, yellow, orange, red, and blue, of certain leaves, flowers, and fruits. All these pigments, as well as chlorophyll, will be fully discussed later.

The Activities of a Plant. If a sunflower plant is to remain alive, grow, and reproduce, it must carry on certain *activities.* These various activities are included among the *functions* of the plant or of its organs. The fundamental activities which are essential to most plants may be listed as follows: (*a*) the *absorption* of water and of substances in solution in water whether from the soil or from the air; (*b*) the *manufacture* of foods, in which process chlorophyll plays an important part; (*c*) the *movement* of substances, including water and foods, from place to place within the plant; (*d*) *respiration*—the release of energy through the breaking down of foods, which may involve an exchange of gases with the atmosphere; (*e*) *transpiration*—the loss of water in the form of vapor from the aerial surface of the plant; (*f*) *assimilation*—the use of raw materials and manufactured foods in the building up of living substance; (*g*) *growth* and *development*—the latter including the changes in form that occur during the life of the plant from its beginning to maturity; (*h*) *irritability*—the perception by the plant of a stimulus, such as a change in temperature, and its response to the stimulus.

Relation of Structure to Function. In order to understand a plant, it is necessary to learn as much as possible about its structure; it is equally important to learn about the activities or functions that are carried on within the plant. Every plant is in general so constituted as to be able to perform its functions successfully; the structure of a plant, then, can not be fully appreciated without a familiarity with its functions, nor can its functions be understood without a knowledge of its structure. Function and structure go hand in hand.

What has just been said of a plant as a whole applies equally to its separate organs. The various activities which have been mentioned, although they may go on throughout the whole or many parts of the plant, are in large measure distributed among the various organs. In fact, there is a considerable division of labor among the organs. Each type of organ is so constituted that it carries on one or more particular functions better than can other organs of the plant. It is essential, therefore, to study not only the plant as a whole, but each separate organ, from the standpoints of both structure and function.

CHAPTER II

THE NATURE OF A CELL

Cells. Every plant or animal, including all its organs, is made up of *cells*, which are usually of microscopic size. These are the units of which the bodies of plants and animals are composed. A cell may exist independently, as is shown by the fact that many simple organisms consist each of a single cell. But in general any of the larger plants and animals is composed of thousands of cells.

Although all cells are alike in fundamental characteristics, they may differ greatly in size and form and in the processes that go on within them. The cells of any organ, such as a root, stem, or leaf, are organized into *tissues*. A tissue may be composed of cells all much alike. However, the term *tissue* is also often applied to groups of cells which differ more or less in structure but which coöperate in carrying on a common activity. For instance, a root or a stem contains conducting tissues, each including cells of several different sorts as to size and form. Just as a plant, unless it is of a very simple sort, is composed of organs, so these organs are made up of tissues, and the tissues in turn are composed of cells.

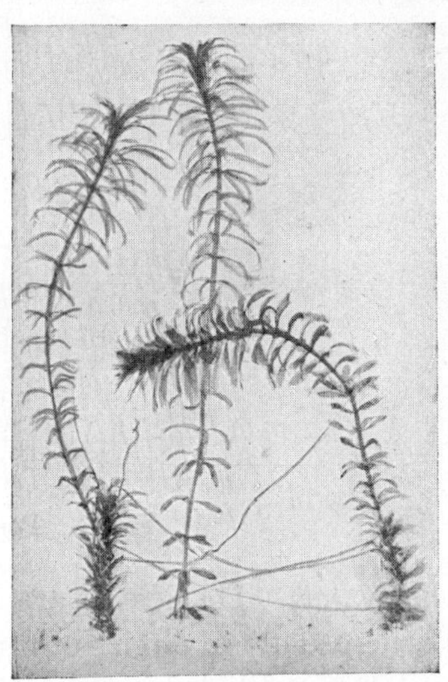

FIG. 4. Elodea plants.

Organization of a Cell. The study of the living cells of one of the more complex plants is made difficult by the fact that its organs are usually of considerable thickness and are composed of many cells. The microscope therefore gives at best only a confused view of an individual cell. For this reason the cells can often be seen more clearly in a leaf, because of its thinness, than in a stem or root; and the thinner the leaf the more distinctly can the structure of an individual cell be made out. A favorable leaf for the study of a mature cell is that of *Elodea* (Fig. 4), an American plant also known as *Anacharis*, and commonly as the "water pest." One species of Elodea grows submerged in streams and ponds throughout the United States. According to the depth and the movement of the water in which the plant is growing, the thin, branching stem varies in length from a few inches to several feet. Slender roots growing from the stem anchor the plant more or less firmly in the soil beneath

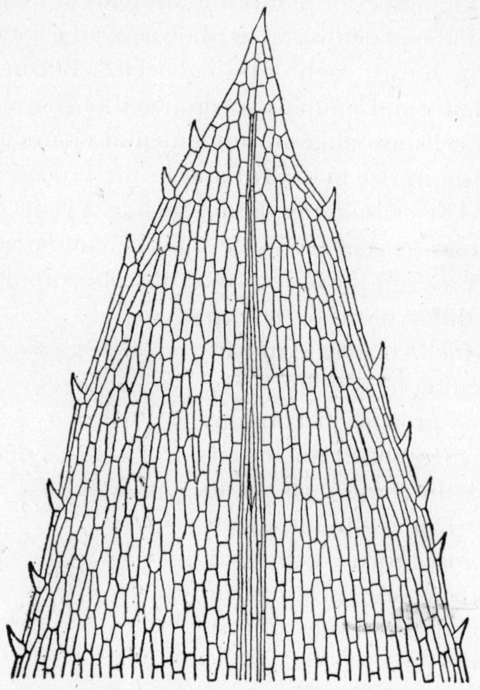

FIG. 5. Portion of an Elodea leaf.

the water. The leaves are small, narrow, and pointed, and are borne usually in circles of three, four, or more.

A leaf of Elodea is one cell in thickness at its margin; elsewhere, except for the midrib, it is two cells in thickness. Viewed from above (Fig. 5), the cells of several rows near the margin appear narrow and rectangular. At intervals, pointed cells project from the edge. Occupying the greater part of the surface of the leaf are a larger number of rows of wider and shorter cells, which are concerned largely in food manufacture. The cells of the lower layer are about half as wide as those of the upper layer. In the central region of the leaf are a few layers of narrow, elongated cells, which constitute the midrib. Although a cell may appear rectangular or square when seen under the microscope (which shows only one plane), it must be remembered that the cell has thickness as well.

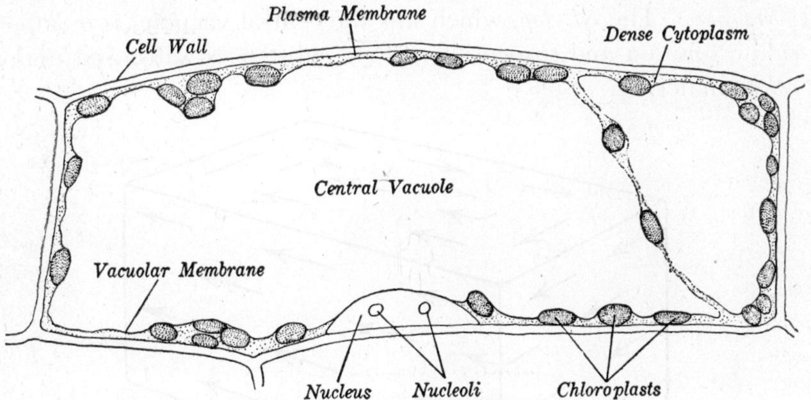

FIG. 6. A living cell of a leaf of Elodea, as seen under the microscope.

Each cell (Fig. 6) is surrounded by a firm, relatively rigid *cell wall*. Where two cells adjoin, they have a single wall in common; this, however, as will appear later, may consist of several layers.

All the material within a cell wall is *protoplasm*. Protoplasm is not homogeneous; it consists of many substances differing in nature, which are definitely arranged within the cell. The whole structure made up by the protoplasm—that is, the body of the cell exclusive of the wall—is the *protoplast*. The protoplasm consists of *cytoplasm* and *nucleus*. Each of these main divisions is in turn composed of various substances. The arrangement of the substances that constitute cytoplasm and nucleus is the *organization* of the cell. Because cells, as well as plants and animals which consist of many cells, have a definite organization, a single cell living alone, or a many-celled plant or animal, is an *organism*.

Structure of Cytoplasm. Just within the wall on all sides of a mature cell, including top and bottom, is a thin layer of the cytoplasm which appears relatively dense and often finely granular; this thin layer will be referred to as the *dense cytoplasm*. The very outermost film of the dense cytoplasm, next the cell wall, is the *plasma membrane*. Included in the dense cytoplasm are many ovoid or somewhat flattened green bodies, the *chloroplasts*. These are the most conspicuous structures in most of the cells of an Elodea leaf. In the central part of the cell and enclosed by the layer of dense cytoplasm is a large, transparent *central vacuole*. The film of dense cytoplasm immediately adjoining the central vacuole is the *vacuolar membrane*. The *cell sap*, which fills the central vacuole, is a rather dilute solution and suspension of food substances, salts, and many other materials.

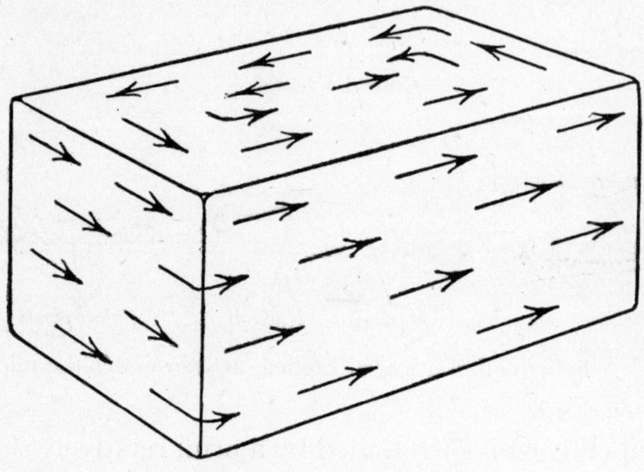

FIG. 7. Diagram showing the direction of rotation of the layer of dense cytoplasm in a cell of an Elodea leaf.

Under certain conditions the layer of dense cytoplasm with the chloroplasts (but not including the plasma membrane) is in motion. The movement is mainly one of rotation (Fig. 7), usually about the vertical axis of the cell. Commonly the movement is in the same direction in all the cells of a leaf; but frequent exceptions to this rule occur. Occasionally a cross strand cuts from one side to another through the central vacuole. The dense cytoplasm is the active substance in this movement; the chloroplasts are carried along by the current, much as pieces of ice may be carried in a river.

The similarity in color and in transparency between most parts of the cytoplasm makes it impossible to distinguish accurately the boundaries of these parts in a living cell. On account of this difficulty it is necessary, in order to study the finer details of structure, to subject a leaf or a portion of a leaf to a rather lengthy treatment. The most important steps in this treatment are: (*a*) immersing the leaf in a poison or combination of poisons which will kill the cells at once but will leave all parts of each cell in as nearly as possible their original positions; (*b*) cutting the leaf into thin sections; and (*c*) staining the sections. The stains used in the last-named process are chiefly aniline dyes which are absorbed differently by different parts of the protoplast. If, therefore, a cell is subjected to the successive action of two or three dyes, its various parts may take on contrasting colors and so stand out distinctly one from another.

The appearance of a cell in a section of an Elodea leaf thus treated (Fig. 8) is very different from that of one in a living leaf. The dense

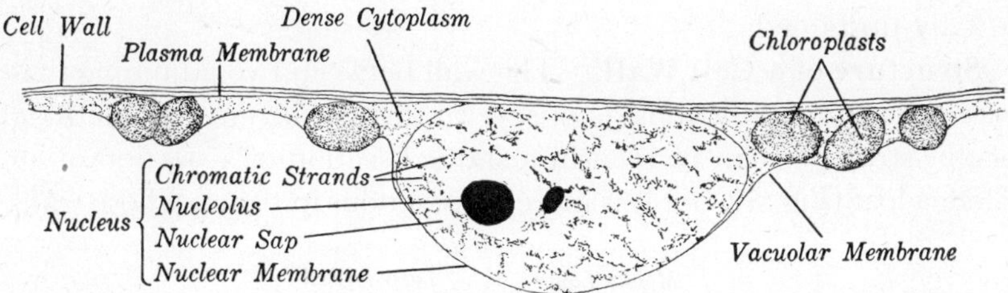

FIG. 8. Portion of a cell in a leaf of Elodea, after it has been killed and stained. Highly magnified.

cytoplasm is seen to be not as nearly homogeneous as it appears in a living cell. Included in it are many clear vacuoles, varying in size and shape but all very small; between these is a somewhat more deeply stained, often finely granular substance. In addition to vacuoles, chloroplasts, and minute granules, the dense cytoplasm includes bodies of varied form, smaller than the chloroplasts, which may be deeply stained. These small cytoplasmic bodies (*chondriosomes*) are more readily observable in a young (Fig. 17) than in a mature cell.

Structure of a Nucleus. The nucleus in a cell of an Elodea leaf is a semitransparent body. In many of the cells it is approximately hemispherical. The nucleus is imbedded, like the chloroplasts, in the layer of dense cytoplasm and therefore close to the cell wall. In a living cell (Fig. 6) the nucleus appears homogeneous except for one or more fairly large, rounded, refractive *nucleoli*. The nucleus may be carried along by the cytoplasmic current, as the chloroplasts are, but more slowly. Consequently, at any given moment it may lie at one side, at the top, or at the bottom of the cell.

In a killed and stained cell (Fig. 8) the nucleus, because of the strong affinity of some of its parts for dyes, is more conspicuous than in a living cell. It is bounded by a *nuclear membrane*, a film similar to the plasma and vacuolar membranes. In addition to the nucleolus or nucleoli, there is within the membrane a set of deeply stained structures appearing like irregular, more or less finely divided strands, which sometimes seem to be interconnected. The substance of these *chromatic strands* is intimately concerned in inheritance. In Chapter X more will be said about the behavior and importance of this hereditary substance. The nucleoius or nucleoli and the chromatic strands lie in a *nuclear sap*, which is usually unstained.

Structure of a Cell Wall. The wall between two adjoining mature cells commonly consists of several distinct layers. Something of this structure can be seen in a stained section of a portion of an Elodea leaf (Fig. 8), but it is more conspicuous in tissues whose walls

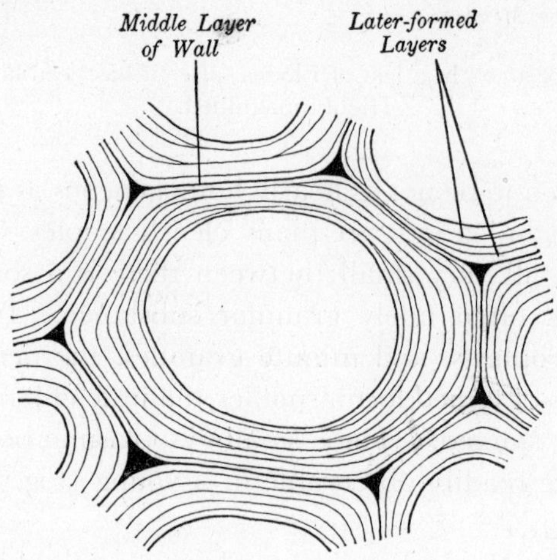

FIG. 9. A cell of the mechanical tissue in the stem of Clintonia. The cell wall consists of many layers deposited one after another. The protoplast has died and disappeared.

have been much more thickened (Fig. 9). The middle layer, which is the oldest, was formed (*secreted*) by the joint action of the two adjoining cells when they were first formed. As these cells matured, each independently secreted new layers, which were deposited successively on the corresponding side of the original layer. Hence the wall, though made up of layers, is essentially a single structure common to the two cells which built it up. If one side of a cell is not in contact with another cell, the wall on that side of course consists only of the layers secreted by the one cell.

The cell walls in many tissues are penetrated by pores, through which the protoplasts of the adjoining cells are in contact. These pores are ordinarily too minute to be seen with the highest powers of the microscope and can be made visible only by a special swelling

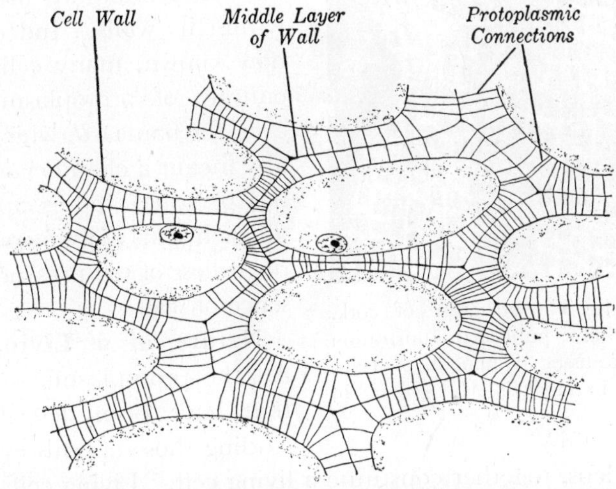

FIG. 10. Cells from the endosperm of a persimmon seed. Except for the middle (oldest) layer, the wall appears homogeneous. The many protoplasmic connections between the cells are conspicuous.

treatment. In some places, however, as in the endosperm (nutritive tissue) of the persimmon seed (Fig. 10), they are large enough to be seen in a stained section.

Cell walls are usually present in plants, usually absent in animals. In plants they constitute an internal framework, or skeleton, holding the individual cells together and giving form and more or less rigidity to the various tissues and organs.

The Discovery of Cells. These units were first recognized by Robert Hooke (1635–1703). He was interested in examining various objects with the aid of the compound microscope, then a new toy, crude as compared with present-day instruments, which had been invented in Holland and recently introduced into England. Among other objects, as reported in his "Micrographia" (1665), Hooke examined a thin slice of cork (Fig. 11) and to his surprise found that it contained many little "pores or cells." Years later it came to be recognized that cork such as Hooke had studied is made up of the walls of dead cells and that the really living part of any cell is the jelly-like or semiliquid protoplasm within its walls. Indeed, as is now known, many cells consist entirely of protoplasm. However, the name *cell*, which originally meant a chamber or cavity, has persisted and is applied to all such units of living organisms regardless of the presence or absence of walls.

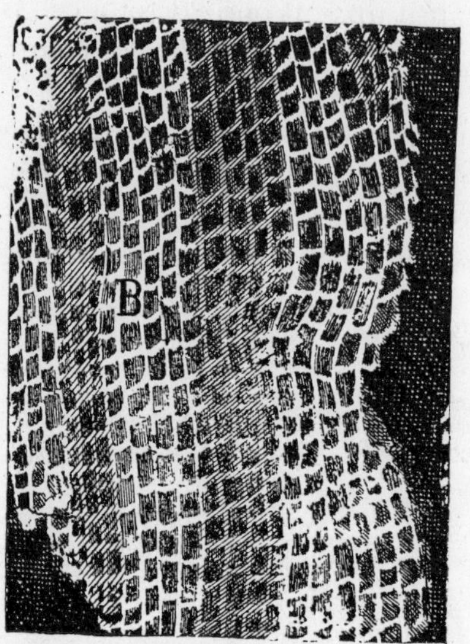

FIG. 11. The structure of cork. This, the first published illustration showing a tissue composed of cells, appeared in Hooke's *Micrographia* in 1665.

Nature of a Living Cell. All the protoplasmic structures that have been described, including those of both cytoplasm and nucleus, together constitute a living cell. Living cells are distinguished from nonliving forms of matter by certain activities or processes that go on within them. It is not possible to define *living matter* so sharply that we can say that certain parts of the protoplast are living and that other parts are nonliving. So far as is known at present, the processes that distinguish living from nonliving matter are carried on within cells which are organized in general much like those of an Elodea leaf. It is possible to say, also, that these processes which characterize living things have their seat primarily in certain portions of each cell—particularly in the dense cytoplasm including the plasma and vacuolar membranes, in the chloroplasts, and in the chromatic strands within the nucleus. To this extent, the parts just mentioned are more living (or more actively living) than such other parts as the cell sap or the nuclear sap.

SUMMARY

A mature cell, such as one in a leaf of Elodea, includes the following parts:

1. Wall (in common with adjacent cells):
    - Middle layer.
    - Later-formed layers.
    - Minute pores.
2. Protoplasm:
    - (*a*) Cytoplasm:
        - Dense cytoplasm:
            - Plasma membrane.
            - Small vacuoles, each with its membrane.
            - Chloroplasts.
            - Chondriosomes.
            - Central vacuolar membrane.
        - Central vacuole, containing cell sap.
    - (*b*) Nucleus:
        - Nuclear membrane.
        - Nucleolus or nucleoli.
        - Chromatic strands.
        - Nuclear sap.

CHAPTER III

SOME PROPERTIES OF CELLS AND TISSUES

Functions of a Protoplast. The activities or functions of a plant as a whole were briefly summarized in Chapter I. In general these activities were mentioned with special reference to the seed plants and their tissues. Essentially all such functions may be and often are embraced in the work of a single cell, and in unicellular organisms they must be so included. The protoplasm of the cell as a whole, the protoplast, actually carries on most of the activities of a complex organism. There is, as will be pointed out later, a certain division of labor among the organs and tissues of higher plants. There are, likewise, for the individual cell special functions which are performed primarily by the nucleus, and others which apparently may be referred to the cytoplasm; but for the most part it is often uncertain which is the master performer and which the helper or accessory in any given process.

General Characteristics of Protoplasm. It has been pointed out (Chapter II) that by the use of appropriate treatments (killing, sectioning, staining, etc.) the various parts of a cell may be differentiated and studied. Progress has been made in applying the knowledge gained regarding the structure and behavior of certain constituents of the nucleus (the chromosomes) to the interpretation of problems of inheritance. On the other hand, the study of the structure of cytoplasm has yielded less of major interest in respect to its organization. Clearly, protoplasm loses certain of its special properties when killed by any means. However, if it is coagulated or properly "fixed" in position, a framework, chiefly of special proteins, results, which may well supply valuable evidence as to certain types of activity.

Structure and Organization. It is perhaps the common verdict of investigators that, although microscopic study of the living protoplast is important, it can not be expected to disclose a finer basic structure than that described by such adjectives as granular, semifluid, foamy—terms which might apply almost as well to non-living substances. It does not appear possible to render visible an organization of protoplasm such as would be helpful in explaining some of its activities. Yet it is with good reason inferred that complexity of organization is a necessary attribute of living substance.

Much light has been shed on the characteristics of protoplasm through the development of methods of microdissection, involving the manipulation of the living protoplast and its parts with minute needles. The ultraviolet microscope and other physical apparatus have contributed something. Many studies have been of a chemical nature. These commonly involve killing the protoplasm by chemical agents and procedures, followed by treatments that eventually permit a determination of many of the simpler constituents of protoplasm—that is, of the organic substances into which it may be broken down.

Matter and Energy. The fact that protoplasm breaks down into relatively simple substances belonging to classes which are well known leads to the conception that the processes characterizing living protoplasm involve the same materials and the same types of energy that are familiar in the nonliving world. Living matter is studied, however, not only with the aid of the procedures and equipment used in the study of nonliving matter but also through the behavior and responses of the organism itself. In any case, a living process is concerned with matter and energy, and these two are the most fundamental scientific concepts. Briefly stated, matter is that which has mass, and energy is the capacity to do work.

Matter may be defined also as material having structure. It occupies space, and its constituent parts are molecules. A molecule is defined as the smallest particle into which any substance, such as water, may be divided without changing its properties. Thus, there are molecules of sugar, of starch, and of thousands of other substances occurring in plants, as well as molecules of inorganic substances. A molecule is in turn made up of atoms. Two atoms of oxygen (symbolized by O) make up a molecule of oxygen (O_2). In a molecule of water there are two atoms of hydrogen (H_2) and one of oxygen (O), so that a molecule of water is a compound (H_2O) and in this respect analogous to such molecules as those of starch or sugar. All compounds are made up of more than one kind of atom.

Energy is any active (kinetic) or latent (potential) force which may bring about changes in or through matter. The kinetic form of energy is in some respects far more familiar than the latent; it expresses itself as heat, as chemical reactions, as electrical phenomena, or as movement. Potential energy may be the energy of position, as in the case of a stone on a hillside, doing work only when dislodged. Or it may be "stored" energy, such as that of any food or fuel or, to take an extreme case, that of an explosive agent whose reaction may be touched off by a spark or a shock.

Matter and Energy in Living Systems. Living matter in its ultimate composition has been found to involve no material unknown elsewhere, nor do its known manifestations of energy take any other form than those just referred to. Living matter is peculiar in the complexity of the materials of which it is made up and in the apparent interrelations of its internal mechanisms. The quality of living implies extreme complexity of organization and, at the same time, extreme variability or pliability in the sense that small changes in its reactions are constantly taking place without throwing the cell out of equilibrium. It is important to appreciate that protoplasm is, of all substances, the most unstable in detail and that it varies from moment to moment in material and energy exchanges, so that the rate and direction of its processes may be expected to vary as its work proceeds. A protoplast may be roughly likened to a great metropolitan population in which groups of individuals are engaged in the most varied enterprises; they come and go, suffer accidents and death, yet the activities and the growth of the whole are measurable from day to day.

Water Content of Protoplasm. The chief constituent of an active protoplast is water. Thin-walled growing cells in the softer tissues of plants may contain 90 per cent water, the cells of certain fruits even as much as 95 per cent. The jelly-fish, a classical biological example of high water content, is credited with 96–97 per cent. Protoplasm in the active state in the average cell, including the cell wall, is more commonly reckoned at 75–90 per cent water, or even less in tissues in which the cell walls are much thickened; in dormant or resting structures a very low level of water content may be tolerated. To prevent winter injury, seed corn is usually dried artificially to a water content of less than 10 per cent. The water content constantly changes with the activity of protoplasm and with the differentiation and maturation of cells. A highly aqueous medium is, however, essential for the rapid and varied chemical and physical processes which take place in a protoplast.

Chemical Constituents of Protoplasm. Naked protoplasm (without enclosing cell walls) may be obtained in quantity by growing certain species of slime molds (Chapter XVII) on appropriate food materials. When subjected to complete chemical analysis, protoplasm has been found to contain somewhat more than 30 identifiable chemical elements. It may be noted, however, that it is not possible to separate completely the protoplasm from contained foods, salts, and any other substances present. Most of the elements found are the commoner ones of the atmosphere and of the earth's crust. Oxygen (O) is the most abundant; next come hydrogen (H), carbon (C), and nitrogen (N) in the order given. An important source of oxygen and hydrogen is water; of oxygen alone, the oxygen (O_2) of the air; of carbon, the carbon dioxide (CO_2) of the air; of nitrogen, the immediate source is the soil, but eventually it is derived from the nitrogen (N_2) of the air.

Compounds in the Soil. The four elements just mentioned (C, H, O, and N) are quantitatively the main elements, but they are not the only ones whose atoms enter into the many known organic materials of various classes. Among those elements functional in the cell which may be thought of as characterizing inorganic materials, derived primarily from the soil and eventually from the rocks of the earth's crust, are potassium (K), calcium (Ca), magnesium (Mg), iron (Fe), phosphorus (P), and sulphur (S). All these are known to be essential to the growth of green plants and occur in quantity sufficient to analyze by usual chemical procedures. Other elements are required in exceedingly low (trace) concentrations. These are known biologically as minor elements and include zinc (Zn), manganese (Mn), boron (B), and copper (Cu); others may be necessary, but it is not yet possible to determine this point definitely since the study of minor-element requirements is by no means completed. Only 14 elements have now been enumerated. Others, such as silicon (Si), sodium (Na), chlorine (Cl), and aluminum (Al), are found in the ash of plants or are otherwise identified as occurring in their cells.

The organic substances present in protoplasm fall largely into such well-known classes of food materials as carbohydrates, fats, and proteins; there are numerous others, present in smaller quantity and belonging to so many groups of compounds that it is not practicable to specify them. The proteins and these miscellaneous groups would include also the enzymes, vitamins, growth substances, pigments (if any), and many other important substances that will be referred to later. The proteins present in living protoplasm may not readily be distinguished from those proteins which are included among the food materials of a cell. In general, the proteins occurring in the vegetative parts of plants have not been extensively studied. Storage proteins of seeds, so much used as foods for man and the lower animals, are better known.

Vacuoles. The solution in the vacuoles of a protoplast contains many substances, including, for example, sugars. When a soluble substance such as a sugar is dissolved in water, for instance, it is molecularly dispersed in the water. The water is then designated the *solvent.* The substance dissolved and distributed in the solvent is called the *solute;* in the case of a cell many solutes may be present. The solution in a vacuole may therefore be regarded as a complex *system.* Since the molecules of the dissolved substances are infinitesimal in size, it is often difficult to determine their presence except by chemical test, although some may be detectable as a result of characteristic odors, colors, or other striking properties.

Colloidal Nature of Protoplasm. There are other types of systems (solutions) in which the particles of many substances are distributed or dispersed as aggregates of molecules or as very large molecules. The dispersed particles of such a system can not be seen under a microscope, good evidence that the particles are still very small; yet they do not settle out. A svstem with such characteristics is called a *colloidal system.* There is abundant evidence to indicate that protoplasm is in the colloidal state. Arbitrary distinctions are made between colloidal "solutions" and "suspensions." In the case of a suspension, the particles will ultimately settle out. There is, from the one type to the other, a gradation. The characteristic of the colloidal state which is most important for present consideration is the extent of the surfaces of the particles. The particles which constitute the dispersed material greatly increase the surface exposure and enormously facilitate chemical reactions and energy exchanges. Proteins, starches, and many other food materials, in addition to prot)plasm itself, are commonly colloidal.

Biological colloidal systems ordinarily imbibe water freely and are termed *hydrophilic* (water-loving). Other substances in the colloidal state which do not imbibe water freely are *hydrophobic* (water-fearing). Examples of hydrophilic colloids include proteins, agar, starch, and dextrins. Colloidal systems often form solid, yet more or less elastic systems called *gels*, illustrated by the familiar gelatin. Protoplasm also may exist in the state of a gel. The liquid condition of a colloidal system is called a *sol*; and just as gelatin and agar melt at high temperatures, so protoplasm displays a change of state with changes in external and internal conditions.

Cellular Processes. All the major processes that characterize a living organism might, with almost equal propriety, be emphasized as strictly cell processes. Only two of these will be discussed in the present chapter. Other activities will be treated in chapters dealing with the form and structure of those plant organs or tissues with which the processes in question are more particularly associated. Photosynthesis, for example, is considered in connection with the discussion of leaves. The two phenomena particularly to be considered here are *absorption* and *respiration.* With respect to the former of these, it is to be noted that every cell requires water and substances in solution. These materials must be obtained from the environment, and absorption is the process concerned whether the environment consists of neighboring living cells or of an external source such as the soil solution. With respect to the second process, respiration, it has already been suggested that every cell requires energy with which to do the work essential to the maintenance of all its activities, including the building up of new protoplasm. The energy-releasing process is respiration.

Diffusion. Absorption, as here considered, is the entrance of material into a cell. Not infrequently there is also an outgo of material, which may be termed *elimination.* Exchanges between the plant and its environment are concerned, under natural conditions, with aqueous solutions only. Even gases actually enter the cell in solution in water. The surface membrane of every cell that absorbs is a moist membrane. Gases go into solution at this moist surface and therefore enter the cell in solution.

The basis of the intake and outgo of materials in solution is in part simple *diffusion.* Attention may be directed first to diffusion in air, since gaseous diffusion is notably rapid. A small amount of ether poured into a beaker in a closed room promptly evaporates and becomes distributed throughout the room, a fact easily established by the noticeable odor. In liquid ether there are vast numbers of molecules close together and in vigorous motion. This vigorous motion indicates that ether has a high molecular kinetic energy. At the free surface of the liquid, molecules promptly fly off into the air as gas molecules, and in very short order the liquid ether disappears. For a brief time there is, in the neighborhood of the beaker, a perceptibly higher concentration of ether molecules than elsewhere in the air. But movement of these molecules in all directions, wholly at random, continues; and as the molecules distribute themselves, they continue to be in motion. Hence, they tend to disperse uniformly throughout the available space. The process of distribution from a region of high concentration to one of low concentration represents an escaping tendency. This process of distribution is diffusion. It should be emphasized that the diffusion of ether in air is independent of the diffusion of any other gas present in the air.

Liquids diffuse in the gaseous state through gases, just as do other gases; but gases also diffuse through liquids. The water that is in contact with the absorbing surfaces of plants contains all the gases of the atmosphere (including oxygen, carbon dioxide, and nitrogen). These gases diffuse into the water (the solvent) of the soil solution until the water is saturated, at which time each gas is distributed uniformly and independently throughout the solvent; and the final concentration of each gas present in the water will depend both upon the concentration of the particular gas in the air and upon its solubility in water. Phenomena of this type will have application later, especially in the discussion of respiration and photosynthesis.

Similarly, solids diffuse through liquids in which they are soluble. A solid such as cane sugar diffuses very slowly, which is one reason why tea is stirred in order to facilitate distribution of the sugar. The solutes in natural waters also are stirred by movement, caused not only by the flow of a stream or by wind action but also by currents (of convection) set up, for example, by unequal heating of the surface of the water.

Diffusion through Membranes. It is evident that water or substances in solution can enter the usual plant protoplast only by diffusing through two membranes, the cell wall and the plasma membrane. Any cell wall which is functional in absorption is therefore *permeable* to water. It *imbibes* water—that is, water molecules enter between the colloidal particles comprising the cell wall—and thus the wall may swell, the limit of swelling being saturation. This limit is an expression of balance between the attraction of the membrane for water and the tendency of the membrane to squeeze out the water. The process is *imbibition.* A membrane permitting the diffusion of water is an imbibition membrane; all absorbing surfaces, including the plasma membrane, are of this type. A rubber membrane is not an imbibition membrane with respect to water.

Permeability. Permeability is a property of membranes, and the rate of diffusion of substances through membranes varies greatly. In general, membranes (living or dead) may be substantially impermeable, such as the outer (cutinized) cell walls of some leaves; or freely permeable, permitting rapid diffusion, as in the case of interior walls; or differentially permeable, permitting a solvent and different solutes to permeate them at different rates. The plasma membranes of living cells are differentially permeable. Hereafter, unless otherwise stated, any mention of a "solution" will refer to an aqueous solution, any reference to a "solvent" will refer to water, and "solutes" will refer to substances soluble in water.

Osmosis. Any system so arranged as to comprise a solvent (water) separated from a solution (for example, cane sugar or salt in water) by a membrane which is differentially permeable—which in this case will mean that it is freely permeable to the solvent but relatively impermeable to the solute—presents a qualitative picture of osmosis and osmotic pressure. In such a system the solvent is pure (100 per cent) water. The solution may be, for instance, 80 per cent water and 20 per cent sugar. In the solution, therefore, the water is diluted to about four fifths of its full concentration. Under these circumstances, the escaping tendency of the water is from the region of its higher concentration to the region of its lower concentration. Since the differentially permeable membrane is permeable to water, water diffuses through the membrane into the solution, increasing the volume of the solution if the latter can expand, tending to increase the pressure in the solution if the volume of the solution is limited. The process of diffusion of the solvent (water) through a differentially permeable membrane into a solution is *osmosis.* The pressure which is developed (conveniently reckoned by the concentration of the solute) is the *osmotic pressure.*

If a suitable differentially permeable membrane in the form of a bag, such as an artificial sausage cover, is filled with a 20 per cent sugar solution and immersed in a vessel of water, the net movement of water molecules will be into the bag, increasing the volume of the solution and in time exerting pressure from within on the wall of the bag, which becomes distended and displays considerable rigidity (Fig. 12, right). A similar bag filled with 20 per cent sugar solution and immersed in a vessel also containing 20 per cent sugar

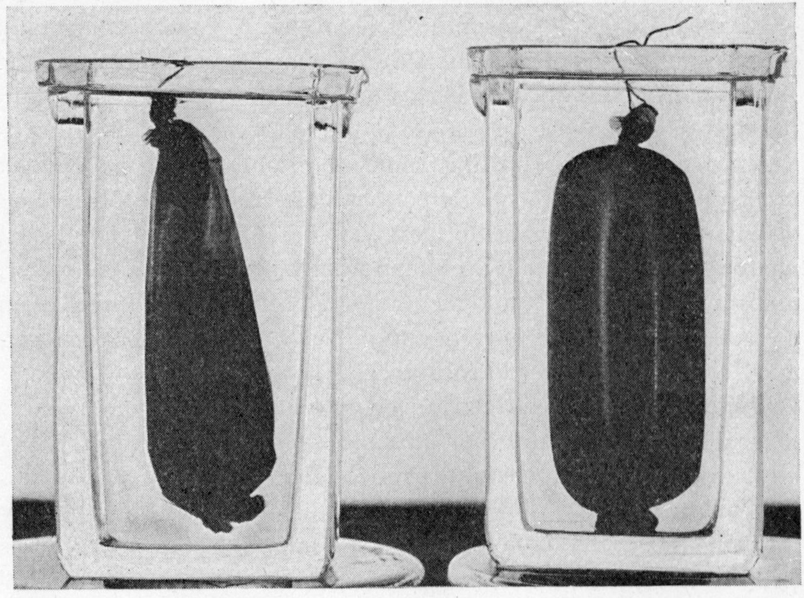

Fig. 12. An experiment illustrating osmosis. The two differentially permeable bags contain similar solutions of sugar. The bag at the left was immersed in a sugar solution of the same concentration as that within the bag. The bag at the right was immersed in water.

solution will exhibit no change, since the concentrations of solvent and of solute are the same inside and outside the bag (Fig. 12, left). If, in the first case (water outside), the sausage membrane is *slightly* permeable to sugar, as membranes usually are slightly permeable to such solutes, some of the sugar will *slowly* pass out of the bag; but distension will nevertheless occur, since water passes inward freely. Distension of the bag will be apparent for some time; but as the solute concentration inside and outside becomes equal, the bag will lose all evidence of distension. It is important to note that the diffusion of any solute through a solvent or through a membrane into the solvent is independent of the diffusion of any other solutes present and that solutions as such do not diffuse, although their components do.

The principle involved in Figure 12 may be illustrated by the use of a thistle-tube apparatus (Fig. 13). An explanation of the rise of water in the tube as indicated should be apparent.

Significance of Osmosis and Permeability. As a biological system for a consideration of osmosis, a cell in a leaf of Elodea offers favorable material. The cell wall is permeable to water and to many dissolved substances, but the plasma membrane is differentially permeable and determines to what extent substances may enter or leave the cell. If substances reach the central vacuole, they must pass the vacuolar membrane, which also is differentially permeable. The permeability of the plasma membrane is not the same for all solutes; and, since each solute enters or leaves the cell independently, the cell exhibits a certain degree of selectivity. Within the cell there is transfer of material between cytoplasm and nucleus, the extent of which is determined by the nature of the nuclear membrane.

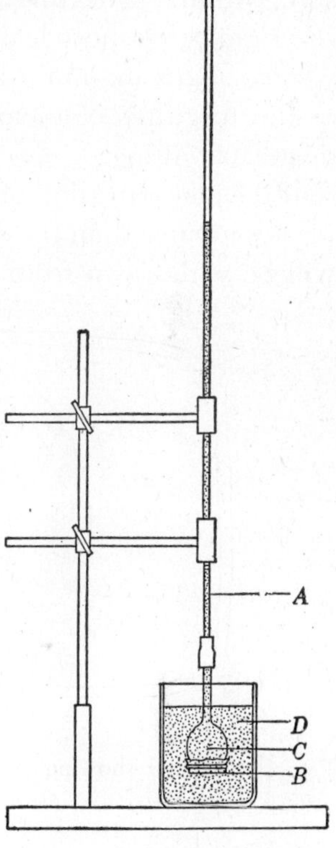

FIG. 13. An apparatus to illustrate osmosis. *A*, a thistle tube whose lower end is closed by the differentially permeable membrane *B*. The lower end (*C*) of the tube contains a concentrated sugar solution. The vessel *D* contains water.

The interchange of materials between cell and environment, however, is by no means simple. Other agencies and forces than those already mentioned may play important rôles. Under ordinary conditions the total concentration of the solutes in the cell sap is higher than that in the liquid surrounding the cell. In consequence, water passes by osmosis into the cell. Continued movement of water into the protoplast results in a pressure exerted by the protoplast on the wall. This pressure is sufficient to distend the protoplast as far as the elasticity of the wall will permit. The pressure so developed within the cell is called *turgor*, and the cell in this condition is said to be *turgid*. A cell may be more or less turgid according to the amount of pressure within. The turgidity of cells is important in maintaining the rigidity of most leaves and of young stems and roots. Non-woody plants maintain a normal habit of growth largely because of the turgidity of their cells. Loss of turgidity results in some degree of wilting.

If the concentration of the solutes in the liquid outside the protoplast is greater than the concentration of those in the cell sap, water will be withdrawn from the protoplast by osmosis. A sufficiently

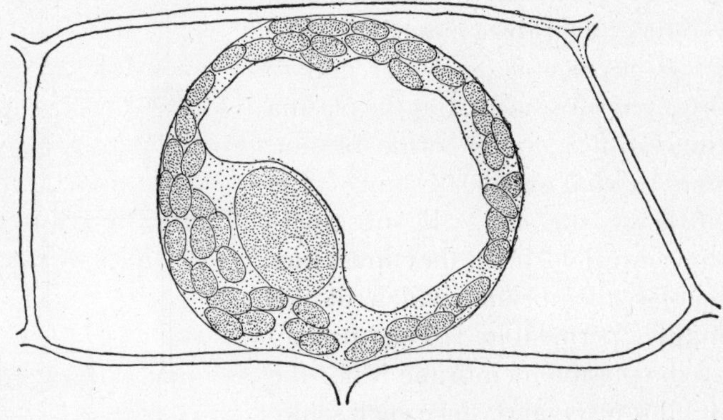

FIG. 14. A cell showing plasmolysis, which resulted from its immersion in a strong solution of common salt.

extensive withdrawal of water from the protoplast reduces the pressure to such a degree that the protoplast is partially or entirely withdrawn from the wall and becomes more or less rounded. In this state of contraction the cell is said to be *plasmolyzed*. The process of becoming plasmolyzed is *plasmolysis*. Plasmolysis may be illustrated by placing a living leaf of Elodea in a rather strong solution of cane sugar or of common salt (Fig. 14). Prolonged plasmolysis is usually fatal to a cell. If, however, a leaf in whose cells plasmolysis has not proceeded too far is removed from the sugar or salt solution and placed in approximately pure water, water will diffuse inward and the cells will return to their former turgid condition.

A demonstration of wilting resulting from plasmolysis may be made with a young tomato plant. If this is placed in a tumbler containing a sufficient quantity of strong salt solution to cover the root system, wilting of the plant will follow promptly. The relation of a root to the absorption of water and to the entrance of salts or other solutes present in the soil solution is discussed in a later chapter.

Each species of plant has a certain range of permeability characteristics. The permeability of the plasma membranes of living cells of any species may vary greatly from time to time, depending upon a variety of conditions internal and external to the cell, such as nutrition, age, temperature, and light. There are great differences in permeability also between the plasma membranes of different cells. Injury generally increases permeability, and death commonly renders the protoplast as permeable as the cell wall.

Respiration. On a previous page it was noted that every living cell of any plant or animal requires energy in carrying on its ordinary life processes. For these purposes the energy of the external environment, such as heat, is useless. Nor is light directly serviceable in this respect, although it is used in special tissues in photosynthesis and becomes available through the products of photosynthesis (Chapter VI). In general, the only directly utilizable energy is the stored (potential) energy of the organic compounds of the cell, that is, of the food material. This food material may be either that which has been made in the cell or that which is transported to the cell from tissues in which it was made or by which it was absorbed. The mechanism and conditions of energy release and transformation in the cell constitute what is known as *respiration.* Respiration is essentially a biological oxidation process and in this sense resembles combustion. It is, however, different from combustion in important respects; for instance, the rate of respiration is relatively slow, and it necessarily proceeds at low temperatures which are favorable for growth or for the maintenance of the cell. There are some analogies, however, notably in the fact that the usual process of burning fuel requires the oxygen of the air. When sugar or other organic material is burned in air, oxygen (O_2) is consumed, the energy released is apparent from the high temperature attained, and the residues or products of complete oxidation are carbon dioxide (CO_2) and water (H_2O).

The Protoplast the Seat of Respiration. It is a fundamental requirement in the process of oxygen (*aerobic*) respiration that molecular oxygen (O_2) shall continually reach the protoplasts of the tissues. Among the higher animals the organs and mechanisms of air intake, distribution, and expulsion are elaborate. In the higher plants there are usually air spaces between the cells, or between groups of cells, which constitute an aeration system. Commonly the intercellular spaces connect with the external atmosphere through stomata (Chapter VI); thus, gases may reach or leave the surfaces of many cells by simple diffusion through air. A supply of oxygen dissolved in the soil water is available to the tissues of a root.

The more active the cell, the more rapid is the rate of respiration, and accordingly the greater is the utilization of foods. In general, respiration in plant tissues does not involve a large loss of energy as heat, and there is no mechanism for the maintenance of body temperature. With changes in conditions the less bulky organs of the plant fairly promptly reach the temperature of the environment. It is essential that the energy set free in respiration should become available for the growth of the cell, but the method of utilization of this energy is largely an unsolved problem. Another complicated problem is that of how a food substance such as sugar is oxidized. It may suffice here to indicate that sugar is transformed by a series of chemical changes effected by means of *enzyme* systems. Enzyme systems are themselves complex compounds (organic catalysts) that promote chemical reactions, each enzyme being rather specific in the type of reaction that it accelerates.

The simple equation of the over-all reaction in respiration is written

$$C_6H_{12}O_6 + 6\ O_2 \rightarrow 6\ CO_2 + 6\ H_2O.$$

This means that one molecule of a simple sugar with much stored chemical energy (absorbed originally from sunlight by leaf pigments) is represented as combining with six molecules of oxygen; and the final products, six molecules each of carbon dioxide and water, indicate an oxidation with the liberation of the stored energy. The reaction is by no means so simple as written; the equation displays only the end results. A contrast of this reaction with that involved in the manufacture of food in the green leaf is deferred to a later chapter. Since CO_2 is produced by the reaction indicated above, it is found practicable to use CO_2 production as one means of demonstrating the respiration of tissues or organs, or of measuring the respiratory rate. The CO_2 produced by any respiring cell or tissue leaves the protoplast by diffusion, if it is not utilized in photosynthesis (Chapter VI).

That large quantities of carbon dioxide are given off in respiration can be determined by passing air freed from carbon dioxide through a vessel containing germinating seeds (Fig. 15) and then testing the air with baryta water for the presence of carbon dioxide—a white precipitate being formed when carbon dioxide is passed into baryta water. If green leaves are used to illustrate the liberation of carbon dioxide in respiration, it is necessary to place them in darkness, since in light the carbon dioxide produced by respiration might be utilized in photosynthesis.

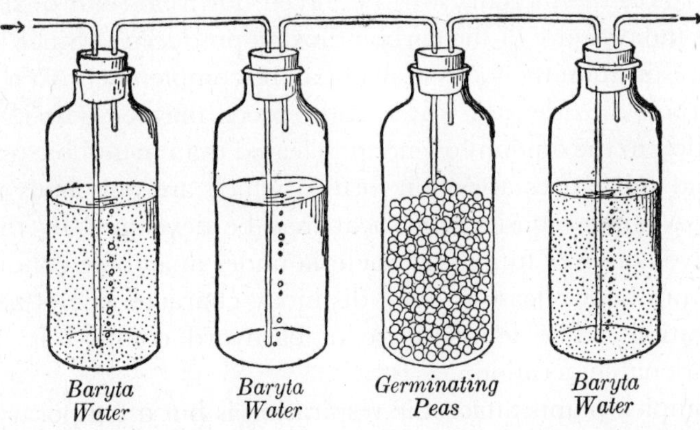

FIG. 15. An experiment demonstrating the evolution of carbon dioxide during respiration. The baryta water in the first bottle removes all carbon dioxide from the air, as shown by the lack of a precipitate in the second bottle; the air then passes into the third bottle, containing germinating peas; the air passing from this into the last bottle again contains carbon dioxide, and a precipitate is formed.

Anaerobic Respiration. In the more complex plants aerobic respiration is characteristic. There is, however, a temporary substitute in a process which by contrast is called *anaerobic* respiration. As the name suggests, anaerobic respiration proceeds in the absence of molecular oxygen. The necessary oxygen involved in the energy release is obtained by a transformation of the molecules of sugar or other food (it was earlier shown that six atoms of oxygen are present in a molecule of a simple sugar). The foods utilized in this way necessarily undergo changes, the atoms being rearranged into new substances (by-products). Continuance of anaerobic respiration for many days would mean an accumulation of such products sufficient to cause injury to the tissues.

Anaerobic respiration may be illustrated by inserting several pea seeds previously soaked in water into the mouth of a test tube filled with mercury and inverted over a dish of mercury. The seeds will rise to the top of the mercury in the test tube. After a time, as the seeds respire, the mercury will be forced down and out of the test tube by the pressure of the carbon dioxide produced. Since in this type of respiration the foods may not all be completely broken down into carbon dioxide and water, more foods may be consumed in proportion to the amount of energy released than in aerobic respiration; and substances are often formed which are poisonous to the plant. At times considerable heat may be developed by the fermentative action of fungi and bacteria under anaerobic conditions, but greater heat release is more distinctly characteristic of aerobic fermentation. The temperature of barnyard compost is higher with reasonable aeration.

In complex plants anaerobic respiration is but a temporary substitute for aerobic respiration, and the plants will eventually perish if permanently deprived of atmospheric oxygen. On the other hand, certain bacteria, yeasts, and molds are unable to grow in the presence of as much molecular oxygen as is contained in normal atmospheric air. Other organisms will live and grow in the entire absence of atmospheric oxygen; and for these, anaerobic respiration is commonly the fundamental process concerned in the release of energy. Anaerobic respiration on the part of these simple organisms is a form of *fermentation*, a process which involves the production in quantity of some by-product such as alcohol, glycerin, or an organic acid, since there is insufficient oxygen to effect complete oxidation.

SUMMARY

The functions of a plant are essentially functions of the protoplasts of its component cells. All these functions may be performed by a single protoplast; but in a many-celled plant there is a degree of division of labor between individual cells and tissues.

Living matter and its activities involve no form of material or of energy that is not common to the nonliving world. Living matter is distinguished by extreme complexity and variability.

A high proportion of water is essential to the activity of a protoplast.

Chemical analysis shows the presence in living matter of somewhat more than 30 elements. Most abundant are O, H, C, and N. Others present in considerable proportions and known to be essential to green plants are K, Ca, Mg, Fe, P, and S. Still others are required in very low concentrations.

These elements form a great variety of compounds; among the compounds present in quantity in living cells are carbohydrates, fats, and proteins. The proteins and other groups of compounds include enzymes, vitamins, growth substances, and pigments. Many substances occur in solution in vacuoles.

Protoplasm, as well as many food materials present in living cells, is in a colloidal state. Like other colloids, protoplasm may take the form either of a more or less solid gel or of a liquid sol.

The passage of materials into and out of a cell is in part simple diffusion. Gases may diffuse through gases or liquids, liquids through liquids or gases, solid substances through liquids in which they are soluble. A membrane that permits the diffusion of water through it is an imbibition membrane. Water and substances in solution in water enter a protoplast by diffusion through the cell wall and the plasma membrane. Some membranes, such as the walls of the outer cells of some leaves, are impermeable to water and to substances dissolved in water; some, such as the walls of interior cells, are freely permeable; some, including plasma membranes, are differentially permeable. The process of diffusion of a solvent such as water through a differentially permeable membrane is osmosis. The pressure which results is osmotic pressure.

Osmosis is illustrated by the passage of substances into and out of a cell of an Elodea leaf. The cell wall is permeable to water and to many dissolved substances; the plasma membrane, being differentially permeable, determines what substances may enter or leave the cell. Vacuolar membranes regulate passage of substances into and out of vacuoles; the nuclear membrane regulates interchange between cytoplasm and nucleus.

Under ordinary conditions the concentration of solutes in the cell sap is higher than in the liquid outside the cell. In this case, entrance of water results in a pressure (turgor) exerted by the protoplast against the wall. The cell is then turgid. If the net passage of water is outward, turgor disappears and the protoplast contracts. The cell is then plasmolyzed.

There are differences in permeability between the plasma membranes of different cells. The permeability of the membrane of any cell varies from time to time, depending upon conditions inside and outside the cell.

Respiration, involving oxidation, renders available the potential energy of organic compounds (foods) within a cell. The respiration of the more complex plants is chiefly aerobic; it involves oxidation by means of molecular oxygen derived directly from the atmosphere or from aqueous solutions with which a plant is in contact. Anaerobic respiration utilizes oxygen obtained by the transformation of the molecules of organic compounds. It results in the formation of by-products. For complex plants, anaerobic respiration is a temporary substitute; but some simple organisms depend upon it partly or wholly as a means of releasing utilizable energy.

CHAPTER IV

STEMS

Kinds of Stems. Plants which develop tall, woody stems capable of standing erect without support are *trees*. Plants which develop relatively short and usually freely branched, more or less erect woody stems are *shrubs*. Since trees and shrubs as groups are not sharply delimited as to size, the words "shrub" and "tree" are convenient, but not particularly exact, terms.

Those plants whose stems develop a small proportion of wood, and therefore remain comparatively soft, are called *herbs*. The distinction between herbaceous and woody plants is likewise not a sharp one, for almost all gradations in the amount of wood developed may be found in different plants.

The stems of many plants can not hold themselves upright, either because of their slenderness or because of the small proportion of supporting tissue. Some such weak-stemmed plants merely creep or clamber along the ground or over rocks. Others (often called *vines*) attach themselves to supports, such as other plants, and so attain an approximately upright position. Clambering and climbing vines may be either woody or herbaceous.

Functions of Stems. Stems of trees, shrubs, vines, and herbaceous plants have in common several primary functions. They constitute the axes which support the leaves, flowers, and fruits. It is obviously a function of the stem or branch to continue the production of new shoots. In large measure the form and direction of growth of its stem and branches determine thc extent to which a plant is exposed to climatic and other environmental factors. The distribution of leaves on the stem follows a variety of patterns (Fig. 70), all permitting advantageous orientation in response to light.

Since leaves are the chief food-manufacturing organs of the plant, the transport of soluble foods between these and other organs—all requiring, but unable to manufacture, food—is necessarily effected through the stem. The stem likewise conducts the water and solutes (mineral nutrients) absorbed by the roots to all parts of the shoot system, and notably to the leaves, where water utilization is greatest and where, also, water loss is highest. Thus, the stem is a major part of the highway of transport and distribution from the sources of supply of foods and other necessary substances to the places where they are to be used.

The green stems of many herbaceous plants and the younger green parts of woody stems contribute somewhat to the general supply of manufactured foods. In plants such as cacti, asparagus, and the greenhouse "smilax" whose minute leaves fall early or persist as scalelike structures, the green stems or branches carry on the process of food making.

Usually some foods are stored for a longer or shorter time in certain parts of the stem. In many plants, especially in those that live for more than a year, food storage is an important function of the stem. For example, during the winter certain cells in the stems of trees and shrubs often contain large amounts of starch and fats. The thickened parts of the stems of kohlrabi, potato tubers, and many other underground stems and branches are especially adapted for the storage of foods.

Offshoots or branches from stems, such as strawberry runners, function in vegetative propagation. Oftentimes after a new plant has established itself at the end of one of these runners, the connecting branch or portion of the stem disappears; and the complete independence of the new plant is then accomplished.

Regions of a Stem. A study of the elongation and development of a stem begins naturally with the growing tip or apex. This is always essentially within a bud. (For a discussion of buds see the chapter next following.) Accordingly, it is convenient to use as illustrative material either the first bud (epicotyl) of a seedling plant or any bud which is the terminus of a growing stem or branch. In all cases it will be found that the growing tip is differentiated into four general regions which merge gradually one into another. Beginning at the extreme tip and proceeding successively downward, these regions are: (*a*) the formative region or *meristem*, in which cell division chiefly takes place; (*b*) the *region of elongation*, in which the cells grow, chiefly in length, although some cell divisions occur here; (*c*) the *region of maturation*, in which various cells take on the characteristics distinctive of particular tissues; and (*d*) the *mature region*, in which cells have become fully differentiated in both structure and function.

Meristematic Region. In the meristematic region (Fig. 16) the cells are all essentially alike in that they are small, closely packed, angular, and substantially uniform in size. The length, breadth, and thickness of any meristematic cell are approximately equal. The cells in this region are distinguished from those of most other parts of the stem by their capacity for indefinitely repeated division. The term *meristematic* is of Greek derivation and means "capable of dividing."

FIG. 16. Lengthwise section of the apex of the stem of a honeysuckle.

A section of a stem treated as previously described (p. 11) shows that meristematic cells differ in structure from mature cells. Since nuclear and cell division (Chapter X) are likely to be going on in many of the cells in the meristematic region, it is necessary to select for the present comparison a *resting cell*—by which, in this connection, is meant one whose nucleus and cytoplasm are not in process of division. Such a cell is not, of course, "resting" in respect to many other activities.

In the first place, the wall of a meristematic cell (Fig. 17) is very thin as compared with that of a mature cell. Second, such a cell contains no central or other large vacuole. The space within the wall is occupied by the nucleus and cytoplasm; the latter contains many minute vacuoles and is similar to the layer of dense cytoplasm immediately lining the wall in a mature cell. Third, a meristematic cell contains no chloroplasts. Among the small darkly

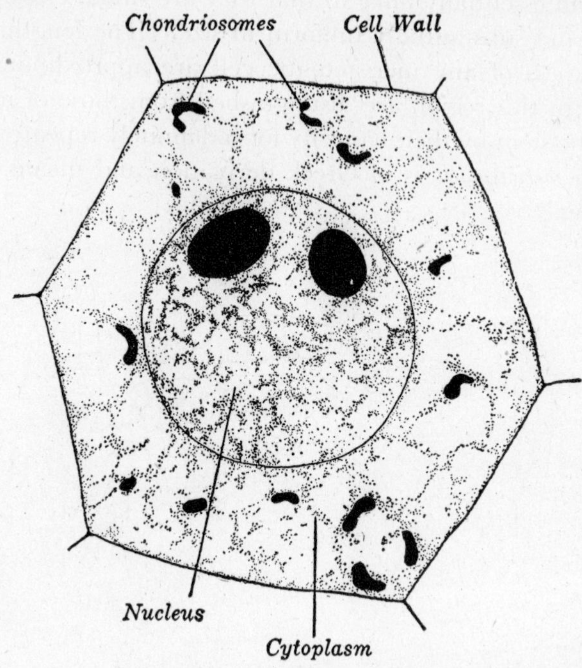

FIG. 17. A meristematic (embryonic) cell from the stem tip of a Coleus plant.

stained bodies (chondriosomes) in the cytoplasm, however, there are some which, particularly in the outer layers of cells, may develop into chloroplasts. Fourth, the nucleus is large in proportion to the size of the cell and is centrally located. The nucleus of a meristematic cell, like that of a mature cell, is surrounded by a nuclear membrane and contains a nucleolus or nucleoli, chromatic strands, and nuclear sap.

The continued division of cells in the meristematic region would result, if nothing occurred to prevent, in a steady increase in number of meristematic cells and consequently in the size of this region. No such increase occurs because the cells which come to lie in the posterior portion of the meristematic region cease to divide; and most of them, except as noted below, begin to enlarge and become constituents of the region of elongation of the stem. The volume of the meristematic region, therefore, remains approximately constant.

Along the sides of the meristem are outgrowths; those closest to the tip are dome-shaped; those somewhat farther back are concave like the bowl of a spoon (Fig. 18). These outgrowths of meriste-

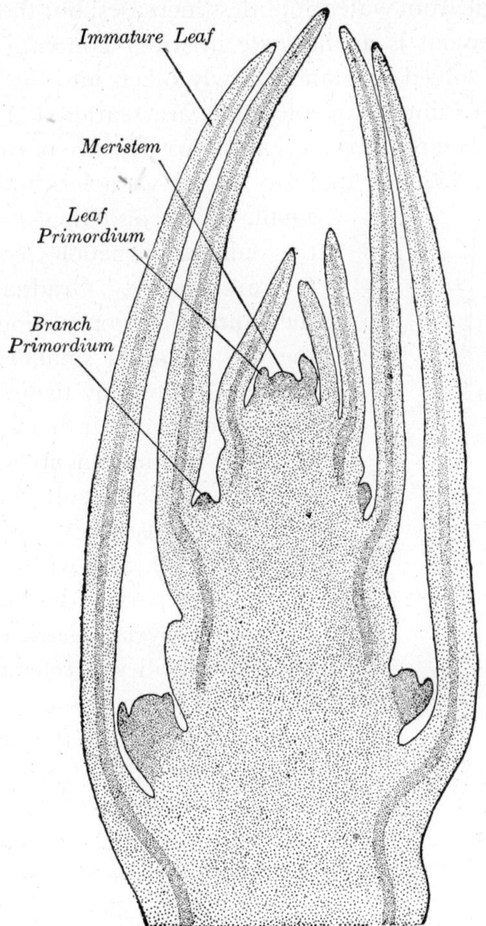

FIG. 18. The apical portion of a honeysuckle stem.

matic cells arise in localized areas by accelerated divisions of some of the outermost cells of the meristem. Such outgrowths, to be referred to as *leaf primordia*, are the beginnings of young leaves. The level or plane of the stem at which one or more leaves are being formed is a node; the meristematic portion of the stem is therefore being set off into nodes and internodes, but the internodes are as yet so short that successive nodes appear to adjoin one another.

Region of Elongation. The cells which lie next below the apical meristem make up the region of elongation. The cells in this region are growing, chiefly in length. As a cell enlarges, the amount of its substance aside from water doubtless increases; but the largest factor in its enlargement is an increase in water content. Most of the water and dissolved substances newly taken into the cell collect in certain of the minute vacuoles that are scattered throughout the cytoplasm. The result is a great increase in size of these particular vacuoles (Fig. 19); the majority of the vacuoles, however, remain small. Now and then two or more of the enlarging vacuoles come into contact and merge. Gradually, therefore, the number of conspicuous vacuoles in the cell becomes smaller; and finally, in the cells of many tissues, the expanding vacuoles unite into one or a few large centrally located vacuoles. The merging of vacuoles results in pushing the dense cytoplasm (except for an occasional strand), and with it the nucleus, to the outer part of the cell. This relatively thin layer of dense cytoplasm just inside the wall was referred to particularly in an earlier description of a mature cell (p. 9). Since the many vacuoles that remain minute are included in it, the dense cytoplasm still has an emulsion-like structure. The nucleus remains imbedded in the dense cytoplasm and is therefore finally located near the cell wall. Since the enlargement of a cell is due largely to pressure resulting from the intake of additional water, it might be expected that the cell would expand equally in all directions. This is not generally the case; most of the enlarging cells of a stem, from causes not fully understood, undergo a greater increase in length than in either lateral direction.

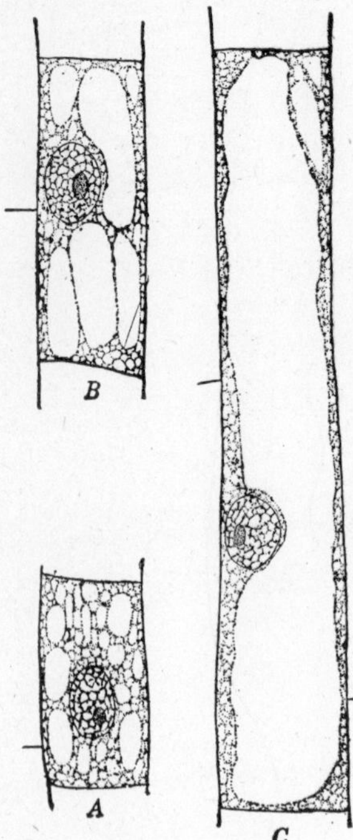

FIG. 19. Stages in the development of a meristematic cell to the mature condition.

In an actively growing stem, rapid elongation usually begins in the third or fourth internode from the stem's apex. The cells of such an internode are growing chiefly, although not exclusively, in length. In the vicinity of each node—often, as in grasses, immediately above the node in the basal portion of an internode—are cells which remain meristematic for a longer or shorter time. The meristematic cells in these interrupting groups or plates may and often do remain undifferentiated and capable of further division and growth, even after those cells above and below them have completed their development. In the region of elongation, certain groups of cells which are to constitute the respective tissues in the mature part of the stem become differentiated in size and shape.

Among the earliest cells to become differentiated in an elongating internode are those immediately beneath the epidermis. These cells enlarge somewhat, and later their protoplasts secrete a few additional layers of wall material. Such thickening of the walls results in the formation of a *mechanical tissue* (Figs. 20, 21) of considerable rigidity. This tissue doubtless functions in support during the early stages of development.

In an elongating internode, at some distance inward from the surface of the stem, strands of cells are differentiated that extend vertically, and parallel with one another, through the internode. These strands, composed chiefly of elongated cells, will eventually mature into *vascular bundles*. They may therefore be spoken of as *provascular strands*.

Seed plants are divided into *gymnosperms*, a group which includes the pines, firs, and spruces; *dicotyledons*, including the majority of trees, shrubs, and herbaceous seed plants; and *monocotyledons*, of which palms, lilies, and grasses—including corn, wheat, and other cereals—are examples. In gymnosperms and in most dicotyledons the provascular strands, as seen in cross section, constitute an interrupted ring. In most monocotyledons the provascular strands are numerous and scattered, although they also extend vertically through each internode.

Generally speaking, after the cells at any particular level in the stem have elongated to their fullest extent, their position with reference to the earth's surface is fixed. Further growth in length of the stem is the result of continued cell division nearer the tip, that is, in the meristem, followed by the elongation of those meristematic cells successively farthest from the tip. The only part of the stem that actually is moved in a lengthwise direction is a restricted portion at the tip. This continued activity at the stem end may then be

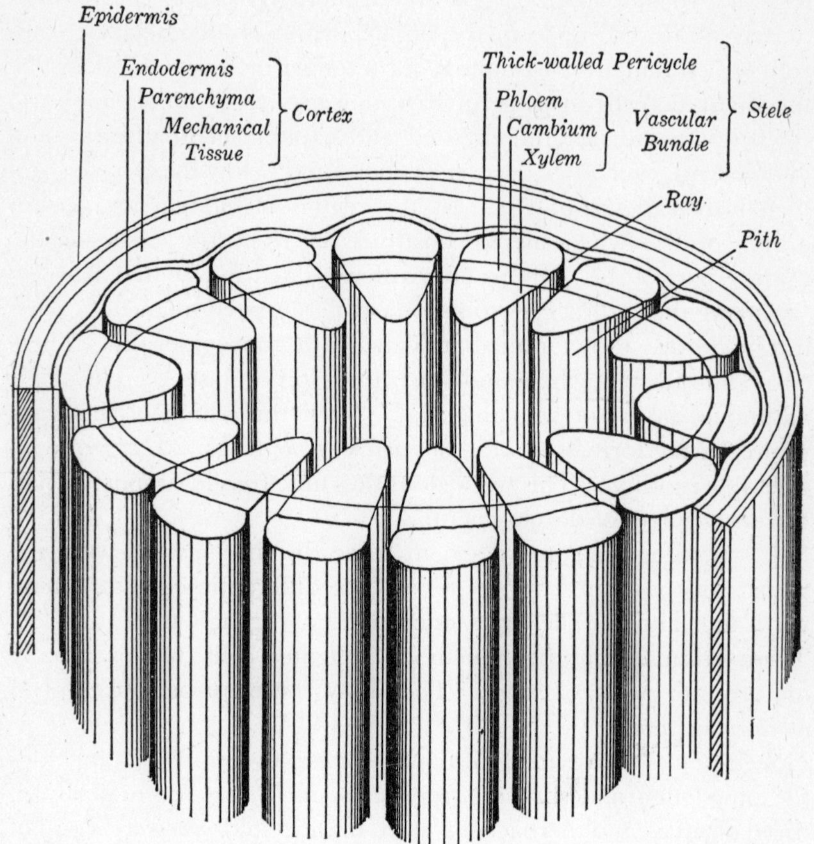

FIG. 20. Three-dimensional diagram of a dicotyledonous stem, showing the primary tissues.

thought of as involving division of cells and a progression of the meristematic region apically; that is, the meristematic region is pushed forward.

Region of Maturation. The differences in size and shape of cells, first evident in the region of elongation, become more apparent as the fully enlarged cells assume their mature characteristics. In general, the walls of maturing cells become thicker by the formation of new layers of wall material. The original thin wall separating

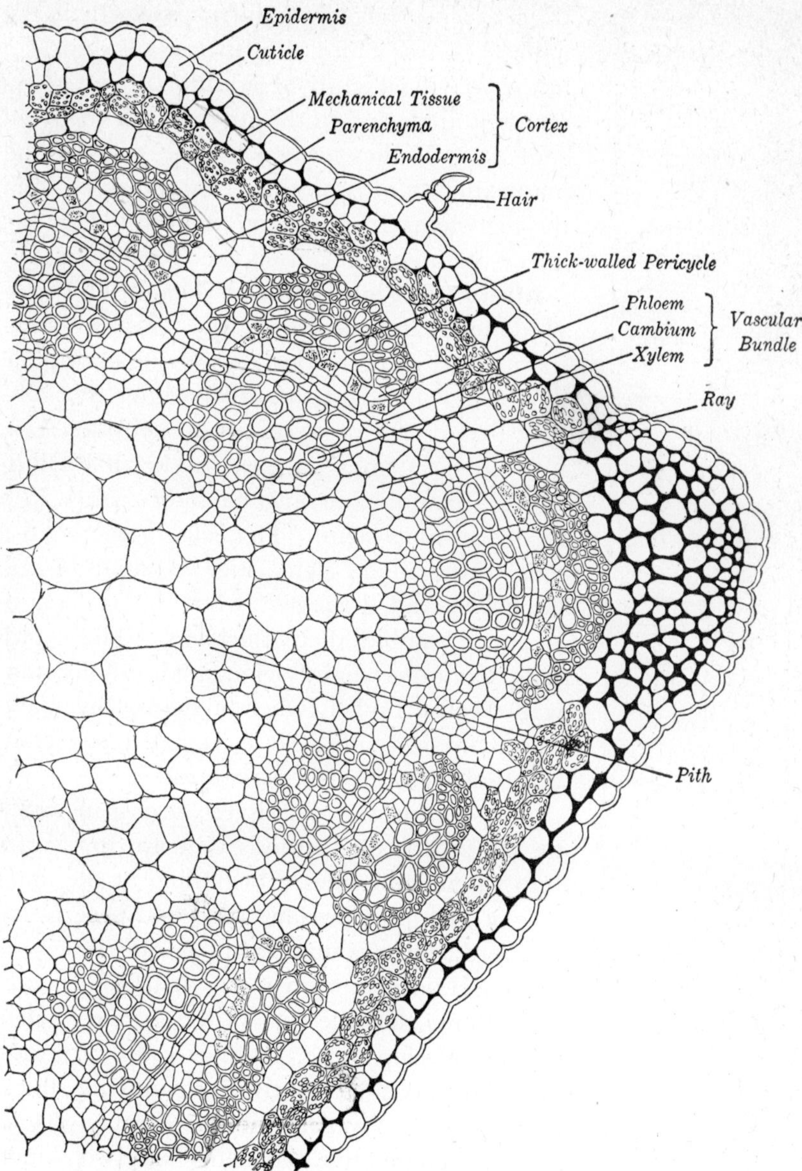

Fig. 21. Portion of a cross section of an alfalfa stem.

two adjoining meristematic cells, somewhat modified in thickness and in chemical composition, remains as the middle layer of the mature wall (Fig. 9). As will appear in the following paragraphs,

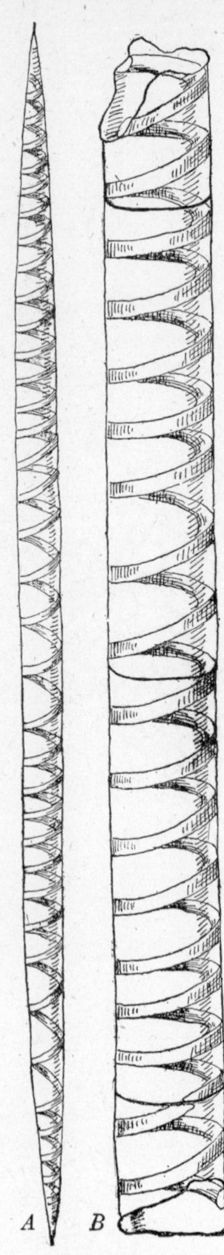

FIG. 22. *A*, a tracheid with spirally thickened wall. *B*, portion of a vessel with spirally thickened wall.

the cells of various tissues differ materially in the amount of thickening that their walls undergo, in the way in which these additional wall layers are deposited, and in the character of their cell contents. Tissues formed by the growth and maturation of cells produced by cell division in the meristematic region or, to a limited extent, in the region of elongation are *primary tissues.*

Mature Region: Primary Tissues of Dicotyledonous Internodes (Fig. 20). Gymnosperms and dicotyledons, on the one hand, and monocotyledons, on the other, differ so markedly that it will be necessary to consider these two types of stems separately. The alfalfa illustrates a common arrangement of tissues in a dicotyledonous stem. The cells in the central part of the alfalfa stem (Fig. 21) mature into large thin-walled *pith cells*, whose vertical length is about double their thickness. These pith cells, like other slightly elongated, usually thin-walled cells found elsewhere in stems, leaves, and roots, are *parenchymatous* cells. A tissue composed of such cells is a *parenchyma.*

Just outside the pith is the region in which lie the provascular strands that are to mature into vascular bundles. Beginning at the inner face of each provascular strand and progressing outward, the cells mature into *primary xylem.* A cross section of a stem made at this particular level shows that the cells of the primary xylem groups develop especially thick walls. In most dicotyledonous stems these strands of thick-walled cells, as well as the later-formed xylem, include conductive elements of two kinds. During maturation the cell walls of single elongated cells with pointed ends are thickened by the addition of new layers. Such cells are *tracheids* (Fig. 22, *A*). In some tracheids the new layers are deposited upon a limited portion of the inner surface of the wall in the form of a spiral band that runs the whole length of the cell; in other tracheids the internal thickening takes the form of a series of parallel rings which encircle the cell transversely. Cytoplasm and nuclei disappear from the tracheids after the formation of these additional wall layers. Mature tracheids, therefore, consist of cell walls only; and each is the result of the maturation of a single meristematic cell.

In addition to the tracheids are cells which mature into *vessels* (Fig. 22, *B*). A vessel is an element resulting from the maturation of a vertical row consisting of a variable number of meristematic

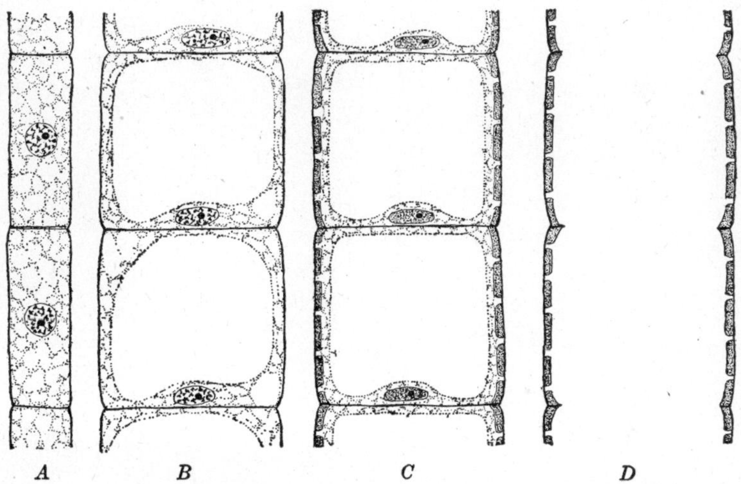

Fig. 23. Stages in the development of a vessel from a row of originally separate cells.

cells joined end to end. After the increase in length which these cells undergo, their maturation begins with a great increase in the diameter of each cell of the row (Fig. 23, *B*). After this enlargement is completed, additional layers of wall material are deposited on the side walls of the cells. In the first vessels to mature, the additional wall material is laid down in transverse rings or in a continuous spiral. The thickened walls of later-matured vessels often contain many thin areas (*pits*) in which the material of the later-formed layers was not deposited. After the thickening of the side walls, the crosswalls between adjoining cells of the vertical row disappear, except for the outer margin of each crosswall. Finally the protoplasts disappear (Fig. 23, *D*). Hence, a vessel is a tube formed from a row of originally separate cells; it differs in this respect from a tracheid, which is at all stages a single cell. Tracheids and vessels are not functionless when mature, in spite of the fact that they are dead; as will appear in a later chapter, water passing from

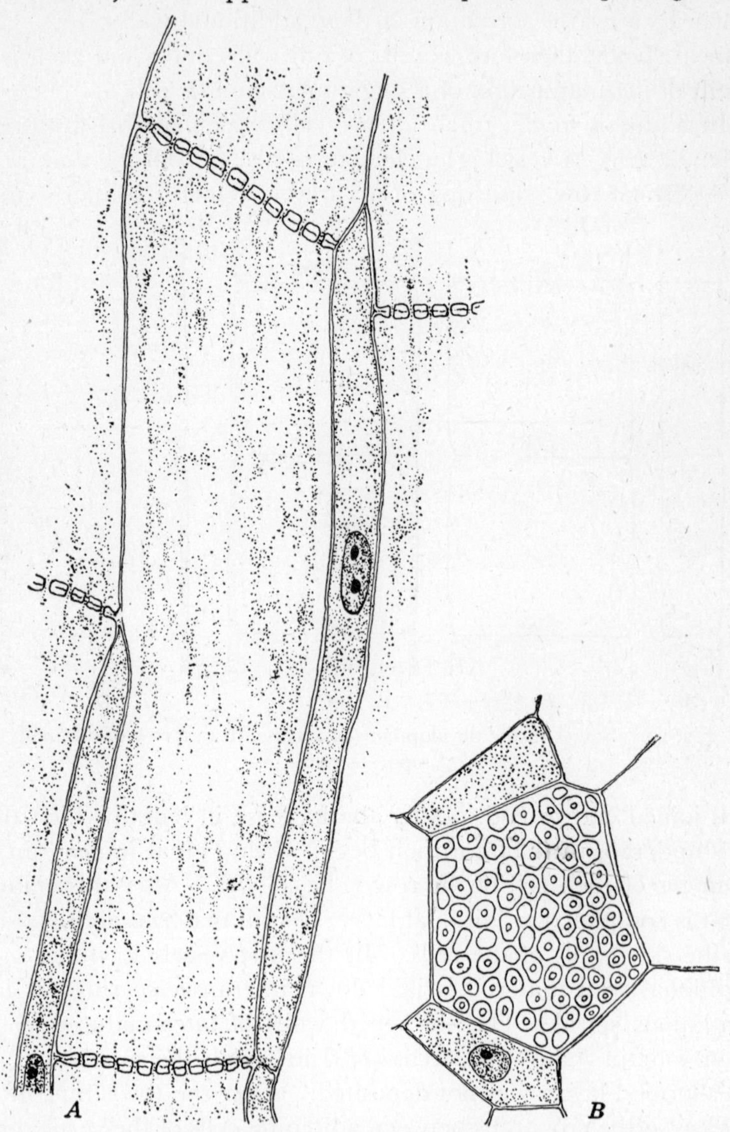

FIG. 24. *A*, lengthwise section of a sieve-tube segment and its companion cell, from the secondary phloem of a squash stem. *B*, the end wall of a sieve-tube segment, showing a group of pores.

the root through the stem and out into the leaf moves chiefly through these dead elements.

Simultaneously with the development of the primary xylem, the cells constituting the outer portion of each provascular strand mature progressively from the outer face inward into *primary phloem.* The *sieve tubes* (Fig. 24) are the most conspicuous elements of the phloem. Each sieve tube is formed much as is a xylem vessel by the elongation and maturation of a vertical row of meristematic cells. It is called a "sieve tube" because the end walls between the cells in the row are perforated, thus satisfying the implications of the "tube" idea. A region of the wall perforated by a group of pores is a *sieve plate.* The pores in such a plate are visible with relatively low magnification, and accordingly are much larger than the minute pores referred to on page 13. As a sieve cell matures, its nucleus disintegrates; and there remains characteristically a thin layer of dense cytoplasm enclosing a large central vacuole, through which extend tenuous strands of dense cytoplasm. The protoplasts of adjacent cells of the sieve tube are connected by cytoplasmic strands which pass through the pores of the sieve plates. The cytoplasmic continuity which results is doubtless important in the transport of foods and possibly of other materials. Interspersed among the sieve tubes are other thin-walled cells whose walls do not develop pores; these cells, which may be long or short, contain cytoplasm and nuclei, whereas the nuclei of the sieve tubes sooner or later disappear. Often a narrow, elongated *companion cell* lies beside and parallel to each sieve cell—that is, beside each segment of a sieve tube.

Thus, the inner and the outer portions of each provascular strand mature into primary xylem and primary phloem, respectively. These vertical columns of xylem and phloem never come into actual contact, however, because a thin strip of cells (the *cambium;* see Fig. 25), extending lengthwise through the center of the strand between xylem and phloem, remains meristematic. A mature vascular bundle, therefore, consists of three main parts: the xylem on the inner side toward the pith, the phloem on the outer side, and the cambium between xylem and phloem. This side-by-side (*collateral*) arrangement of xylem and phloem in vascular bundles is characteristic of the structure of stems; as will be seen, it is very different from the arrangement found in roots.

The vascular bundles are separated from one another by radial strands of parenchymatous cells—the *rays* (Figs. 20, 21). Immediately surrounding the cylinder of bundles is the *pericycle*. The portion of the pericycle just outside each vascular bundle consists of

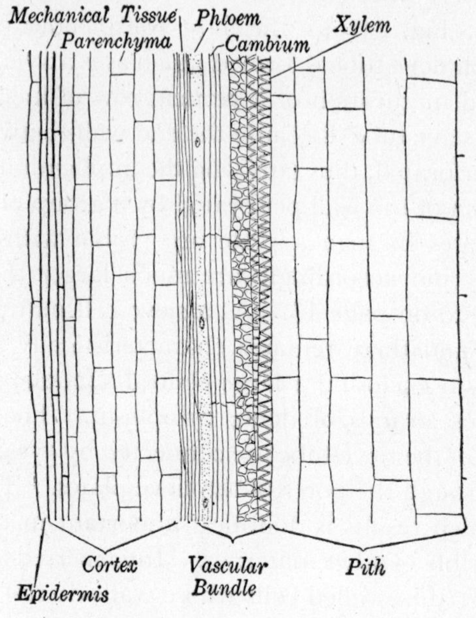

FIG. 25. Portion of a lengthwise section of a sunflower stem.

long needle-shaped cells with greatly thickened walls. These walls become impregnated with substances that greatly increase their stiffness. Since this change does not take place until the internode is well along toward maturity, these stiffened cells help to hold erect only the mature portions of the stem. The pericyclic cells at the outer end of each ray are parenchymatous and scarcely distinguishable from the cells of the ray. The zone of pericycle consisting of alternating vertical strips of thick- and thin-walled cells constitutes the outermost layer of the whole central core of the stem which has thus far been described. This central core is the *stele*.

A relatively thin *cortex* surrounds the stele. In the alfalfa stem the innermost layer of the cortex as seen in cross section is made up of large thin-walled cells with no intercellular spaces. This cylindrical layer, one cell in thickness, is the *endodermis*. Just outside the endodermis are loosely packed parenchymatous cells, most of which contain chloroplasts. In the stems of many plants, however, it is difficult to distinguish the cells of the cortical parenchyma from those of the endodermis. As already mentioned, cells with greatly thickened walls in the outer portion of the cortex constitute a mechanical tissue.

The cortex is bounded on its outer face by an *epidermis*—a layer of slightly flattened, vertically elongated cells. The outer walls of the epidermal cells are thickened and impregnated with a waxy substance (*cutin*), which makes them almost impermeable to water. Comparatively little water is lost, therefore, from the surface of a stem whose epidermis is intact. Here and there an embryonic epidermal cell matures into a long, pointed *hair*. *Stomata* (which can be more satisfactorily studied in the leaf) also occur sparingly in the epidermis of the stem.

Structure of a Dicotyledonous Node. Although the vascular bundles are parallel throughout each internode and most of them are continuous with those of the internodes above and below, at the nodes there are cross connections between the bundles. Extending through the cortex of each node too are other vascular strands, each connecting at its inner end with a vascular bundle of the internode below and at its outer end with the base of a leaf. Thus, during development some of the bundles in each internode, instead of extending vertically through the node above, project outward in that node into the base of the leaf. Such vascular connections (*leaf traces*) provide paths of transfer for water and soluble materials between the leaf and the rest of the plant.

Secondary Thickening in Dicotyledons and Gymnosperms. *Secondary tissues*, in distinction to primary tissues, are the result of activity of the cambium. One important respect in which monocotyledons differ from gymnosperms and dicotyledons is that monocotyledons usually produce no secondary tissues, whereas gymnosperms and dicotyledons usually form secondary tissues, although in varying amounts.

After primary xylem and primary phloem have been formed in the stem of a dicotyledon or of a gymnosperm, the cambial cells lying between the primary xylem and the primary phloem of each bundle begin to divide tangentially (Fig. 25). The new cells formed on the inner face of the cambium mature into secondary xylem elements, and those formed toward the outer face develop into secondary phloem elements. The process of division extends to those layers of ray cells which lie between the cambial regions of adjacent bundles; hence, the cambium in time becomes a continuous zone or cylinder (Fig. 21). The secondary xylem matured from the cambium now also constitutes a cylinder, continuous except where it is interrupted by rays. Similarly, a cylinder of secondary phloem, continuous except for the rays, is formed outside the cambium. A few cells produced both to the inside and to the outside of the cambium remain thin-walled and are added to the rays, so that these structures remain continuous, vertical parenchymatous layers connecting cortex and pith.

Increase in diameter of the cylinder of secondary xylem is accompanied by a compensating increase in number of cambial cells. This results from the fact that now and then one of the cells in the cambium divides in a radial instead of a tangential plane. Both daughter cells enlarge to the full size of a cambial cell, but they enlarge in a direction parallel to the circumference of the cambium. It is by means of such occasional radial divisions that the diameter of the cambial cylinder is gradually increased.

In an aerial stem of alfalfa the cambium ordinarily produces secondary xylem and secondary phloem for one season only, after which the stem dies. In the stems of many perennial plants, especially trees and shrubs, the cambium continues to form secondary xylem and phloem from year to year.

Structure of Secondary Phloem (Figs. 26, 27). Secondary phloem may be simple or relatively complex in structure. In most gymnosperms the secondary phloem consists chiefly of sieve tubes, on whose side and end walls are sieve plates; intermingled with the sieve tubes are a few parenchymatous cells. In the sieve tubes of a dicotyledon, sieve plates may occur in both end and side walls or in the end walls only. In the secondary, as in the primary, phloem of dicotyledons, a companion cell lies beside each segment of a sieve tube. The secondary phloem of dicotyledonous stems also includes parenchymatous cells, which are often densely filled with reserve foods. Vertically elongated cells (*bast fibers*), having pointed ends and thick walls, occur in the secondary phloem of most woody dicotyledons and of some gymnosperms.

Toward the end of the growing season, further functioning of the sieve tubes is usually prevented by the development of pads of additional wall material over each sieve plate. During the next growing season the nonfunctioning sieve tubes with their companion cells become crushed between the rigid layers to the outside and the expanding cylinder of newly formed secondary xylem and phloem within. Such parenchymatous cells and bast fibers as are included in the secondary phloem are more resistant to this crushing and usually persist in a more or less unmutilated state for several years.

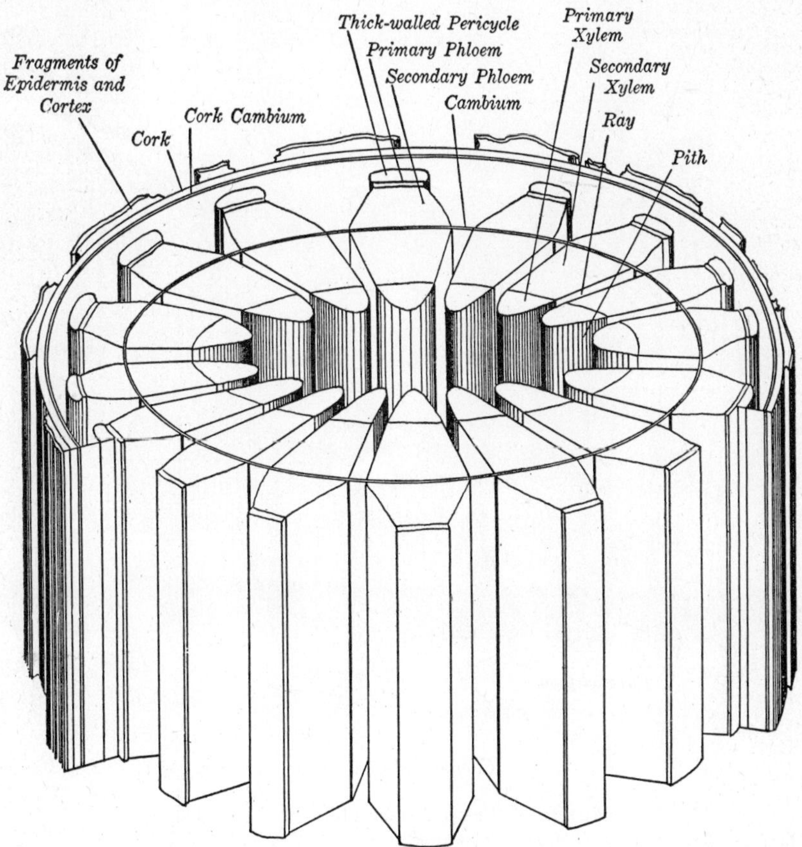

FIG. 26. Three-dimensional diagram of an internode of a dicotyledonous stem, showing the results of cambial activity.

Structure of Secondary Xylem (Figs. 26, 28). The secondary xylem in the stems of gymnosperms consists chiefly of tracheids. Secondary xylem in stems of woody dicotyledons, with very few exceptions, contains vessels and may contain tracheids in addition.

The remaining portion of the mature secondary xylem in stems of dicotyledons consists largely of elongated, empty, pointed cells with thick, rigid walls. Such *wood fibers*, which are much like the bast

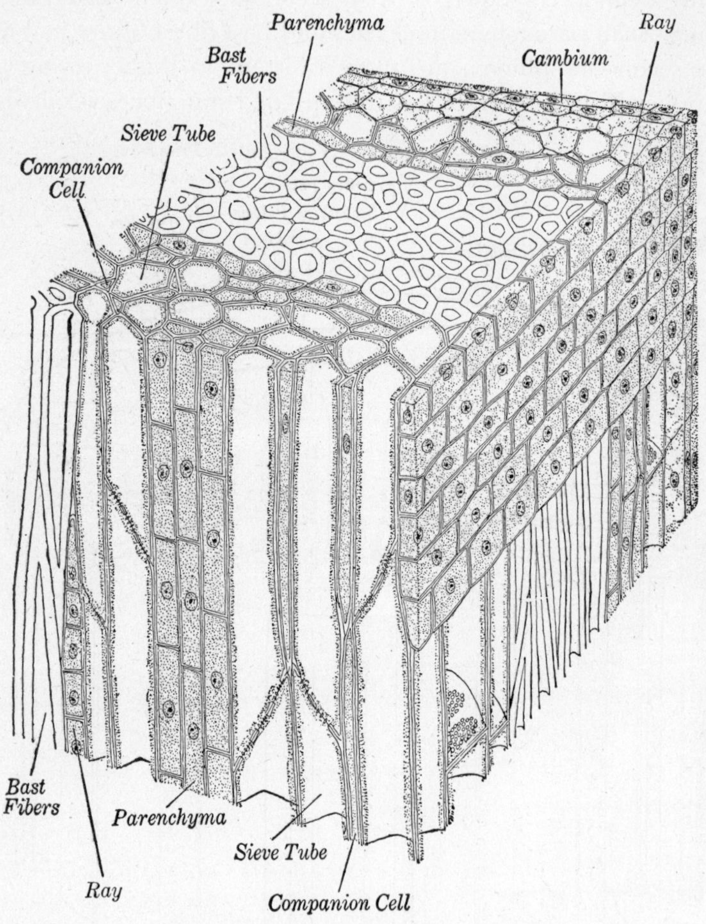

FIG. 27. Portion of the secondary phloem of a basswood stem.

fibers of the secondary phloem, contribute to the rigidity of the stem. The secondary xylem of woody dicotyledons contains also parenchymatous cells. In the secondary xylem of some stems, such as those of walnut and hickory, parenchymatous cells are numerous; in other stems, as those of willow and cottonwood, only a few parenchymatous cells occur in the secondary xylem.

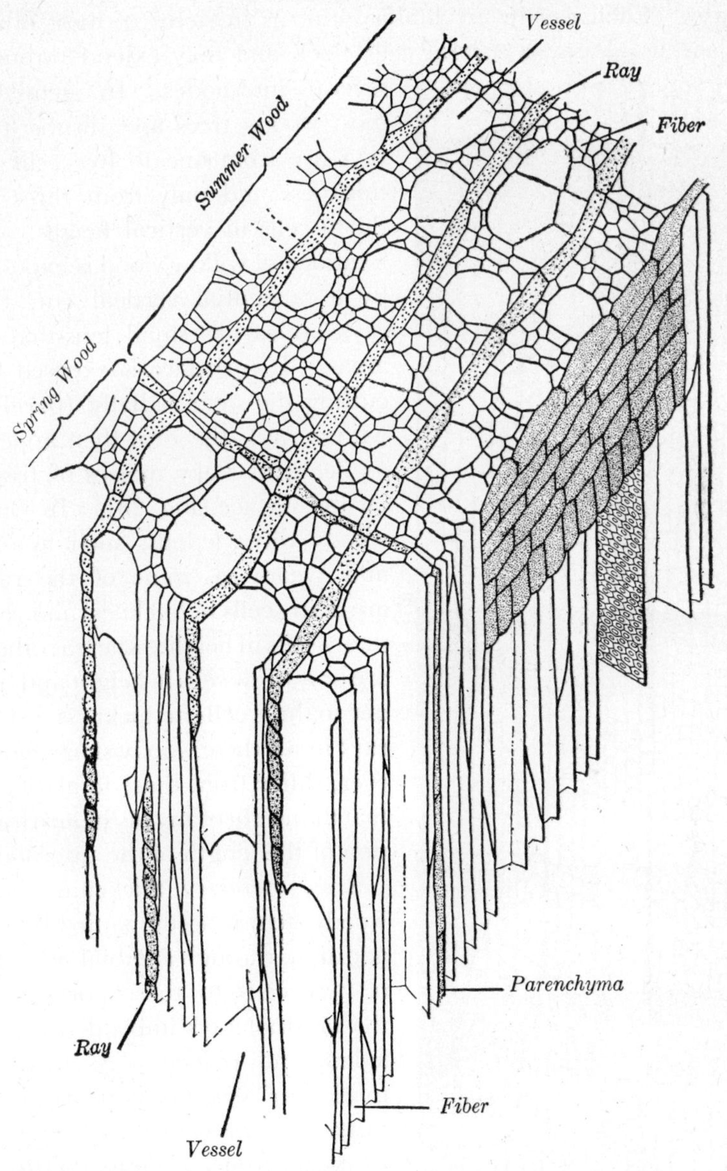

FIG. 28. Portion of the secondary xylem of a willow stem. The only parenchymatous cells here present constitute the last-formed layer of the summer wood. This layer of parenchyma, therefore, marks the boundary between the summer wood of one year and the spring wood formed the next year.

Rays. Each ray in an alfalfa stem, as in stems of most other herbaceous plants, is several cells thick and may extend through several internodes. In stems of most woody trees and shrubs, the rays are from one to five cells in thickness and only from three to thirty cells in vertical height. If a surface of willow wood is exposed by a tangential vertical cut, the rays appear as small lens-shaped areas. If a surface is exposed by cutting the stem radially (parallel with a ray), the rays then appear as flecks or flaky masses of tissue on the surface (Fig. 28). In some woody dicotyledons, such as oak and sycamore, some of the rays are many cells in thickness and very many cells in height, whereas others are only a few cells in height and but one to three cells in thickness. The rays in all these woody stems, however, differ from those in alfalfa in that the height of any ray is but a fraction of the length of the internode.

The secondary thickening of a woody stem is accompanied by the addition, through cambial activity, of new cells to those portions of the original rays imbedded in the xylem and phloem. As the formation of secondary tissues continues, new rays originate from year to year from various points in the cambium. Such rays extend

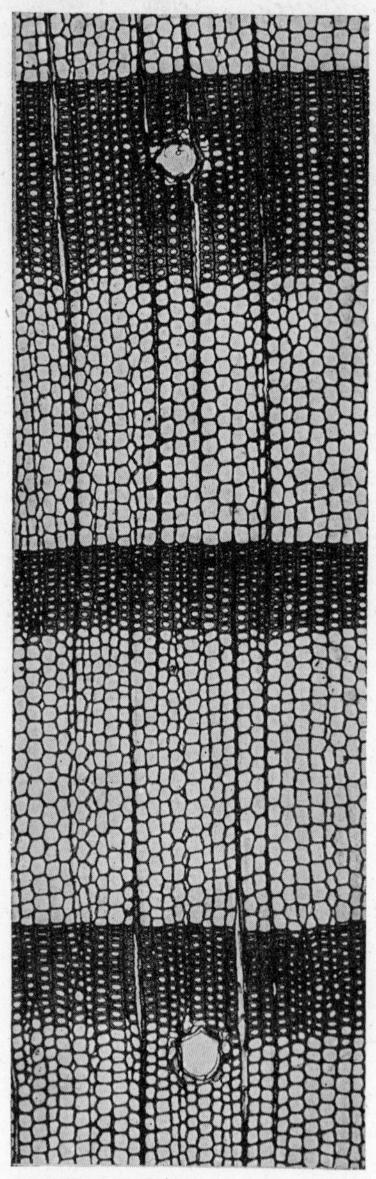

FIG. 29. Portion of a cross section through the secondary xylem of a trunk of the shortleaf pine. Two annual rings and parts of two others are shown. In this, as in other gymnosperm stems, no vessels are present. Photograph by the Forest Products Laboratory, Madison, Wis.

outward radially from the point of origin. In a cross section of an older woody stem it can be seen, therefore, that the number of rays increases progressively from the center outward and that this increase in the number of rays is proportional to the increase in circumference of the woody cylinder. The rays of a woody plant serve as a pathway between the inner and the outer parts of the stem for the crosswise transfer of water and substances in solution, including foods and mineral nutrients.

Annual Rings. In the stems of woody trees and shrubs, where the formation of new secondary xylem and phloem continues from year to year, the xylem elements formed at the beginning of each season of growth usually differ greatly from those formed later in the season. The xylem elements formed early in the growing season (the *spring wood*) are large and relatively thin-walled. As the season advances, the successively formed elements do not develop to so large a size; but their walls become thicker. The xylem elements produced toward the close of the growing season (the *summer wood*) are smallest and thickest-walled of all (Fig. 28). In the late summer or early fall the cambium ceases to form secondary tissues. When, in the following spring, the cambium again begins to form new secondary xylem, the first elements matured are large and thin-walled. Consequently a cross section of a stem shows a sharp line of demarcation between the small-celled, thick-walled summer wood of the previous year and the large-celled, thin-walled spring wood of the current year. This is the explanation of the occurrence of concentric *annual rings* which are so conspicuous in stumps and in cut ends of branches of many trees and shrubs. In some woods, as in that of black ash (Fig. 30, *A*), many very large vessels are formed in the spring wood; but the summer wood is composed chiefly of fibers, with a few small scattered vessels and some tracheids. Such a wood is *ring-porous*. In certain other *diffuse-porous* woods, such as that of the quaking aspen (Fig. 30, *B*), vessels are more or less uniformly distributed throughout the spring and summer wood. However, in the wood produced toward the end of the growing season, there is a larger proportion of elements other than vessels. Hence, even though the vessels throughout each annual ring are more or less alike and uniformly distributed, sufficient difference exists between late summer wood of one year and spring wood of the following year to make the rings distinguishable.

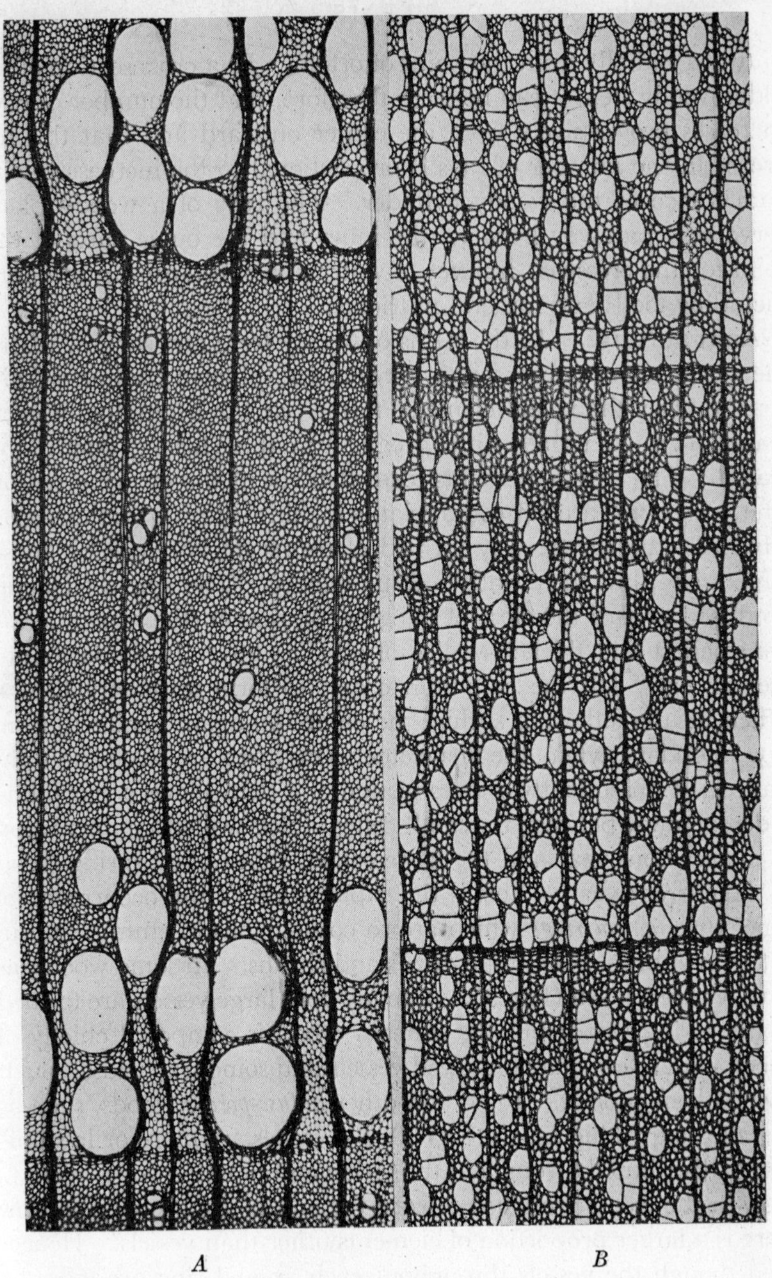

A *B*

Fig. 30. *A*, secondary xylem of the black ash. *B*, secondary xylem of the quaking aspen. Photographs by the Forest Products Laboratory, Madison, Wis.

The number of rings in the xylem is not a perfectly accurate measure of the age of a tree, because sometimes, as a result of exceptional weather or other conditions, two rings are formed in a single year. Annual rings in the trunk or branch of a tree are sometimes consistently thicker on one side than on the other. If a tree is growing at the edge of a clearing in a close stand of timber,

FIG. 31. *A*, cross section of a trunk of lodgepole pine, showing the greater width of annual rings produced after a thinning of the stand. *B*, cross section of a portion of a trunk of black spruce, showing the greater width of annual rings produced after draining the swamp in which the tree grew. Photographs by the Forest Products Laboratory, Madison, Wis.

there is a greater development of branches on the side toward the clearing, which receives more light. Each annual ring is broader on the side of the trunk which bears the heavier and more numerous branches. In older branches of many trees, and especially in those branches which diverge at a relatively wide angle from the trunk, much more xylem is produced by the cambium on the lower than on the upper sides. Hence, the annual rings of such branches will be thicker on the under sides of the branches. These differences become more apparent as the branches become longer and heavier and as the under surfaces of the branches are consequently put under progressively greater compression.

The thickness of annual rings produced in successive years is often greatly influenced by variations in environmental conditions, especially in the supply of water to the plant. Seasonal weather variations recorded by weather bureaus have been correlated with variations in thickness of annual rings. The agreement is found to be close, thin rings having been produced in years with low rainfall and thick rings in years with abundant rainfall. A permanent change in the environment, such as the felling of surrounding trees or the draining of a swamp in which a tree has been growing, may result in marked differences in thickness between the annual rings produced before and those produced after the change (Fig. 31). It has been possible in many instances to date the clearing of land by early settlers or to establish the time of logging operations in particular areas by an examination of the annual rings of trees that were left uncut at those times.

In many tropical regions, where the amount of available moisture varies but little throughout the year, there is little or no difference between wood produced in different seasons. Consequently the growth of successive years can not be distinguished. However, in parts of the tropics where rainy seasons alternate with dry periods, trees reflect these periodic changes in their environment by producing annual rings.

Sapwood and Heartwood. As the number of annual rings in the wood increases, there comes a time when, in the trunks of many trees, the vessels and tracheids of the inner rings become filled with gums and resins or blocked by bladder-like growths (Fig. 32) from neighboring parenchymatous cells. Such blocking of the water-conducting elements is usually followed by the death of all cells which are still alive in the annual ring, and frequently by an impregnation of the cell walls with dark-colored substances. The xylem of rings so modified becomes dry and then is known as *heart-*

wood. Water and dissolved substances from the roots now travel upward only in the outer, younger rings which constitute the *sapwood.* From year to year more rings in the inner part of the sap-

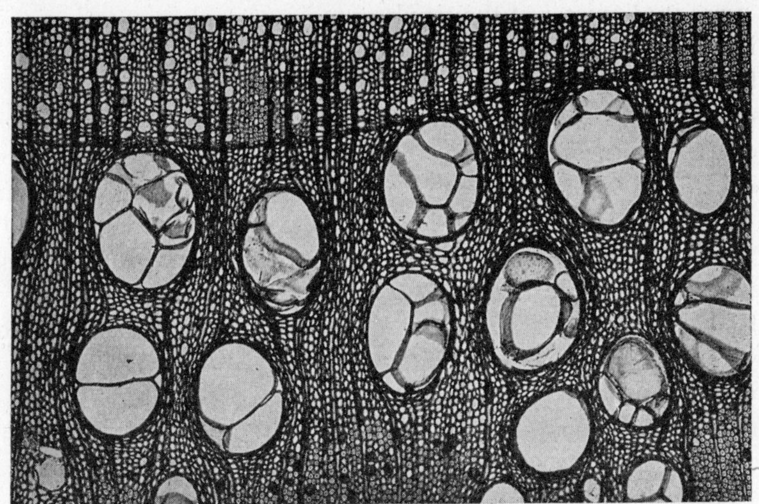

FIG. 32. Portion of a cross section through the heartwood of an oak. The vessels are filled by growths from neighboring cells. Photograph by the Forest Products Laboratory, Madison, Wis.

wood are changed to heartwood. Hence, the sapwood of any particular tree remains of about the same thickness from year to year, whereas the heartwood is continually increasing in diameter. The sapwood may include only a few annual rings, as in the black locust or the black cherry; or, as in the hickory and the maple, it may be many rings in thickness. Xylem that has been changed to heartwood is often stronger mechanically than it was when it was sapwood. The development of heartwood in a tree may, therefore, increase the rigidity of the stem independently of any increase in the number of cells.

If often happens that in very old trees the heartwood has decayed and disappeared, leaving the now hollow trunk composed almost wholly of sapwood. Sycamores are among the largest trees of the eastern United States, often in rich, moist river bottoms of the Ohio Valley becoming three to eight feet in diameter at the base, sometimes even larger. It is uncommon to find sycamore trees two or three or more feet in diameter which are not hollow. Evidently these trees go on living for a very long time after becoming hollow—

producing by cambial activity new sapwood to the outside and meanwhile undergoing progressive decay on the inside of the woody cylinder. The enlargement of the cavity thus keeps pace with the increase in diameter of the trunk.

Bark. The portion of a woody stem external to the cylinder of xylem is usually called the *bark*. The plane of separation between wood and bark is, therefore, the cambium. If the bark is peeled from an older woody stem or branch, only the cylindrical core of wood is left. Bark, freshly peeled from the wood of a living trunk or branch, has on its inner side a layer of relatively soft, white or light-colored tissue that is obviously composed largely of living cells. This zone is often called the *soft bark*. The *hard bark* is a layer of varying thickness which extends beyond the soft bark to the weathered outer surface of the stem.

Cork Cambium. In a very young branch or stem the bark is composed of phloem, pericycle, cortex, and epidermis. The stems of most trees and shrubs and of some herbaceous plants develop a *cork cambium* during their first growing season (Fig. 33). This cork cambium usually arises in the outermost portion of the cortex; but it may develop from the epidermis, as in the apple, or within the pericycle, as in the currant. When the cork cambium is about to form in any of these regions, the mature living cells of one layer lose their central vacuoles, and their dense cytoplasm increases in amount. A tangential division of each of these cells then results in the establishment of a new cylinder of meristematic cells which is similar to the true cambium in appearance and in the capacity of its cells for division. The cork cambium, however, instead of forming phloem and xylem, produces *cork cells* on its outer face and parenchymatous cells on its inner face. These cells derived from the cork cambium are arranged in more or less uniformly radial rows. The walls of cork cells become impregnated with a fatlike substance; hence, the layer of cork so formed is impermeable to gases, water, and dissolved food substances. Consequently, all the living cells lying outside the cork layer die as a result of being cut off from supplies of food and water, and usually sooner or later are sloughed off. These dry, hard, dead tissues, together with the cork, constitute the hard bark. The soft bark, which is located between the hard bark and the wood (bounded on the outside by the cork cambium and on the inside by the true cambium), is a zone composed of secondary phloem, ray extensions, and parenchyma derived from the inner face of the cork cambium.

The cork at the inner face of the hard bark in many trees is usually but a few cells in thickness. In some trees, however, including the

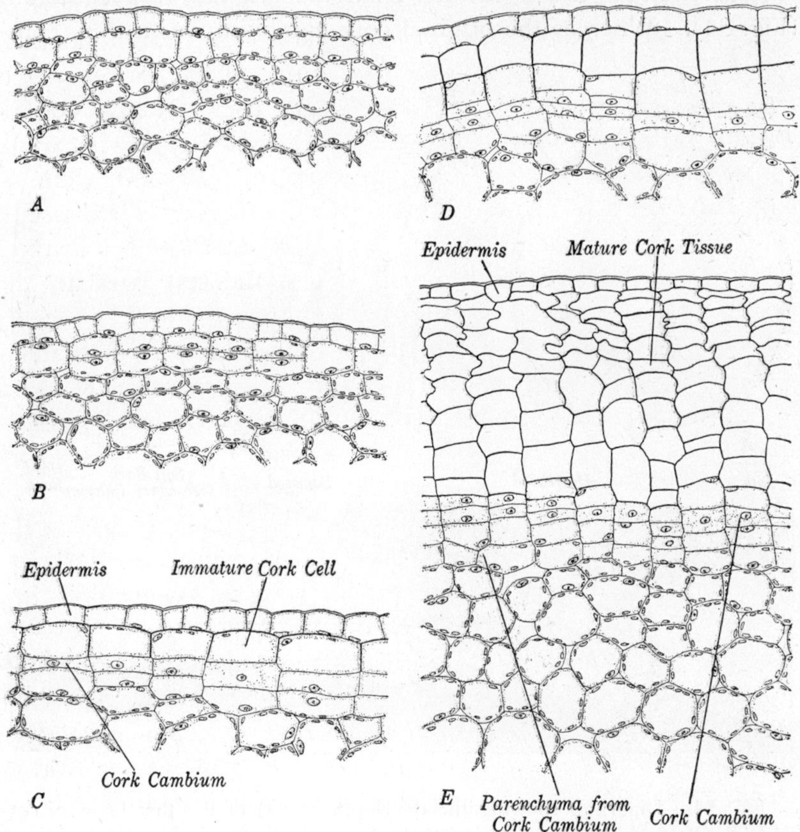

FIG. 33. Portions of cross sections of the outer region of a geranium (Pelargonium) stem. *A*, from a young stem. *B*, cells of the outermost cortical layer are dividing to function as a cork cambium. *C*, the first layer of cork cells is being differentiated. *D*, *E*, successively later stages; cork forming on the outer face of the cork cambium, parenchyma on its inner face.

cork oak, a native of the Mediterranean region which supplies the cork of commerce, many more layers of cork cells are formed and are retained. The cork may attain a thickness of an inch or more. In most woody plants the original cork cambium becomes inactive after a few years, although this layer in some trees, such as birch, beech, cork oak, and some cherries, continues for many years to form new cork cells.

In woody plants whose first-formed cork cambium becomes inactive after a few years, additional cork cambia are developed in living parenchymatous tissues inward from the original cork cambium (Fig. 34). Whereas the original cork cambium was a thin, com-

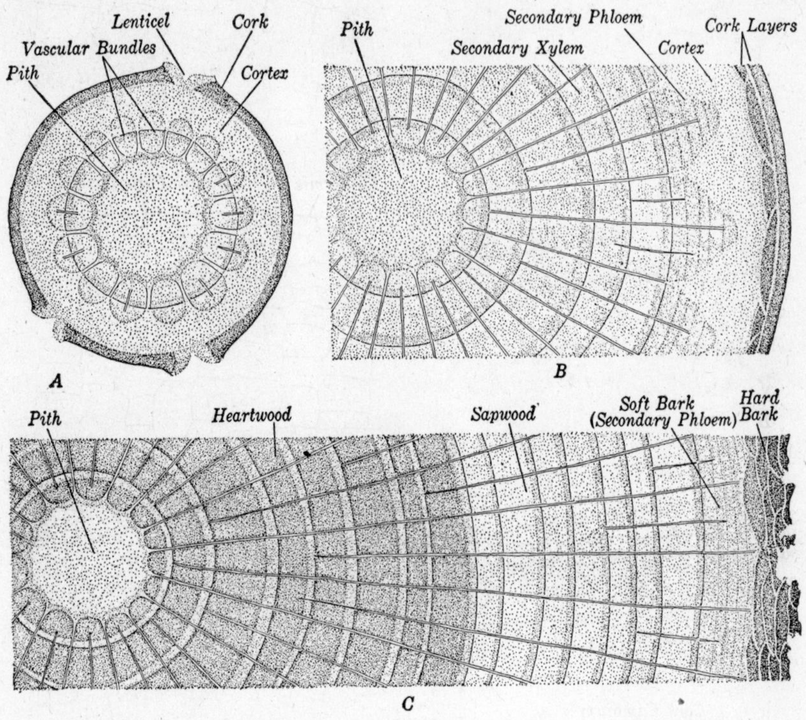

FIG. 34. Diagrams showing the development (*A*) of the first layer of cork and (*B*, *C*) of additional layers inside the first. In *C*. the development of heartwood is shown.

plete cylinder, concentric with the epidermis and with the layers of the cortex, the newer cork cambia which develop successively in the inner portion of the cortex, in the pericycle, and in the outer layers of the phloem have the form of troughlike strips. These strips of cork cambium are convex on their inner sides, and their edges abut upon the convex surfaces of previously formed strips. Seen in cross section, they appear as relatively short intersecting arcs. Each successively formed cork layer shuts off the supply of water and foods to such living cells as lie outside it. These starved groups of cells die, their walls become hard and dry, and so more hard bark is added inside that previously formed.

The cell layers constituting the hard bark often become cracked in consequence of the pressure exerted from within by the expanding cylinder of xylem and phloem, and portions of the hard bark may become separated from the underlying tissues and fall away. The size and form of these separating portions of hard bark are influenced by the relative positions of successive cork cambia, which, as just seen, are usually not concentric zones but troughlike strips. The manner and pattern of cracking of the hard bark are often distinctive of the species. Examples of characteristic cracking are seen in the shaggy bark of hickories, the rough, deeply furrowed bark of oaks, and the shredded bark of grapes. Smooth bark, like that of a birch, is usually produced by the continued activity of the first-formed cork cambium, which is maintained as an uninterrupted continuous cylinder by occasional radial divisions. In this way the cork cambium accommodates itself without cracking to the expansion of the cylinder within.

Lenticels. In the young portions of many stems certain limited regions of the cork cambium, usually beneath stomata, become par-

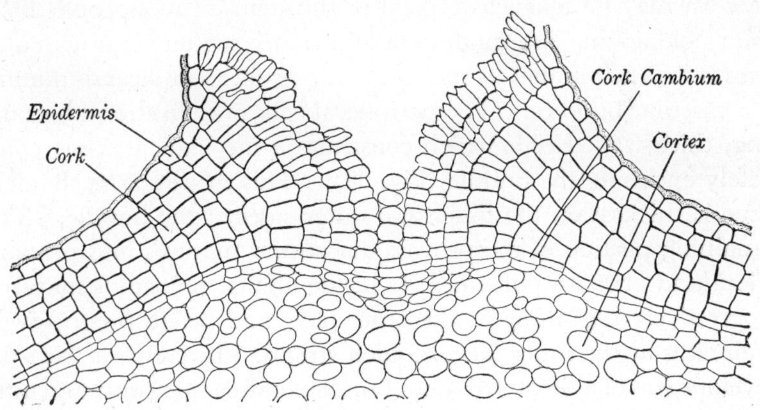

FIG. 35. Cross section of a lenticel of Forsythia.

ticularly active. Repeated tangential divisions in each such region produce a mass of cells, whose enlargement causes a pressure that ruptures the epidermis. The cellular mass then protrudes as a small rounded or elongated swelling called a *lenticel* (Fig. 35). The characteristic horizontal markings of birch (Fig. 36) and cherry stems, as well as the rounded markings on young twigs of the horse chestnut, are lenticels. Between the cells of a lenticel are intercellular spaces continuous with those of the cortex. Through these spaces oxygen may diffuse inward to the living cells of the stem, and the carbon dioxide given off by the living cells may diffuse outward.

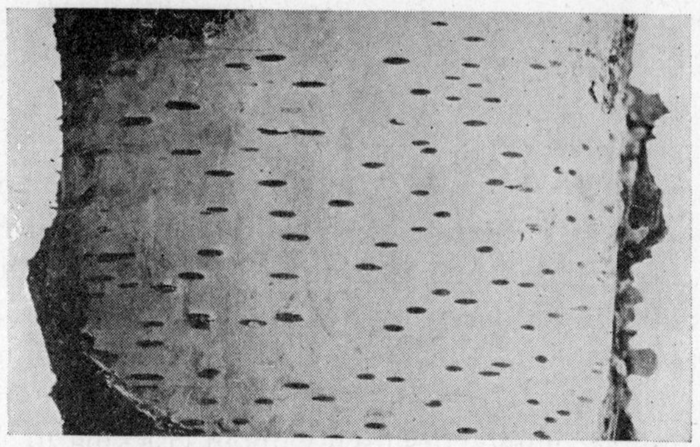

FIG. 36. Portion of a birch stem with horizontal lenticels.

Tissues of a Monocotyledonous Stem (Fig. 37). The stem of the corn may be taken as typical of the stems of monocotyledons. Young elongating internodes contain many scattered provascular strands that lie parallel to one another. Later these strands mature into vascular bundles. The peripheral cells of each strand become long, thick-walled cells which constitute a mechanical tissue completely enclosing the bundle (Fig. 38). This sheath of mechanical tissue is thickest on the inner and outer sides of the bundle. The remaining portion of the provascular strand matures into primary xylem and primary phloem. As in the alfalfa, phloem is matured progressively beginning at the outer face, and xylem progressively beginning at the inner face, of each strand. In contrast with the development of a dicotyledonous bundle, maturation continues until the whole strand, except the sheath of mechanical tissue, is converted into xylem and phloem. There is, therefore, no meristematic region (cambium) separating xylem and phloem, and no possibility of the formation of secondary elements between primary xylem and primary phloem. The phloem consists of regularly arranged sieve tubes and companion cells. The xylem of each mature bundle includes two large vessels with pitted walls, adjacent to the phloem, and between these vessels a few tracheids. The innermost portion of the xylem contains one or two vessels whose walls have spiral or ring-shaped thickenings. Just outside the latter vessel or vessels is a large intercellular space that separates this region of the xylem from the sheath of mechanical tissue.

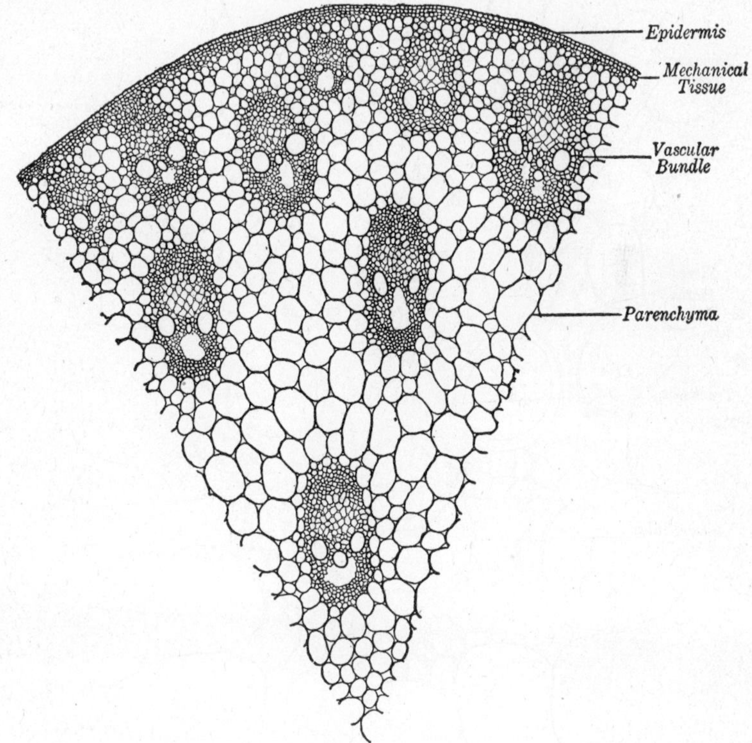

FIG. 37. Cross section of a portion of a corn stem.

The greater part of the stem consists of large parenchymatous cells. Scattered throughout this tissue are vascular bundles. The parenchymatous cells in the central part of the stem may be compared with the pith, and those in the outer portion with the cortex, of the alfalfa. It is impossible, however, to distinguish sharply between pith and cortex in the corn stem. Outside the parenchymatous tissue is a narrow cylinder of mechanical tissue, most of whose cells are small and thick-walled. Outside this is an epidermis of relatively small, thick-walled cells.

Since the corn lacks a cambium, its stem can not increase in diameter after the primary tissues mature. The absence of a cambium in the vascular bundles (Fig. 38) is the chief feature distinguishing most monocotyledonous stems from those of gymno-

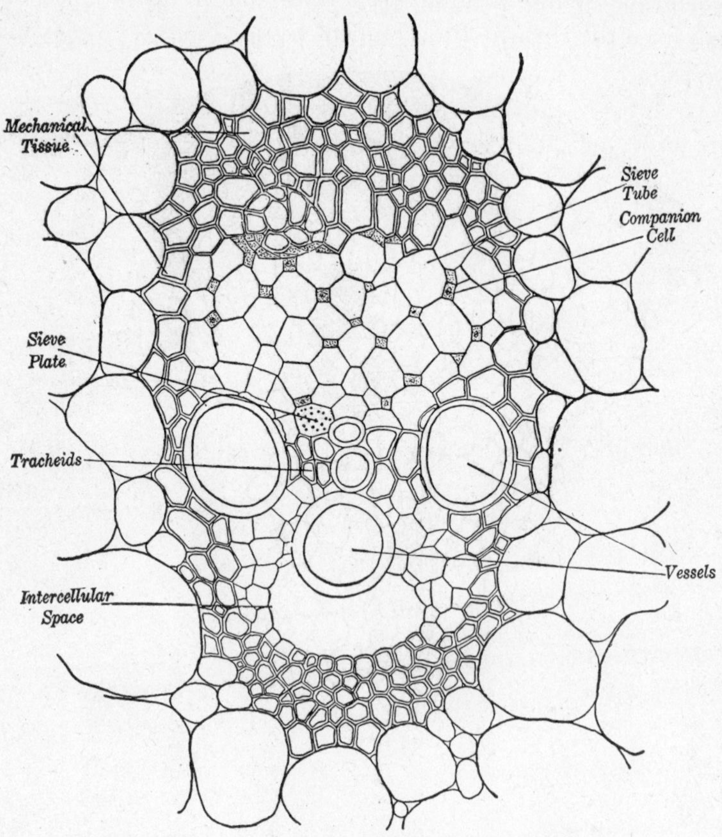

FIG. 38. A vascular bundle from a corn stem.

sperms and dicotyledons. Other respects in which monocotyledons differ from the majority of dicotyledons and from gymnosperms are the scattered arrangement of the vascular bundles, the presence of a sheath of mechanical tissue partially or completely surrounding each bundle, the lack of a well-defined cortex, and the absence of rays.

Growth in Thickness of Monocotyledonous Stems. The stems of most monocotyledons, since they contain no cambium, are incapable of growth in thickness after the cells in any particular region have attained their full size. Hence, certain monocotyledons, such as some bamboos, although they grow rapidly to a considerable height, sometimes extending many inches upward each day during the growing season, remain slender. The trunks of some other monocotyledons, like the date and the coconut palm, taper gradually from base to apex. In these, cells enlarge and mature progressively from the apex of the stem to the base. The greater diameter of the basal portion of the trunk is due, therefore, not to the formation of new cells but to the delayed enlargement of the cells which were formed when that region was meristematic.

FIG. 39. The Joshua tree (*Yucca brevifolia*), a monocotyledonous tree of the Mojave Desert. Photograph courtesy of Forrest Shreve.

The stems of a few monocotyledons, such as the Joshua tree of the Southwest (Fig. 39), aloe, and dracaena (the dragon tree), undergo a true secondary thickening, although their vascular bundles are without cambium. In the Joshua tree, a cylinder of meristematic cells in the pericycle functions as a cambium, by means of which the stem grows slowly in thickness from year to year. Groups of new cells formed on the inner side of this cambium develop into entire vascular bundles; the new cells formed on the outer side of the cambium remain parenchymatous.

Wound Tissue. As illustrated in the origin of cork cambium and in the completion between vascular bundles of the cylinder of true cambium, many thin-walled mature cells are capable on occasion of resuming the characteristics of meristematic cells. When the stems, roots, or even leaves of some plants are exposed to unusual stimuli such as that of wounding, as for example when a branch is cut from the stem, the exposed thin-walled living cells are stimulated to divide. Such cambium cells and cells of the soft bark as are exposed by the wounding become particularly active. The

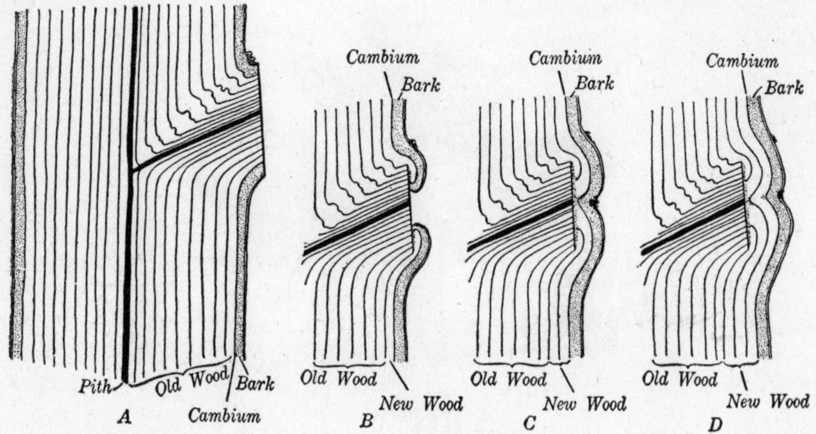

FIG. 40. The process of healing of a wound produced by cutting off a branch. *A*, just after the wounding. *B*, *C*, *D*, successive stages in the development of a callus. *Old Wood*, the layers present at the time the branch was removed; *New Wood*, later-formed layers.

result is the formation of *wound tissue* or *callus* (Fig. 40). The walls of the outer cells of the callus become impregnated with waxy compounds, and these cells function as do cork cells in preventing the evaporation of water from tissues beneath. Certain deeper-lying callus cells become a cambium which is continuous with the cambium in the stem (Fig. 40, *B*). The cambium in the callus, like that in the body of the stem, forms secondary xylem on its inner side and secondary phloem on its outer side. These secondary tissues, together with the callus tissues outside them, gradually grow inward from all sides over the cut surface. The circle of exposed wood becomes progressively smaller, and the callus may in time extend completely over the wounded surface (Fig. 40, *C*). As additional elements are added by the cambium, which is now continuous, the original cut surface exposed in the wound becomes more and more deeply buried (Fig. 40, *D*). The healing or covering over of exposed surfaces largely prevents the entrance into the wound of decay- and disease-producing fungi.

Grafting and Budding. The formation of wound tissue on cut surfaces makes *grafting* possible. Grafting is commonly practiced in the propagation of such woody plants as do not readily form roots on cuttings. Grafting also makes possible the perpetuation of plants which, because of some change in their normal behavior, have lost the ability to produce seeds; and seedlessness in fruits is often commercially desirable. Familiar examples of seedless plants are certain raisin grapes and the navel oranges. Grafting is conveniently used also to obtain duplicates of a desirable plant which, because of its hybrid nature, will not breed true by means of seeds.

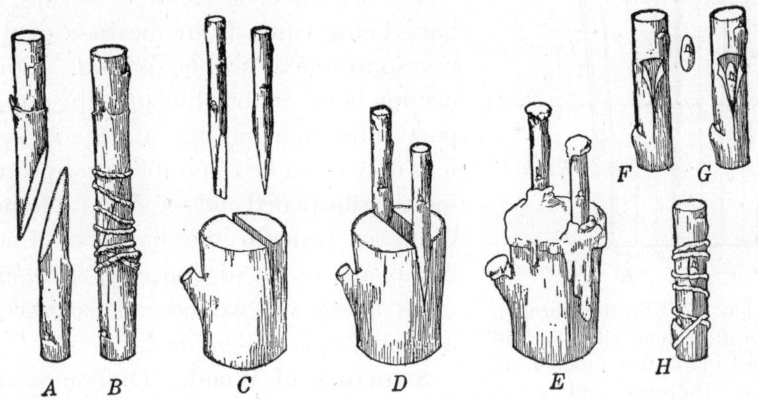

FIG. 41. Methods of grafting. *A*, *B*, between stock and scion of similar size. *C*, *D*, *E*, between a large stock and small scions. *F–H*, bud-grafting.

In order to make a graft, a *scion* and a *stock* are required. The scion is usually a part of a branch bearing one or more buds. This is the part that is to grow into a shoot system, eventually bearing the flowers or fruits characteristic of the plant from which the scion was cut. The stock is commonly a piece of a root or of a stem which will produce roots; or it may be a growing, rooted plant cut back for the purpose but not removed from the soil. The two parts of the graft are so cut that the exposed cambial regions of stock and scion fit closely when the two are brought together (Fig. 41). Immediately after the graft is made, the region of the graft is covered with a waterproofing material or with adhesive tape. With renewed cambial activity a union is effected (Fig. 42), and the main bud of the scion becomes the terminal shoot of the new plant. Budding is similar to grafting except that the scion is a single bud cut out with neighboring bark and cambium and inserted under flaps made by slitting the bark of the stock. Grafts are usually successfully established only when the stock and scion are from plants of the same or of closely related species.

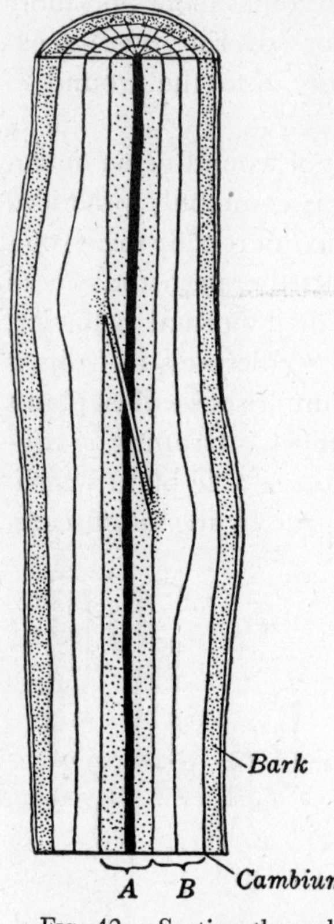

FIG. 42. Section through a grafted stem; the diagonal lines mark the junction of stock (below) and scion. *A*, wood layers present when the graft was made. *B*, layers formed after the grafting.

Fruit trees are often "girdled" in the winter by mice or rabbits—a ring of bark being eaten from the base of the tree so as to expose the sapwood. Connection between the phloem in the upper part of the tree and that in the root system may often be re-established by forcing the sharpened ends of pieces of living branches beneath the bark on either side of the break so that each piece extends across the wound. This process is known as *bridge-grafting*.

Structure of Wood. Differences in strength, elasticity, and weight, as well as differences in surface patterns of lumber cut from various woods, are directly correlated with differences in microscopic structure. Workability, resistance to splitting or splintering, and general usefulness as sources of lumber or fuel also are characteristics which vary with differences in wood structure. Some of these differences are due to variations in width of annual rings, in relative amounts of spring and summer wood in each ring, and in thickness and extent of the rays. Depending upon differences in the kinds of xylem cells which are present, the thickness of their walls, the diameters of cell cavities relative to wall thickness, and the proportions in which various types of xylem cells occur, woods may be light or heavy, tough or brittle. The woods of hickory and ash, which contain many long fibers as well as thick-walled vessels and tracheids, are tough, elastic, and heavy, well suited for tool handles and implement parts. Willow and poplar woods, in which thin-walled vessels predominate, are light and brittle.

Some woods have a large proportion of thick-walled conductive elements but lack sufficient fibers to make them tough. Such woods are heavy but brittle. Balsa, one of the lightest of woods (Fig. 43, *A*), and the tropical lignum vitae, one of the heaviest (Fig. 43, *B*), represent extremes in wood structure. Just as the presence of many thick-walled fibers and other wood cells lends strength and toughness to certain woods, so also the presence of broad layers of thick-walled summer tracheids in the annual rings of southern yellow pine results in a timber that is most suitable for use where strength is especially required. Sharp differences between spring and summer wood or the presence of masses of fibers may, however, cause a timber to be hard to work and therefore less desirable than one which, like that of the white pine, has a uniform texture. Even when the secondary xylem of two species is composed of similar types of cells and includes like proportions of spring and summer wood, differences in the length of the elements and in the nature of the cell walls may make the two sorts of timber markedly different in character. It is because of such differences that spruce is much tougher and lighter than most pines.

Woods differ greatly in color, in figure or grain, and in surface texture. Color is affected chiefly by changes which occur when sapwood is transformed into heartwood; the heartwood may be black as in ebony, brown as in walnut, or red as in mahogany. The patterns produced on a cut surface by rays, fibers, and other xylem elements, as well as by the alternations of summer and spring wood, make lumber from certain species especially valuable for furniture and for the interior finish of buildings. The pattern or grain which is exposed when boards or veneers are cut from logs depends largely upon the manner in which the log is sawed. There are two general methods of sawing (Fig. 44): "plain-sawing," the

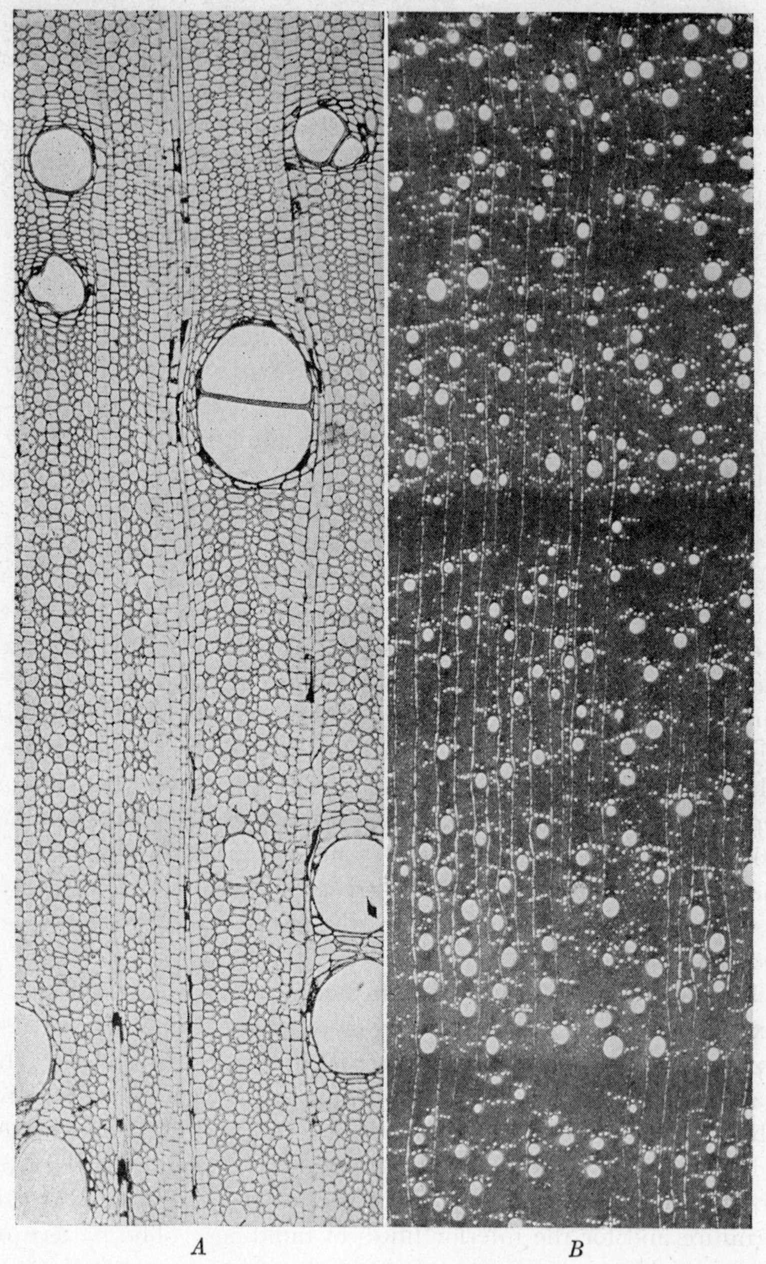

A B

Fig. 43. Portions of cross sections through the wood (*A*) of balsa, (*B*) of lignum vitae. Photographs by the Forest Products Laboratory, Madison, Wis.

lumber being cut at right angles to the rays; and "quarter-sawing," the cutting being parallel to the rays. The term "quarter-sawing" arose from the fact that the log after being slabbed off and squared

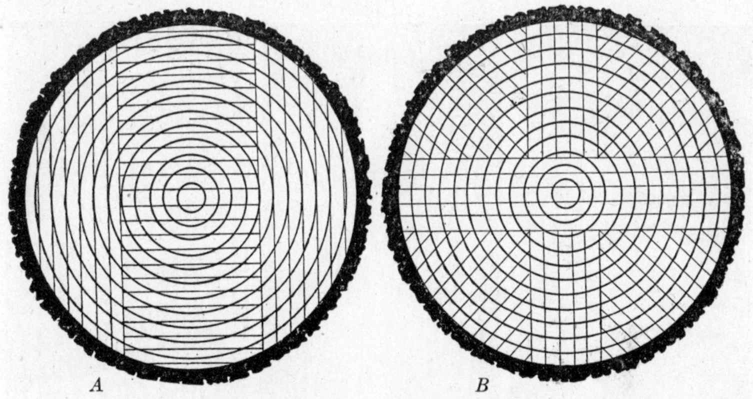

FIG. 44. Methods of sawing a log. *A*, plain-sawing. *B*, quarter-sawing.

is first quartered before any further cuts are made. Even in plain-sawed lumber one or more boards cut from the center of the log are actually quarter-sawed because of cutting parallel with the rays, so exposing the surfaces rather than the cut ends of these rays. Plain-sawing is especially desirable in woods such as southern yellow pine, cypress, and redwood, which have contrasting cylinders of spring and summer wood; woods with elevations or depressions in the cylinders of summer wood also are usually plain-sawed. Plain-sawing of this latter type of wood, as in curly and bird's-eye maple (Fig. 45, *A*), produces a pattern of circular and wavy summer-wood lines against a background of spring wood. Quarter-sawing, on the other hand, may expose a surface with a more striking pattern than does plain-sawing (Fig. 45, *B*, *C*). In oaks and sycamores this pattern results largely from contrasts in color between rays and other tissues. Quarter-sawing of maple, birch, and mahogany gives a surface view that appears wavy. In some mahoganies, the exposing of alternately inclined fiber masses in adjacent rings produces a ribbon-like surface view. Because of irregularities of grain, valuable cabinet woods of unusual pattern may be cut from walnut stumps or from the crotches or burls (abnormal swollen outgrowths) of mahoganies and other woods.

Veneers (thin slices) were formerly produced only from the more expensive woods; but the demand is now so great that the making of veneers from cheaper woods has become an important industry. Veneers cut from red birch are used in the manufacture of door

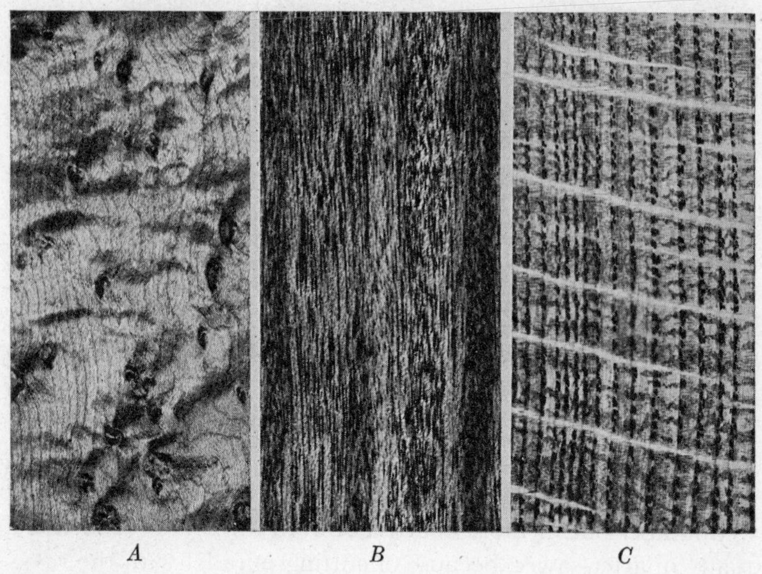

FIG. 45. *A*, plain-sawed bird's-eye maple. *B*, ribbon effect of quarter-sawing "Philippine mahogany." *C*, quarter-sawed oak. Photographs by the Forest Products Laboratory, Madison, Wis.

panels, furniture, and partitions. Besides covering cheaper woods, sometimes even metals or plastics are covered with such very thin slices of expensive woods. Veneers an eighth of an inch or more in thickness are cut from cheap woods and are glued together in layers to build up boards known as *plywood*. Each sheet of veneer is placed so that its grain lies at right angles to the grain of the sheets above and below it. Because of the arrangement of the wood fibers in plywood, this material is far stronger than is an ordinary board of the same thickness and the same weight. Plywood, therefore, is used where lightness or thinness is desired in addition to strength of material. Sawmill wastes such as slabwood, edgings, planer chips, and sawdust which were formerly burned in outdoor incinerators at the mill are now used in a variety of ways. Sheet "presswood," for example, is made by cementing together under pressure the fragments of finely shredded wood. In paper-making, lignin, a substance impregnating the walls of wood cells during their development, is dissolved out and was formerly discarded as waste. Experiments are now being conducted which are leading toward the utilization of lignin as the basis for a cheap plastic from which a vast number of articles, many formerly pressed from hard rubber, may be made. Basswood, cottonwood, and yellow pine are made into excelsior, used for upholstering, packing, and filtering.

Branches. A branch begins as a small rounded hump of meristematic tissue in the axil (the angle between leaf and stem) of a young leaf just back of the meristematic region of the stem (Fig. 18). Although there is usually such a *branch primordium* in the axil of each leaf, only a few of the primordia ultimately develop into branches.

If the plant is one whose normal span of life is a single year, the primordia destined to become branches begin to elongate soon after they appear. Elongation is soon followed by an organization in each elongating primordium of regions corresponding to those present in the stem—namely, a meristematic region, a region of elongation, a region of maturation, and a mature region. The tissues matured in a branch are similar to those of the stem, and each tissue of the branch is continuous with the corresponding tissue of the stem. Water and food materials can therefore pass from the xylem of the stem to that of the branch, and foods manufactured in the branch can pass through its phloem to that of the stem. The secondary tissues of the branch are similarly continuous with those of the stem.

Branch primordia of most trees and shrubs do not develop into branches during the year that they appear; but after developing to a certain stage, they remain dormant or continue to grow very slowly. Such *buds* may begin to elongate rapidly the year after they are formed, or they may remain dormant for several or many years.

The growth in length of a stem and of its branches is accompanied by the formation of an ever-increasing number of new branches. If all such branches were to persist and to increase in diameter by secondary thickening, the system of branches might become so closely crowded that they with their leaves would densely shade one another. Such a condition is rarely found in trees, however, because many of the young branches, especially those toward the inside, die within a few years of their formation. In many trees this dying of smaller inner branches results in the formation of a continuously expanding hollow "crown." In some trees, such as the cottonwood, the death of a branch is due to the development of a basal transverse *abscission layer*, which causes the branch to become separated from the stem or older branch bearing it. In most trees no abscission layer is formed at the base of a branch; a dead branch remains attached to the tree until it is broken off by storms or by other means.

Knots. If a dead branch remains on a tree for some time, the secondary tissues of the stem formed each year imbed more and more of the basal portion of the branch which, for a time at least, is still covered by remains of dead bark. In some trees, such as the white pine, dead branches may persist for many years. When the branch finally breaks off, the broken end may become completely overgrown as the trunk continues to increase in diameter. A board sawed from a log through the buried base of a branch will therefore contain a portion of the branch, which appears as a *knot*. The base of a dead branch often loosens because of shrinkage of the wood around it and falls out, leaving a knot hole. If trees are in a close stand, their lower branches, because of lack of light, die while they are still slender; the knots which are left are therefore small. Lumber cut from such logs is relatively "clear." Trees in a scattered stand receive adequate illumination not only upon their tips but upon their sides as well. The lower branches of such trees are retained in a living condition, often for many years, and continue to increase in diameter along with the increase in girth of the trunk. Lumber cut from such trees contains many large knots and hence is of poorer grade than "clear" lumber.

Variations in Stems. The height of a tree and the thickness of its trunk vary with the species, with the age of the tree, and with the environment. At high elevations, plants of species which at lower levels develop into large trees often have small, twisted, gnarled, and more or less prostrate stems (Fig. 46). Under conditions that favor growth, trees of certain species attain a great height and develop huge trunks. The "big trees" of California (Fig. 47) are notable illustrations. Some of the dimensions to which they attain will be noted in Chapter XXVIII. The numbers of annual rings counted in the stumps of a few of these trees indicate that they were more than 3,000 years old when felled, the oldest one thus far counted having been somewhat more than 3,200 years of age. The closely related redwoods reach even greater heights than do the "big trees" but remain of smaller diameter.

FIG. 46. A pine growing at a relatively high altitude (Sentinel Dome, Yosemite), showing the dwarfing and distorting effects of snow and wind. Photograph by Phillips D. Schneider, received through the courtesy of G. J. Peirce.

Some vines, such as the morning glory and the lima bean (Fig. 48), climb by means of the twining of their stems, the terminal portion of such a stem moving through a rather large spiral as a result of periodicities in growth on different sides. If a stem of this type comes in contact with a support, the spiral movement of the terminal portion causes the stem to twine about the supporting object. The coils are at first often very loose; but later, through a straightening of the stem, the spirals become steep and firmly bound about the support. Other vines climb by means of tendrils. The tendrils of the garden pea (Fig. 66, *A*) correspond to leaflets; those of the grape (Fig. 49), to branches. Tendrils are usually sensitive to contact, especially toward their tips. Contact with an object serves as a stimulus, and in the cases of most tendrils the end within a short time becomes tightly wound about the object touched. In the Japanese ivy and the Virginia creeper, the small branches of the tendrils end

Fig. 47. "Big trees" in the Mariposa Grove, Yosemite National Park. Copyrighted photograph by Gabriel Moulin. Courtesy of Save-the-Redwoods League.

in knobs. Upon contact with solid objects the knobs broaden into disk-shaped structures that adhere with extreme tenacity to the surface with which they are in contact. If these disks happen to be fastened to soft rock, bits of the surface often come loose with the branch ends when such a vine is forcibly removed from its support.

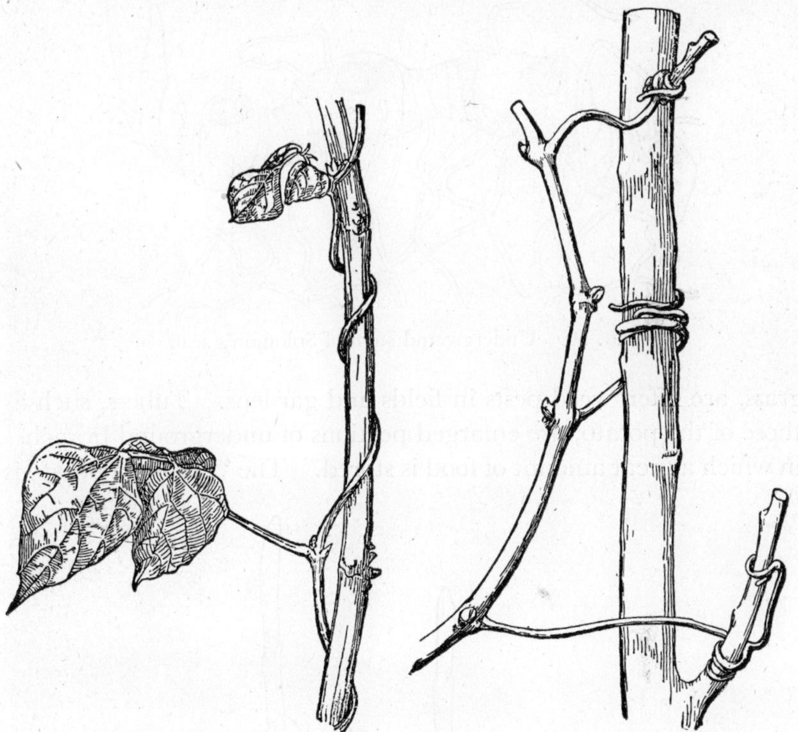

FIG. 48. The twining stem of a bean. FIG. 49. Tendrils of the grape.

Certain plants, such as the English ivy, climb by means of aerial roots growing from the stem; the roots wedge themselves into crevices and cracks of the supporting surface.

The stems of many plants grow underground. A whole stem with its branches may be underground, as is the case in many ferns, of which only the leaves appear above the surface; or, more frequently in seed plants, the underground stem produces aerial branches which bear foliage leaves and flowers. The latter case is illustrated by cattails, sedges, grasses, and goldenrods. Underground stems (Figs. 50, 51) often contain a considerable amount of food. If such a stem is broken into numerous parts, roots and aerial branches may be developed at each node, new plants being so produced. It is for this reason that certain grasses, like the quack

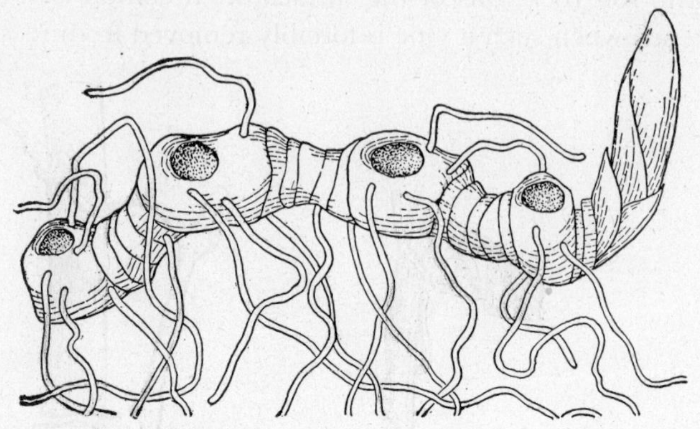

FIG. 50. Underground stem of Solomon's seal.

grass, are often weed pests in fields and gardens. Tubers, such as those of the potato, are enlarged portions of underground branches in which a great amount of food is stored. The "eye" of a potato is

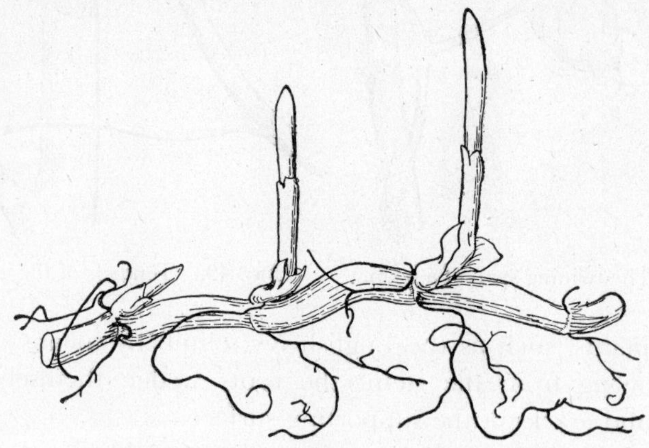

FIG. 51. Underground stem of quack grass.

a node at which is an undeveloped leaf with buds in its axil. Each bud is capable of forming a shoot and thus a new plant.

Many plants have very short stems that are partly or wholly buried in the ground. Short stems of this type are often associated with large, fleshy roots containing reserves of food, as in the parsnip, carrot, beet, and dandelion. In other cases, as in the jack-in-the-pulpit and the crocus (Fig. 52, *A*), the short stem with a few scaly leaves attached is itself the storage organ and is consequently enlarged and fleshy.

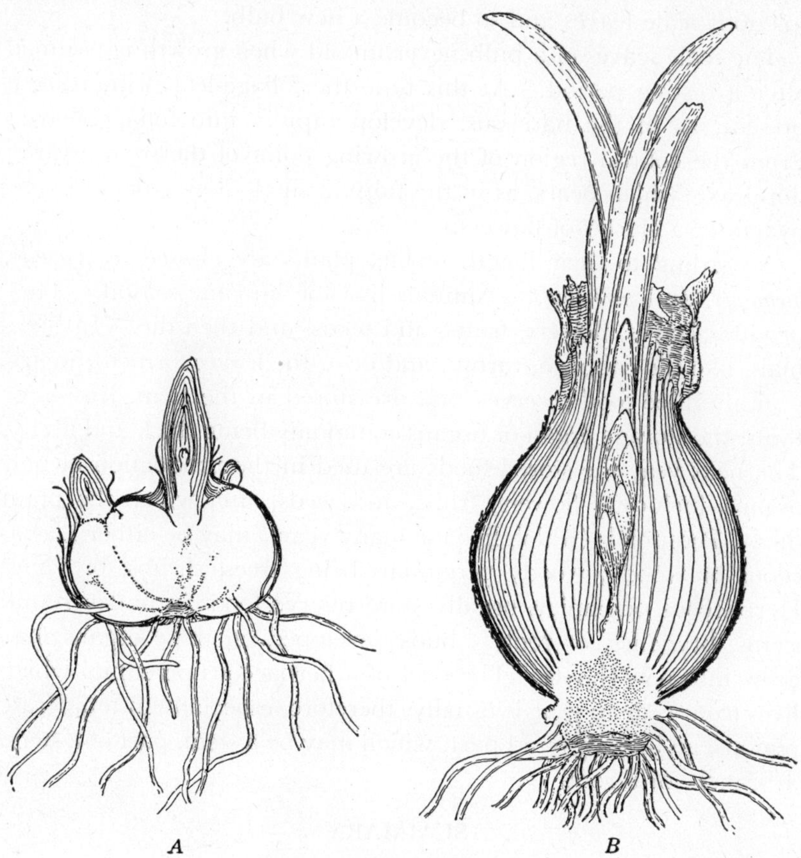

Fig. 52. *A*, the short, thick underground stem of a crocus. *B*, the bulb of a hyacinth. Both in vertical section.

Some plants produce underground bodies commonly known as *bulbs*. Among such plants are the hyacinth, narcissus, onion, and tulip. A median lengthwise section (Fig. 52, *B*) of one of these bulbs shows that it has a short conical stem. The upper surface of the stem bears many broad, fleshy scale leaves enclosing the terminal growing point and, in some plants at least, the primordia of foliage leaves and flowers. The short stem and many of the scale leaves are storage organs containing abundant reserve food, often in the form of sugar. From the outer lower edge of the stem grow many roots. Among the new growing points which arise in the axils of the scale leaves, an occasional one may itself develop conspicuous scale leaves and so become a new bulb.

The scale leaves of a bulb never unfold when growth is resumed after a resting period. At this time the foliage-leaf primordia, if present, as in the narcissus, develop rapidly into foliage leaves. From the central region of the growing point of the stem arises a floral axis which bears, as in the tulip, a single flower or, as in the hyacinth, a cluster of flowers.

According to their length of life, plants are classed as *annuals*, *biennials*, and *perennials*. Annuals live for but one season. They produce leaves, flowers, fruits, and seeds, and then die. In biennials, like the cabbage, turnip, and beet, the leaves formed the first year produce food reserves that are stored in the stem, leaves, or roots, the storage organ or organs commonly being thick and fleshy. The next year the stored foods are used in the production of new organs, including flowers, fruits, and seeds, after which the plant dies. Perennials (which live for many years) may be either herbaceous or woody, woody perennials being trees, shrubs, or vines. Herbaceous perennials usually store reserve foods in underground stems, branches, or roots. Buds developed on these organs may grow into new shoots. The part of a herbaceous perennial which lives from year to year is usually, therefore, especially in temperate regions, an underground part, which may be a stem, part of a stem, a branch, or a root.

SUMMARY

A convenient grouping of the seed plants takes consideration of size, the proportion of wood, and the extent of the stem. On this basis there are trees, shrubs, and herbs. A plant whose stem can not hold itself erect may creep or clamber; if the stem can attach itself to a support and so grow upward, the plant is a vine. Vines may be woody or herbaceous.

The functions of a stem include, besides the varied activities involved in its own growth, the development and support of leaves and flowers, the conduction of substances, and the manufacture and storage of foods.

The growing apex of a stem includes a meristematic region, a region of elongation, a region of maturation, and a mature region. The three latter regions are differentiated into nodes and internodes. In the stems of dicotyledons and gymnosperms the vascular bundles are characteristically arranged in the form of a hollow cylinder. In stems of monocotyledons the vascular bundles are as a general rule numerous and scattered.

Internodes of a dicotyledonous stem consist of stele, cortex, and epidermis. Tissues of the stele include pith, xylem, cambium, phloem, rays, and pericycle. The cortex includes mechanical tissue, parenchyma, and endodermis. A node differs from an internode in that there are leaf traces present in its cortex.

A stem of a dicotyledon or of a gymnosperm develops a cambium, the division of whose cells results in the formation of secondary xylem and secondary phloem. The secondary xylem (with included rays) formed in each growing season constitutes an annual ring. Annual rings are distinguishable because of differences in size between elements formed at the beginning and those formed at the end of each growing season. Older annual rings toward the center of a tree may be modified into heartwood. In such a case, movement of sap is restricted to the outer annual rings, the sapwood.

Bark includes all tissues outside the cambium. In a young stem the bark is composed of phloem, rays, pericycle, cortex, and epidermis. The bark of an older stem includes also a cork layer (or layers) produced by a cork cambium, which usually arises in the outermost portion of the cortex. Several successive cork cambia may be formed by a stem. Lenticels may be present in the outer surface of the bark.

Internodes of monocotyledons are ordinarily not sharply differentiated into cortex and stele. In the numerous scattered vascular bundles there is no cambium between xylem and phloem. Most monocotyledonous stems have no secondary thickening. Those which thicken secondarily have a cambium which produces complete new vascular bundles.

A wounded portion of a stem may form a wound tissue (callus). Grafting (including budding) is made possible by the ability of tissues in the vicinity of a wound to proliferate. Differentiation of cells then results in the establishment of vascular connection between stock and scion.

Branch primordia are formed in the embryonic regions in the axils of leaves. A branch primordium may develop immediately into a branch or may remain dormant for one or more years.

Trees vary in size according to species, age, and environment. Stems that grow underground are either erect or horizontal. They may be entirely subterranean or may produce aerial branches. According to their length of life, plants are classed as annuals, biennials, and perennials.

CHAPTER V

BUDS

Nature and Positions of Buds. As noted in the previous chapter, leaf primordia (Fig. 18) arise from the apical meristematic region of a stem or branch. Immediately below the tip of this region the leaf primordia appear as small protuberances. Still farther down, the young leaves developed from older primordia have grown and curved so as to enclose the meristematic region. Such an end portion of a stem or branch with its unelongated internodes bearing leaf primordia, as well as partially or fully developed leaves which curve and enclose the growing point, is a *terminal bud.*

As the older internodes within the bud elongate, the leaves adjoining them are separated by greater distances. With growth, these older leaves become flattened and spread out, no longer enclosing the bud. But as long as the stem continues to grow, new leaf primordia may be formed near the apex; and these are covered by the young leaves just behind them. The terminal bud, therefore, is continuously present as long as the stem tip remains alive.

In the axil of each leaf primordium is a small portion of the stem which remains meristematic. In such a meristematic axillary region a protuberance often develops which becomes a *branch primordium* (Fig. 18). As the older internodes within the terminal bud grow, some of the branch primordia elongate, produce leaf primordia near their own tips, and so become *axillary buds* (Fig. 53). An axillary bud has essentially the same structure as a terminal bud.

Buds which may appear in other than terminal or axillary positions are *adventitious buds.* These are similar in structure to terminal and axillary buds. Adventitious buds arise from various tissues of leaves, as in the begonia and the African violet, from the cortex of a stem, from the pericycle of a stem or root, or from the callus tissue produced on the wounded surface of a stem or root. The sprouts that appear on the cut surfaces of tree stumps, on exposed portions of roots, or on such fleshy food-storage roots as those of the sweet potato, result from the elongation of adventitious buds.

Content of Buds. Buds, whether terminal, axillary, or adventitious, are of various types with regard to the immature parts that they contain. A bud which, as already described, includes a meristematic stem tip with its nodes and unelongated internodes and the primordia of leaves is a *foliage bud.* Leaf primordia within a foliage bud may or may not have primordia of branches in their axils. Buds of another type (*floral buds*) include, as in the buttercup (Fig. 54), the primordia of the various parts of a flower or, as in the cherry, plum, or peach, of a cluster of flowers. If, as for example in the apple, lilac, or horse chestnut, a bud contains primordia of leaves and possibly of branches in addition to those of a flower or flowers, the bud is a *mixed bud* (Fig. 55). While these three types inter-

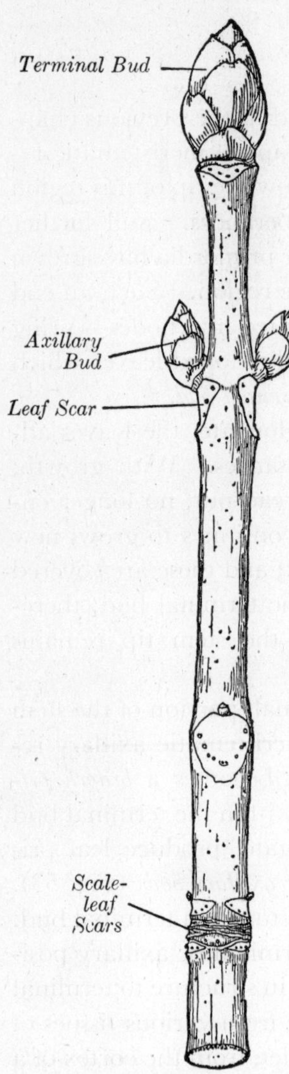

Fig. 53. A branch of the horse chestnut bearing terminal and axillary protected buds.

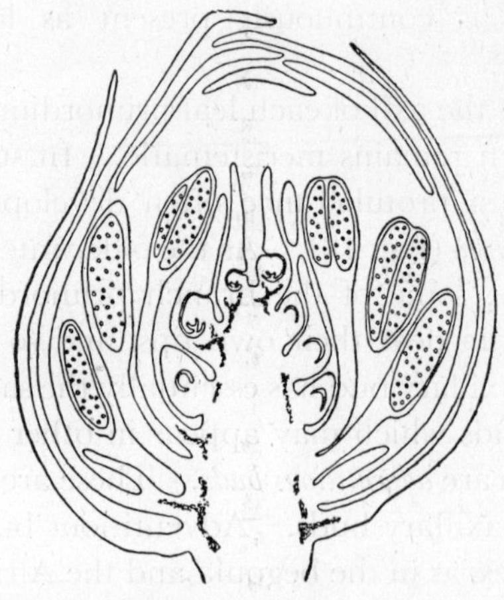

Fig. 54. Lengthwise section of an axillary naked floral bud of the buttercup, containing the parts of a single flower enclosed by foliage leaves. Diagrammatic.

grade to some extent, buds in general fall into the three categories mentioned.

Protected and Naked Buds. If the outermost leaves of a bud are scalelike, it is a *protected bud* (Fig. 56). Most trees and shrubs of temperate regions form buds of this type. In a protected bud the outermost scale leaves commonly overlap and are often heavily cutinized or covered with waxy or resinous substances. In addition, hairs may be borne on the surfaces or margins of the scales. Such secretions and outgrowths tend to prevent the loss of water and the consequent drying of the enclosed immature parts of the bud. Scale leaves afford protection also against mechanical injury.

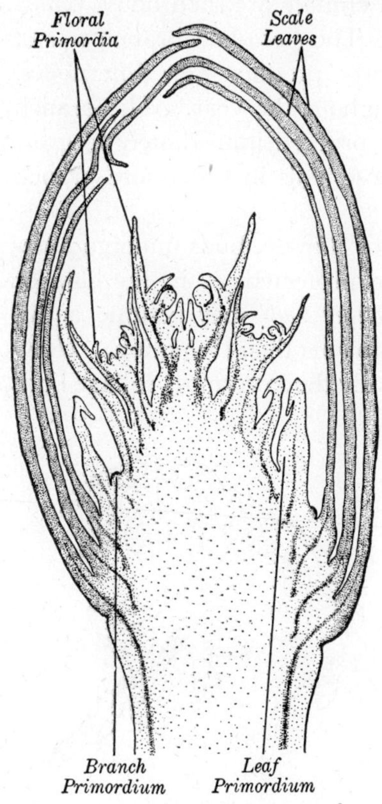

Fig. 55. Lengthwise section through an axillary protected mixed bud of the apple. Diagrammatic.

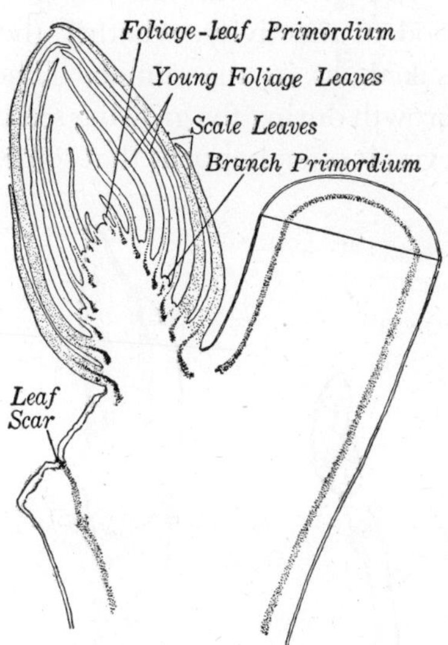

Fig. 56. Lengthwise section through an axillary protected foliage bud of the elm. Diagrammatic.

If the leaves borne by a bud, including the outermost one, are all foliage leaves, the bud is *naked*. Such buds, with no scale leaves, are characteristic of all annuals, of most biennials, and of a few perennials such as juniper and sumac.

Time of Development of Buds. Naked buds in which there is no cessation of continued growth are *active buds*. All foliage buds of annuals are active buds; so, also, are those of most biennials. Perennials with active buds are chiefly those native to regions where the climate is mild throughout the year. Familiar examples of these perennials from regions with a mild climate are such house plants as geranium, begonias, and coleus. The stem and branch tips of plants with active buds continuously produce new internodes, leaves, and branch primordia throughout the year. The branch primordia or many of them usually proceed immediately to grow into branches bearing leaves in whose axils in turn more branch primordia may be produced.

In regions with seasonal changes of climate, buds undergo a period of inactivity, whether they are protected, as in the elm, or naked, as in the sumac. These *resting buds* may resume active growth during the growing season following their formation. However, it often happens that some, usually the lowermost, foliage buds

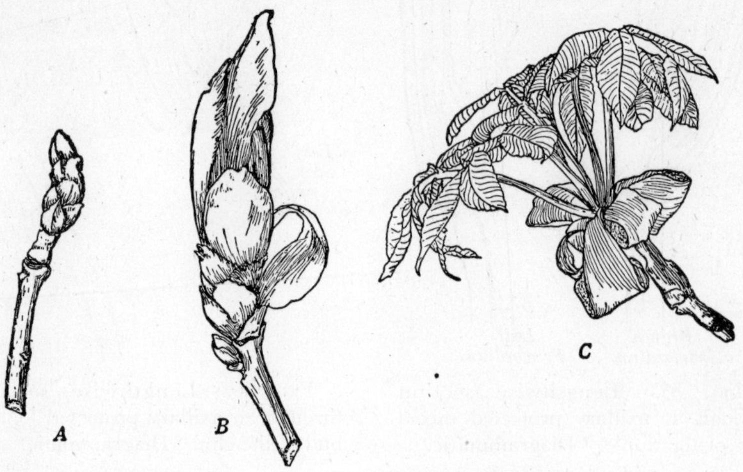

FIG. 57. Axillary protected leaf buds of the hickory in successive stages of development. *A*, winter condition. *B*, beginning of elongation in the spring; scale leaves greatly expanded. *C*, after the foliage leaves have emerged; scale leaves still present.

on a twig or branch are delayed in their further development for several or many years if, indeed, they develop at all. Such delayed or *latent buds* may be stimulated to resume activity after years of latency if the resting or developing buds above them die or are removed. If an unusually late spring frost kills the unfolding buds on a tree, the latent buds are stimulated to unfold.

Unfolding of Resting Buds (Fig. 57). When a protected foliage bud resumes growth, the scale leaves expand, and sooner or later they are shed. The opening of the bud is accompanied by a very rapid elongation of the internodes within it and by a rapid development of the immature foliage leaves to maturity. This rapid maturation of immature leaves accounts for the suddenness with which a tree puts forth new leaves in the spring. All the leaves borne by some trees, such as the horse chestnut, were present in an immature condition in protected buds at the beginning of the growing season; in other trees additional foliage leaves are formed from the meristematic region of the stem tip. In most woody plants the terminal bud persists and becomes a resting bud at the end of the growing season. But in certain other woody plants, including the elm, the tissues at the end of the stem die during the course of the growing season. In the case of the elm (Fig. 58), an axillary foliage bud ordinarily develops at the living node of the stem nearest the dead stem tip. At this bud grows, it crowds the dead stem end over to one side; when the leaves fall, the axillary bud seems to occupy a terminal position on the stem. It is this bud which will extend the stem during the following growing season.

After the shedding of the scale leaves, the former place of attachment of each is marked by a scar on the stem. Since the internodes between the places of attachment of the scale leaves elongate but slightly, the scars left by the scale leaves form a ring about the stem (Fig. 53) instead of being scattered along it. In parts of the world where scale leaves are shed each year, it is therefore possible to determine the age of a branch by counting the spaces between successive circles of scale-leaf scars. With increase in diameter of the stem, however, these rings are eventually obliterated.

Protected floral buds are usually axillary. When such a bud opens, the scale leaves, as in the case of foliage buds, expand and fall, leaving a group of scale-leaf scars. The undeveloped portion of the branch within the bud elongates somewhat, and the floral primordia which it bears expand into one or more flowers. In many plants the unfolding of floral buds occurs before the unfolding of foliage buds. Indeed, as in the elm (Fig. 58), the flowers may

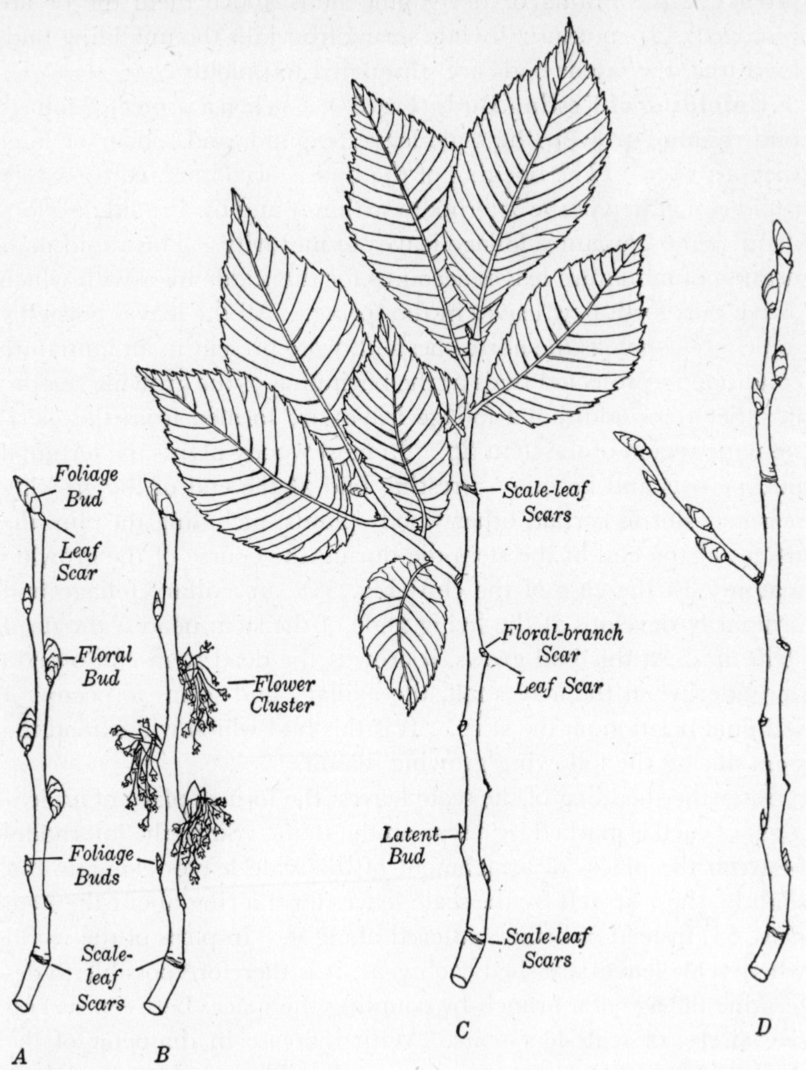

FIG. 58. The seasonal history of an elm twig and of its protected buds. *A*, winter condition. *B*, early spring; the floral buds have developed into floral branches bearing clusters of flowers. *C*, midsummer; two foliage buds toward the tip of the twig have developed into branches bearing leaves; two foliage buds toward the base have remained latent; the floral branches have developed mature fruits and have fallen, leaving floral-branch scars. *D*, late autumn; the leaves have fallen: in the axils are protected foliage and floral buds.

produce mature fruits, the fruits may be shed, and the floral branch itself may have fallen, leaving a floral-branch scar, before the foliage leaves have developed fully. In other cases, as in the cherry, although the floral buds unfold early, the fruits do not mature until some weeks after the foliage leaves have developed.

FIG. 59. The larch, a tree with a conspicuous central shaft; growth from the terminal bud of the stem is more rapid than growth from the terminal buds of branches.

In the unfolding of a protected mixed bud, floral and leaf primordia may mature simultaneously; or the floral primordia may mature more rapidly than the primordia of leaves. The horse chestnut is an example of the former type; the apple, of the latter.

Buds and Plant Form. The form of a plant is dependent largely upon the number and positions of its buds and upon the time and manner of their development. Many conifers, such as the pine,

FIG. 60. The elm, a tree in which the terminal growth of branches is nearly as active as that of the central axis. Photograph by the Maryland State Department of Forestry; received through the American Forestry Association.

spruce, and larch (Fig. 59), produce at the ends of their stems or branches terminal protected buds which possess the capacity to grow more vigorously than the smaller axillary buds produced immediately below and in close proximity to each terminal bud. During successive growing seasons, development from the terminal bud of the main stem is more rapid than development from the terminal buds of the branches, with the result that a single strong shaft or trunk is produced. Trees like the maple and the elm (Figs. 60, 61), although they differ in the arrangement of their buds, show much the same growth tendencies; but the growth of one or more of the

Fig. 61. An elm in summer. Photograph by James A. G. Dewey; received through the American Forestry Association.

lateral branches may be nearly or quite as rapid as that of the original trunk, and so several large branches are formed. The development of many of the axillary buds on these branches results finally in the production of a much-branched, spreading crown, very different from the top of a spruce or larch.

Sometimes, as in the lilac, a mixed bud is terminal. Since this bud includes a meristematic stem tip terminated by a cluster of floral primordia, further extension of the leaf-bearing portions of the plant must be brought about by growth from axillary buds. If many of these axillary buds continue their development, a densely branching plant is produced. Some plants, like the elm (Fig. 58) and the poplar, form several or many axillary floral buds and relatively few axillary foliage buds back of the foliage bud at the end of the stem. In the late spring, after the fruits are ripe, the floral branches fall from the tree, leaving conspicuous bare spaces on the twigs which bore them.

Although each kind of tree tends to develop a characteristic form, it is still true that environmental factors play an important part in determining its shape. Among these environmental factors are wind (Fig. 46), shade, and temperature. The form of a tree may be profoundly influenced by the presence of surrounding vegetation. A pine tree growing in the open takes a very different form from that which it would assume in a dense forest. The effects of the human element in the environment, aside from the far-reaching results of such activities as logging operations, drainage of swamps, and the burning of cut-over areas, are illustrated by the results of pruning trees, shrubs, and woody vines. Peach and other fruit trees, for example, may be induced by proper pruning to grow flat against a wall. In formal gardens, certain shrubs including box are commonly pruned so that the plants grow in such unnatural shapes as cones or spheres. "Headers"—the main shoots of fruit or shade trees that tend to grow tall with little side-branching—are often pruned so that more side branches are stimulated to develop. This practice induces lower, fuller crowns and in the case of fruit trees tends to increase the production of fruit-bearing twigs. The fruit of such trees, also, is made more accessible.

SUMMARY

Buds are classified according to the positions they occupy as terminal, axillary, or adventitious.

If the meristematic stem tip within a bud bears only leaf primordia, it is a foliage bud; if only floral primordia, it is a floral bud; if both leaf and floral primordia, it is a mixed bud.

Buds covered on the outside by scale leaves are protected buds; naked buds are covered by foliage leaves only.

Meristematic stem and branch tips which produce new leaf and branch primordia continuously throughout the year are active buds. Protected buds in general, at least in temperate regions, undergo a resting period. A resting bud ordinarily resumes activity and unfolds during the spring next following the growing season in which it was formed. Some protected resting buds remain indefinitely in an inactive (latent) condition unless they are induced to develop by some special stimulus.

When a protected bud opens, the scale leaves fall, leaving scars at their former places of attachment. The unelongated stem tip then develops, as do also the primordia of leaves, flowers, or branches previously enclosed within the scale leaves.

The form of a plant is determined largely by the number and positions of its buds and by the type and degree of the development that takes place from them.

CHAPTER VI

LEAVES

External Structure. The most conspicuous and fundamentally the most important organs of larger plants are their leaves. Importance is not measured by the size of individual leaves but by the amount of their combined surfaces which are exposed to sunlight. Nor is leaf size necessarily correlated with plant size. For example, a leaf of the "big tree," the largest of all living things, is individually some thousands of times smaller than the leaf of a banana plant. This latter plant, which reaches a height of only 20 to 30 feet, may have leaves 6 to 10 feet long and 1 to 2 feet broad. There is very little proportional difference in thickness, however, between the leaves of the big tree, those of the banana (Fig. 62, *B*), and those of many more familiar plants such as corn, tobacco, tomato, oak, elm, or apple.

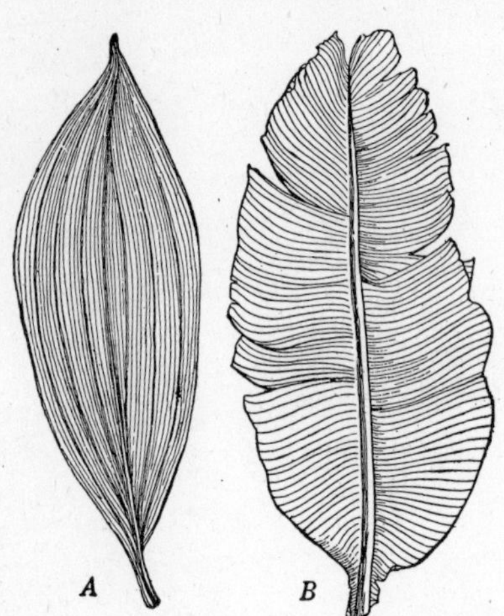

Fig. 62. *A*, parallel-veined leaf of lily-of-the-valley. *B*, pinnately parallel-veined leaf of banana.

Leaves ordinarily can be recognized as such without difficulty—broad, flattened, green structures extending outward usually at an oblique angle from the stem or branch. A foliage leaf often is composed of *blade*, *petiole*, and *stipules;* but many foliage leaves lack petioles or stipules or both. In the grasses and in some other monocotyledons, neither petioles nor stipules are present. Leaves which lack petioles have a *sessile* position on the stem. Corn, an example of a large grass, has leaves whose bases surround the stem and almost completely cover it. Such a basal portion of a leaf is the *sheath* (Fig. 63).

The expanded portion of a leaf, the blade, presents an unlimited variety of shapes. The margin of the blade may be smooth as in the lily-of-the-valley (Fig. 62, *A*), toothed as in the elm (Fig. 64, *A*), or still more deeply indented as in a maple leaf (Fig. 64, *B*). The *lobes*, portions of the leaf between deep indentations, may themselves be toothed or may have smooth margins. The blade, as so far described, would be that of a *simple* leaf. If the lobing extends to the midrib (main vein) or to the base of the blade, the individual portions of the blade are *leaflets*, and the leaf is *compound*. Compound leaves may be *pinnately* compound (like a feather), as are those of the ash (Fig. 65, *A*), the pea (Fig. 66, *A*), and the rose (Fig. 66, *B*), or *palmately* compound (resembling a hand) like those of the horse chestnut (Fig. 65, *B*). The leaflets may themselves be divided, as in many ferns. Some compound leaves are three times divided, and the common meadow rue (Fig. 65, *C*) has a four-times-divided leaf.

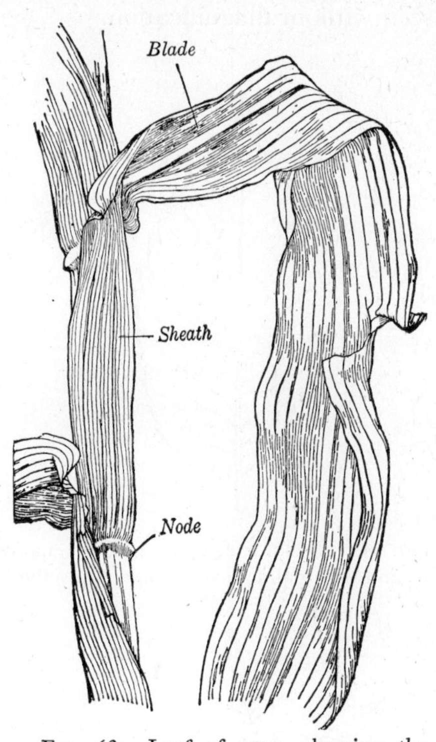

FIG. 63. Leaf of corn, showing the sheath, a portion of the blade, and the arrangement of veins.

In spite of the great variation in shape of leaf blades between plants of different kinds, the arrangement of the veins is according to one of two main plans. In the majority of monocotyledons, as the corn (Fig. 63) and the lily-of-the-valley (Fig. 62, *A*), several main veins run approximately parallel to the leaf axis, extending from the base to the apex of the blade. Such leaves are *parallel-veined*. The leaves of the banana (Fig. 62, *B*) and of some other monocotyledons show a deviation from the ordinary parallel-veined arrangement. The leaf blade of such a plant has a midrib and many branch veins; the latter extend, parallel with one another, from the midrib nearly or quite to the margin. In both types of parallel-veined leaves the conspicuous veins really are connected by a network of fine branches, but these slender branches are not easily seen without magnification.

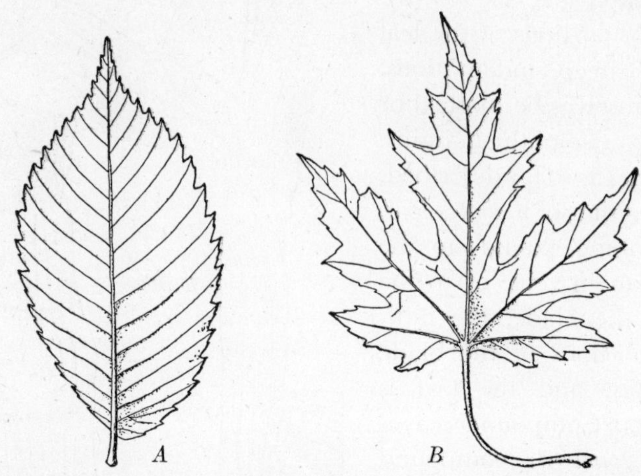

FIG. 64. *A*, elm leaf, with pinnate venation. *B*, leaf of maple, palmately lobed and with palmate venation. Only the larger veins are shown in each case.

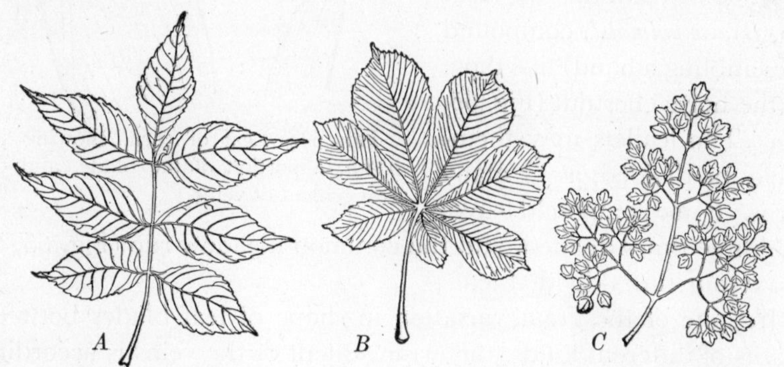

FIG. 65. Compound leaves. *A*, pinnately compound leaf of ash. *B*, palmately compound leaf of horse chestnut. *C*, four-times-divided leaf of meadow rue.

In the second main plan of vein arrangement, characteristic of the leaf blades of the majority of dicotyledons, the main vein or main veins branch repeatedly, many of the ultimate branches being connected so as to form a rather conspicuous network (Fig. 67). Such leaves are *netted-veined*. A netted-veined leaf with a conspicuous

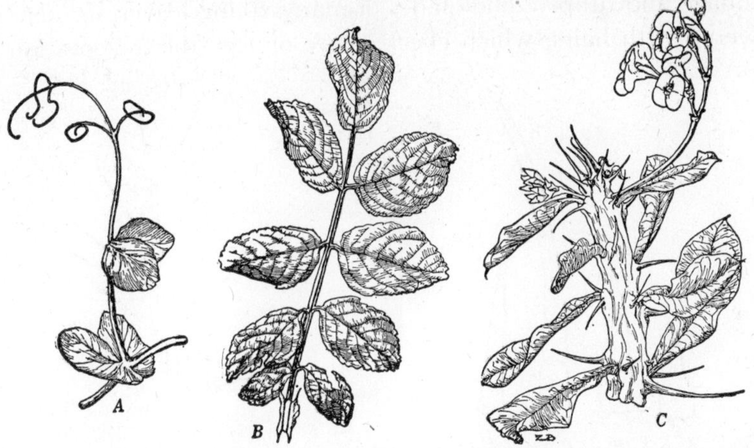

FIG. 66. Leaves with stipules. *A*, leaf of pea; some leaflets replaced by tendrils. *B*, rose leaf. *C*, twig of Euphorbia, with spinelike stipules.

midrib from which large branch veins diverge at different points, as in the leaf of the elm (Fig. 64, *A*), is *pinnately* netted-veined. If several main veins diverge from a single point at the base of the leaf, as in the maple (Fig. 64, *B*), the arrangement of veins is *palmate*.

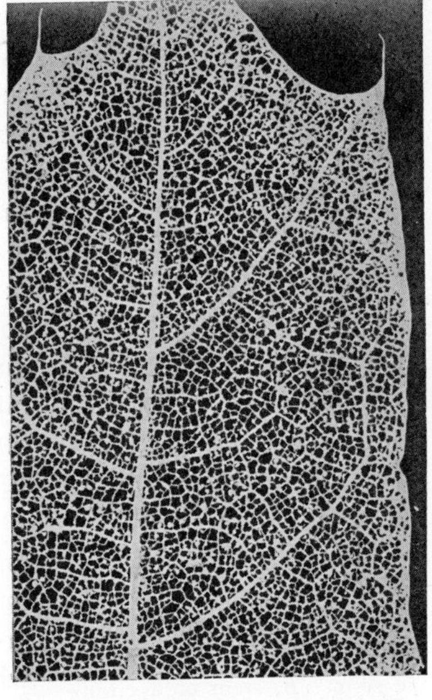

FIG. 67. The system of veins of a netted-veined leaf (black oak).

In leaves having blades whose margins are lobed, the arrangement of the veins usually corresponds to the way in which the leaf is lobed; hence, if a leaf is pinnately lobed, the chances are that it is pinnately veined. If the leaf is palmately lobed, the veins are usually palmately arranged.

The surface of the blade of a foliage leaf may be smooth, rough, or hairy. The surfaces of most leaves are cutinized, and some are coated with wax; when the waxy coating is broken up into minute rods or plates, it appears as a "bloom," like that on the leaves of cabbage and tulip. The blades of many young leaves are densely covered with hairs, which check, more or less, the evaporation of

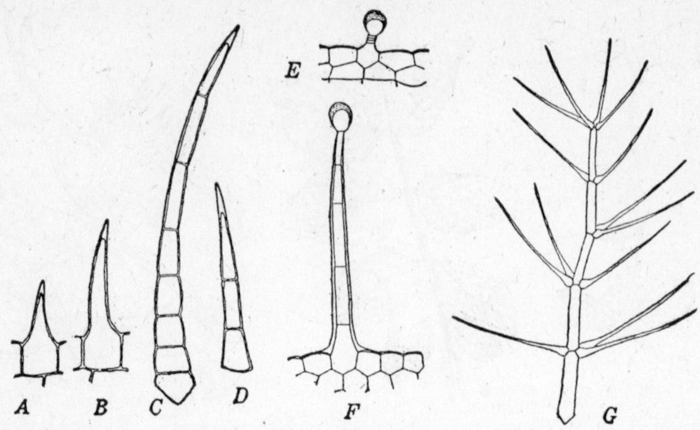

FIG. 68. Epidermal hairs from various leaves. *A–D*, from the sunflower. *E*, *F*, young and old glandular hairs of geranium. *G*, branching hair of mullein.

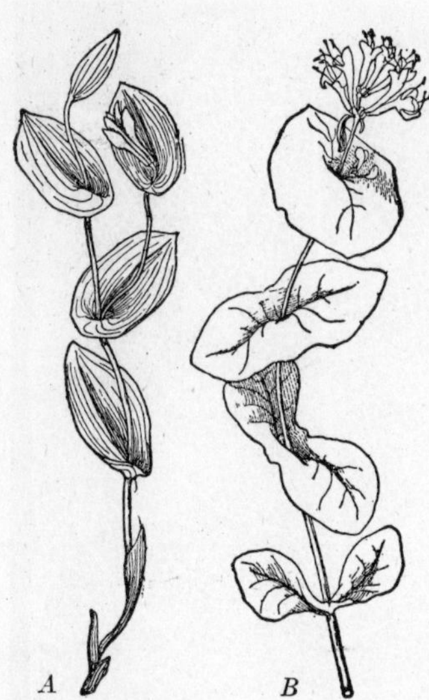

FIG. 69. *A*, stem of bellwort with leaves that encircle the stem. *B*, stem of a climbing honeysuckle with opposite leaves, the two of each pair united about the stem.

water from the immature blades. As the blade matures, the hairs may shrivel and disappear, or they may persist. Some leaf blades, like those of the mullein, are covered by a dense matting of hairs (Fig. 68, *G*); the leaves of some plants bear glandular hairs (Fig. 68, *E*, *F*) which secrete special substances. The strong odors given off by mints are due to volatile oils secreted by the terminal cells of glandular hairs on the leaves and stems.

When a petiole is present it may be long or short, stout or slender, cylindrical or flattened, and in some cases grooved or winged. At its base, where it is attached to the stem, the petiole may be swollen; or it may clasp or ensheathe the stem. The bud which is present in the axil—the angle between leaf and stem—is completely covered in some plants by the enlarged base of the petiole. The blades of some sessile leaves partly surround the stem, as in wild lettuce; or, as in the bellwort (Fig. 69, *A*), they completely encircle the stem. When sessile leaves are opposite, the blades of a pair may be united around the stem, as in some of the wild honeysuckles (Fig. 69, *B*) and in the common boneset.

Stipules may be either bladelike or spinelike. When present they are borne one on either side of the base of the petiole. Certain

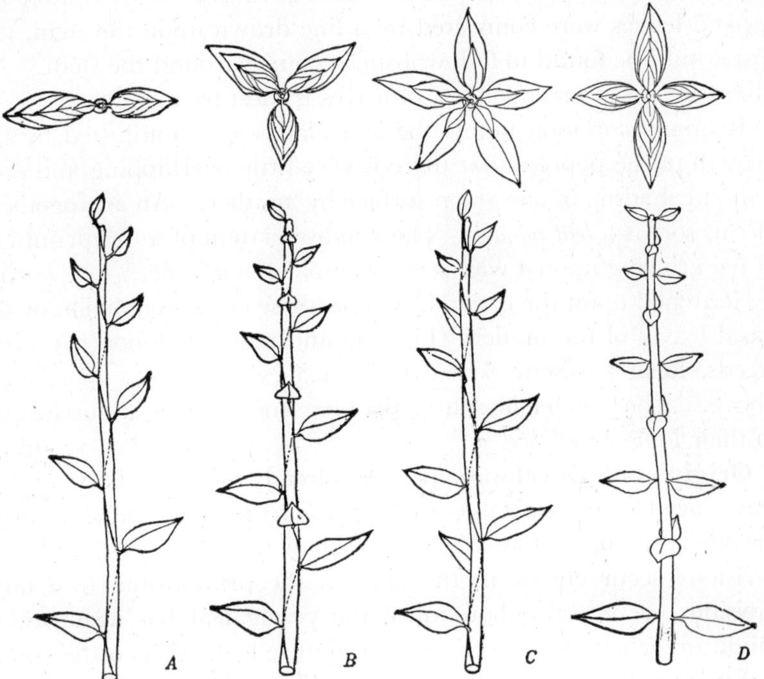

FIG. 70. Types of leaf arrangement. *A*, *B*, *C*, various alternate arrangements. *D*, opposite arrangement. The upper figure in each case represents the leaf arrangement as seen from above.

bladelike stipules are green and, like the leaf blade, manufacture foods. In this respect such stipules are usually of minor importance as compared with the blade, but in the pea (Fig. 66, *A*) and in some other plants their importance in food manufacture approaches that of the rest of the leaf. Other bladelike stipules furnish a protective covering for immature leaves and, as in certain oaks and willows, are shed after the leaves are mature. The common black locust and the crown-of-thorns (Fig. 66, *C*) are examples of plants whose stipules are spinelike and persist after the other parts of the leaves are shed.

Arrangement of Leaves (Fig. 70). Leaves of some plants are borne in pairs at each node, those of a pair being *opposite* each other and each pair usually standing at right angles to the pair below. If three or more leaves are borne at a single node, as in Elodea, they are *whorled*. Leaves are *alternate* when but a single leaf occurs at each node. If the bases of successive alternately arranged leaves were connected by a line drawn upon the stem, this line would be found to follow a spiral course around the stem. An alternate spiral arrangement of leaves is most frequent.

In many common plants the leaf blades are so adjusted by the growth of the petioles that there is very little overlapping and consequent shading of one green surface by another. An arrangement of this sort is a *leaf mosaic*. The leaf association of a nasturtium or of ivy growing upon a wall is an example of a mosaic. Leaves that lie flattened upon the ground, such as those of the dandelion or the basal leaves of the mullein (Fig. 71) and many common perennial weeds, form a rosette whose lower leaves are longer than those above. The greater length of the lowermost leaves is due largely to their longer petioles.

Origin and Development. As already noted (Chapter IV), leaves are first recognizable as leaf primordia—small humps of embryonic cells upon the sides of the stem meristem. At first, cell divisions occur chiefly in the apex of the primordium; but later divisions occur throughout until the young leaf has assumed, in miniature, the form and shape of a mature leaf. When the young leaf in a winter bud resumes activity in the spring, its rapid increase in size is due in large part to the enlargement and maturation of cells already present and not primarily to an increase in number of those cells followed by their enlargement. In the leaves of some plants, however, a considerable number of cell divisions occur while the young leaf is maturing. Such a leaf owes its increase in size not only to an enlargement of cells already present, but in part to the formation and enlargement of new cells. However, leaf development may be greatly influenced by the environment. Contrasting conditions during the growing period, such as sunlight and shade, high and low temperature, abundant moisture and drought, produce contrasting effects in the form and structure of leaves of the same species or strain. Such conditions affect, for example, the extent of cell division and of differentiation, the character of the internal aerating system, and the magnitude of the surface secretions. Of all environmental factors, light probably is most important in its influence upon the forms of leaves, as well as of stems. When light intensity has been reduced to about one tenth that of ordinary sunlight, the leaves of tobacco are larger but thinner than

Fig. 71. The rosette arrangement (leaf mosaic) of the first-formed leaves of mullein.

typically. Individual palisade cells (see below) are longer, and the spongy tissue is less compact.

Since all or almost all the cells of a typical leaf enlarge and mature more or less nearly simultaneously, there are no localized regions in which at any given time cells are dividing, elongating, and maturing. The lack of such distinct regions is one important respect in which the development of most leaves differs from that of stems or roots. Another difference is that relatively early the cells of a leaf have been formed once for all, cell division then ceasing; whereas division, and therefore growth, may continue indefinitely in the tips of roots or stems.

In certain monocotyledons, however, especially in some grasses, the basal portion of each leaf remains meristematic even after the apical portion is mature. The leaf continues to grow in length as cells formed in the basal region successively enlarge and mature. In the pine, also, cell division continues longer at the leaf base than toward the apex. In the leaves of some few dicotyledons, such as tobacco, there is a limited amount of cambial activity in the larger veins and in the petioles. The existence of cambium in leaves, however, is the exception rather than the rule.

Tissues of a Leaf Blade. The blade of a dicotyledonous leaf (Fig. 72) typically includes several distinct tissues. On its upper

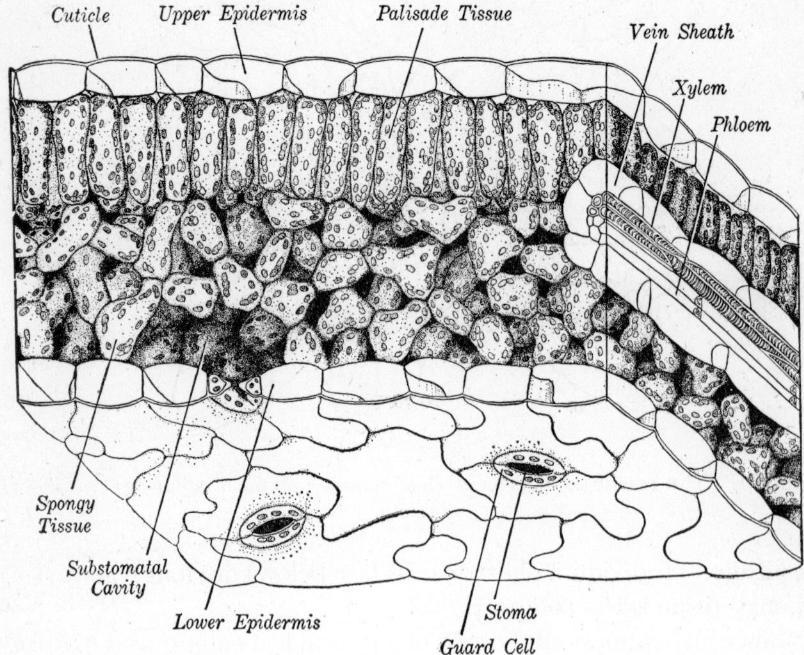

FIG. 72. Portion of the blade of a sunflower leaf.

side is an *epidermis*, whose cells are often irregular as seen in surface view but appear nearly rectangular in cross section. In some varieties the individual epidermal cells look like pieces of a jigsaw puzzle. The outer walls of the epidermal cells are cutinized. Next beneath the upper epidermis is a region of *palisade cells* which may be one, two, or more cells in depth. The long axis of each of these cells is perpendicular to the surface of the leaf. The palisade cells are in general compactly arranged; but there may be spaces between them, particularly at their lower ends. They contain many chloroplasts. Next beneath, commonly making up the greater part of the thickness of the leaf, is a region of rounded or irregularly lobed cells which are loosely packed since each of the cells has but a small portion of its surface in contact with the surfaces of neighboring cells.

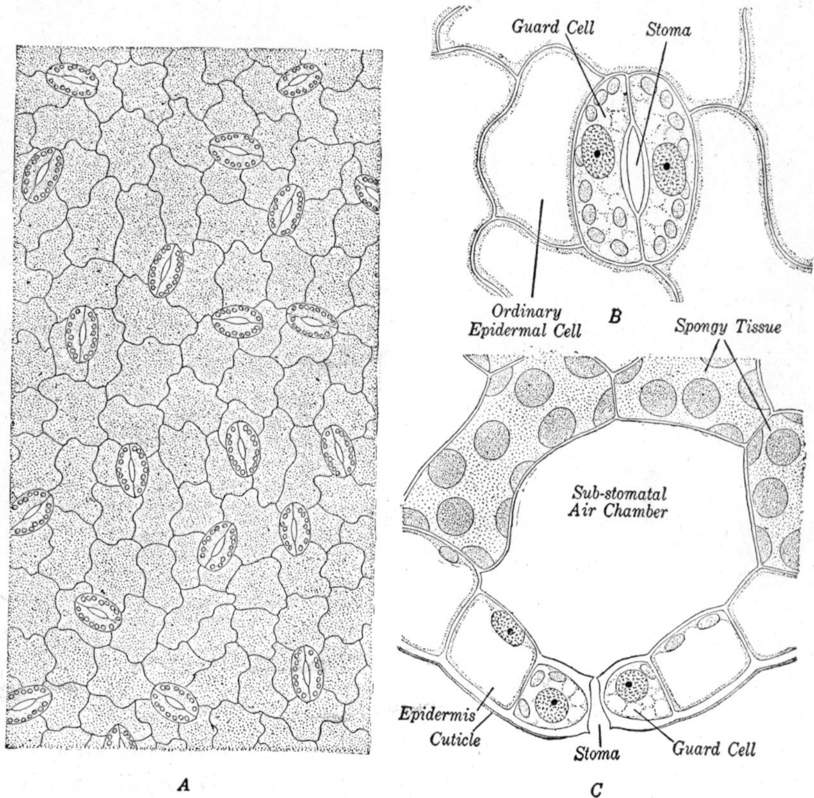

FIG. 73. *A*, lower epidermis of a sunflower leaf in surface view, showing distribution of stomata. *B*, single stoma and adjacent cells in surface view. *C*, vertical section through a stoma and the adjacent portion of the leaf.

This region is the *spongy tissue*. Between the cells are numerous, often large, *intercellular spaces*. The cells of the spongy tissue also contain chloroplasts, although usually not as many in proportion to their size as do the palisade cells. Adjoining the spongy tissue is the *lower epidermis*, whose cells are similar to those of the upper epidermis. Here and there in the lower epidermis is an opening called a *stoma* (plural, *stomata;* Fig. 73). Each stoma is bordered by two bean-shaped or kidney-shaped *guard cells* which are smaller than the other cells of the epidermis and which contain chloroplasts. The wall of each guard cell adjacent to a stoma is somewhat thicker than

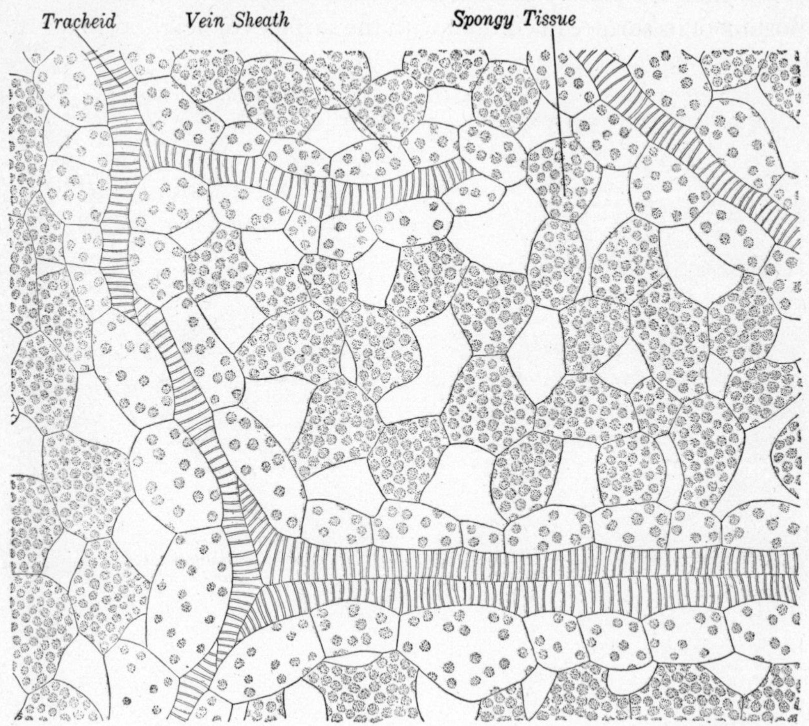

FIG. 74. Horizontal section through the spongy tissue of a sunflower leaf.

the walls on other sides of the cell. The stoma opens into an intercellular space (a *substomatal cavity*), which in turn is continuous with spaces between the cells of the spongy tissue. All the intercellular spaces in the spongy tissue are likewise connected with one another and with such spaces as may occur between the palisade cells. Thus, the stomata and the intercellular spaces constitute an aerating system lined with a large area of wet wall surface, by means of which gases may be freely interchanged between the atmosphere and the interior cells of the leaf. In many leaves stomata are present also in the upper epidermis.

Both the upper and the lower epidermis may bear hairs (Fig. 68). Some hairs are merely single elongated epidermal cells. In other cases a hair is a row of two or more cells resulting from the growth and division of an epidermal cell. In still other instances a hair is composed of more than one row of cells.

The veins of a leaf are vascular bundles which are continuous through the petiole with the vascular bundles of the stem. Like a stem bundle, a vein contains xylem and phloem; the xylem is toward the upper side of the blade and the phloem toward the lower surface. It has been seen that a vascular bundle in a stem has xylem toward the inner side of the stem and phloem toward the outer side. If such a bundle could be bent outward at an angle to the stem axis, the xylem which was on the inner side in the stem would then be on the upper side; and the phloem which was on the outer side in the stem would be on the lower side.

Xylem and phloem in a vein of a leaf consist, respectively, of the same types of elements as are found in the bundles of the stem. As the branches from the midrib and the main veins become progressively smaller, the phloem and xylem contain fewer and smaller elements. Each of the ultimate fine veins in which the system terminates may possess no phloem and may be but a single tracheid in diameter (Fig. 74). Surrounding the xylem and phloem of a vein is a sheath whose thickness varies with the size of the vein. The sheath surrounding the midrib, or often that surrounding one of the larger veins, is usually a compact mass of cells consisting of parenchyma and mechanical tissue, extending from upper to lower epidermis and occupying in this particular region the place of palisade and spongy tissue. The sheath about one of the smaller veins consists usually of but a single layer of parenchymatous cells and lies within the spongy tissue.

Tissues of a Petiole (Fig. 75). A petiole may contain one, three, five, or more bundles which run lengthwise, connecting the vascular supply of the stem with that of the leaf blade. If more than one are present, the various bundles may be parallel throughout the length of the petiole; or they may lie so close to one another that at the outer end of the petiole they appear to be a single bundle. The bundles of the petiole, like the veins of the blade, include xylem and phloem. The xylem serves as a direct bridge between the water-conducting tissue of the stem and that of the blade; the phloem connects the food-transporting tissue of the blade with that of the stem,

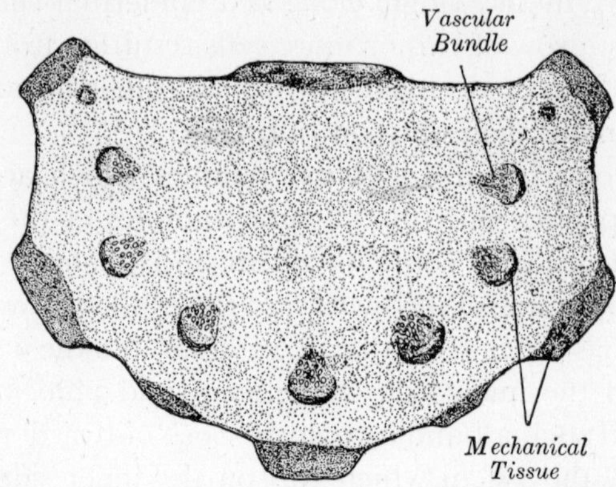

FIG. 75. Diagram of a cross section through the petiole of a leaf of beet.

so serving as a direct pathway for the transfer to the stem of food manufactured in the blade. Surrounding each bundle is often a sheath of thick-walled mechanical cells. There may be similar cells

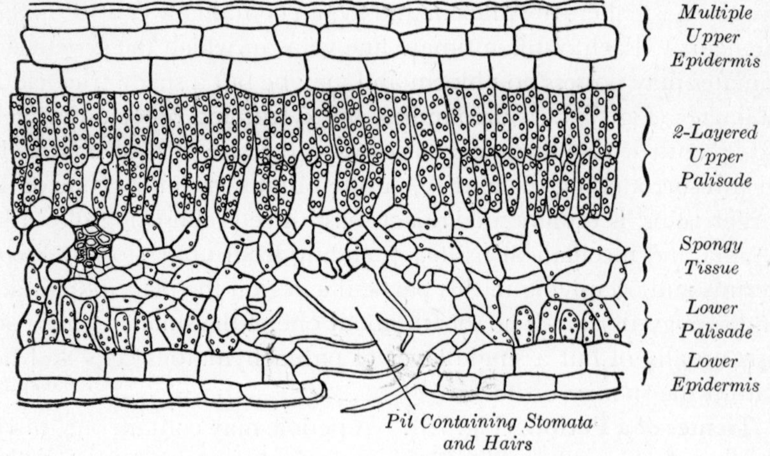

FIG. 76. Cross section of a portion of an oleander leaf.

also just within the epidermis of the petiole. Both systems of mechanical tissue aid materially in the functioning of the petiole as a support for the blade. The remaining cells of the petiole, except those in the epidermis, are parenchymatous.

Variations in Foliage Leaves. It was noted earlier that leaves borne by plants of different kinds often differ greatly in form, struc-

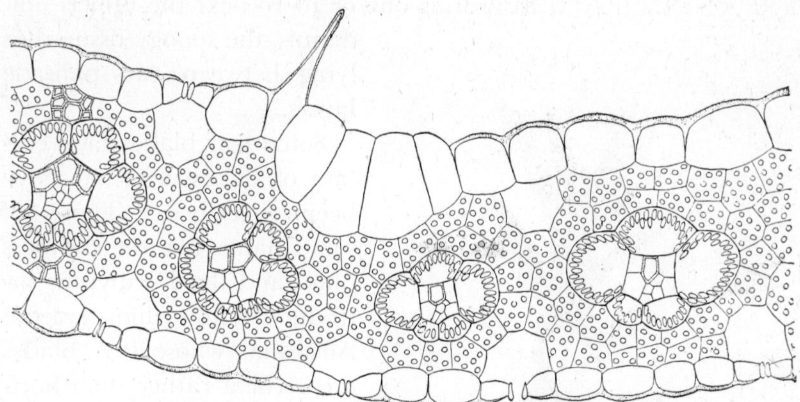

FIG. 77. Portion of a cross section of a leaf of corn.

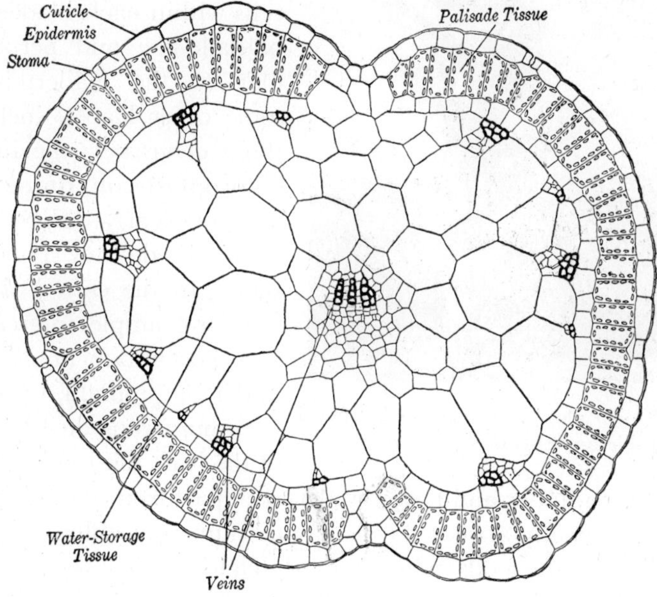

FIG. 78. Cross section of a leaf of Russian thistle, with large parenchymatous water-storage cells.

ture, and even in function. Such variations are due chiefly to differences in the arrangement and proportions of the various tissues rather than to the presence of tissues of different sorts. A special type of arrangement is found in such leaf blades as those of the oleander (Fig. 76) and the rubber plant, which have a palisade layer next the lower, as well as one or more next the upper, epidermis, the spongy tissue thus lying between two palisade layers.

Fig. 79. An aloe, in whose thick leaves considerable amounts of water are stored.

Some leaf blades lack certain of the tissues that have been described. Those of some plants, like the compass plant and the Eucalyptus introduced into California from Australia, whose leaf blades are vertical rather than horizontal, have no spongy tissue, all the chloroplast-containing cells within each blade being palisade-like and perpendicular to the epidermis. In some other leaves, including those of grasses, the interior chloroplast-containing cells are not clearly differentiated into palisade and spongy tissues. In the corn leaf (Fig. 77), for example, intercellular spaces occur only immediately under the stomata, which are very numerous on both sides of the leaf; the remaining tissue between upper and lower epidermis, apart from the veins, consists of compactly arranged cells having numerous chloroplasts.

Ordinarily the foods manufactured in a foliage leaf do not remain long in the leaf but are transferred to, and stored in, some other organ such as root or stem. Sometimes, however, as in the cabbage and the century plant, considerable amounts of foods are stored in foliage leaves, which in such plants are usually relatively thick.

The foliage leaves of many plants characteristic of dry regions have thick, fleshy leaves composed chiefly of water-storage tissue.

This tissue may be an epidermis several cells in thickness, as in the leaf of the begonia; but more commonly water-storage tissue is internal, as in leaves of the Russian thistle (Fig. 78), the century plant, and the aloe (Fig. 79). In either case this tissue consists of large parenchymatous cells containing few or no chloroplasts. The imbibing power of mucilaginous substances in the dense cytoplasm and in the central vacuoles of these cells greatly increases their water-absorbing and water-retaining capacity. Water so held within the storage tissue may, however, move to other parts of the plant after the water supply of the soil is exhausted, enabling the plant to remain alive for some time.

FIG. 80. A pitcher plant (Sarracenia).

Insectivorous Plants. The leaves of certain plants obtain a part of their food from the bodies of insects. An example is the common pitcher plant (Fig. 80) growing in marshes, whose pitcher-like leaves are usually partly filled with water. On the inside of the tip of each leaf are stiff hairs pointing inward and downward, and glands which secrete a fluid attractive to insects. After insects enter the pitcher, some of them are prevented by the hairs from escaping; and many insects ultimately drown in the water at the base of the pitcher. Substances from their decomposing bodies are used as foods by the plant. Another plant growing in similar situations is the sundew (Fig. 81, *A*). Its leaves are provided with slender, sticky hairs which are sensitive to contact with protein-containing bodies. If a small insect touches one of the hairs, it sticks to the hair and in its struggles comes into contact with neighboring hairs which then bend over and hold the insect fast. After the death of the insect, the soft parts of its body are dissolved by secreted digestive juices. In time the hairs resume their ordinary position.

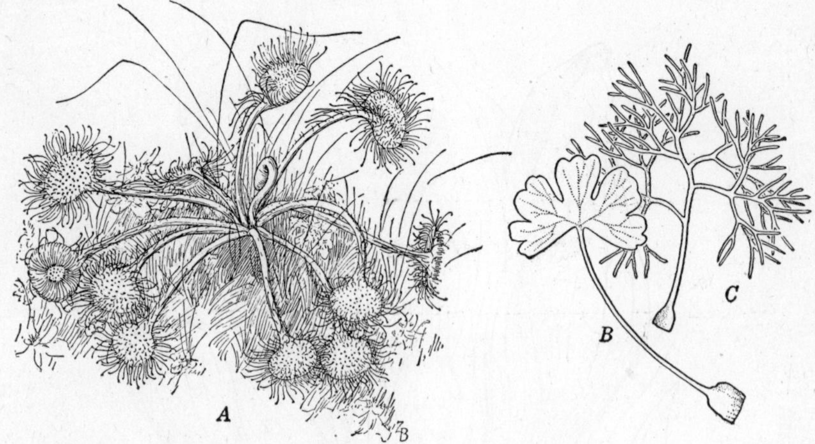

Fig. 81. *A*, a sundew (Drosera), whose leaves trap insects. *B*, aerial leaf, and *C*, submerged leaf of a water crowfoot (Ranunculus).

Variations in Leaves on the Same Plant. Foliage leaves borne on different parts even of the same plant may differ considerably in form and structure. Those leaves of a tree which are freely exposed to sunlight frequently have a thick, heavily cutinized epidermis, a palisade tissue two or three cells in depth, and a spongy tissue with small intercellular spaces; whereas the leaves in the interior of the crown or on the shaded side of the same tree may have a thinner, less heavily cutinized epidermis, a palisade layer but one cell thick, a spongy tissue with large intercellular spaces, and a relatively high chlorophyll content.

Even more striking differences appear between thc aerial and the submerged leaves of some water plants. The aerial leaves of the water crowfoot, for example (Fig. 81, *B*), have well-defined palisade and spongy tissues; the submerged leaves, on the other hand (Fig. 81, *C*), have no palisade tissue, and the intercellular spaces in their spongy tissue are small. The aerial leaves are few-lobed; the submerged leaves are divided into many narrow, thin segments.

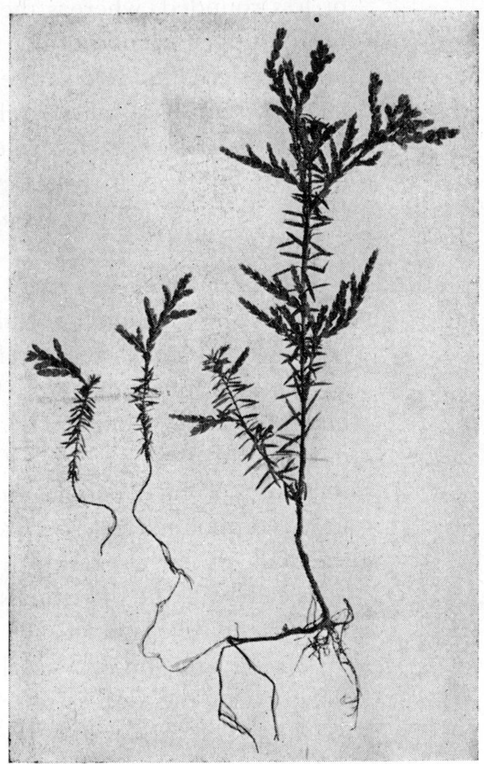

Fig. 82. Seedlings of the arbor vitae bearing leaves of juvenile and adult forms.

Differences may appear also between the leaves first produced by a plant and those formed later. The leaves of a young seedling of arbor vitae are needle-shaped (Fig. 82); but after one or more seasons' growth, scalelike appressed leaves develop and ordinarily continue to be formed during the life of the tree. Another example of "juvenile" leaves is seen in the bean, whose first-formed foliage leaves are undivided whereas those formed later are compound.

Leaves of juvenile form are not confined to seedlings; not uncommonly, leaves borne on branches developed from adventitious buds formed in a callus are of the juvenile type. A change in the environment of an older plant, too, may result in the formation of juvenile leaves. The basal (juvenile) leaves of the harebell are broad and more or less rounded, whereas the leaves borne on the upper portion of the stem are long and slender (Fig. 83). An environmental change, such as a marked change in illumination, causes a stoppage of terminal growth, followed by the development of lateral shoots whose basal leaves are rounded.

FIG. 83. Harebell (*Campanula rotundifolia*), with leaves of juvenile form at the base and of adult form on the upright stalk.

Fall of Foliage Leaves. In temperate climates the autumnal shedding of leaves by dicotyledonous trees and shrubs is a well-known phenomenon. It is brought about by the development of a special layer of cells (an *abscission layer*, Fig. 84) across the base of each petiole and sometimes, in a compound leaf, across the base of the stalk of each separate leaflet as well. The cell walls of the abscission layer are thin; the middle layer of each wall becomes dissolved, and finally nearly the whole thickness of the wall is softened and dissolved. The abscission layer does not extend across the vessels and tracheids of the bundle or bundles, whose walls, however, are easily broken by the wind or by the weight of the leaf after the disintegration of the walls of other cells. In some oaks and other trees, the abscission layer is not well developed in the autumn; dead leaves, therefore, may remain on such trees well into the winter or even into the spring. The cells of the basal part of a petiole immediately below the abscission layer usually develop a cork cambium producing a corky tissue, which is externally visible on the stem as a *leaf scar*. Upon the surface of a leaf scar can commonly be found one or more *vascular-bundle scars*.

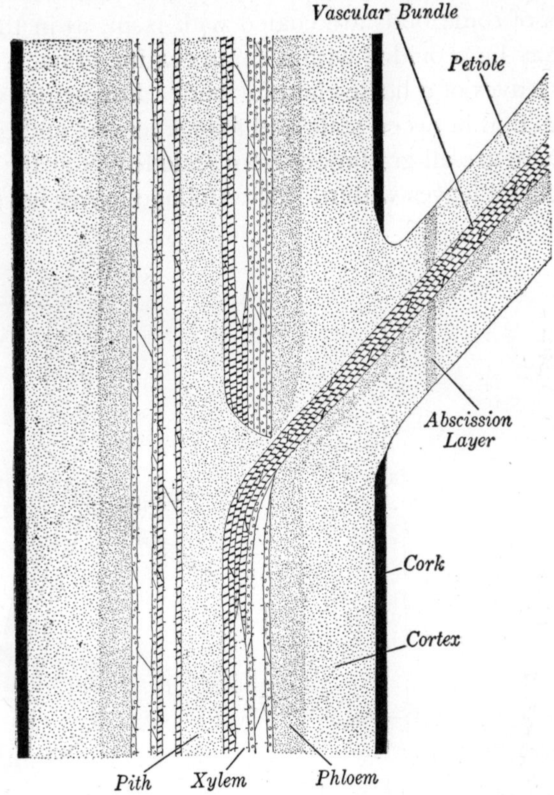

FIG. 84. Diagram showing the attachment of the petiole of a leaf to the stem, and the position of the abscission layer.

Many trees and shrubs indigenous to regions without pronounced seasonal changes do not shed all their leaves simultaneously. Plants of this type, such as eucalyptus, oranges, live oaks, and some species of holly, form new leaves and shed old ones continuously throughout the entire year. Such "evergreen" plants are always in foliage.

Scale Leaves. In many cases a leaf primordium matures into a flattened leaf, which is attached to the stem by a broad base and which carries on little or no food manufacture. Such a *scale leaf* is usually relatively small, without chloroplasts, and brownish or yellowish in color. Scale leaves about a protected bud aid in checking evaporation from structures within the bud and so minimize the harmful effects of sudden changes in temperature. They also prevent mechanical injury of the embryonic parts within. The scale leaves of some buds are coated with resin, as in the poplars, and they may be provided with a dense coating of hairs, as are the inner scale leaves of a horse-chestnut bud. Frequently there is no sharp distinction between scale and foliage leaves; and often, as in the lilac, there are all gradations from scale leaves at the outside of a bud to foliage leaves within. After foliage leaves have emerged

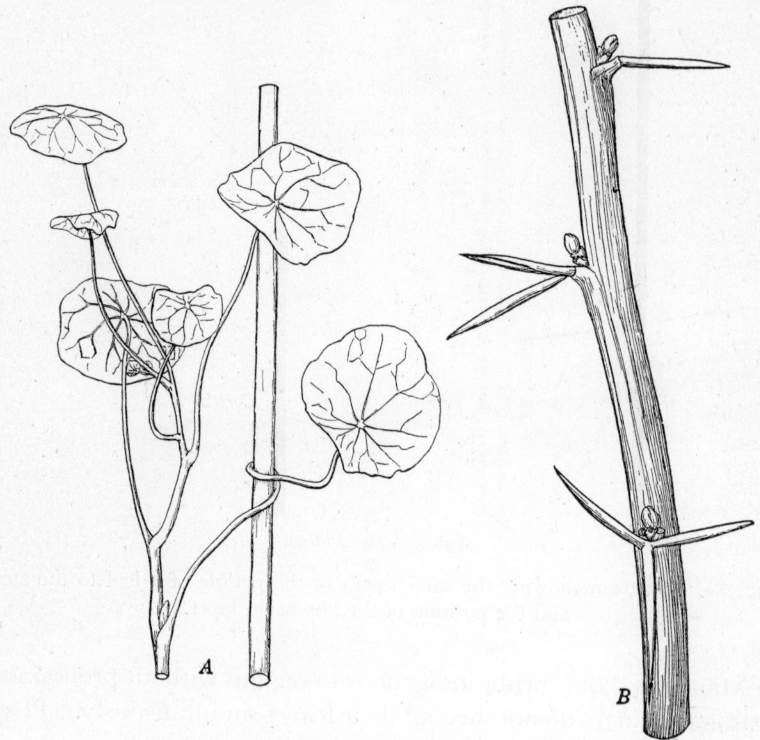

FIG. 85. Leaves of special forms. *A*, those of nasturtium (Tropaeolum), whose petioles function as tendrils. *B*, portion of stem of common barberry (in winter condition); the spines represent leaves.

from the bud, each scale leaf usually falls away. Since the internodes between nodes at which scale leaves are attached elongate very little or not at all, a condensed ring of scars is left at this level on the stem. In some buds, like those of the hickory, the inner scale leaves become large and brightly colored before they fall. The fall of a scale leaf, like that of a foliage leaf, is brought about through the formation of an abscission layer.

Scale leaves develop on subterranean, as well as on aerial, stems and branches. The scale leaves surrounding the embryonic region of a subterranean stem or branch constitute a protective sheath which prevents the abrasion of the meristematic region as the stem pushes through the soil.

Tendrils and Spines. An entire leaf primordium or a portion only of such a primordium may mature into a *tendril*. A tendril, therefore, may represent a whole leaf or only a part of a leaf. In peas (Fig. 66, *A*) and vetches one or more leaflets toward the terminal end of the leaf are tendrils. In some smilaxes (not including the greenhouse "smilax," which is an Asparagus), the stipules are tendrils. In clematis and the nasturtium (Fig. 85, *A*) the petioles may function as tendrils, winding about a support and enabling the plant to climb. The term "tendril" is, in fact, applied to any twining portion of a plant which helps to attach the plant to a supporting object. The twining organs of the grape (Fig. 49) are tendrils, although they are branches rather than leaves.

Fig. 86. Portion of the stem of a cactus bearing spines and flowers. Photograph courtesy of D. T. Macdougal.

Spines and thorns, likewise, may be branches, leaves, parts of leaves, or in some cases roots. The common barberry (Fig. 85, *B*) has one to five (typically three) spines at each node, the spine or group of spines in each case representing a leaf. The foliage leaves are borne in clusters on very short branches in the axils of these spinelike leaves. Some of the spines of the cacti (Fig. 86) are leaves, and some are branches.

Functions and Processes. The great majority of the cells that make up the body of a leaf are living cells, active throughout the life of the organ. Accordingly, in the leaf as a whole all the processes common to living cells generally are proceeding at a rate characteristic of the kind and state of the plant in the given environment. Even the dead cells of the vascular bundles, as in stems and roots, are functional, especially in support and in the transport of solutions. In addition, the usual green leaf is primarily concerned with two processes which fall to its lot by virtue of its chlorophyll content, its structure, surface area, and position. It is the function of the green leaf—supplemented by any other green organs—to manufacture an organic substance as a basis of the food supply of the plant. This process will be described in the sections dealing with *photosynthesis.* It is the lot of the leaf also to account for the larger part of the water given off by the aerial parts of the plant to the atmosphere in the process of *transpiration.*

PHOTOSYNTHESIS

The Green Leaf in Food Manufacture. Green plants are the eventual source of essentially all the foods used by living organisms, whether plant or animal; and they are likewise indirectly the source of the organic matter of the world, including coal and oil. This statement merely calls attention to an end result of reactions beginning in the green cell, extending to many interrelations of organisms, and finally including in part complicated natural processes requiring great time. It is considered certain that the earth in geologically ancient times was without great stores of organic matter but that carbon dioxide (CO_2) and water (H_2O) were present as they are today. Out of these substances, with the addition of a few other chemical elements and sources of energy, have come eventually organisms and their products. Food manufacture from carbon dioxide and water proceeds only when these substances are available to living, active cells (as in leaves) containing chlorophyll and exposed to light.

Photosynthesis. Photosynthesis in the sense here used may be briefly defined as the process whereby carbon dioxide and water are transformed into an organic substance through the agency of the protoplasm of the living cell and of energy absorbed by chlorophyll from visible light. Since this process involves a putting together (synthesis) of two simple substances into one that is more complex and since light is absorbed, with an ensuing photochemical reaction as one essential step in the sequence of changes, the process is called *photosynthesis*.

Photosynthesis is a complex process. It has been studied for a century and a half, and the information accumulated is important; but the exact mechanism is not yet certainly known. It is convenient to express the process by an equation in which six molecules of CO_2 and six of H_2O, plus light energy, produce one molecule of a simple sugar and six molecules of oxygen, the light energy in this process being stored in the molecule of sugar as potential energy:

$$6\ CO_2 + 6\ H_2O\ (+\ \text{light energy}) \rightarrow C_6H_{12}O_6 + 6\ O_2.$$

This equation, like the respiration equation, does not disclose the actual reactions. It does not mention chlorophyll, which absorbs the energy utilized. It does, however, serve to indicate that CO_2 and H_2O are the materials out of which an organic product, eventually a simple sugar (glucose), is made. It appears certain that the reaction is very indirect, as it would necessarily be when six molecules of each reactant must ultimately be combined. The factors or agencies which absorb the CO_2 and mobilize the energy add to the complexity. It will be noted from the equation just given that the volumes of CO_2 consumed and of O_2 evolved are equal. For the continuance of photosynthesis there must be an external source of CO_2, constantly diffusing into the protoplast; and the oxygen produced will ultimately diffuse out of the protoplast into the environment. The photosynthetic process is energy-storing, since glucose has a high energy content. Glucose is a food that may be used in various ways in the cell, as will be indicated later. For the moment it will be emphasized that glucose may be built up into starch and that during photosynthesis starch commonly accumulates in the plastids of many plants as starch grains. Since starch is not directly soluble, the building up of starch prevents an excessive osmotic concentration in the cell during active photosynthesis.

Respiration and Photosynthesis. It has been shown that respiration is an energy-releasing process and photosynthesis an energy-storing one. The equations representing these processes are counterparts of each other. It is convenient to consider that glucose is the first identifiable energy-storing product in photosynthesis, and this sugar may be regarded as commonly the product destroyed when energy is released in respiration. In producing glucose, photosynthesis utilizes carbon dioxide and water, oxygen being the by-product. On the other hand, in the respiration of glucose, oxygen is used, and carbon dioxide and water are the by-products. A healthy leaf exposed to sunlight will display a rate of photosynthesis which, by comparison with respiration, is very high. The net result in the gas exchange is then a high absorption of carbon dioxide over and above that supplied by respiration. There is an equivalent oxygen elimination. At night, or in very low light intensity, the reverse is true. Unlike photosynthesis, which proceeds only in the presence of light, respiration is going on all the time, night and day, in every active living cell. Under favorable conditions the rate of photosynthesis of the green tissues so considerably exceeds the rate of respiration that the manufacture of food by photosynthesis in the course of the day is in excess of the utilization of food in respiration by all the tissues of the plant combined; hence on the whole there is a daily increase in weight. A green plant placed in the dark begins immediately to lose in dry weight, because respiration involves the use of food substances.

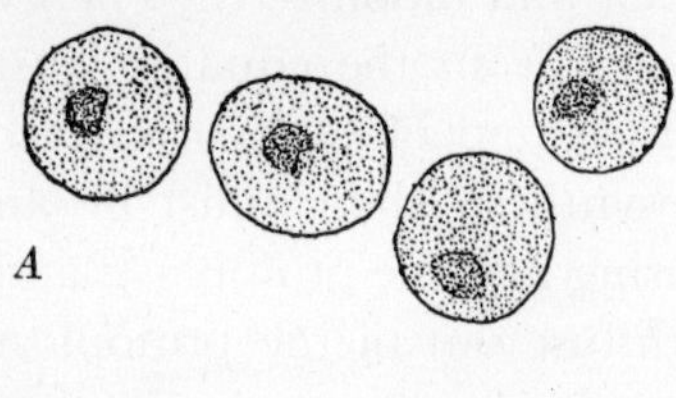

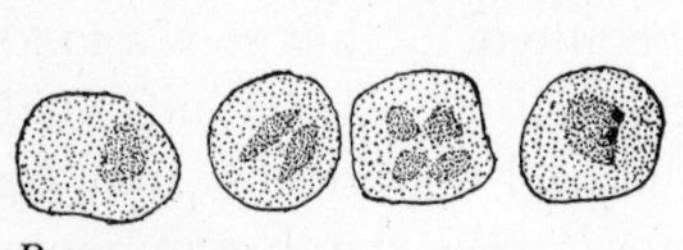

Fig. 87. Chloroplasts. *A*, from the leaf of Elodea, each chloroplast containing one starch grain. *B*, from the leaf of a moss, each chloroplast containing one or more starch grains.

Plastids: Chloroplasts. The photosynthetic aspect of the work of food manufacture in living cells is carried on by bodies of a class known as *plastids*. The plastids of mature cells, at least in the more complex green plants, develop from some of the chondriosomes of embryonic cells (Fig. 17). Those plastids which are green in color are chloroplasts (Fig. 87). Certain types of plastids other than chloroplasts will be discussed later.

The chloroplasts of most of the larger land plants are usually small and spheroidal, ellipsoidal, or (if crowded) polyhedral; the number in a cell varies from few to many. In tissues active in photosynthesis, such as the palisade tissue of a leaf, many chloroplasts are present in each cell. A chloroplast appears to be of a spongy nature; except for an apparently firmer consistency, it does not greatly differ in appearance from the surrounding cytoplasm. It is highly proteinaceous but contains also fatlike substances. It may be slightly vacuolate and invariably displays masses of granules which seem to be peculiar to it and which are often aggregated in a form known as *grana* (Fig. 88). Apparently a chloroplast possesses a definite membrane.

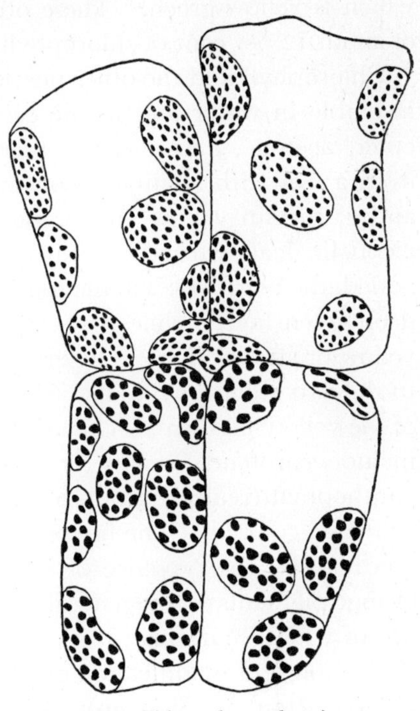

FIG. 88. Chloroplasts showing granular inclusions; from the spongy tissue of a leaf of Colocasia. The grana are of different sizes in the cells of different layers. After Heitz.

When plants are grown in darkness, the plastids lack chlorophyll but contain some of the yellow pigments. In some plants growing in light, chlorophyll fails to develop in the plastids of certain cells. In the silver-leaf geranium, chlorophyll development is limited to certain areas of the leaf blade, other areas being white or yellowish-white (Fig. 92, *A*). Sometimes a whole leaf or branch is entirely devoid of chlorophyll. The plastids in the lighter portions of such a plant contain carotene and xanthophyll (see below), whereas in the plastids of the green areas chlorophyll also is present.

Plastid Pigments. The green color of a chloroplast is due mainly to the presence of two green pigments, together called chlorophyll. The chloroplast contains also certain yellow pigments, which will be considered later. Apparently all the plastid pigments occur together in a finely divided state in the grana of the plastid. That the pigments are readily released from the body of the plastid is shown by killing a leaf in boiling water and then immersing it for some time in alcohol. The alcohol becomes green; and when the leaf is removed, it is found to be colorless, the chlorophyll having been dissolved in the alcohol. Microscopic examination discloses the now colorless chloroplasts not appreciably modified in form. Chlorophyll is a mixture of chlorophyll *a*, which is blue-green, and chlorophyll *b*, which is yellow-green. These ordinarily occur in the proportion of about 72 per cent of chlorophyll *a* to 28 per cent of chlorophyll *b*.

Chlorophyll and the other pigments contained in chloroplasts are insoluble in water and in the cell sap but are soluble in alcohol, ether, acetone, and various other liquids. The extract obtained from a leaf with a suitable solvent includes, besides chlorophyll *a* and *b*, certain yellow and orange pigments (carotenoids). If an alcoholic leaf extract is diluted with water and benzol is then added, the benzol rises to the top of the mixture as a sharply defined, deep-green layer, while the water and alcohol below show a pale yellow or straw color. The green solution at the top is due chiefly to the two chlorophylls, the yellow solution at the bottom to some of the yellow pigments. The yellow pigments occurring in plastids include carotene, usually deep yellow or orange in color, and xanthophyll (really a group of xanthophylls), which is light yellow or lemon-colored. The intensity of the green of leaves is of course modified by the presence of these yellow pigments. Yellow and orange pigments of this general type in animals and animal products are of wide occurrence; they have been shown to result from the utilization and modification of plant carotenoids.

Formation of Chlorophyll. Chlorophyll is found in chloroplasts, except in some very simple plants which lack identifiable plastids; therefore it may be assumed that conditions in the cytoplasm outside chloroplasts are not usually favorable for its production. The formation and the maintenance of a normal amount of chlorophyll are usually dependent upon light. Within limits, variable with the species, chlorophyll concentration increases with light intensity. Actually, the most intense sunlight, or conditions associated with it, reduces somewhat the chlorophyll content of the leaves of many species. Seedlings germinated in the dark and then placed in three lots to receive red (long wave length), green (medium wave length), and blue (short wave length) light, respectively, will become green first in the red and last in the blue, provided the radiation in each case is of equal intensity. Many species of green plants lose their green color when placed in darkness for a few days. This fact has been taken to indicate that chlorophyll must be decomposed even more rapidly in light but that, since it is likewise formed in light, decomposition is not apparent. This assumption seems scarcely justified, since many plants, such as parsnip, carrot, certain ferns, and cacti, maintain the green color of their leaves or stems for days, weeks, or even months in darkness. It seems more probable that in darkness the scarcity of food and the interaction of other internal conditions may induce chlorophyll decomposition, promptly or very slowly according to the species. When green leaves turn yellow it is a symptom of unhealthfulness, of which there are many possible causes. Other factors necessary in chlorophyll formation will be referred to later.

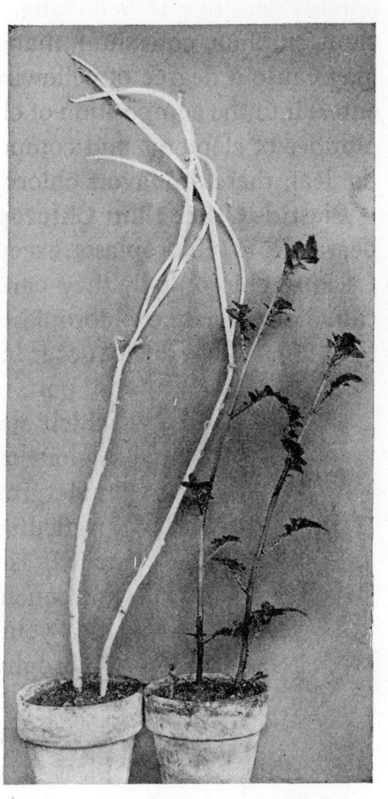

Fig. 89. Potato shoots grown in darkness (*left*) and in the light (*right*).

In general, plant parts which would be green if grown in light do not form chlorophyll when grown in darkness, but they may contain some of the yellow pigments and usually appear pale yellow or whitish. Plants grown in darkness, as compared with those grown in light, also frequently show marked differences in the forms of their aerial organs; these differences, together with the absence of green color, are summed up under the term "etiolation." Etiolated shoots of the potato (Fig. 89) or of the bean have small leaf blades, elongated petioles, and long, slender internodes. Etiolated shoots of wheat, barley, or corn have greatly elongated leaves; and sometimes the internodes are unusually long.

Chlorophyll is formed only within a relatively narrow range of temperature. In etiolated plants brought into light, chlorophyll is produced most rapidly between 18° and 30° C. A chlorophyll molecule, whether of chlorophyll *a* or *b*, contains the elements carbon, hydrogen, oxygen, nitrogen, and magnesium; chlorophyll *a* is $C_{55}H_{72}O_5N_4Mg$. These elements must be available in appropriate combinations. Carbohydrates also must be present if chlorophyll is to be formed. Although iron is not a constituent of a chlorophyll molecule, its presence is another necessary factor in chlorophyll formation; plants grown under conditions of iron deficiency are notably sensitive to yellowing. Variations in the amounts of calcium, sulphur, potassium, manganese, and phosphorus present also may cause a degree of yellowing, although none of these elements enters into the composition of chlorophyll. The presence of a large number of elements and compounds, contributing to the health of the leaf, therefore favors chlorophyll formation.

Plastids Other than Chloroplasts. *Leucoplasts* are similar in appearance to chloroplasts except that they contain no pigments. Lacking chlorophyll, they can not carry on photosynthesis; they can, however, like chloroplasts, manufacture starch from sugars (Fig. 90). They do not occur in green leaves or leaf parts but chiefly in parts of plants not exposed to light, in which starch is stored, such as the cortical regions of aerial stems and various tissues of underground stems and roots. They are particularly abundant in many seeds and fruits, as in those of the cereal grains. Not infrequently, if such an underground organ as a young potato tuber is exposed to light, chlorophyll appears in the leucoplasts, which thereby become chloroplasts. In this case, whether a particular plastid is to be a leucoplast or a chloroplast is determined by external conditions, particularly by the presence or absence of light. Some colorless plastids, however, like those in the marginal cells of the silver-leaf geranium, can not under any conditions become chloroplasts.

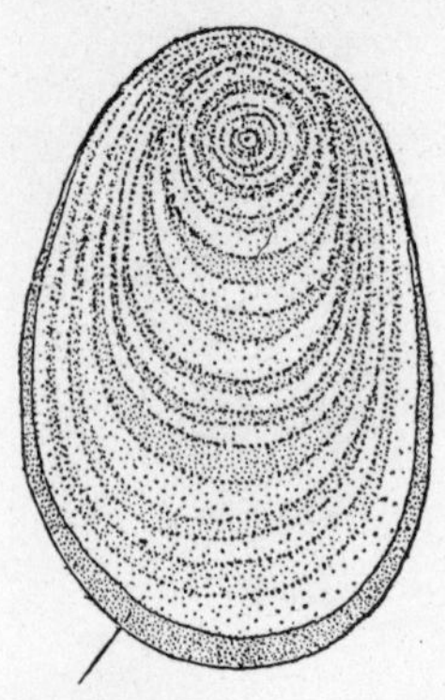

Fig. 90. Starch grain formed in a leucoplast; from a potato tuber.

Chromoplasts lack chlorophyll but contain some of the other pigments, especially carotene and xanthophyll. While carotene and xanthophyll are typically yellow or orange, they may vary in depth of color to orange-red, red, or reddish brown. These colors, occurring in certain flowers, fruits, and various other organs, are often due to the presence of chromoplasts. It will be shown, however, that the red (and other colors) of many leaves and other plant parts, and especially certain of the autumnal colors, belong to an entirely different group of substances, mostly water-soluble. Chromoplasts are more variable in form than are either chloroplasts or leucoplasts. In the cells of some of the floral parts of the nasturtium (Fig. 91), the chromoplasts are angular and orange-red. Those in the fruits of the climbing bittersweet are crescent-shaped and reddish brown. Other fruits whose colors are due to the presence of chromoplasts are those of the tomato, rose, and red pepper.

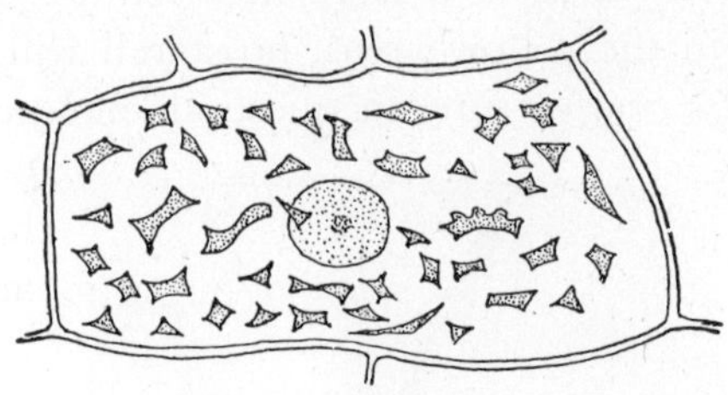

FIG. 91. Chromoplasts in a cell of a flower of nasturtium. After Strasburger.

Elaioplasts, whose particular function seems to be the storage of fats, occur in some plants.

The Rôle of Chlorophyll. It has been indicated that photosynthesis is possible only at a suitable temperature and in the presence of living matter, chlorophyll, water, carbon dioxide, and light. That the process is dependent upon the presence of chlorophyll may be shown by a simple experiment. If a leaf of the silver-leaf gera-

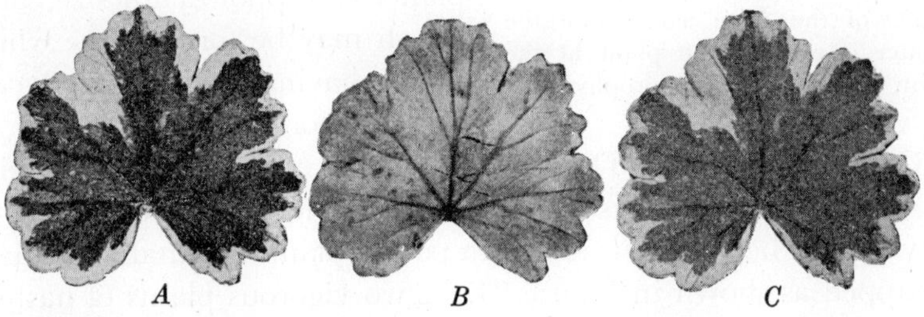

FIG. 92. Experiment illustrating the necessity of the presence of chlorophyll for photosynthesis. *A*, fresh leaf of the silver-leaf geranium. *B*, the same leaf with chlorophyll extracted. *C*, the starch-containing portion of the leaf has turned dark blue after treatment with iodine. Note that the starch pattern in *C* corresponds with the chlorophyll pattern in *A*.

nium, already referred to, after being exposed to the light for several hours is killed with boiling water, the chlorophyll extracted with alcohol, and the leaf placed in a solution of iodine, the portions which formerly contained chlorophyll turn blue, but those which lacked chlorophyll remain white or become merely yellowish (Fig. 92, *C*). The basis of this reaction is that starch turns blue (often brownish in a leaf) with iodine. Even if leucoplasts are present in the yellow areas, no starch will be formed by them during the period of time in question, since the formation of starch in them occurs only after considerable food has been produced in the green areas and some of this has been transported to the pale areas.

FIG. 93. Green and white corn plants of the same age. Note the greater growth of the plant at the right, which contains chlorophyll.

The importance of chlorophyll may be illustrated also by planting selected kernels of corn, some of which will produce green, and others white, plants (Fig. 93). For the first few days plants of both types grow with equal rapidity; but after the food reserves of the kernels have been used by the seedlings, the green plants continue to grow while the white plants die. Because of the presence of chlorophyll the green plants can photosynthesize, and starch may be formed; the white plants, having no chlorophyll, can not carry on photosynthesis.

Carbon Dioxide. That carbon dioxide (as supplied by the air) is used in photosynthesis, leading to the formation of starch in leaves, may be demonstrated with potted plants in suitable bell jars equipped as shown in Figure 94. Two vigorous plants of nasturtium or coleus are placed in the dark until the iodine test no longer discloses the presence of starch in the leaves. Each plant is placed on a base over which a tubulated bell jar is sealed. A stream of air is drawn slowly through each jar by a water pump or an aspirator. In one case (*A*) the air entering the bell jar is deprived of its content of carbon dioxide by being conducted through or over some substance, such as soda lime, which absorbs the carbon dioxide but no other gas of the atmosphere. For additional precaution small dishes containing a solution of soda lime are placed under the bell jar. The second bell jar (*B*) is similarly equipped; but instead of soda lime some inert material (which does not absorb carbon diox-

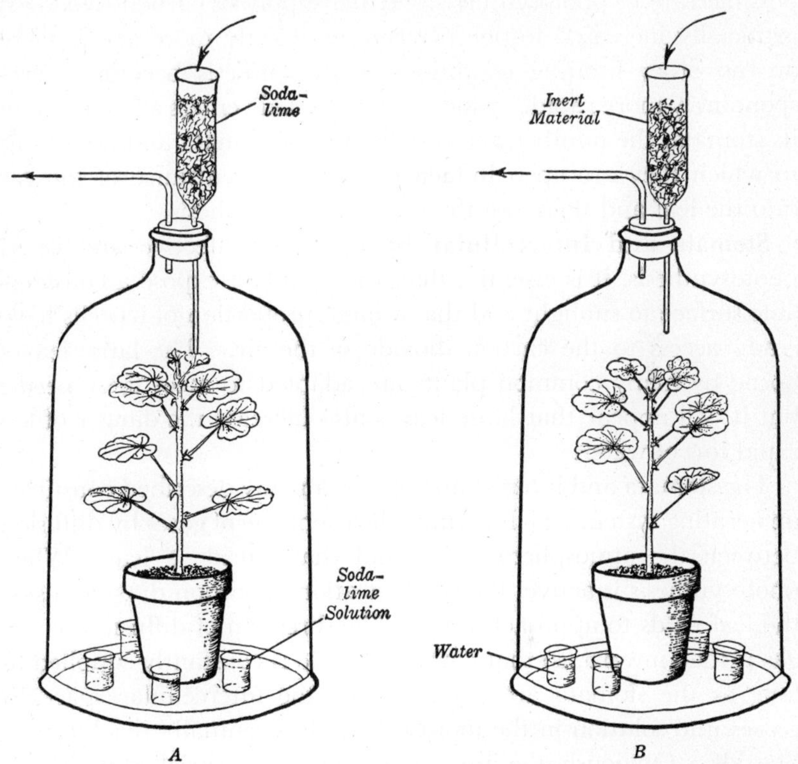

FIG. 94. Experiment showing the necessity of carbon dioxide for photosynthesis. Explanation in the text.

ide) is used, and dishes of water are placed under the bell jar. In *A*, therefore, no carbon dioxide is available; in *B* there is the usual amount found in air. If, after an exposure of at least six hours to sunlight, leaves from each plant are tested with iodine, those from the plant in jar *A* will give no starch test; but those of the plant in jar *B* will turn blue, showing that starch was formed only when carbon dioxide was available and hence that the presence of carbon dioxide is essential to photosynthesis.

The amount of carbon dioxide in the air is only about 3 parts in 10,000 (0.03 per cent). In some localities, as at the surface of the soil or in the neighborhood of cities and factories, the proportion may be slightly higher. Although a large amount of leaf surface which can absorb carbon dioxide is exposed to the atmosphere, the ordinary supply of this gas is often insufficient for the greatest possible rate of photosynthesis. If the supply of carbon dioxide is artificially increased to one per cent or slightly more and if there are no other limiting conditions, photosynthesis becomes correspondingly more rapid. Since carbon dioxide enters a leaf through its stomata, the number and distribution of stomata and the extent to which they are open influence the rate of entrance of the gas into the leaf and therefore the rate of photosynthesis.

Stomata and Intercellular Spaces. For effective and rapid photosynthesis, it is essential that a green plant expose a considerable surface to sunlight and that a large proportion of its cells have ready access to the carbon dioxide of the air. The large leaves borne by many common plants are adapted to meet these needs; but it will appear that large leaves also increase the danger of too rapid loss of water.

The stomata and intercellular spaces already described constitute an aerating system which permits the exchange of gases by diffusion between the atmosphere inside and that outside a leaf. When photosynthesis is active, the concentration of carbon dioxide inside the leaf tends to approach zero. The direction of diffusion of this gas is then inward, so that carbon dioxide is constantly supplied as long as the stomata are open. From the intercellular spaces it passes into solution in the moist cell walls, eventually reaching the plastids. Obviously the internal atmosphere is enriched with oxygen during photosynthesis, and the diffusion gradient for this gas is then outward.

When fully open, a stoma of average size is invisible to the eye; its area is less than one millionth of a square centimeter. In spite of the minute size of a stoma, an epidermis with the usual distribution of stomata is an effective multiperforate system in diffusion, with a capacity far greater than the sum of the stomatal areas. It has been estimated that a vigorous leafy plant with an area of one square meter produces about one gram of organic matter per hour, involving the use of the carbon dioxide contained in 2.5 cubic meters of air. A grape vine with a leaf area of 10 square meters would, if active for a day of 10 hours, produce about 100 grams of sugar, equivalent to 400 grams (about 14 ounces) of new growth. This would consume as much carbon dioxide as ordinarily occurs in 250 cubic meters of air.

Guard Cells. It is generally true that stomata are open in light and closed in darkness. However, the striking characteristic of the functioning of stomata in many plants is the ability of the guard cells to undergo changes in turgidity. The turgidity of these cells is only the immediate cause of the opening and closing of stomata. The mechanism controlling the movements of guard cells is rather complex, and the responses of the cells to environmental conditions also are complex. In general, when guard cells are turgid, as is usual in light, they are arched, and the included stoma is wide open; but when they are not turgid, they straighten and close or reduce the size of the stoma (Fig. 95). But, assuming the response to light as well as an adequate water content in the leaf, the problem is to account for the change in turgidity which occurs in light. This has been connected with changes in the contents of the guard cells in comparison with those in neighboring cells, but there is difference of opinion regarding the exact mechanism. When water is abundant in leaves, the stomata are usually open; they are commonly closed when water is deficient.

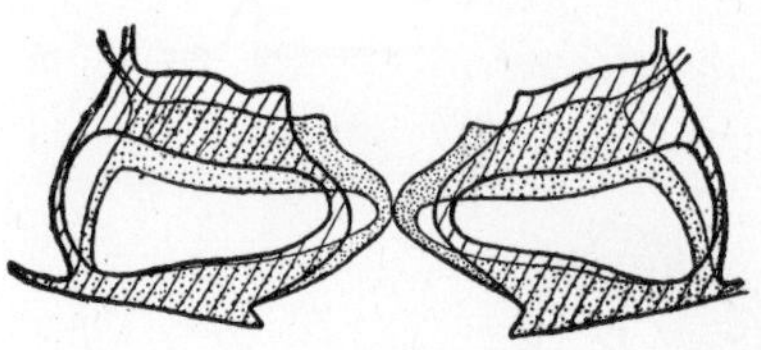

Fig. 95. A stoma in cross section, showing its opening and closing in consequence of changes in the turgidity of the guard cells. The thick walls of the guard cells in the open (turgid) condition are indicated by diagonal shading; in the closed (nonturgid) condition, by stippling. Adapted from Schwendener.

The behavior of guard cells varies in different species. In some common plants, such as potato, cabbage, and beet, stomata are usually open both day and night if the water supply is abundant. On the other hand, in cereals such as wheat and oats, stomata are always closed at night and may close even in the daytime if there is a slight deficiency in the water content of the plant. In very many plants the behavior of the stomatal apparatus is intermediate between the extremes just mentioned.

Light. The necessity of light for photosynthesis can be shown by covering the whole or a part of the surface of a green leaf with a screen made of some opaque substance, such as tinfoil or black paper (Fig. 96, *A*), so arranged that it will exclude the light but will not interfere with the exchange of gases between the inside and the outside of the leaf. It is best to select a leaf on a vigorously growing plant which has been kept in the dark for one or more days, because leaves on such a plant do not ordinarily contain starch. If, after adjusting the light screen, the leaf is exposed to the sun for an hour or more, then removed from the plant and tested, it is found that the portions exposed to the light contain starch (Fig. 96, *B*) but that no starch is present in the portion from which light was excluded. With other information available, this experiment shows, not that light is concerned directly in the formation of starch, but that light is necessary to the manufacture of some simple product which may be transformed into starch.

FIG. 96. *A*, light screen attached to a leaf. *B*, leaf after exposure to light under a light screen. The dark portions of the leaf show the distribution of starch, as demonstrated by treatment with iodine.

Under natural conditions in field and forest, photosynthesis proceeds most favorably for any particular species in that intensity of sunlight to which the species is adjusted. Many species grow normally under the varying conditions of full sunshine; others grow best in partial shade—that is, at lower average light intensity—with which may be associated other differences in the environment. Plants may be grown successfully under artificial illumination, employing electric light from such sources as tungsten, fluorescent, and vapor lamps.

Energy and the Function of Chlorophyll. In the study of photosynthesis it is relatively easy to determine, at least in outline, the *material* changes that are involved in the combination of carbon dioxide and water into such a carbohydrate as glucose. Intimately connected with these material changes are those that involve *energy*. Every substance contains, or possesses, a certain quantity of energy. Some of the energy possessed by a substance may more or less readily be changed into another form. For example, chemical energy is

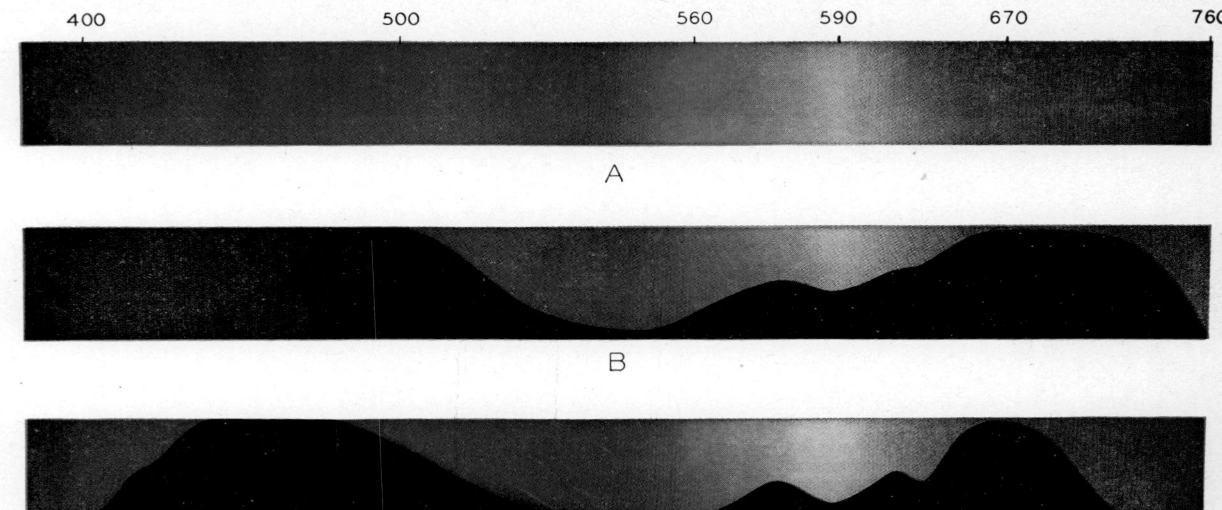

FIG. 97. *A*, distribution of colors in the spectrum of sunlight. *B*, spectrum of sunlight after passing through a relatively thick leaf; the black parts indicate proportions of light absorbed in each region of the spectrum. *C*, spectrum of sunlight after passing through a leaf extract. The numbers at the top indicate the wave length in millimicrons of the light in each region of the spectrum. (1 millimicron (mμ) = 1/1,000,000 of a millimeter.)

changed in the process of combustion (burning) to heat energy. Energy which may thus fairly readily be changed is *available* energy. Great amounts of energy are locked up, as it were, in the atoms of any substance and are not available by any ordinary means. The available energy content of carbon dioxide and that of water are relatively low; but the available energy content of glucose or of any other carbohydrate is relatively high. It may be repeated that, through the agency of chlorophyll, carbon dioxide and water have been combined to form a sugar and that the newly formed sugar possesses a stock of energy which was not present in the water and carbon dioxide but was obtained from sunlight by the plant cell through the agency of chlorophyll. In this process, light energy was changed into chemical energy.

Usually a part of the energy of the light which strikes any substance is absorbed by that substance. No effect can be produced by light unless it is absorbed. An important characteristic of chlorophyll is its capacity to absorb a considerable fraction of the radiant kinetic energy of the light falling upon it. A considerable part of this energy is transformed eventually into the potential energy stored in the products of photosynthesis.

Sunlight is composed of different kinds (wave lengths) of light. When a beam of light passes through a prism, it is split into its component parts, the visible ones of which produce on the human eye the sensations of the colors red, orange, yellow, green, blue, and violet. The splitting of the beam is due to the different degrees to which its component rays are dispersed by the prism. The display of varied colors so produced is the *visible spectrum* (Fig. 97, *A*). If a dilute alcoholic extract of chlorophyll from a leaf is placed in the path of a beam of sunlight and the beam after passing through the extract is dispersed by a prism, the spectrum appears interrupted by several dark regions; these correspond to the portions of the beam of light which have been absorbed in larger amounts by the extract. Recalling that a weak solution of chlorophyll was used, the dark regions may be regarded as the zones of relatively high absorption. Actually, a suitable concentration of chlorophyll, whether as extract or in the active leaf, will show a small and varying degree of absorption practically throughout the visible spectrum (Fig. 97, *C*). Some of the dark regions located toward the red end of the spectrum, and some toward the violet end, are caused by the absorption of the corresponding rays of light by chlorophyll *a* and chlorophyll *b*. Two or three toward the violet end of the spectrum are caused by the absorption of light by carotene and the xanthophylls. Experiments show that the light of any particular wave length which is absorbed by chlorophyll shares in the energy used in photosynthesis. Plants which lack chlorophyll, with the exception of certain bacteria to be mentioned later, can not transform the energy of sunlight into the chemical energy used in photosynthesis. In strong direct sunlight, the energy of the red end is relatively intense; and since it is strongly absorbed, it dominates photosynthesis. In reflected light from the sky the energy of the blue end is relatively more intense, so that it becomes correspondingly important. It has been calculated that only about 0.5 to 3 per cent of the light energy falling upon a leaf in direct sunlight is used in photosynthesis; some of the light is reflected, some is transmitted, and a considerable proportion of that which is absorbed is transformed into heat; the heat in turn is concerned in the evaporation of water lost in transpiration from leaves and other aerial parts.

From the preceding discussion it follows that photosynthesis involves a complex of internal and external conditions. Presupposing the active protoplast, as well as the plastid with no doubt several unknown mechanisms, the chief factors easily identified are the chlorophyll concentration, the carbon dioxide of the air, light, and temperature. In the process of photosynthesis light energy has been transformed into the energy of carbohydrates. These and other foods represent not only reservoirs of the energy of sunlight but also a source of building materials for growth.

TRANSPIRATION

Importance of Water. It will appear in the following chapter that water enters the absorbing surfaces of roots from the soil solution. Solutes, many of which constitute the required mineral nutrients, also enter; both water and solutes eventually reach the vascular tissues; thence they are conducted through roots, stems, and branches to leaves, buds, and floral organs. An ample supply of water is necessary for all the activities of a plant, particularly for photosynthesis and growth. A young leaf not infrequently contains up to 90 per cent of water. The water content of a leaf at any moment, however, represents only a fraction of the water reaching the leaf during the growing season. This large water requirement is occasioned by the fact that water is constantly being lost by evaporation from cells of all aerial parts, especially from the leaves; and the loss can be compensated only by an intake of water from the soil or from other available source.

Transpiration. Water evaporates from a free water surface or from any surface containing water; that is, it changes from a liquid state to a vapor and passes into the atmosphere. The evaporation of water from the exposed surfaces of a plant is *transpiration.* Since in most familiar plants transpiration is chiefly from the cells of leaves, it is in the leaves that this process is most readily studied. It has been pointed out that the expanded form of the leaf and its intricate system of air spaces and stomata (which are usually open in light) constitute it a remarkably perfect structure for capturing, by diffusion, the carbon dioxide of the air, which during active photosynthesis is in higher concentration outside than inside the leaf. Efficiency of form and structure in the *intake* of a gas means a similar efficiency in the *outgo* of any gas that is in higher concentration inside. The concentration of water vapor is usually higher inside, for the spongy tissue of a leaf is constantly evaporating water into the intercellular spaces, from which the water vapor passes into the outer atmosphere by diffusion, mainly through the stomata—that is, by *stomatal transpiration.* A rapid loss of water is therefore a necessary consequence of leaf structure and a hazard in the life of a plant whose leaves are well constructed for the absorption of carbon dioxide and for the photosynthesis of organic food. The epidermal cells of a leaf permit some water to pass, but the amount of water lost to the atmosphere in this way is relatively small in land plants because of the presence in and on their walls of the relatively impervious cutin. Transpiration through a cutinized surface is *cuticular transpiration.* In various cases from 85 to 97 per cent of the water lost by transpiration passes through stomata, the remainder being lost through the cutinized epidermis.

Amount and Rate of Transpiration. A reasonable indication of the quantity of water loss in the transpiration of potted plants may readily be obtained. Selecting a vigorous geranium plant growing in good, adequately watered soil, the entire pot and soil surface are covered with a rubber cloth which is tightly wrapped around the base of the stem (unless special pot containers and soil covers are provided), so that no water vapor can escape except through the plant. The potted plant is carefully weighed, a record made, and the plant set aside, under any growing conditions desired, for 24 hours. It is then weighed again. Subtracting the final weight from the initial one, the difference represents the loss of water during the time of the experiment. A measure or estimate of the area of the leaves being obtained, the rate of loss of water per unit of area can be calculated.

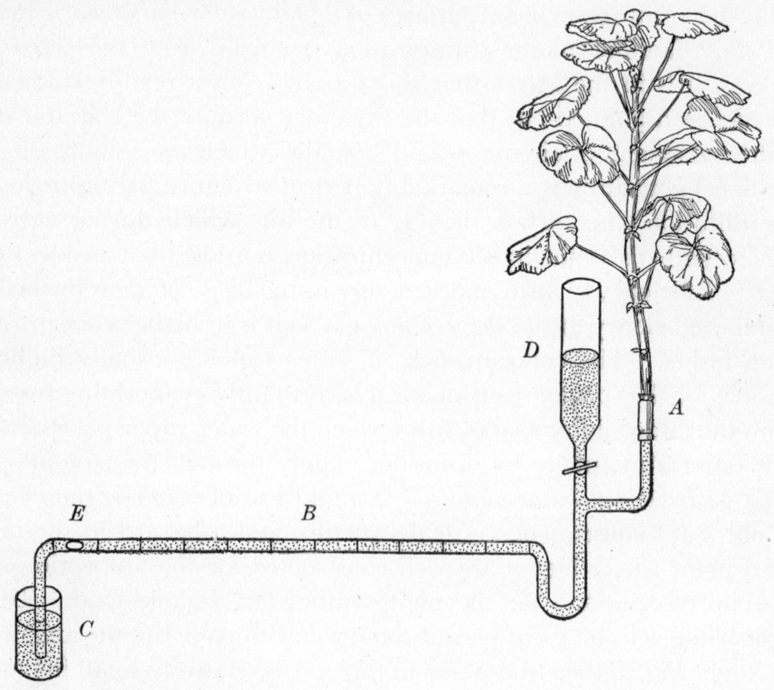

FIG. 98. A potometer, used to determine the amount and rate of water absorption and water loss by a plant during transpiration.

The approximate rate of transpiration over short intervals of time may be determined by the use of a potometer (Fig. 98). A cut shoot, or a branch bearing leaves, is fitted snugly into a rubber stopper suitable for arm *A*. The system *A–B* is tilted and filled with water, so that when the stopper with the shoot is inserted in *A* water will be forced out into *C*, previously nearly filled with water. The reservoir *D* is then filled. By lifting the apparatus slightly, arm *B* is raised above the water in *C*; then, allowing the plant to transpire for a short time, a bubble of air (*E*) is introduced; the apparatus is then lowered so that the bent tip of *B* is below the water level in *C*. Now, as water evaporates from the leafy shoot, it is replaced by water drawn from tube *B*; the result is a shifting of the bubble *E* toward the plant. By noting the time required for the bubble to move a certain distance, the rate of transpiration may be estimated. If the apparatus is placed under different external conditions, the effects of the environment on transpiration may be studied. The method just described is not a strictly accurate one for determining the rate of transpiration because it measures the rate at which water is being absorbed by the shoot, and the amount of water transpired may be at least slightly different from the amount absorbed.

By far the greater part of the water absorbed by plants is lost by transpiration, and the amount lost is surprisingly large. Under ordinary growing conditions, a vigorous sunflower plant is estimated to transpire about 400 pounds of water in a growing season of 100 days. A single corn plant growing in Kansas has been shown to remove 54 gallons, or 1⅘ barrels, of water from the soil in a single season, which is 90 times as much water as is needed by the plant for all purposes except to replace the loss by transpiration. On the basis of the rate of water loss of apple shoots observed in Illinois during July, it appears that a single mature apple tree may lose 95 gallons per day. At this rate an acre of 40 apple trees would transpire 480 tons of water during a midsummer month.

Experiments show that the amount of water transpired by a plant fluctuates from hour to hour, from day to day, and from season to season. Such fluctuations are due largely to variations in the external conditions, although conditions within the plant and within its individual cells also affect the rate of transpiration.

The Mechanics of Transpiration (Fig. 99). It has been pointed out that, since transpiration is concerned with water in the gaseous state, the diffusion of water vapor from leaves is in every way comparable with that of other gases. Within the leaf, water evaporates from the moist surfaces of the cell walls abutting on any part of the system of intercellular spaces. The air in these spaces therefore tends to become saturated with water vapor. This vapor can diffuse from the internal atmosphere of the leaf through open stomata to the external atmosphere so long as the water-vapor concentration of the external air is lower and the internal temperature is not appreciably higher. It is assumed also that there is sufficient external air movement to prevent a local atmosphere of high vapor concentration just outside the stoma.

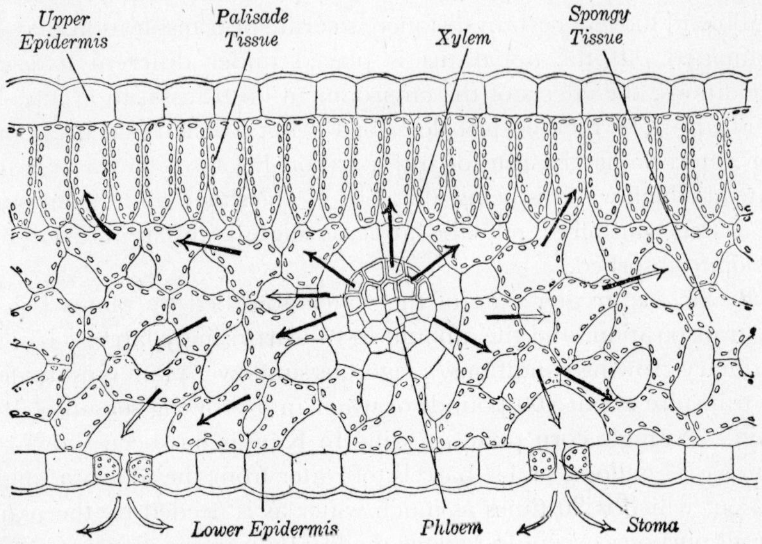

Fig. 99. Diagram showing the paths of movement of water through and out of a leaf. The movement of water in liquid form is indicated by black arrows; that of water in the form of vapor, by light arrows.

Stomatal transpiration consists, therefore, first, in the evaporation of water from the saturated walls of cells lining the intercellular spaces, and second, in the diffusion of the water vapor through stomata. The evaporation of water from the walls of cells adjoining an intercellular space tends to create a water deficit in the walls. As a result of this deficit, the walls of each such cell imbibe more water from the included protoplast. Withdrawal of water from the protoplast increases the concentration of substances dissolved in the cell sap, and this cell tends to draw water by osmosis from neighboring cells that contain proportionally more water. The latter cells in like manner draw from their neighbors, and eventually water is withdrawn from the tracheids and vessels of the veins of the leaf. These vascular elements are connected by the tracheids and vessels in the xylem of petiole, stem, and root with the cortex of the root; and through the cortex connection is established with the root hairs

(p. 152). Thus, a continuous stream of water is made possible through root, stem, and branches to the leaf, compensating for the loss of water in the form of vapor from the stomata.

External Factors Influencing Transpiration. Most important among the external atmospheric factors influencing the rate of transpiration are radiant energy (including light), humidity, temperature, and air movement. Factors are operative also through the soil. Since the stomata of the great majority of plants are open in light, radiant energy is a dominant factor in transpiration. Typically, a curve representing the transpiration rate throughout the day shows a maximum corresponding more or less with light intensity, although actually, because of other considerations, the maximum usually occurs somewhat later than noon. There is some absorption of radiant energy beyond the range of visible light, especially in the longer wave lengths (infrared). The radiant energy absorbed at any wave length which is not used in photosynthesis is transformed into heat and so becomes a factor in the vaporization of water.

The humidity conditions of an atmosphere are commonly expressed for many purposes as *relative humidity*, meaning percentage of saturation at any stated temperature, so that a relative humidity of 50 per cent at 90° F. indicates that the air has 50 per cent of the vapor it can hold at that temperature. With the air in the intercellular spaces near the saturation level, there would be a steep diffusion gradient into an outside air with a relative humidity of 50 per cent. Usually transpiration varies inversely as the relative humidity of the atmosphere. It is worthy of mention that at two different temperatures each with a relative humidity of 50 per cent, the higher temperature will imply a higher actual water-vapor content, since at a higher temperature more vapor can be held in the air. Many botanists prefer, therefore, to express humidity values as vapor pressures—that is, in millimeters of mercury—just as air pressures may be expressed.

A rise in temperature promotes the rate of transpiration, just as it increases evaporation, by facilitating molecular activity. Also, the evaporating power of the air varies with the temperature, since the capacity of the air to hold water is greater at a higher temperature. A rise in temperature of the air without an actual increase in water content necessarily means a decreased relative humidity.

Other conditions remaining constant, a rise in the temperature of leaves, as from the absorption of radiant energy or from respiration, tends to increase the rate of transpiration; but in general it appears that such causes of temperature rise are not often serious, since losses of heat from a plant are rapid.

It has been seen that a local atmosphere of high humidity on the surface of a broad leaf, such as might occur in a still atmosphere, retards transpiration, whereas moderate air currents, preventing any accumulation of vapor, facilitate water loss. Leaf movement also increases the rate of transpiration. Except at high altitudes, atmospheric pressure is a factor of slight importance; but at high altitudes air pressure is sufficiently low to increase the rate of transpiration and in conjunction with other agencies tends to develop a desert-like environment. Soil factors influence transpiration indirectly by affecting primarily the rate of absorption of water by the roots. So long as the water-supplying power of the soil is adequate, transpiration is facilitated; but as soon as this power is reduced from any cause, incipient wilting of leaves begins, and transpiration is cut to a minimum.

Factors Influencing the Loss of Water. When the stomata are completely closed, stomatal transpiration is of course stopped. However, a decrease of 50 to 75 per cent in the diameter of stomata apparently affects transpiration but slightly; a further decrease in diameter, however, results promptly in a reduction of the rate of transpiration.

The shape and size of a leaf markedly affect the amount of water transpired. Some plants of dry regions, like the century plant and the aloe (Fig. 79), have large, thick leaves. Loss of water from such leaves tends to be slow, because even though the area of the leaves may be considerable it is small in proportion to their volume. In some plants, such as certain cacti (Fig. 100), the loss of water from the plant as a whole is relatively low because the leaves are small or absent or in some cases spinelike, the transpiring surfaces being chiefly those of the stems. Some desert shrubs and trees have leaves during the rainy season but shed them in dry periods.

In general, plants such as the sunflower and the cactus represent in surface relations two extreme types, the sunflower growing normally under conditions of average soil moisture and the cactus typifying one of the desert *succulents* which as a class constitute only a fraction of the large group of desert species. The sunflower has numerous expanded leaves and no great bulk of stem. The surface-to-volume ratio (S/V), which may be used as a kind of index of growth form, is high in this plant; and such a ratio suggests a high capacity to transpire and at the same time to photosynthesize. On the other hand, in a cactus the leaves are a negligible factor, and the stem is bulky, therefore S/V is uncommonly low, suggesting a correspondingly low over-all capacity for transpiration and photosynthesis. In every case in which transpiration is limited by restriction of surface, the rate of growth is correspondingly limited.

Fig. 100. A cactus (*Cereus giganteus*), adapted by its structure to life in a desert. Photograph courtesy of D. T. Macdougal.

In the cells of thick, fleshy stems or leaves, substances of a mucilaginous nature are often present, which tend to imbibe and retain water. As already mentioned, the leaves of Russian thistle (Fig. 78), of the century plant, and of the aloe have internal water-storage tissues which can hold certain quantities of water. Such a plant usually has a root system near the surface of the soil which absorbs water quickly after a rain, the water being collected in the stem and leaves. So long as this stored water is available, the activities of the plant may continue at a rate approaching the normal.

Perhaps the most important internal factor which may or may not be associated with structural modifications is the capacity of many nonsucculent dry-land plants to suffer water loss, wilting, and suspended activity without losing the capacity to revive when water becomes available. In fact, the leaves and stems of many desert plants may transpire as much or more per unit area of surface when moisture is available as those of plants growing in moist situations also with ample available moisture. Frequently desert species are not protected against transpiration. They merely endure it. Under extreme conditions they dry out severely, transpiration being reduced practically to zero; and so they exist until water is available. In respect to water such plants are truly opportunists. The capacity to endure drying is probably associated with the capacity to bind water. Bound water is held with considerable force by the colloidal materials, and so some of the changes otherwise introduced by rapid drying are prevented. Other factors influencing the rate of transpiration are to be expected from differences in behavior of the stomata and also in the osmotic concentration of the cell sap. Prompt response of stomata to incipient wilting and relatively high osmotic concentration of the sap tend to reduce evaporation from cell surfaces and consequently materially affect the rate of transpiration.

Impregnation of the outer walls of the epidermis with cutin tends to check transpiration. Cutinized walls are characteristic of epidermal cells of leaves and stems that are exposed to the air. In some leaves so much cutin is present that it forms a thin layer (cuticle) on the surface. Another form of wax, often flaky in

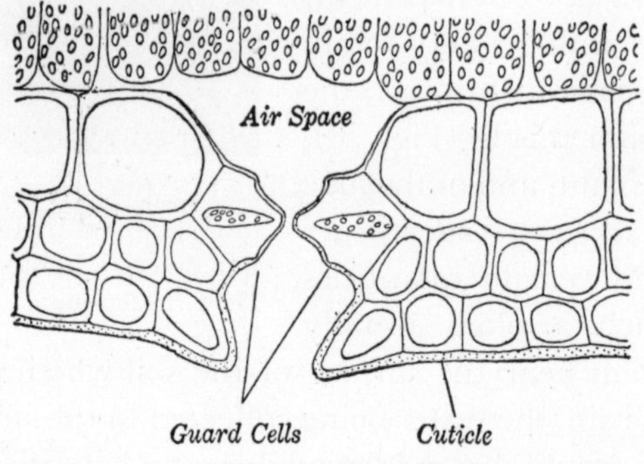

FIG. 101. Cross section of a portion of the lower surface of a leaf of the rubber plant. The heavily cutinized epidermis and the sunken stomata tend to limit transpiration.

texture, occurring on the surfaces of certain fruits and on the leaves of cabbage and other plants, also checks epidermal evaporation. An exposed layer of cork acts in the same manner as a cuticle or waxy coating. The location of stomata at the bases of pits, as in the leaves of the pine and of the rubber plant (Fig. 101), has a similar effect. The presence of hairs on the surface of a leaf or stem, so conspicuous in the mullein, may limit transpiration only slightly if at all.

Generally speaking, plants native to regions or conditions in which the supply of available water is very limited, such as the semi-deserts of the southwestern United States, possess the most highly developed means of checking transpiration, whereas plants living in habitats permitting access to an abundance of water rarely have special means of limiting this process. Plants whose structure and functional adjustments fit them to live in deserts and other very dry localities, or in other situations in which the availability of water is limited, are *xerophytes;* those fitted for life in water or under extremely moist conditions are *hydrophytes;* and those which stand midway between these two classes, being suited to approximately average conditions with reference to a supply of water, are *mesophytes.* The differences between xerophytes, mesophytes, and hydrophytes illustrate the general rule that living organisms are adapted by their structure and functions to existence in particular types of environment.

The Water Balance in Plants. From what has been said, it is evident that the movement of water in a plant is affected by the rate and amount of absorption of water from the soil and by the rate and amount of transpiration. It has been seen that soil factors such as the water content or the concentration of solutes in the soil water usually affect the rate of transpiration. However, transpiration and absorption are not always directly proportional, and water may be transpired by a plant more rapidly than it is absorbed by the roots. Conversely, water may be absorbed more rapidly than it is lost by transpiration.

When water is lost more rapidly than it is absorbed, the water balance is changed, and a deficit exists. A considerable water deficit is likely, therefore, to exist in a plant during periods of active transpiration. About midday on bright, sunny days many plants lose considerably more water than they can absorb; the resultant water deficit in a sunflower plant may reach 28 per cent of its maximum water content. Fluctuations in the water content of leaves of common plants (such as wheat, sugar beet, or pumpkin) may be, under some climatic conditions, as great as 20 per cent. Even in plants with an extensive water supply and with transpiration limited, a daily deficit may occur. When transpiration is excessive, as on very warm, dry days, a plant can not make up the water deficit during the night, so that the deficit may persist the next morning.

With continued drought and consequent lack of water in the soil, the daily water deficit in the plant increases. The loss of turgidity in the cells leads to a loss of rigidity; and the leaves and young stem and branch tips droop or wilt, although elsewhere in the plant the water content may be relatively high. Such wilting often occurs at midday when transpiration is active; but ordinarily toward evening, when transpiration decreases, the water deficit is relieved and the plant recovers its rigidity. This may occur without appreciable absorption of water from the soil, the water already in the plant being redistributed. Under certain conditions the water content may become so depleted that the plant recovers from a wilted condition only with difficulty, if at all. Permanent wilting occurs when soil water is no longer available to the plant; and the living cells of all organs, including root hairs, gradually lose their turgor. After permanent wilting the plant absorbs water, if at all, very slowly from moist soil and not until new root hairs are formed.

Loss of Water in Liquid Form. Under certain conditions some plants give off water as a liquid. At the ends of the veins of the leaves of such plants as the cabbage, nasturtium, and fuchsia are large water pores (Fig. 102) which differ from ordinary stomata in that they always remain wide open. Immediately beneath each water pore is a loose tissue devoid of chlorophyll, which is in contact with the end of a vein. When there is an abundant supply of water and the transpiration from such a leaf is limited, water in liquid form escapes through these pores. In the strawberry (Fig. 103) and primrose, water pores occur at the tips of the teeth of the leaves. Similar pores are present also at the tips of the leaves of most grasses, such as wheat and barley. The process of exudation of water from water pores may be easily observed if a pot of young,

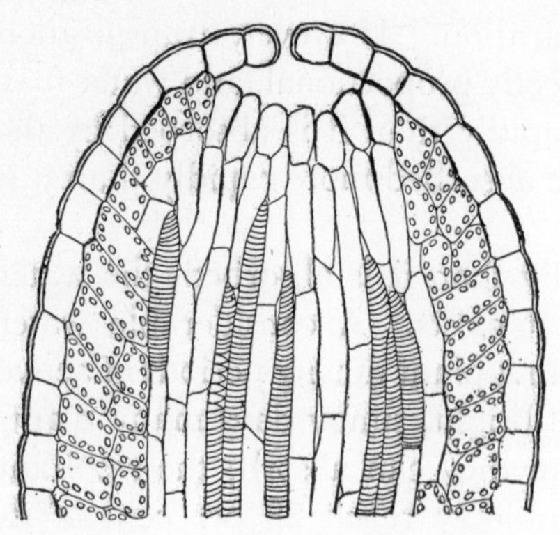

FIG. 102. Water pore at the tip of a leaf of fuchsia. Water in liquid form exudes from such a pore.

well-watered wheat or barley plants is covered with a bell jar. In a short time, drops of water appear on the tips of the leaves at the ends of the veins.

FIG. 103. The exudation of droplets of water from pores at the ends of veins in strawberry leaves.

SUMMARY

Leaves of seed plants differ from other vegetative organs in that in general all or almost all their cells enlarge and mature simultaneously.

Mature leaves may be opposite, whorled, or alternate in arrangement on the stem. A foliage leaf is commonly composed of blade, petiole, and stipules; but some lack petiole, stipules, or both. Leaf blades are either parallel-veined or netted-veined. In the latter case the arrangement of veins may be palmate or pinnate. When marginal lobes of a blade extend to the midrib or to the base of the blade, the leaf is compound. Leaflets of a compound leaf may be pinnately or palmately arranged. Leaflets may themselves be divided.

Apart from veins, the blade of a dicotyledonous leaf usually consists of upper epidermis, palisade tissue, spongy tissue, and lower epidermis. Both lower and upper epidermis may contain stomata. A stoma is a space between two guard cells.

Veins are vascular bundles, continuous with those of the stem and consisting of the same primary tissues. Surrounding a vein is a sheath composed of parenchyma and including, in the cases of many large veins, mechanical tissue as well. A petiole contains one or more vascular bundles which connect the bundles of the stem with the veins of the leaf blade.

Structural differences between leaves of various plants are due largely to differences in the proportional amounts of the tissues already mentioned. Leaves other than foliage leaves may be scale leaves, tendrils, or spines. The separation of leaf from stem is due to an abscission layer formed at the base of the petiole.

Photosynthesis is a process by which carbon dioxide and water are combined to form a simple sugar. Oxygen is given off, equal in volume to the carbon dioxide utilized. Photosynthesis occurs only when living cells containing chlorophyll are exposed to light. It is an energy-storing process—the counterpart of respiration, which releases energy.

Photosynthesis is carried on in or by the activity of a type of plastids known as chloroplasts. Chlorophyll is contained in the chloroplasts, along with certain yellow or red pigments—carotene and xanthophyll. Chlorophyll consists of chlorophyll *a* and chlorophyll *b*.

Chlorophyll is usually formed only in the presence of light of not too great intensity. In many plants it disappears in darkness. Chlorophyll production occurs only within a narrow range of temperature and in the presence of carbohydrates and of iron. It is necessary also that the constituent elements of chlorophyll (C, H, O, N, and Mg) be available in suitable form.

Types of plastids other than chloroplasts are leucoplasts, which are colorless but which, like chloroplasts, can manufacture starch from sugars; chromoplasts, which lack chlorophyll but contain carotene and xanthophyll; and elaioplasts, which store fats.

The stomata and intercellular spaces in a leaf constitute an aerating system which permits exchange of gases (oxygen and carbon dioxide) between the atmosphere and the cells of the leaf. The opening and closing of stomata result from changes in the turgidity of the guard cells, which in turn are influenced by external conditions.

The energy stored in the process of photosynthesis is derived from light. Chlorophyll absorbs varying proportions of the light of different wave lengths.

Transpiration is the evaporation of water from the exposed surfaces of a plant. In most familiar plants transpiration is chiefly from the cells of leaves. Most of the water transpired by leaves of the usual type passes through the stomata. The greater part of the water absorbed by a plant is lost by transpiration.

The rate of transpiration is influenced by radiant energy (including light), humidity, temperature, and air movement; also by the open or closed condition of stomata, by the shape, size, and thickness of leaves, and by the presence or absence of mucilaginous substances which imbibe and retain water. Plants adapted to situations of limited water supply are xerophytes; those fitted for very moist conditions are hydrophytes; and those suited to approximately average conditions are mesophytes.

The water balance of a plant is determined by the relative rates of absorption and transpiration. If loss of water is more rapid than absorption, a water deficit occurs. A considerable deficit in any part of a plant may cause wilting.

Some plants under certain conditions exude water in liquid form through pores which differ from ordinary stomata in being always open.

CHAPTER VII

ROOTS

Functions of Roots. It is obvious that the roots of a typical seed plant growing in the soil are the only organs by means of which the plant establishes and maintains effective contact with the soil solution, thereby being able to absorb water and salts. *Absorption* is therefore a fundamental function of roots. It has been seen that the volume of water required by a plant is large and that its salt requirement also is considerable, so that the wide distribution or ramification of roots in the soil and the great extent of surface exposed have special significance in the absorption process. The idea conveyed by absorption suggests another function, that of *transport*, or disposal of materials absorbed, since substances moving into the root must also be passed along to the plant as a whole. A third function is the evident one that the plant requires all-sided support for the weight and spread of its top; the effective *anchorage* of the roots in the soil assures this result as well as the protection of the delicate absorbing structures. Further, *food reserves* commonly accumulate in roots to an extent more or less comparable with that in stems; and roots specialized as storage organs are frequent, particularly among biennial species. Finally, it will be apparent that all the living cells of root tissues display the various activities that characterize corresponding cells in other parts of the plant.

Types of Root Systems. Structurally, two main types of root systems are recognized: *tap-root* (Fig. 104) and *fibrous-root systems* (Fig. 105). In a system of the former type, the primary root (tap root) commonly grows much more rapidly than do any of the branch roots; and it also constitutes a central axis from which smaller branch roots arise. Sometimes, as in the pine, the primary root may die early. In such a case a branch root acquires the appearance of a tap root. For at least a short distance below the surface of the soil the tap roots of many plants may attain a diameter approximately equal to that of the stem. Young hickory trees form thick, woody tap roots of large diameter, extending several feet downward; but, as the tree grows and large bracing side roots develop near the surface of the soil, the preponderance of the tap root may be lost. In some plants, especially in herbaceous annuals or in biennials like the radish, turnip, carrot, and beet, the diameter of the tap root may exceed by many times that of the stem. The great diameter of such a root is due chiefly to the formation of parenchymatous cells by cambial activity. The economic importance of many plants with fleshy tap roots results from the storage of large amounts of reserve starch or sugar in these parenchymatous cells.

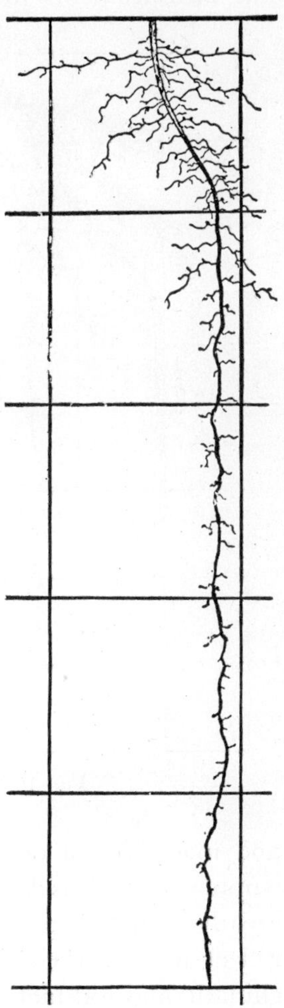

FIG. 104. The tap-root system of alfalfa. This and Figure 105 are from Weaver, Jean, and Crist, *Development and Activities of Roots of Crop Plants*, published by the Carnegie Institution of Washington.

A fibrous-root system has no central axis. Instead, the primary root, if it persists, and many of the branch (or adventitious) roots grow to approximately the same length and diameter. Such a root system may be composed of relatively slender roots, as in many annual plants; or, if secondary thickening is long continued, various members of the root system may grow to a large diameter, as in most familiar trees. In the fibrous-root systems of some plants, such as the sweet potato or the dahlia (Fig. 106), some of the branch roots become much swollen and enlarged for a part of their length, the tissues being filled with food and water. The enlargement of a root of this sort is usually the result of an increase in size and number of the parenchymatous cells which are present. Fibrous-root systems with such enlarged branch roots are often termed *fascicled-root systems*.

Distribution of Root Systems. Extensive studies of the distribution of root systems of native and crop plants have been made by trenching and gradually washing away the soil, using care to support the finer roots as excavation and washing proceeded. The observations and measurements made have shown that in general the extent

FIG. 105. The fibrous-root system of corn.

and mass of root development had previously been inadequately emphasized. It is demonstrated also that, while growth habits vary greatly with the species, the details of root distribution in the soil reflect to a marked degree a definite response to the complex of climatic and soil factors.

Some plants have relatively shallow root systems in proportion to the height of stem and branches. The tamarack (larch) is notably shallow-rooted, growing as it does in cold and boggy regions. In fact, contrary to the popular impression, the roots of trees growing under the conditions usually prevailing in a forest or in a meadow are found chiefly to a depth of about four feet. Looser soils and special drainage conditions may permit penetration to ten feet or more. The lateral spread of the roots also is variable, depending upon the density of the stand. Commonly it is much greater than the spread of the branches, and within limits it increases with decrease in water content of the soil. Cacti too in the drier parts of their range are shallow-rooted. Corn is an example of a crop plant with a large development of shallow roots, but at the same time with a considerable spread and depth of penetration, particularly under favorable conditions of growth. It is reported that two-months-old alfalfa plants grown in a prairie region of the Missouri valley developed roots that extended but one and one half feet below the surface of the soil, whereas plants from the same lot of seed and of the same age grown under conditions of the more arid grasslands to the west had roots extending to a depth of five feet.

FIG. 106. Fascicled roots of dahlia.

Regions of a Root (Fig. 107). As in the case of a stem, the growing tip of a root includes a meristematic region in which the cells are small, angular, closely packed, and all substantially alike; back of this is a region of elongation in which cells are enlarging, mainly in length; next comes a region of maturation in which cells are differentiating and beginning to take on mature characteristics; and finally a mature region in which most of the cells have completed their development. There are, however, certain differences to be noted between roots and stems. (*a*) Covering the meristematic region of a root tip is a thimble-shaped *root cap*, to which there is no corresponding structure at a stem tip. (*b*) In contrast with the condition in a stem, the transition from the meristematic to the mature region of a root is continuous, since there are no nodes or internodes such as are present in the stem. However, the continued formation and elongation of cells steadily increase the length of a root, and accordingly the apex is forced continually farther and farther into the soil or other substrate in which the root may be growing.

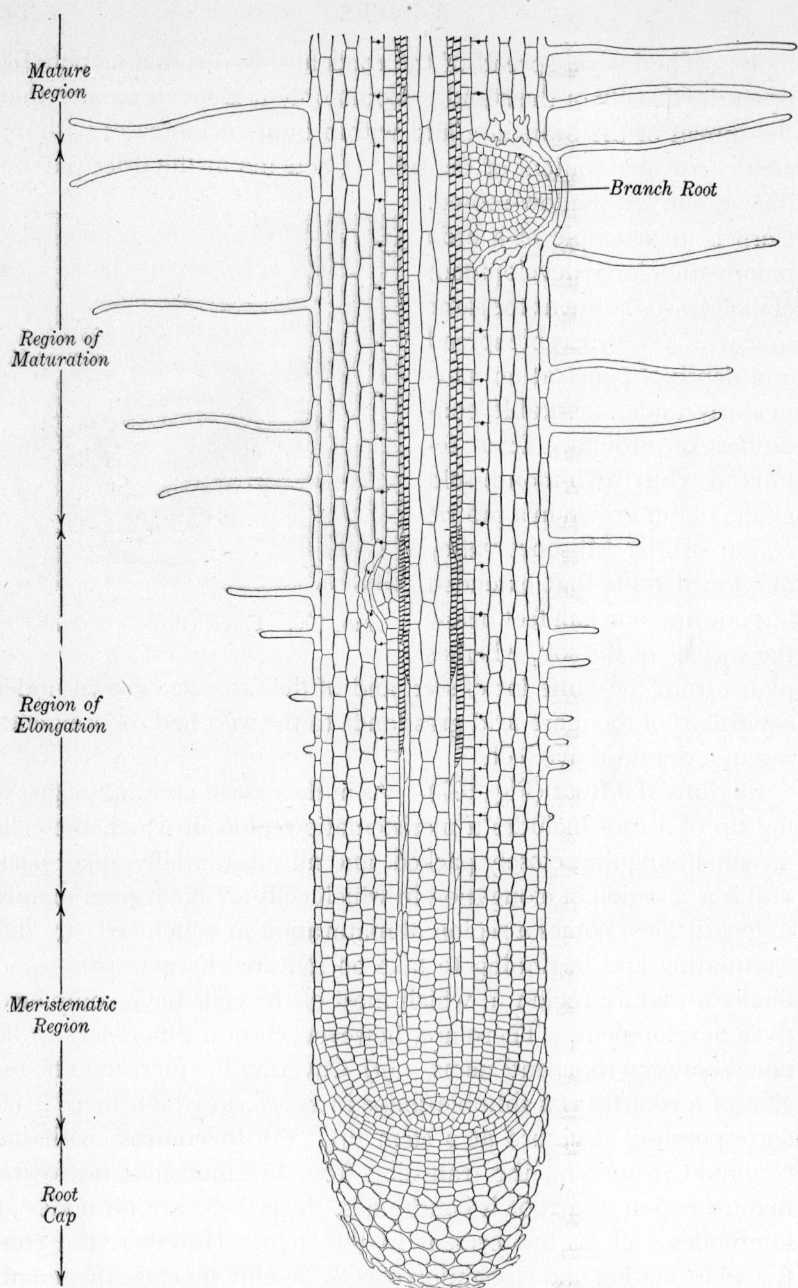

FIG. 107. Lengthwise section of the apical portion of a root, showing its various regions. Diagrammatic.

The position of the region of elongation in a root may be very simply demonstrated by making a series of equidistant, parallel cross marks perpendicular to the root axis, using a pen and India ink, the

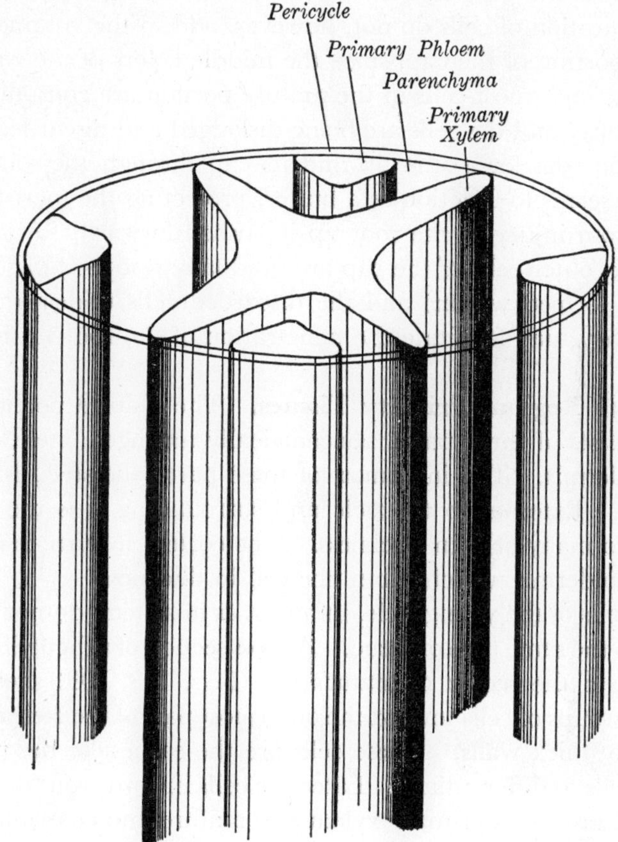

FIG. 108. Three-dimensional diagram of the stele of a root before secondary thickening has begun.

first mark being immediately back of the tip. On examination after 24 hours, it will be found that the root apex is being advanced by growth not at the extreme tip but at a short distance back.

Root Cap. The cells of the root cap, like those in other parts of a root, are formed by divisions in the meristematic region. Beginning in this region and progressing forward through the cap, there are, successively, a short region of elongation, one of maturation, and, at the apex and outer sides of the cap, a mature region. Since the cells in these three regions go through the same course of development, though within a very restricted distance lengthwise, as do the cells in the corresponding regions of the main body of the root, their history need not be followed in detail. The continued elongation and maturation of cells do not, however, add to the volume of the mature portion of the cap, since the middle layers of the walls between the outermost cells in the mature portion are constantly dissolving away and the cells are being dislodged and discarded as the elongating root forces the tip and its cap through the soil. The root cap seems to function as a buffer, protecting the meristematic region from injury as the root tip is pushed forward. Also, since the older, outer cells of the cap are gradually sloughed off (as new cells are formed within) and the discarded cells undergo a slimy decay, they may facilitate the penetration of the root tip into the soil.

Mature Region: Primary Tissues. The mature portion of a root consists of three parts, concentrically arranged: stele, cortex, and epidermis. The innermost of these parts, the stele, is a solid cylinder. External to the stele and surrounding it is the cortex, several to many cells in thickness. The cortex, in turn, is covered by the epidermis, which is but one cell in thickness.

The cells of the young stele, in a root as in a stem, do not all mature into the same type of tissue. A cross section of a dicotyledonous root cut in the region of maturation (Figs. 108, 109) shows that several groups of cells toward the outermost part of the stele develop especially thick walls. These cells are the earliest of the primary xylem cells to differentiate. Later the cells inward from these first-matured groups of primary xylem also mature into elements of primary xylem which are of larger diameter. When maturation is complete, the primary xylem often constitutes a mass that fills the entire central portion of the stele. Projecting outward from the central mass are a number of longitudinal ridges—the first-matured strands of primary xylem. The outer cells of these ridges are tracheids (single-celled xylem elements with pointed ends). Many of the cells inward from those that become tracheids mature into vessels (elements which result from the maturation of vertical rows of meristematic cells).

In the angles between the radiating ridges of primary xylem are strands or columns of cells that mature into *primary phloem*, including,

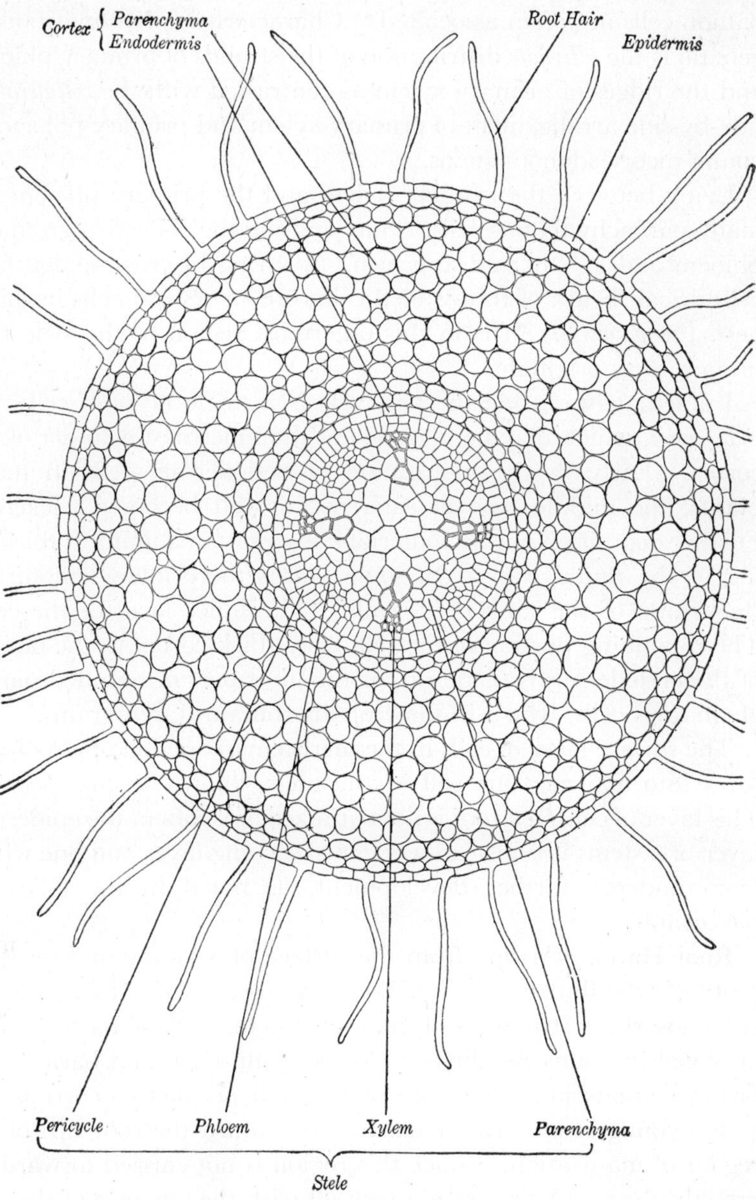

Fig. 109. Cross section of a sunflower root at a level at which secondary thickening has not yet begun. Diagrammatic.

like the primary phloem of the stem, sieve tubes with which companion cells are often associated. Characteristic of young roots in general is the *alternate* distribution of the strands of primary phloem and the ridges of primary xylem as contrasted with the *collateral* or side-by-side arrangement of primary xylem and primary phloem in young dicotyledonous stems.

Lying between the primary xylem and the primary phloem are many parenchymatous cells. Surrounding the collective groups of phloem and xylem, and appearing as a ring in cross section, is a cylindrical sheath of thin-walled cells, one or several cells in thickness, the *pericycle*. It is in this outermost region of the stele that branch roots originate.

Immediately outside the pericycle is a single layer of cells, the *endodermis*, which may be regarded as the innermost cylinder of the cortex. Early in the maturation of endodermal cells in many plants, the middle part of each radial wall becomes thickened. Further deposition of wall material may result in a uniform thickening of the radial walls. In some plants there follows in turn a thickening of the tangential walls at the inner faces of the cells. The remaining portion of the relatively thick cortex to the outside of the endodermis is made up for the most part of rounded parenchymatous cells, which in some plants contain starch grains.

The surface layer of cells in the meristematic region of a root matures into a tissue, one cell in thickness, known as the *epidermis*. This layer of cells in a root is not cutinized as is, often, the epidermal layer of a stem; it is instead a water-absorbing layer and one which is to undergo further development, as noted in the following paragraph.

Root Hairs. Arising from the surface of a young and growing root, a few millimeters back of the apex, are *root hairs* (Fig. 107), the chief absorbing structures of the root system. These hairs are best observed in young seedlings. Collards, mustard, and barley offer favorable material. The zone of root-hair production corresponds to the youngest part (the part, that is, toward the root tip) of the region of maturation. Since this region is not carried forward by growth, the root hairs are not torn off with the advance of the root tip. The younger hairs are invariably nearer the tip; a little farther back they have attained their full length, a length often greater than the diameter of the young root. Commonly the root-hair zone occupies a region only a few millimeters in length, since usually the oldest hairs—those farthest from the apex—gradually disintegrate as new ones develop progressively toward the apex. Each root hair is a tubular outgrowth or prolongation of an epidermal cell, of which it forms a part. The cells which develop hairs are characterized by soft, gelatinous walls and by a very vacuolate cytoplasm. When seeds are germinated in moist air, the root hairs formed on the primary root may be straight; but the hairs of roots growing in the soil become irregular in shape or contorted, in consequence of close contact with soil particles. When a young plant is pulled from a moist, friable soil, the soil adheres to the roots. This is because the root hairs have grown about the soil particles and thus are brought into intimate contact with the soil solution (Fig. 110).

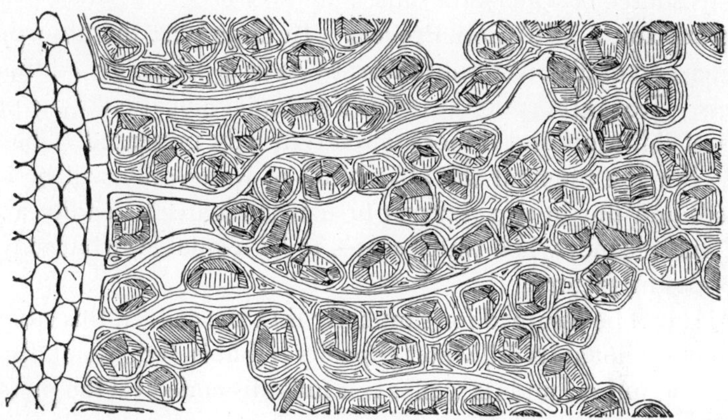

FIG. 110. Diagram showing the relation of root hairs to the soil. The concentric lines about the soil particles show the distribution of water in the soil; the clear areas represent spaces filled with air.

Absorption by Root Hairs. It is evident that, other conditions being similar, the larger the surface exposure of a root system the greater is its capacity to absorb. Root hairs greatly increase the absorbing surface, and there is good evidence that they are much more efficient in absorption than the unmodified epidermal cells. Measurements have been made of the extent and area of roots and root hairs of winter rye grown in soil in a greenhouse. It was found that for one plant the total root surface (not including root hairs) was 2554 square feet, the total length of the root system being 387 miles, and that the total root-hair surface was 4321 square feet.

With plants grown in soil, it is then chiefly through the root hairs that water is obtained. Mineral salts and other substances dissolved in soil water also are similarly but independently absorbed. The number of root hairs that may develop in any particular case depends in part upon the kind of plant and in part upon environmental conditions. In moist, well-aerated soil, root-hair production is commonly far greater than in wet, poorly aerated soil. Grown in water cultures (to be described later), many plants produce few or no root hairs. Ordinarily, after root hairs have ceased to function, they die and decay; or the entire epidermal layer in the older region of the root may progressively disintegrate. It is obvious that as the plant grows in height and the roots spread downward and laterally, the new shoot becomes gradually more remote from its source of water and salts.

Absorption a Diffusion Process. In large part the absorption of water and of dissolved substances by roots is primarily a diffusion process. Root absorption presents a special application of the principles of diffusion and osmosis already briefly presented (Chapter III). For the moment the absorption of water only will be considered, and this in two aspects: first, when water is readily available; and second, when water ceases to be available, what may be the opposing factors?

(*a*) It can be assumed for simplicity that the cell (in this case the root hair) is not at its full water capacity—that is, it does not display maximum turgor, and its wall is not fully distended by the pressure of the protoplast. The root hair is in contact with the soil solution through its moist cell wall and plasma membrane. The cell sap has usually a much higher concentration of solute particles per unit of its volume (and hence a relatively lower concentration of water molecules) than the soil solution, and the latter accordingly has a higher concentration of water molecules. Under such circumstances soil water must diffuse from its higher concentration (the soil solution) into the root hair. Diffusion of water into the root hair actually does take place, but only until the increasing volume of the protoplast, caused by the entry of water, so distends the cell wall that the pressure which the wall exerts backward on the protoplast is sufficient to balance the tendency of the water to diffuse inward. When this point is reached, no more water can be absorbed by the root hair, and the cell is at its maximum turgidity.

To continue to absorb water from the soil solution, the root hair must deliver water to the adjacent cortical cells (Fig. 111), these to other cells, and so on. If there is no movement of water inward and upward, a state of maximum turgidity soon prevails in the root, and absorption temporarily subsides.

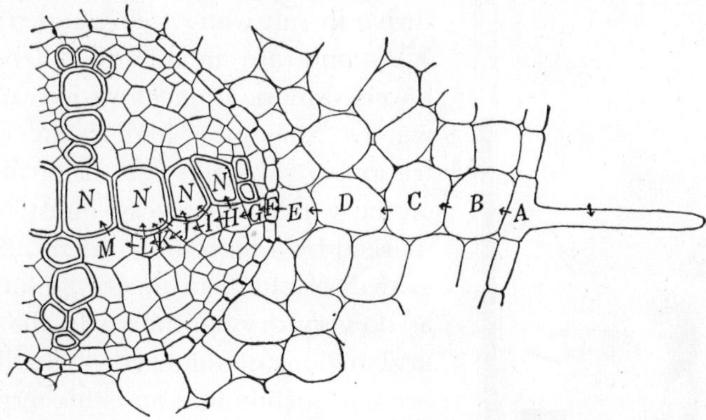

FIG. 111. Diagram showing the path of water movement from the soil into a root. Water passes into and through a root hair (*A*), through cells *B–M*, and from these into the xylem elements (*N*).

(*b*) Under conditions of decreasing soil moisture the soil solution becomes more concentrated, and eventually some plants might experience serious difficulty in absorption—in the particular case, that is, in which the concentration of solutes in the soil solution approaches that in the cell sap. Another result of soil-water depletion is the bringing into action of other forces of considerable magnitude operating against water absorption; for example, organic matter in the soil holds water by imbibition, and in addition the thinning films of soil water become more and more tenaciously bound to the surfaces of soil particles. Therefore, a stage is reached at which soil water is not available to the plant; and the latter, continuing to lose water to the atmosphere, undergoes permanent wilting and eventually death. The percentage of water in the soil at the stage of permanent wilting is the *wilting coefficient*. This quantity varies greatly with the type of soil but not materially with the species of plant.

If the soil solution contains a higher salt concentration than the cell sap of the absorbing root cells, water moves out of the root.

Plants not adjusted to high salt concentrations are not found along sea beaches or on marine flats where inundation with salt water is frequent. A few species of plants, however, can grow in these locations, so that the vegetation in such areas is marked by distinctive species. Many algae thrive in salt water (see Chapters XIV, XV) and are unable to tolerate the lower osmotic concentration of fresh water. Since the higher the concentration of salts the less the availability of the water, even very moist habitats marked by a high salt content affect the growth of plants in much the same way as do very dry habitats. In the soils of arid regions of the earth "alkali" lands are not uncommon, and this term often denotes both an alkaline condition and a higher salt concentration than usual.

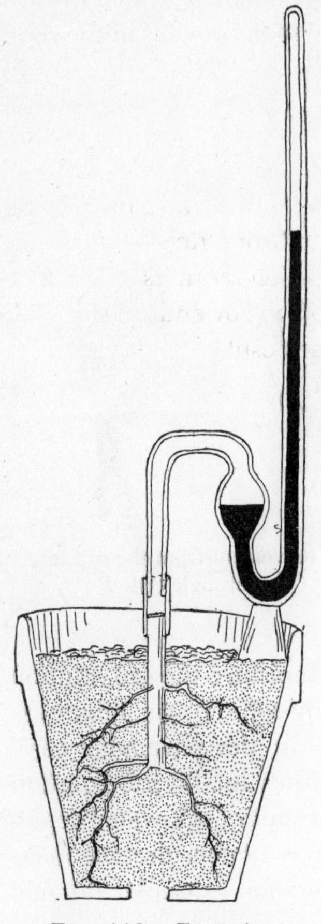

FIG. 112. Experiment demonstrating root pressure. The stem of a potted cutting of a geranium is cut; its upper part is replaced by a bent closed tube containing mercury. Water exudes from the cut end of the stem, forcing the mercury upward.

There is also a restricted number of species of plants inhabiting the typical bogs of the northern United States. In these situations it seems probable that several conditions aside from water saturation and low temperature render absorption difficult. These habitats all abound in water, but in each case some one or more factors seem to limit the rate of absorption; and in general only such plants thrive as can withstand not only the special chemical characteristics of the bog, but also the restricted possibility of absorption.

Given a well-developed root system, the conditions which in general promote water absorption are a favorable temperature, adequate aeration, and a limited salt concentration.

Root Pressure. The exudation of sap from wounds in the trunk of a tree, a birch or elm for example, is not an uncommon phenomenon in later winter or early spring. Grape vines pruned at this time of year may show extensive "bleeding." The name *root pressure* is intended to indicate that such exudation results from a pressure which under certain conditions arises from, or is associated with, absorption by roots. It is simple to demonstrate that many herbaceous plants display root pressure. If a vigorous, potted fuchsia plant is cut off an inch or two above the soil and a glass tube is attached to the cut end by means of soft rubber tubing, sap rises in the tube (Fig. 112). By using a bent glass tube and beaker, the volume of the sap may be determined. More important is the determination of the exudation pressure, which requires that a mercury manometer be promptly attached to the cut end. This pressure is seldom more, often less, than two atmospheres. In order to obtain favorable results, the potted plant used should be well watered and should remain under favorable growing conditions.

The maple-sugar industry is made possible by the fact that the sap of a maple flows freely when the tree is tapped; a single tree may yield as much as six to eight quarts per day; the sugar content is higher than that of any other tree known, and the natural flavor enhances its value. Certain species of palm yield more sap than the maple, but its economic value is inconsiderable. The exudate of the century plant (Agave) is the source in Mexico of two alcoholic beverages.

The mechanism of root pressure is still imperfectly understood. Several facts oppose the view that it plays an important part in the rise of water or the "ascent of sap" in trees. Root pressure is infrequent in the maple when the tree is in leaf; and here, as in certain other plants, bleeding is attributed to living cells in the neighborhood of the wound. When water is being lost from the plant at a maximum rate, that is, when there is the greatest need for water, there is no root pressure; and in fact under such circumstances a negative pressure is often demonstrable.

Secondary Thickening (Fig. 113). The production of secondary tissues in a dicotyledonous root results, as in the stem, from the activity of the cambium. First to function as cambium are cells lying just within each phloem strand and outside the central mass of xylem (Fig. 114, *A*). In a root with four strands of phloem there appear four trough-shaped cambial regions. Each cambial cell divides tangentially into two daughter cells. As tangential division proceeds, the cells that come to lie toward the inner face of each strip begin to enlarge, chiefly in a radial direction; then they mature gradually into secondary xylem. Repetition of this process results in the continued formation of additional secondary xylem elements between the outer face of the xylem mass and the inner face of the

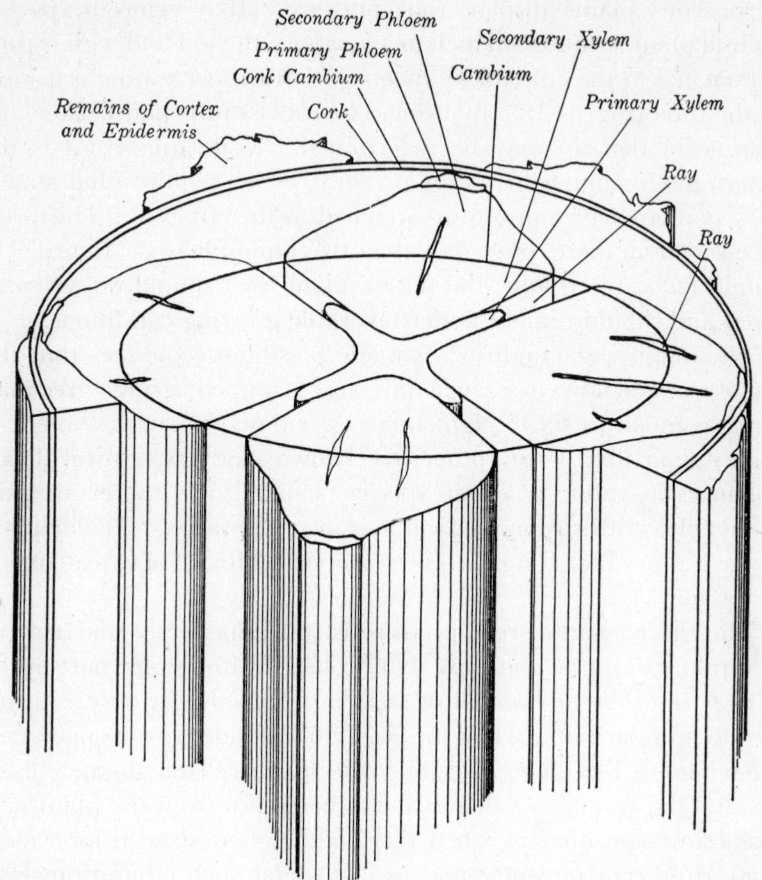

FIG. 113. Three-dimensional diagram of a portion of a root after cambial activity has resulted in secondary thickening.

cambium (Fig. 114, *B*). Occasional cells on the outer face of the cambium mature into secondary phloem elements, which lie, therefore, between the cambium and the inner side of the primary phloem strand.

Soon after cambial activity begins between the primary xylem and the primary phloem, some of the cells of the pericycle on the outer face of each ridge of primary xylem also begin to function as cambium. The cambium now forms a continuous sheath which completely surrounds both the primary xylem and whatever secondary xylem has already been formed (Fig. 115). As in the stem, the secondary xylem and the secondary phloem constitute two concentric cylinders that lie, respectively, within and without the cambium (Fig. 116). The cylinders of secondary xylem and secondary phloem are not continuous, however, because at occasional narrow regions in the cambium (at first opposite the ridges of primary xylem, later at any place in the cambium) cells are formed which

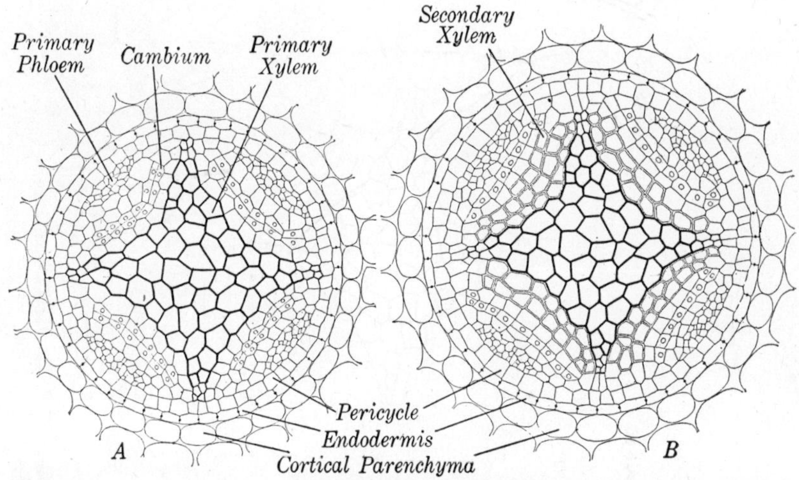

Fig. 114. Cross sections of the stele of a dicotyledonous root. *A*, at a level at which cambial activity is beginning. *B*, at a level at which the cambium has begun to produce secondary xylem and phloem. Both diagrammatic.

remain thin-walled. These radial, perpendicular strips of parenchymatous cells constitute the rays. The rays, extending outward through the secondary xylem and the secondary phloem, are similar in structure and function to those of the stem.

Secondary Tissues. As noted for stems in Chapter IV, the secondary xylem is variously organized in the roots of different plants. Roots of some plants contain a large proportion of water-conducting elements. These elements may consist of tracheids only, as in the pine; of vessels only, as in the willow; or, as in the oak, of both tracheids and vessels. Ordinarily, in roots the water-conducting elements constitute a greater proportion of the secondary xylem than in stems. On the other hand, in the roots of some plants the greater portion of the secondary xylem is composed of elements other than tracheids and vessels. Such elements, not primarily

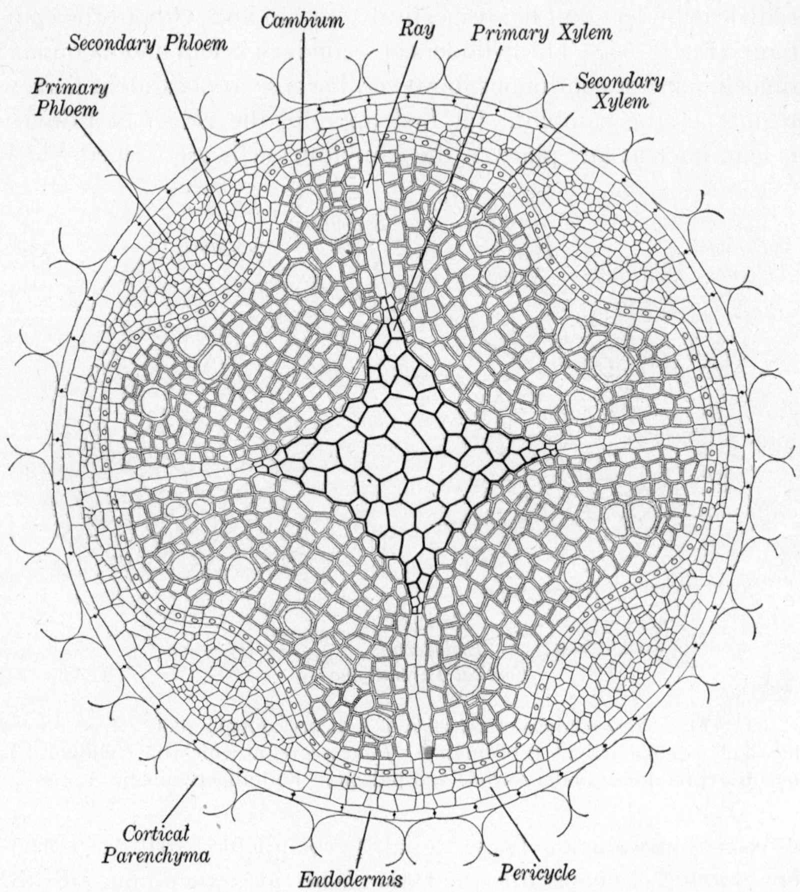

FIG. 115. Cross section of the stele of a dicotyledonous root at a level at which the cambium has become a continuous sheath and considerable amounts of secondary tissues have been produced. Diagrammatic.

concerned in conduction, may be thick-walled (mechanical) elements which contribute to the efficiency of the root as an organ that anchors and supports the stem; or many of them may be parenchymatous cells in which reserve foods are stored.

While still very young, the elements of secondary xylem and secondary phloem are arranged in definite radial rows in consequence of the method of their formation by repeated tangential divisions of the cambial cells. In such plants as the pine, whose secondary elements do not enlarge greatly during maturation, this radial arrangement persists. However, in many roots vessels enlarge greatly while other elements of the secondary xylem remain small; in the mature secondary xylem, therefore, while there is some

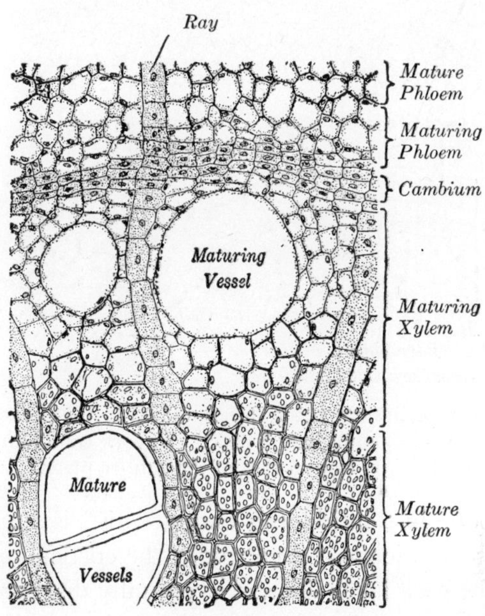

FIG. 116. Small portion of a cross section of a root of Ficus (rubber plant), showing the formation of secondary phloem and secondary xylem by the cambium.

indication of the original radial arrangement, the various elements are in general irregularly disposed.

Annual rings are formed in the roots of woody plants, although they are not usually so sharply defined as are the annual rings of stems.

Cork Cambium (Fig. 117). In the roots of many plants which form secondary phloem and xylem, there are pericyclic cells which retain the power of division. The tangential division of these cells results in the establishment of a cork cambium which, as in the stem, produces cork cells on its outer face and parenchymatous cells on its inner face. Like the walls of similar cells elsewhere in the plant, the walls of cork cells in the root become impregnated with a fatty material; consequently the layer of cork formed so deeply

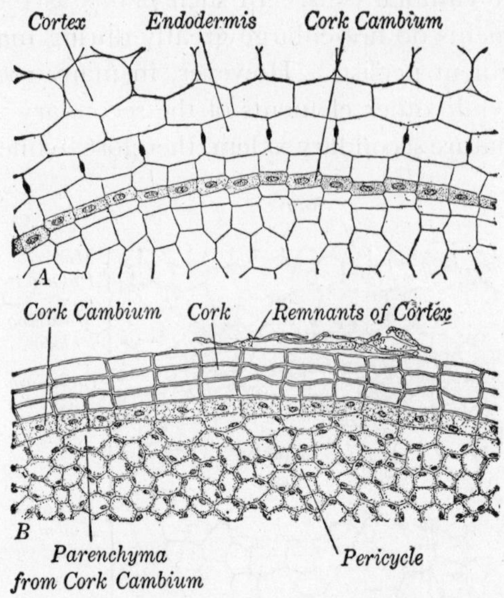

FIG. 117. *A*, cork cambium being differentiated in the pericycle of a root of the grape; adapted from Bonnier and Sablon. *B*, cork cambium, and secondary tissues formed by its activity, from a root of the rubber plant.

within the root—just inside the endodermis—is impermeable to water and dissolved foods. As a result, the cortical and epidermal cells outside the cork layer die and eventually disappear. For this reason, the older portions of a root are derived entirely from the stele, except in some plants whose roots form a cork cambium in the cortex rather than in the pericycle.

The cork cambium just described ordinarily forms new cork cells for a few years only and then becomes inactive. Additional layers of cork cambium are successively developed in the parenchymatous cells of the pericycle and phloem inward from the original cork cambium; and therefore, no matter how old the root becomes, new cork cells are continuously being formed.

Branch Roots. It has already been said that branch roots may arise from a primary root. They may arise also from other branch roots. The development of such a root begins with the division of pericyclic cells adjacent to the group of tracheids in a ridge of primary xylem (Fig. 107). As a result of these divisions and of successive divisions of new cells, a small lens-shaped mass of meristematic tissue is formed. The outermost cells of this mass develop into a root cap; the innermost cells form the meristematic region of the branch root. The branch root grows out through the cortex of the primary or other root to the surface (Fig. 118) and then pushes

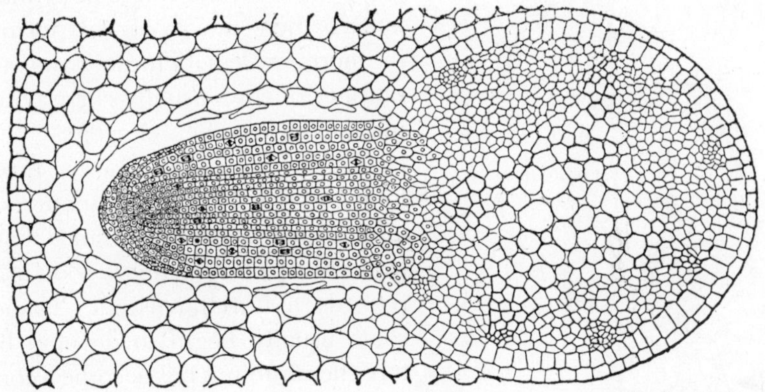

FIG. 118. Cross section of part of a primary root of the sunflower, showing the origin of a branch root from the pericycle and its growth through the cortex of the primary root.

through the soil exactly as did the parent root. In penetrating the cortex, a young branch root does not necessarily push aside the normal, growing cortical cells; it may in fact secrete enzymes which soften or digest the materials of these cells, especially the walls, so that the branch root then grows into an area of softened or collapsed cells, sometimes actually a cavity formed by the dissolution of the cortical cells. Early in the development of a branch root, the cells in the anterior and posterior portions, respectively, of its meristematic region begin to undergo the processes of elongation and maturation already described—the cells maturing from the anterior portion forming the root cap, those maturing from the posterior portion becoming part of the body of the branch root. The various tissues matured in the body of the branch root are continuous with corresponding tissues of the parent root. Hence, water and dissolved mineral salts can pass through the xylem of the branch root into the xylem of the main root and thence into the stem. Manufactured foods entering the phloem of the primary root from aboveground parts of the plant move into branch roots or into branches of these roots through the continuous system of phloem. In plants whose primary roots produce secondary tissues, each branch root also may develop a cambium.

Since the development of branch roots begins adjacent to the groups of tracheids in the ridges of primary xylem, these new roots are formed in more or less definite rows, the number of rows usually corresponding to the number of ridges. For example, in the sunflower three, four, or five rows of branch roots are formed at some distance back from the tip of the primary root, in its recently matured portion. Branch roots usually begin to develop before the cambium has become a complete cylinder; if they develop after it has become continuous, the branch roots originate in the cambium rather than in the pericycle. Branch roots so formed are not in regular vertical rows.

FIG. 119. A corn plant.

The repeated formation of new branch roots, together with the growth in length of roots already formed, results in a continuous extension of the root system through the soil. The increase in number of roots, each bearing root hairs, increases the absorptive surface of the root system; the expansion of the water-absorbing surfaces thus meets the growing need of the plant for water which results from the continuous enlargement of the aerial portion of the plant.

Adventitious Roots. Roots may develop directly from stems and leaves much as they regularly develop from other roots. Roots arising directly from stems and leaves are *adventitious roots*. Most plants with trailing or horizontal underground stems, such as the iris, most grasses, many ferns, and various vines, regularly produce numerous adventitious roots on their stems. Some plants with erect stems, like the corn, also regularly form adventitious roots.

Adventitious roots supplement the work of primary and branch roots in absorbing water and dissolved materials from the soil. In some plants, such as corn and certain other cereal grains, the primary root and its branches may entirely disappear, all movement of water into the plant then being through the fibrous system of adventitious roots. Adventitious roots may function also as supports that help to hold erect the stem or its branches. Instances of this sort are seen in the corn (Fig. 119), whose "prop roots" grow downward at an angle from the lower nodes of the stem into the soil; or in the banyan tree of India (Fig. 120), whose adventitious

Fig. 120. A banyan tree, with many vertical adventitious roots. After Baillon.

roots grow directly downward from horizontal branches to the soil. Some climbing plants, including English ivy, develop many short adventitious roots along the internodes of their stems; these roots aid the plants in clinging to their supports.

Many plants that do not ordinarily form adventitious roots do so under special conditions. When the tip of a raspberry stem bends over and touches the ground, the end in contact with the soil forms adventitious roots. Stems and branches of other plants, including the rose, geranium, and coleus (Fig. 121), ordinarily form adventitious roots only when a stem or branch has been severed from the plant and placed in damp soil.

The common practice of propagating many greenhouse and garden plants by cutting a stem or branch into pieces is founded upon

FIG. 121. A cutting of coleus forming adventitious roots after being placed in soil.

the ability of such pieces (*cuttings*) to form adventitious roots when placed under good growing conditions. The production of certain field crops also depends upon the application of this principle, as for example in the potato, which is grown from tubers, and in sugar cane, which is grown from stalks. Propagation by cuttings has the great advantage that it almost always results in the production of new plants precisely like the parent. In this way it is possible to multiply indefinitely any desirable variety of strawberry, raspberry, or rose which, because of its hybrid nature, will not breed true by means of seeds.

Variations in Roots. The roots of plants growing in unusual situations may function in ways other than the usual ones already mentioned. For example, the roots of many submerged water plants, as well as those of many swamp plants, are provided with large intercellular spaces which accumulate the gases (chiefly carbon dioxide and oxygen) that diffuse into the plant or are given off by its cells. The roots of certain tropical plants that grow on rocks in swiftly running streams are flattened and bladelike, and their cortical cells contain numerous chloroplasts. These roots function like leaves in the manufacture of foods.

FIG. 122. Aerial roots of an orchid. After Kerner.

Other plants, including some tropical orchids (Fig. 122), growing high above the soil, often for example on the stems and branches of trees, bear roots which are exposed to the air. Not infrequently such an aerial root has a spongy outer cell layer which holds and absorbs rain or which facilitates the condensation of dew on its surface. Although these roots never penetrate the soil, they perform much the same absorptive functions as do roots growing in soil. Aerial roots often also contain chlorophyll and are concerned in photosynthesis. In a few orchids the leaves are much reduced or lacking, and the green roots carry on essentially all the food manufacture of the plant. Roots which function as food-storage organs have already been discussed.

THE ENVIRONMENT OF ROOTS

The Soil. Because of its almost universal commonness and because of its location—something that is walked on rather than observed—soil in general receives less attention than do the plants that are anchored in it. Frequently half, oftentimes far more, of the volume of a plant body is imbedded in the soil. Sugar beets, parsnips, and carrots, for example, are plants the greater part of whose bulk is below ground. Soil provides a solid yet penetrable material in which plants from an inch or two to a hundred or more feet in height can fasten themselves firmly against such a force as that exerted upon their aboveground parts by wind pressure. That it serves also as the source for essentially all the water and the dissolved mineral substances that are necessary for the growth of the plant has been pointed out. Quack grass, thistles, poplars, and other common plants extend structures (underground stems and roots) through the soil which serve as means for the establishment of new individuals. Such plants in this fashion are able to increase their numbers within more or less limited areas.

In addition to the familiar plants which inhabit the soil, this substrate is literally teeming with microscopic animals and plants. In a teaspoonful of rich soil there may be billions of bacteria. Various other minute plants, including larger fungi and algae, also are regularly present in the upper soil layers.

The color of ordinary upland soil is usually at least an indicator of its usefulness to plants. Generally speaking, the darker a soil the more suitable is it for plant growth. The color of the rock fragments which make up the bulk of the soil, as well as various climatic conditions and the amount of moisture present, influence to a certain degree its general appearance. However, the browns and blacks of decaying plant remains are chiefly responsible for its depth of color.

Rock Particles. If a quantity of rich loamy soil is allowed to dry in the air, it is found that about 90 per cent of its weight is the weight of the rock particles which constitute its foundation material. A closer examination of these rock fragments reveals enormous differences in their sizes. They may range from gravel (of which there is little in a rich soil) through sand grains to silt and clay. Although clay particles ordinarily occur in small aggregations or clumps (floccules), individually they are extremely minute. These clay particles may be so small that the combined volumes of some millions of them would but equal that of a large sand grain. The pulverizing of bedrock into such particles of different sizes has been accomplished largely by the grinding or erosive action of glaciers, by friction of water-borne fragments of rock upon bedrock, or by the sand-blasting of exposed rocky outcrops by wind-borne abrasive particles. Rocks can be split by alternate heating and cooling if the temperature range is appreciably great. Cracks so produced may be widened by the expansion of water within them as it freezes and later by the wedging effect of growing roots.

Chemical changes also are of importance in the disintegration of rocks. Decay of once-living material, as well as the respiration of roots, small animals, and microscopic plants in the soil, results in the production of carbon dioxide. As this goes into solution in the soil water, a weak acid is formed which slowly etches and dissolves rock. A limy sandstone so attacked will ultimately crumble into almost pure sand as the more easily dissolved limestone cementing substance is dissolved from between the sand grains. Granite and other hard rocks disintegrate much more slowly. Lichens, often found on bare rock, grow very slowly and hence occupy the same general area for relatively long periods of time. They sometimes occur in slight depressions which have resulted from their dissolving effects. Such lichens, as well as mosses and other small plants which can obtain a foothold in the minute crevices and irregularities of rocky surfaces, are often pioneers in soil-building. They not only provide obstacles against which wind- and water-borne particles of material may lodge; they add their own substance also as their parts die and decay. Such changes from rock to soil were not accomplished only in the distant past; they are going on everywhere at the present time.

Humus. As plants and animals die and as plant parts such as leaves fall to the ground, their once-living (organic) material begins to decay as a result of the action of bacteria and other fungi. The partially broken-down brown or black material which results is *humus*. As this disintegration proceeds, the substances from which the plant or animal parts were originally constructed are set free and made available for use by green plants. In properly drained and aerated soils, humus does not accumulate much beyond five or ten per cent, partly because it is constantly being transformed and utilized as a source of food by small organisms living in the soil.

In wet or boggy places decay is so retarded that the soil may be almost entirely organic. Indeed, the gradual filling in of shallow ponds and lakes by the growth about their margins of water plants and the deposition of remains of dead plants on the bottom is one of the ways in which soil is built. This concentrated, partially decomposed organic matter is *peat*.

Humus is for several reasons an important constituent of soil. It increases the porosity of the soil so that proper drainage and aeration are possible. It increases the water-holding and water-absorbing powers of the soil, since particles of humus act as minute sponges. Humus supplies also, as has been suggested, a source from which may occur slow liberation of materials necessary for plant growth.

Soil Texture and Structure. Deposits of rock fragments upon bedrock may vary in thickness from a fraction of an inch to hundreds of feet. Where the soil is more than a few inches in depth, however, the upper few inches contain materials other than rock fragments. This uppermost layer is the *topsoil;* underlying layers constitute the *subsoil*.

The *texture* of soil is determined by the proportions of sand, clay, and silt which it contains—sandy soils, clay soils, and loam soils being some types based upon the relative content of rock particles of various sizes. Loam, for example, is approximately one half sand and one quarter each of silt and clay.

The *structure* of soil depends upon the way in which the soil particles are arranged. A loam favorable for plant growth is composed not merely of certain quantities of sand, clay, silt, and other materials mixed indiscriminately, but of definite aggregations (*crumbs*) of these particles. These crumbs are maintained more or less as units of soil structure by the adhesive action of extremely fine clay and humus particles. Such a composition is of the greatest importance, since it makes possible drainage of water from between the larger crumbs. As the water seeps away, air enters the larger spaces, but water remains in the smaller spaces. The soil is then structurally able to provide sufficient supplies of water, and of oxygen from the soil atmosphere, to the roots of plants growing in it. Field and garden soils can be kept in this condition by cultivation when the soil is moist but not when it is saturated with water. Heavy, beating rains tend to "puddle" bare soil, as also does cultivation when the soil is too wet. Puddled soils, in which the crumbs are disorganized, become hard, crack upon drying out, and are no longer favorable for root growth. Under natural conditions, growth of roots, followed by their eventual death and decay, helps to maintain the looseness of soil. The burrowing of earthworms and other small animals also plays a part in this process.

Water in the Soil. The chief source of soil water is rain and snow. Much of the water falling as rain runs off, and some of it evaporates; but some passes by gravity into the soil between the soil particles. The amount of *gravitational water* which thus enters the soil and its rate of entry depend upon the nature of the soil, the kind, amount, and character of the vegetation, the amount of precipitation, the slope of the land, and the amount of water already in the soil. After a rain, some of the water gradually sinks under the influence of gravity until it arrives at the *water table*, the level at and below which all the spaces in the soil are filled with standing water. The water table may be thought of as an underground reservoir filled with boulders, gravel, and sand, within which the water is dammed by rocky ledges or clay deposits often many feet below the surface. If the bedrock which underlies such a region is stratified, the water from this underground reservoir may move for miles in the crevices between the rock layers and emerge as springs on some hillside where the layers happen to be exposed.

As water enters the soil and passes downward, much of it is retained at each level for a time in the form of thin films about the soil particles as well as in the more minute spaces between them. This *capillary water* adheres so closely to the soil particles that it is not influenced by gravity. The films about adjacent soil particles are united, forming a continuous water system which is the source of most of the water absorbed by plants. The amount of water that a given volume of soil may hold under ordinary conditions is influenced to a considerable degree by the sizes of the rock particles of which it is composed. For example, a one-inch cube of rock exposes six square inches of surface to which water may adhere. If this cube were cut in two, the exposed surface would be increased by two additional square inches. If these pieces of rock in turn were cut into smaller pieces such as are present in gravel and these in turn were reduced to the size of those of sand, the total exposed surface would obviously be increased at each step. At a conservative estimate, a million clay particles could be made from a single sand grain. It follows that by a transformation of rock into clay the total exposed surface is enormously increased.

As water evaporates from the surface of the soil or is absorbed by plants, capillary water moves slowly from adjacent regions where the films are thicker to regions where they are thinner. This movement tends to bring the film system into equilibrium. Loss of water from the surface of the soil causes an upward movement of capillary water; the effect of this upward movement may extend as far downward as the water table, which is then lowered. Lateral movements of capillary water in the soil occur also from regions where water is more abundant to regions where it is less abundant. The mobility of capillary water varies, however, with the character of the soil.

In soils that have lost their capillary water by evaporation, there still remains about each soil particle a thin film of water which is held so firmly that it can be removed only by heating the soil to a relatively high temperature. This *hygroscopic water* (bound water) adheres so tenaciously to the soil particles that plants are unable to absorb it.

The water in the soil is not pure but contains many dissolved substances, some derived from humus and others from inorganic rock particles. Among these dissolved substances are compounds of nitrogen, sodium, potassium, calcium, magnesium, iron, phosphorus, and sulphur, all of which are important in the nutrition of plants. The soil water contains also many other solutes that are of less significance to plants. The actual proportions of the substances in solution in soil water are usually small, although in some soils relatively large amounts of solutes are present. In some cases much lime is present; "alkali" soils are rich in soluble salts.

Soil Temperature. The temperature of the soil plays an important part in the growth and activities of the root systems of plants. Since the speed with which molecules move is directly dependent upon temperature, the movement of the molecules of water and of soluble materials into roots is more rapid at higher, and slower at lower, temperatures. Hence, soil temperature is a factor in the rate of movement of dissolved substances into roots. At low soil temperatures there is relatively little absorption. If the air temperature becomes unseasonably high while the soil is still very cold or even perhaps still frozen, the evaporation from the leaves of pine seedlings, for example, may go on more rapidly than the absorption of water; in such a case the plants dry out and die. Death of seedlings under these conditions is often erroneously attributed to the results of freezing rather than to those of drying. The root systems of black spruce and tamarack trees growing in bogs are usually very shallow and widespread. Only the top few inches of the peaty soil in which they are growing becomes warmed during the summer. Frost remains in the underlying layers long after the air temperatures become relatively high, and these lower layers are cold even in the hottest part of the summer. The roots do not grow into such cold regions of the soil but extend only through the warmer upper layers where, because the movement of water and solutes is facilitated, adequate absorption is possible.

Air in the Soil. If the spaces in the soil are filled with water, most of the air present is driven out. Ordinarily when water enters the soil, it passes downward or evaporates, and the spaces between the soil particles not occupied by water become filled with air. The proportion of carbon dioxide increases and that of oxygen correspondingly decreases with the depth of the soil. The texture of the soil influences the rate at which oxygen enters and carbon dioxide escapes. Since oxygen is necessary for the continued respiration and growth of roots, an adequate supply of air in the soil is of great importance. In poorly aerated soils not only does the absence of oxygen retard growth, but the concentration of carbon dioxide may directly or indirectly exert a toxic action which hinders root growth. The reactions of different plants to the aeration of the soil vary greatly. Most cereal grains and some other plants turn yellow and die when the soil in which they grow is saturated with water for a long period, not only because of lack of oxygen but also because of many other changed conditions.

Erosion of Soils. Much time and money are being expended in efforts to curb the loss of valuable topsoils and subsoils that are being carried away by wind and water. Planting of windbreaks and the re-establishment of sod on land that should never have been broken are methods which have proved more or less successful in curbing wind erosion. Dams and log cribs are built in dry washes and gullies as impediments to slow down the velocity of run-off water from land that has been denuded of its natural cover of forest or of undergrowth on the forest floor by careless cutting of timber, by burning, or by excessive pasturing. As the flow of water is retarded, the soil particles may settle and so begin to fill up and flatten badly gullied areas. Later run-off water then will not attain a speed sufficient to cause further erosion.

SUMMARY

The functions which roots ordinarily perform include absorption of water and dissolved substances, transport of absorbed materials, anchorage, support of the stem-borne parts, and often, in large fleshy or woody roots, storage of considerable quantities of reserve foods.

The root system may be either a tap-root or a fibrous-root system. Fibrous-root systems with enlarged branch roots are fascicled-root systems.

The extent and distribution of the root system in the soil depend in part upon the species of plant and in part upon environmental factors.

As seen longitudinally, a root is divided into the following general regions: root cap, meristematic region, region of elongation, region of maturation, and mature region. The mature region, as in the stem, consists of three concentric cylinders: stele, cortex, and epidermis. The stele is composed of xylem, phloem, parenchyma, and pericycle. The cortex ordinarily includes endodermis and parenchyma. The epidermis is the outermost layer of the root, one cell in thickness; many of its cells produce tubular outgrowths—root hairs.

The zone in which root hairs are developed from epidermal cells of the root is commonly a few millimeters in length, lying in the younger part of the region of maturation. Usually the older root hairs die and disintegrate as new ones develop progressively toward the root apex.

The absorbing surface of a root system is generally vastly greater than the surface of the aerial parts of the plant. The larger part of this absorbing area consists of the surfaces of the root hairs despite their limited zone of occurrence and their temporary nature.

Under conditions favorable to growth, the cell sap of root cells contains usually a much higher concentration of solute particles per unit of its volume than does the soil solution. Conversely, the soil solution has the higher concentration of water molecules. Accordingly, osmotic movement of water into the surface cells of the root occurs so long as these cells are kept below maximum turgidity through their continual delivery of water to the cortical cells within.

The exudation of sap (bleeding) from wounds is characteristic of certain trees in the spring. This exudation is thought to result from a pressure developed as a result of, or associated with, root absorption and is usually termed root pressure. Root pressure can be demonstrated in herbaceous plants. It is, however, inconstant in many trees, absent entirely in some plants, and always fails when there is rapid loss of water from the aerial parts of a plant.

Some roots develop primary tissues only. Others develop secondary tissues as a result of cambial activity. The functioning of cambium results in the formation of secondary phloem and secondary xylem, through which extend the rays. The secondary xylem produced in a single year's growth constitutes an annual ring. Cork cells and cork parenchyma also are secondary tissues.

Branch roots, arising before secondary thickening has started in the parent root, originate in the pericycle; later branch roots arise in the cambium. As these roots grow through the cortex, they become differentiated into the parts characteristic of the parent root. Roots developing directly from stems or leaves are adventitious roots.

The root system of a mature plant may consist finally of the primary root and its branches, or of the primary root, its branches, and adventitious roots, or of adventitious roots alone.

Soil, the environment of roots, provides for most plants the source of water and of the necessary dissolved substances. Soils vary in their water-holding capacity and in their ability to supply necessary soluble materials according to the sizes and proportions of rock particles (soil texture), the proportion of humus present, and the ways in which the various soil constituents are arranged (soil structure).

CHAPTER VIII

NUTRIENTS AND FOODS, METABOLISM, AND TRANSPORT

Sources of Material and Energy. It has been seen that, in relation to its external environment, a green plant obtains energy from the sunlight, carbon dioxide and oxygen from the air, and water and salts (in solution, as is also oxygen) from the soil. Assuming that absorption and diffusion, respiration, and photosynthesis are proceeding, it is clear that the chief basic materials and energy sources available within a cell for the building and growth of its substance are: water, both a building substance and an essential medium; organic food substances such as glucose, which are energy-containing products of photosynthetic activity; soluble mineral salts; and oxygen. These materials are all essential in a further consideration of mineral nutrition, food storage and utilization, and processes of translocation within the plant.

MINERAL NUTRIENTS

Essential Mineral Elements. Salts represent the mineral constituents. These are not placed in the category of foods, since they do not directly undergo further oxidation and yield energy. Some of the mineral constituents enter into the composition of complex foods or of other essential products, some undoubtedly influence or condition chemical reactions in the cell, and still others (as salts) seem to function in various ways, not all clearly understood but concerned in general with the regulation of such phenomena as permeability, osmotic pressure, and mobilization of materials.

The various salts dissolved in the soil solution enter a plant through the absorbing surfaces of its roots and so become a part of the solutes contained in the sap, as pointed out earlier. It has been indicated also that not less than thirty chemical elements may be found in a plant, since they are constituents of compounds usually present in the soil. Fresh plant material such as green corn fodder consists of 80 per cent water and 20 per cent solid matter. If the solid matter (as dried material) is burned in an open fire, it is almost exclusively the organic material which is consumed, representing chiefly C, H, O, and N; most of the mineral constituents remain in the ash. In corn the total ash amounts to only 1.2 per cent of the fresh substance, so that usually any single mineral element will represent only a fraction of 1 per cent. Several of the trace elements may be present in such small quantities as to render their estimation in the ash difficult, which accounts for the fact that they were long overlooked as a requirement of plants.

Of the necessary elements required in larger amounts, the ash contains chiefly potassium (K), calcium (Ca), magnesium (Mg), phosphorus (P), and sulphur (S); among those required in minor quantities are such as iron (Fe), manganese (Mn), zinc (Zn), copper (Cu), and boron (B). Because of its ultimate incorporation into organic nitrogenous products, nitrogen (N) was not enumerated above. This element, however, is a constituent of soils, and it is available in several salts, for example, as a nitrate such as KNO_3. The ash contains also a considerable fraction of sodium (Na) and chlorine (Cl), the two elements of common salt (NaCl); but these last mentioned, and many others in lesser quantity, while they enter the plant are not usually considered requisite to plant development.

The question naturally arises as to how the necessity for these particular chemical elements has been determined. For one thing, the composition of the ash is suggestive, but, since this is also misleading, it is not a safe criterion; rather, the matter has been determined by experiments which were illuminating though laborious. Such experiments have been carried on for more than a century. A few studies were made even earlier; in 1758 Duhamel grew plants to maturity in water cultures. He used water from the River Seine and hoped to derive from his experiments information regarding the nutrition of plants. In later studies the water- or solution-culture method became the standard procedure, although supplemented by sand and soil cultures when practicable.

In small-scale solution cultures in which seedlings are grown for a few weeks only, it is possible to use as containers vessels such as tumblers, fruit jars, or wide-mouthed bottles. The seedlings are supported in any one of various ways, and the roots then grow freely in the solution. Obviously the solution-culture method has disadvantages, since support for the plants must be arranged. More practicable is the use of a pure grade of quartz sand as a substrate for the solution. In this substrate, as in soil, the roots become established and so furnish the necessary support for the aerial parts of the plants.

The value of solution cultures lies in the possibility of studying the salt requirements under simplified conditions, with all salts in soluble and available forms. The six major mineral elements (N, P, K, Ca, Mg, S) may be supplied in the form of three soluble salts: calcium nitrate, $Ca(NO_3)_2$, potassium phosphate, KH_2PO_4, and magnesium sulphate, $MgSO_4$. It is necessary or desirable to use these salts in higher concentrations than the others to be mentioned, for two chief reasons: (*a*) they are absorbed in relatively larger quantities; (*b*) they are comparatively nontoxic in a full nutrient solution, and in relatively high concentration they tend to keep the solution constant. Iron is supplied as any soluble salt of this metal, often as iron tartrate, and in much lower concentration than those given above. The other minor elements that are considered serviceable are added as a mixed salt solution, giving in the final solution concentrations much lower than those of the major mineral elements and usually lower than one part per million, since the soluble salts containing, for example, zinc, copper, and boron are exceedingly toxic at higher concentrations. If the salts used to furnish the major mineral elements are not of high purity, the minor elements may be unwittingly introduced as impurities.

A series of solution cultures may be so prepared that each element—or each major element—may be omitted successively from one of the cultures by omitting the salt containing it and substituting therefor another salt supplying a component which is not to be omitted. For instance, to prepare a solution with nitrogen deficiency, calcium chloride may be substituted for calcium nitrate. The lack of any particular element is made apparent by more or less characteristic symptoms in the plant, and these symptoms in leaves and other parts of the plant are often spoken of as "deficiency diseases." As an example, a young tomato plant lacking phosphorus appears unthrifty; its leaves are pale or yellowish, often being set at an acute angle with the stem; veins, petioles, and stem display gradually a higher content of red pigment (anthocyan); the plant as a whole exhibits immaturity.

Fertile soils contain all the necessary plant nutrients, but, to maintain or to restore fertility, rotation practices and natural fertilizers are supplemented by adding to the land dressings of artificial

FIG. 123. Radishes from cultures grown in a mixture of sand and soil to which were added: (*A*) a solution containing all the essential mineral elements; (*B*) a solution lacking potassium; (*C*) one lacking phosphorus; (*D*) one lacking nitrogen. Such a series demonstrates the importance of these three elements, which are the ones most likely to be lacking in soils. Photograph courtesy of S. F. Thornton and Purdue University Agricultural Experiment Station.

fertilizers, which are simply salts (or products furnishing these) less pure and less expensive than the "chemicals" used in the laboratory. Fertilizers containing nitrogen, phosphorus, and potash are the usual components of commercial products. Lime (calcium), when required, is commonly added separately and in larger quantity. In modern agriculture and gardening, watch is kept for iron, boron, manganese, copper, and zinc deficiency or unavailability.

Recently popular interest has been aroused in the so-called "soilless" culture of plants. This is merely an application of the solution- or sand-culture method to the production of plants on a large scale in the greenhouse or out of doors. Instead of growing the plants for weeks with their roots in glass or jar containers, crops are grown to maturity in trays, tanks, and benches. The wide publicity given the earlier successes with these procedures took little account of costs or requisite conditions, and some extravagant claims were made as to the place of this type of culture in the gardening of the future. Nevertheless, in greenhouse work particularly, sand, pebble, and shale substrates used in connection with selected mineral nutrient solutions are apparently proving practicable substitutes for soil in certain types of propagation, especially where large, clean root systems and high-quality planting stock are required. The soilless system permits greater control of conditions; it requires better equipment and more skillful technical work.

Rôles of Essential Elements. Nothing further need be said regarding the significance of the elements carbon, hydrogen, and oxygen, which constitute a great part of the dry matter of plants. In general, however, it is difficult to determine definitely the rôles of those mineral elements which do not enter into the composition of the more permanent or identifiable organic compounds. A chief consideration is the fact that, in the absence of any one of these elements from the nutrient solution, a general unhealthy condition soon prevails in the cells, and often it is not clear which effects are directly traceable to the deficiency and which are only indirectly induced.

Since nitrogen forms no less than 16 per cent of proteins, and accordingly a considerable part of protoplasm, its ultimate significance is evident. Nitrogen is present also in many classes of organic compounds roughly designated "nitrogenous." It has been seen that green plants commonly absorb and utilize nitrates, and often a nutrient solution is arranged to contain an ammonium compound, such as ammonium sulphate, $(NH_4)_2SO_4$, which also is readily available. Organic nitrogen-containing compounds are not satisfactory in nutrient solutions for seed plants. In the soil, nitrogenous substances are converted by bacteria (Chapter XVI), and the nitrogen eventually appears as ammonium compounds and nitrates. Molecular nitrogen (N_2) constitutes about 78 per cent of the atmosphere, but this vast source is unavailable for green plants except as it is to some extent combined into mineral salts by the action of a few species of bacteria and in a certain measure also by electric discharges in the air. The original rocks are devoid of nitrogen; so that the air is actually its ultimate source, the soil and its contained plant and animal remains being the immediate sources.

Phosphorus is a constituent of certain proteins, especially those of the nucleus. It occurs also in other complex organic substances. Phosphorus is utilized in relatively large quantity in meristematic tissues, and to such regions of growth it moves freely from older organs. Developing seeds likewise accumulate phosphorus. Many plant proteins contain sulphur also, and this element is associated with substances which are important as oxidizing (and reducing) agents. It is a constituent of such substances as mustard oil.

So far as known, the chief organic compound in plants of which calcium forms a part is calcium pectate, which constitutes the outer layer of the walls of such cells as root hairs, as well as the middle layer of the wall between any two adjacent cells. Calcium accumulates in leaves but not in seeds. It seems to take part in certain regulatory processes in cells, and in the soil it plays some analogous rôles. The chlorophyll molecule contains magnesium; but this element has other functions, since it is required by all organisms. It appears to take part in the formation and utilization of fats, and it is often associated with phosphorus.

Potassium is almost universally present in cell sap in the form of a salt, and it seems to aid in processes concerned with the condensation, or manufacture, of carbohydrates as well as with the conditions facilitating movement of foods from cell to cell. Iron is one of the factors essential to the formation of chlorophyll, but it is not a constituent of the chlorophyll molecule. With iron deficiency the normally green plant displays a general yellowing. Iron has other rôles, probably associated with enzymes. It appears certain that the metallic minor elements manganese, copper, and zinc may be associated with enzymatic activity of certain types. No plausible part has been assigned to boron; but when it is present in an amount inadequate for normal growth, old leaves wither, and new leaves differentiate incompletely.

METABOLISM AND FOODS

Metabolic Processes. It is hardly possible to realize the variety of the reactions which take place in the living cells of a plant. This whole complex of material and energy changes or any aspect of it is *metabolism*. Metabolism includes constructive processes such as photosynthesis, other forms of food manufacture or utilization, and assimilation—the last a vague term often implying the incorporation of food materials into protoplasm. Destructive processes, such as digestion and respiration, also are included under metabolism. An excess of constructive over destructive metabolism results in an increase in materials and in possibilities of growth and development. An excess of destructive over constructive metabolism results in a decrease in the amount of materials and in a running-down of the mechanism.

Many metabolic processes are no doubt carried out as simple chemical reactions and energy exchanges, but metabolism is known to be particularly characterized by complexity. Numerous reactions that are not easily or not at all effected by the strongest inorganic agents in the laboratory proceed continually in the cell; thus, glucose is made into starch, and out of simple substances new protoplasm is fabricated. Such reactions are effected or accelerated in the living cell through the intermediary of cell products known as *enzymes*. The exact mechanism of their action is not clear, but a hint is offered in the idea that they are catalysts—meaning that, while they take part in a reaction, they are not used up; rather, they are recovered when the reaction is over and are available for succeeding reactions.

Carbohydrates. On the basis of probability and of a certain amount of evidence, glucose, a six-carbon sugar ($C_6H_{12}O_6$), is generally considered a precursor of other organic substances in plants. It is certain that glucose may be transformed, in the cell in which it is produced or in other cells to which it has passed, into any one of a number of compounds. Among these are other sugars having the same general formula as glucose but in whose molecules the atoms are differently arranged. Others are more complex than glucose, such as cane sugar ($C_{12}H_{22}O_{11}$), found in the sugar beet, sugar cane, and sugar maple; and malt sugar, having the same formula as cane sugar, which is present, for example, in sprouted barley. It is of interest to note that the general formula for cane and malt sugars contains just twice the numbers of atoms in glucose less the numbers of those in a molecule of water. Actually, the linking-together of two molecules of six-carbon sugars (glucose + fructose) and the splitting-out of water yield cane sugar. This is another aspect of food manufacture; it is also a synthesis—a synthesis by condensation —and there is every indication that this process is catalyzed by an enzyme.

It has been seen that another important carbohydrate—starch—is formed from glucose. In a cell in which photosynthesis is going on, starch is usually deposited in the form of one or more small grains within each chloroplast (Fig. 87). The amount of starch formed in such a cell is often approximately proportional to the rate at which photosynthesis is proceeding. In the production of starch it is thought that the equivalent of a molecule of water (H_2O) is extracted from each molecule of glucose, being split out during the condensation process. A new unit results of the composition $C_6H_{10}O_5$, instead of $C_6H_{12}O_6$; many such units are combined to form a molecule of starch. The formula of starch, therefore, is written $(C_6H_{10}O_5)_n$, the *n* indicating an indefinite but large number of units.

Another carbohydrate produced by the transformation of sugars is cellulose, which frequently forms a large proportion of the substance of cell walls and which exists in an almost pure state in cotton fibers. More readily transformable kinds of cellulose (hemicelluloses) are deposited in the cells of some plants—for example, in the seeds of dates—as a reserve food. Other carbohydrate foods produced by certain plants are glycogen (in certain fungi) and inulin, as in the tubers of some species of sunflower.

Fats. Simple sugars or the products derived from these serve as the chief building materials for fats. The fats of plants are chiefly in the liquid state—that is, they are oils, such as olive oil, cottonseed oil, and linseed oil. Many seeds and fruits, including the castor bean, soybean, peanut, cotton seed, and olive, are particularly rich in fats. Although composed of the same elements as carbohydrates (carbon, hydrogen, and oxygen), a fat molecule differs markedly in its organization from a carbohydrate molecule, one important difference being its lesser content of oxygen. As an illustration, olein, the fat most largely present in olive oil, has the formula $C_{57}H_{104}O_6$. The energy content of fats is higher in proportion to their volume than is that of carbohydrates, and consequently fats are foods by means of which a large amount of available energy may be stored in a very limited space. Fats, like starch, are insoluble in the cell sap.

Proteins. The most complex organic compounds that have been identified as distinctive chemical entities are the proteins. They constitute an essential part of the living matter of all plant and animal cells. They are often present also as reserve foods, being especially abundant in peas, beans, and similar seeds and in the outer portions of the kernels of wheat, oats, and corn. The enzymes that have thus far been isolated and crystallized are proteins.

All proteins contain carbon, hydrogen, oxygen, and nitrogen; many contain also phosphorus and sulphur. There is strong evidence that every active cell can synthesize proteins. The building materials required trace back eventually, first to carbohydrate products of photosynthesis, and second to salts containing nitrogen derived from the soil—also to phosphates and sulphates similarly derived in the case of proteins which contain phosphorus and sulphur. The presence of protein-synthesizing enzymes in the cell is assumed. Phosphorus-containing proteins are particularly characteristic of nuclei, and such proteins are known as nucleoproteins; but some cytoplasmic proteins also contain phosphorus. There are many different kinds of proteins in plants, and there is good evidence that they consist invariably of chains of *amino acids*, these acids containing one or more groups with a nitrogen atom (such as an amino group, NH_2). Much has been learned regarding the amino acids of which proteins are composed; and a considerable number of these simpler compounds have been artificially combined into substances that may be considered comparatively simple proteins.

Proteins are extremely complex, their molecules being composed of a very large number of atoms. For example, the formula of gliadin, found in the wheat kernel, is $C_{685}H_{1068}O_{211}N_{196}S_5$. Although formulas of this nature have been determined for a few proteins, the exact chemical constitution—that is, the arrangement of the amino acids and of their atoms in the molecule—is not known for any protein that occurs in living cells.

Proteins, as well as many other components of living matter, occur in the colloidal state—which, it will be recalled, is marked by the distribution of the substances in question in a more or less finely divided condition through a continuous medium. This medium, in protoplasm, is always water which contains numerous substances in solution. Egg albumen is a colloidal mixture of proteins in water, in which, however, various other substances are suspended or dissolved. A colloidal suspension of proteins varies in consistency from that of a viscous liquid like egg albumen to that of so solid a substance as a firm gelatin. The differences in consistency depend in part upon the proportion of water present and in part upon the size and arrangement of the protein particles.

An important characteristic of many proteins in the colloidal state is their tendency to undergo, under high temperatures and other conditions, the change known as *coagulation*. This change involves modifications in the physical state and probably in the chemical constitution of a protein. Many proteins of plants are coagulable, but the best-known example of coagulation is that of the albumen (white) of a cooked egg. In many cases coagulation is irreversible; the coagulated protein can not again be brought into suspension in the medium from which it was separated.

Another significant characteristic of proteins and of other substances in the colloidal state is their general inability to pass through ordinary membranes, even through so permeable a membrane as a cell wall. Protein foods can not, therefore, pass from one cell to another unless the two cells are connected by openings of some size through the dividing walls. Such openings, it has been seen, are present in the walls between the cells of sieve tubes; and it is probable that sieve tubes serve for the translocation of protein foods. It seems probable that some protein transport from cell to cell may occur through the minute protoplasmic strands that connect the protoplasts of actively metabolizing cells.

Pigments. Certain pigments, especially the chlorophylls, carotene, and xanthophyll, which are present in plastids, have already been described. Other pigments that are produced by plant cells occur, not in plastids, but in solution in the cell sap. Most abundant of these water-soluble pigments are the *anthocyans*, which are usually red, purple, or blue. In some plants anthocyans are present in varying amounts at all times. In others they appear only in the spring or in the autumn. They are abundant in the roots of the red beet, in red onion bulbs, in the leaves of some plants, such as Iresine, coleus, and red cabbage, and in many red and blue flowers and fruits. In some plant parts these pigments appear only in cells of the epidermis; in others, they occur in cells of various tissues.

The formation of an anthocyan is dependent especially upon the presence of large amounts of sugars. Light also is essential. The anthocyan molecule contains sugar. When conditions are such that sugars are being used rapidly by a plant so that they do not accumulate, anthocyans are not usually formed. At low temperatures sugars accumulate, and anthocyan formation results. Many plant parts are brilliantly red in early spring and in autumn, because of the low rate of respiration at the lower temperatures, the abundance of sugars, and the consequent formation of anthocyans.

Although the functions of anthocyans have not been definitely determined, it is considered possible by some that they aid in the absorption of certain rays of light which would be injurious to chlorophyll. Anthocyans absorb some light energy, which is converted into heat, so that under like conditions red leaves have a higher temperature than green ones. Such rise in temperature may accelerate the activities of cells, but the general advantages of a slight temperature rise are problematic.

The brilliant colors characteristic of autumn leaves in temperate regions (Fig. 124) result from the presence of pigments. The yellow colors are often due to the yellow pigments present in chloroplasts. During the summer a fairly uniform chlorophyll content may be maintained; but, as autumn progresses, the destruction of chlorophyll proceeds so that the green color fades, leaving only the color of the yellow pigments. Frost is not necessary to the disappearance of chlorophyll. Leaves often become yellow during dry periods even in summer. Bright red colors are commonly due to anthocyans, which are produced in many plants in the autumn. Autumnal conditions favor the accumulation of sugars in leaves and hence the formation of anthocyans. When a leaf is alive, the cell walls are usually light-colored and translucent. They may become brownish upon the death of the cells and the accumulation of various products. The protoplasts often blacken after death. In these ways the brown colors of autumn leaves are caused. Various combinations of yellow, red, brown, and black pigments produce intermediate shades or cause a mottling of leaves.

UTILIZATION AND STORAGE OF FOODS

Digestion. The term *digestion* is usually applied to the processes in living organisms whereby various complex food materials are converted into simpler compounds. These latter may be at once or by further conversion may become soluble and capable of diffusing through cell membranes. Many stored foods such as starch are insoluble or practically so in cell sap and hence must be digested before they can be utilized or translocated. By the complete digestion of

Fig. 124. Autumn colors of leaves. The yellow of the birches is due to carotenoids which persist after the disappearance of chlorophyll. The red of the maple is due to anthocyans.

starch, glucose is produced. In describing earlier the formation of starch $(C_6H_{10}O_5)_n$ from glucose, it was pointed out that a molecule of water is lost for each glucose molecule used, thus:

$$\underset{\text{glucose}}{n\, C_6H_{12}O_6} \rightarrow \underset{\text{starch}}{(C_6H_{10}O_5)_n} + \underset{\text{water}}{n\, H_2O}.$$

The reverse of this reaction shows the end result in starch digestion:

$$(C_6H_{10}O_5)_n + n\, H_2O \rightarrow n\, C_6H_{12}O_6.$$

A reaction involving the incorporation of water, as this does, is *hydrolysis*. All the usual food-digestive processes are hydrolyses, whether the food substance converted is a carbohydrate, fat, protein, or other product. The reverse process—the building up or manufacture of such foods—has previously been designated *condensation*. Some other stored foods, such as cane sugar, are soluble in cell sap; nevertheless, cane sugar is a condensation product and may be digested in a manner similar to that described above:

$$\underset{\text{cane sugar}}{C_{12}H_{22}O_{11}} + H_2O \rightarrow \underset{\text{glucose}}{C_6H_{12}O_6} + \underset{\text{fructose}}{C_6H_{12}O_6}.$$

Here it will be seen that each molecule of cane sugar, with the incorporation of one molecule of water, produces two molecules of six-carbon sugars (of the same composition though structurally different).

Enzymes. The protoplasts of plant and animal cells produce special substances known as *enzymes*, whose function it is to bring about or to accelerate chemical changes. Each class of compounds, such as starch, fat, or protein, is in general acted upon by particular types of digestive enzymes. Starch is digested by *diastases;* fats are digested by *lipases;* proteins, by *proteases;* and cane sugar, by *sucrase* (invertase). In the course of any such process the enzyme concerned is not used up; on the contrary, it is released with the completion of the reaction, and exceedingly small quantities of a digestive enzyme are capable, consequently, of digesting large amounts of the particular food upon which it acts. Some foods are converted outside a living cell in the same manner as in it, when they are brought into contact under appropriate conditions with the proper enzyme. An extract of diastase, for example, derived from barley kernels, will digest starch if placed with the starch in a little water in a test tube. Experiments such as this demonstrate that these enzymes are distinct from living matter, since they can be extracted from cells, without loss of their characteristic properties, by processes that remove or kill the living matter. So far as they have been isolated and crystallized, enzymes are proteins; but in some cases they appear to be associated with nonprotein groups. Their properties are destroyed by high temperatures and by strong chemical reagents. As hydrolytic agents, these enzymes play a conspicuous and important part in digestive changes, and they were first studied in relation to digestion. There is good evidence, however, that the same enzymes are equally important in processes of condensation. Diastases, for example, play as large a part in the making of starch as in its digestion. As has been indicated, starch manufacture and other similar reactions are *reversible*, and this fact is expressed by the reversed arrows in the following equation:

$$n\,C_6H_{12}O_6 \rightleftharpoons (C_6H_{10}O_5)_n + n\,H_2O.$$

Enzymes of a dozen or more classes have been identified, and it seems probable that most of the complex chemical changes occurring in the living cell are catalyzed by enzymes. It follows that every living cell contains a great variety of enzymes.

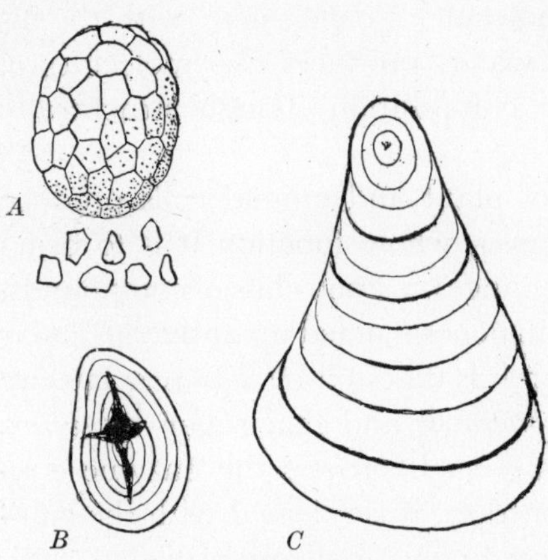

FIG. 125. Starch grains. *A*, compound and individual grains from the oat. *B*, grain from a seed of bean. *C*, from the stem of canna.

Food Storage. Most of the foods whose manufacture has been discussed are often produced by a plant in far greater amounts than are immediately used. The surplus is stored. If photosynthesis is more rapid than the removal of its products, these products accumulate in the cells in which they originate and are ordinarily stored as starch in the chloroplasts; hence there may be a temporary storage in the chlorophyll-containing cells of leaves or of other organs. When starch is once formed, therefore, being a solid not readily soluble in water, it can not be moved. It must first be converted into the simpler, soluble units from which it was condensed, such as glucose, if it is to be translocated. When a sugar reaches a storage cell, some of it may be changed to starch, this change being effected by plastids, usually leucoplasts. Undoubtedly equilibrium conditions within the cell determine the direction of these changes.

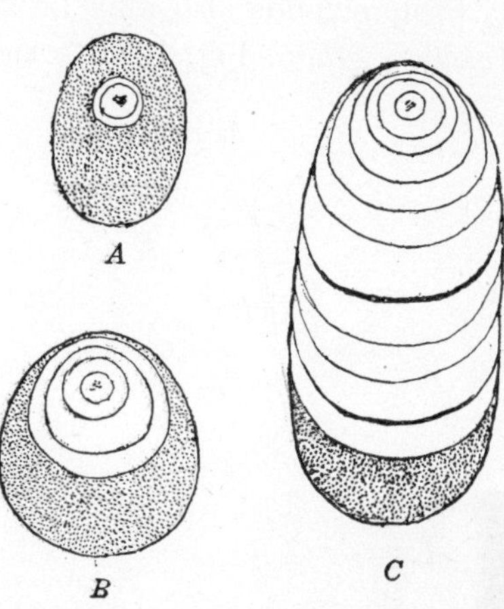

FIG. 126. Stages in the development of starch grains in chloroplasts of cortical cells of a stem of Pellionia. The chloroplast is shaded in each case. *A*, *B*, grains composed of but few layers. *C*, older grain with many layers.

The starch grains formed in leucoplasts are commonly larger than those formed in chloroplasts. Starch grains deposited in leucoplasts are stratified, being composed of successive layers deposited about an original small core. Their shapes vary greatly, those starch grains produced by each kind of plant having a more or less characteristic form (Figs. 90, 125). The layers that make up a grain are commonly of two different sorts. Some layers allow light to pass through rather freely and therefore appear clear in transmitted light. Layers of a second sort, alternating with those of the former type, do not allow light to pass through so readily; they appear, therefore, as comparatively dark, usually narrow, zones. In many plants, including oats (Fig. 125, *A*) and rice, several starch grains are formed within each leucoplast; as these grains grow, they come into contact and commonly remain together as compound grains.

In occasional instances, comparatively large storage-starch grains are formed in chloroplasts instead of in leucoplasts. An example of this type of starch formation is furnished by the relatively thick stems of Pellionia. The stems are green, since many of their cells contain chloroplasts. Photosynthesis may go on in these cells; and the accumulating sugars are transformed into starch. But the stems serve also as storage organs. Hence, many of the starch grains, instead of being small temporary structures, as are most starch grains formed in chloroplasts, become large (Fig. 126) and similar in structure to the grains commonly deposited in leucoplasts.

Stored fats appear in various parts of cells as droplets of varying size. They occur in vacuoles and in the cytoplasm as well as in, or attached to, chloroplasts, leucoplasts, and elaioplasts.

Protein foods also may be stored in the form of small globules (*aleurone grains*, Fig. 127). Aleurone grains are especially charac-

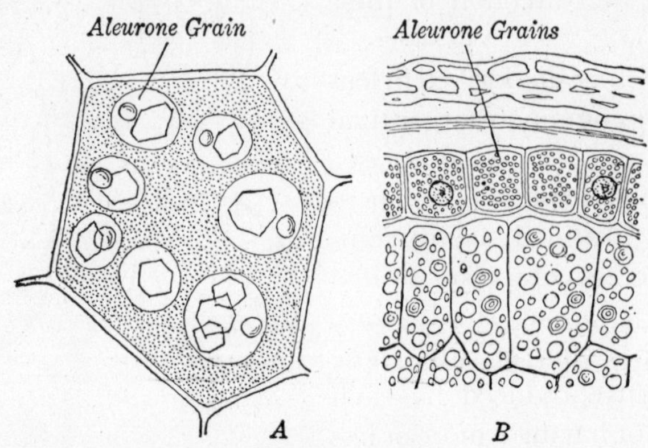

Fig. 127. Aleurone grains. *A*, cell of the castor bean containing large, complex grains. *B*, cross section of the outer portion of a corn kernel, showing the layer of cells which contain many small aleurone grains. After Strasburger.

teristic of the storage cells of the seeds of beans, peas, and other members of the same family, as well as of a particular layer of the kernels of cereal grains. In the castor bean, the aleurone grains are comparatively large and of complex structure.

The portions of different plants in which foods are stored vary greatly, depending largely upon the length of life of the plant. In annual plants foods are stored chiefly in seeds and fruits. The corn kernel is a fruit in which are stored quantities of starch and fats and some proteins; the bean seed is rich in carbohydrates and proteins. In trees and shrubs, as well as in other perennials, storage may occur in any of the living tissues of the vegetative organs, most frequently in those of stems and roots. A potato tuber is an enlarged underground branch or part of a branch, many of whose cells are packed with starch; a head of cabbage consists chiefly of leaves containing much water as well as some fats, carbohydrates, and proteins. The sugar beet has a much-enlarged root in the sap of whose cells large quantities of cane sugar are dissolved.

Food Utilization in Respiration. Respiration as a fundamental cellular process has been considered in Chapter III. It constitutes an important part of food utilization, since oxidative reactions furnish the energy for essentially all the constructive and mechanical work of tissues. Energy release in final analysis involves relatively simple compounds such as glucose and organic acids, but obviously these products are maintained at certain levels through other enzymatic processes. An adequate available food supply is essential during respiration in order that the living matter itself may be better protected from partial disintegration and use. This suggests that the rate of respiration increases directly with an increase in the food level. To a limited extent this is true, but apparently only to the extent that the food is being utilized in growth and differentiation of tissues; for example, the respiration of the sugar beet at maturity is exceedingly low.

Assimilation. In the complex phenomena of metabolism certain aspects have been emphasized. The term, as defined, includes all the chemical reactions and essentially all the energy changes involved in the utilization of materials in the cell. One aspect of these reactions which must be considered, but whose mechanism is highly hypothetical, is that phase of metabolism concerned with the actual incorporation of nonliving substances into the living matter. This process is *assimilation.* Obviously it can not be clearly differentiated from digestion, from building-up processes, or from other enzymatic effects concerned with the mobilization and incorporation of the materials that may be suitable. One of the characteristics of living matter is its power of growth and repair, which implies the ability to manufacture new matter like itself out of foods. It has been noted that another characteristic is its instability—the readiness with which it undergoes changes, in part at least induced by changes in the conditions which surround it. The concept of living matter is a dynamic one; it may be constantly built up, yet it may also be continually broken down; *assimilation* and *dissimilation* express these ideas, although the terms are often much more broadly applied.

Vitamins and Auxins. The terms *vitamin* and *auxin* are applied to substances, now recognized as constituting two fairly distinctive groups, which produce striking effects upon metabolism, growth, and development. Unfortunately, there is no well-stabilized nomenclature applying to these substances. However, "growth substances" may be regarded as a term embracing all such materials.

In the study of animal metabolism, vitamins are often spoken of as *growth factors*. In work with plants the auxins are classed as *hormones* (or plant hormones). Most of the ten or more known vitamins important to the growth and health of animals are produced by green plants, or at least the precursors or sources of these substances are so produced. For this reason it is not a simple matter to determine the vitamin requirements of green plants. On the other hand, some of the fungi lack the capacity to produce certain vitamins and, like animals, must obtain these with their foods. Auxins also are produced by plants and, while they are found in the animal body and in excretions, they may be derived from plant products or from bacterial action in the digestive tract. Several of the animal hormones, however, are produced in animals only, arising from the activity of the ductless glands. Both vitamins and hormones are effective at low concentrations, in some instances at concentrations even lower than those which are essential for boron and manganese.

Secretion. The production by the protoplast of a cell or by the protoplasts of a group of cells of substances which are extruded constitutes what is commonly recognized as *secretion*. The term is

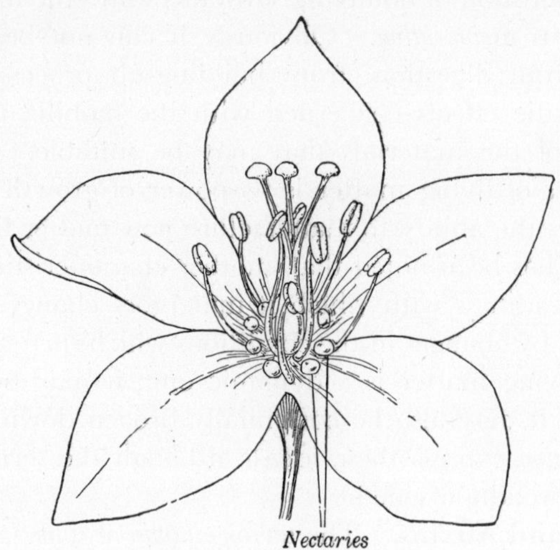

FIG. 128. Flower of buckwheat, with nectaries at its base.

none too well distinguished from *excretion*, but the latter is used in a broader sense. Typically, *glands* are functional in secretory processes. Glands are often special epidermal hairs; others are more complex structures, such as floral *nectaries*. Nectaries are characteristic of the flowers of a large number of species of plants (Fig. 128). These exude a modified sap, a solution containing sugar and other substances in solution. The relation of nectaries to the pollination of flowers by insects is discussed elsewhere. Glandular hairs of leaves and stems not infrequently produce certain volatile oils or resins. The sticky hairs or tentacles of a leaf of sundew (Fig. 81, *A*) are glands whose secretions trap small insects, which are subsequently digested by means of enzymes similarly secreted. Also, certain leaf glands exude water—that is, water in which the solute concentration is exceedingly low. In general, the mechanism of glandular secretion is not well understood, but it appears that the forces concerned develop within the glandular tissue. The production of a cellulose wall or the deposition of a new layer of cellulose on the inside of a cell wall by the protoplast is usually regarded as a type of secretory activity. The development of cutin and other waxes on epidermal cells is an analogous function.

MOVEMENT OF WATER AND SOLUTES

Water Movement in Root, Stem, and Leaf. As previously indicated, water is absorbed by the root system, and the leaves are the organs through which water loss chiefly occurs. It is obvious that in the regions intervening between the absorbing root surfaces and the transpiring leaf surfaces a movement of water must take place. In a very small plant, such as duckweed, the water transpired may be replaced merely by osmotic movements from cell to cell—the forces concerned in these movements being those already discussed in connection with osmosis (Chapter III). The conditions in such a plant are very different, however, from those in a sunflower or in a tree. Osmotic movement of water from cell to cell can not possibly suffice to replace amounts lost by transpiration in these larger plants. The great resistance offered to the passage of water from cell to cell and the great distances to which water is conducted in large plants imply the existence of some means for rapid conduction. The long conducting elements of the xylem permit the mass movement or flow of water, carrying along, of course, substances in solution and moving at a more rapid rate than would be possible if there were many interposing membranes to be traversed. This movement of water is mainly in the cavities of tracheids and vessels.

Water moves in those tracheids and vessels only which are unobstructed and entirely filled with water. The mass of water and solutes moving in the conducting elements of the xylem is the *transpiration stream*, and the movement of this mass is the *sap flow*.

The path of the transpiration stream may be shown by cutting off the shoot of a plant which, like Impatiens, has a translucent stem and placing the shoot in a solution of a dye such as eosin or fuchsin. The general course of the dye can be traced through the stem, the petioles, and the veins of the leaves. Microscopic examination of cross sections of the stem will show that the only elements containing the dye are those of the xylem.

But not all the vessels and tracheids of the xylem necessarily conduct water. As has been seen, the water-conducting elements in trunks of trees become blocked when sapwood changes to heartwood. Hence, there can be no movement of water through heartwood. Conducting elements even of the sapwood may become partly or completely filled with gas at certain seasons of the year, in which case there is no conduction through these vessels and tracheids. Such blocking of conducting elements with gases is often so extensive that half of the vessels and tracheids in an annual ring of sapwood are temporarily nonfunctional.

There is a general relation between the volume of transpiration and the amount of conducting tissue developed by a stem. Submerged water plants have relatively few vessels and tracheids. When plants of the same species are grown on land or when water plants bear branches and leaves above the surface of the water a proportionally greater amount of xylem is produced.

Forces Concerned in Sap Flow. In some trees water is raised for great distances. Such trees as oaks, maples, and elms often reach heights of 50 to 100 feet or more. The redwood, the big tree, the Douglas fir, and the sugar pine of the Pacific Coast of North America grow to a height often greater than 200 feet. The amount of work necessary in lifting enough water to these heights to supply transpiration needs is very great—sufficient not only to raise the water but also to overcome the resistance encountered in its passage.

Xylem elements, being tubular structures without protoplasm, can in themselves exert no force that may cause the movement of water. Capillarity is a force which can not be responsible in this process, since in these vessels water could rise by capillarity no higher than about 30 centimeters (12 inches). Root pressure plays apparently a minor part, if any, in the rise of sap in the stems. It has been held that the parenchymatous cells of the stele force water into tracheids and vessels with which the living cells are in contact. Root pressure, however, can not be of prime importance in this transport of water, since it is least, or even negative, when transpiration and water movement in the stem are most rapid.

The force which chiefly accounts for the ascent of sap is that exerted by the transpiring cells of the leaves. As water evaporates from the cell walls bordering upon the intercellular spaces, there results a water deficit in the walls, so that water moves into them from the protoplasts. The accruing deficit in the protoplasts of these transpiring cells necessitates the entrance of water from adjoining cells of the spongy tissue and so in turn shortly from cells in contact with the tracheids which in part conduct the water in the leaf. Loss of water by these tracheids exerts a tension on the water columns, and this tension is ultimately transmitted through the tracheids and vessels of the veins of the leaf, which are connected through the petiole with the xylem elements of branch, stem or trunk, and root. The tensions in these columns must be regarded as extending throughout their length and influencing directly the movement of water from the pericycle and cortex of the root. It has been convincingly shown that considerable tensions, or negative pressures, do occur in the vessels when the transpiration rate is high; and under normal conditions of water loss it is estimated that a force sufficient to balance this water deficit is adequate to raise water to the height of the tallest trees if efficiently applied and if the columns of water in the conducting tracts are not broken.

Tensile Strength of Water. Contrary to what would be imagined from ordinary experience with water, experiment shows that a column of water has great tensile strength. When the tensile strength of a bar of metal is tested, the force required to break it is considered equal to the force of cohesion of its molecules. In liquids, the molecules are more mobile and their cohesive force is more difficult to measure. However, by means of proper apparatus it can be shown that the molecules of water enclosed in a tube tend very strongly, like those of a metal bar, to cohere. Because of the cohesion of the water columns in the xylem, the pull exerted by the leaf cells lifts the columns. In a tree 100 feet in height, the effect of the pull is felt for 100 feet plus the distance to the most remote root. The pull upon the water columns is continuous so long as transpiration is active. If intake of water by the roots is ample, a stream of water is kept flowing continuously upward through the xylem to the leaves.

Conduction of Solutes. The movement of solutes from one cell to another by diffusion, together with protoplasmic movement within the cells, is apparently adequate to take care of the needs of tissues of limited extent. However, any process conditioned by diffusion must be slow. Accordingly, it is not to be expected that by this means solutes absorbed by the roots or solutes derived from photosynthetic activity in the leaf would be effectively transported for the distances required to reach all parts even of such a plant as the potato. A tree presents the extreme aspect of the problem. It is clear that salts and soluble organic materials are transported through these relatively great distances upward, downward, and to some extent laterally, and the channels of such movements of nutrients and foods are the vascular elements, with water as the medium.

It has long been held that the transport of mineral salts is primarily by way of the tracheids and vessels of the xylem. In recent years a controversy has developed over this point. Evidence for the transport of salts by the xylem route is based in part on the content of salts in the sap of the vessels and in part on the continuance of transport, though often at a slower rate, when a stem or branch is girdled. Girdling consists in removing a ring of bark down to the cambium, so that the phloem is disconnected and can no longer conduct. The controversy has renewed interest in this problem, and it is considered reasonable to conclude that salts do move into the phloem to some extent; but it is not yet generally conceded that the phloem is a primary factor in conduction up the stem.

Sugar is found not uncommonly in low concentration in xylem sap, and it no doubt enters from cells adjacent to the xylem. It is generally agreed, however, that the translocation of soluble organic foods is chiefly through the phloem. Evidence for this view comes in part from girdling experiments, which clearly indicate an accumulation of food above the girdle. Organic substances, such as sugars and proteins, are readily identified in the sieve tubes; and structurally these elements of the phloem seem admirably constructed to play a primary part in conduction. It has not been shown that there is mass movement of materials through the pores connecting rows of sieve tubes, but the appearance of the cytoplasm in active sieve tubes and the absence of a nucleus are themselves suggestive of such movement. Nevertheless, the precise mechanism of the movement of organic materials and the forces involved have not been clearly identified.

It seems possible to suggest the main steps in the process of translocation from the leaf, beginning with the accumulation of starch in the chloroplasts during active photosynthesis. This accumulation ordinarily occurs during the daytime; but during the night, or chiefly during the night, the conditions are favorable for the conversion of starch to sugar. It is probable also that in the cells of the leaf, where sugar is available, the materials are formed which will enter into the construction of proteins and other products. All these diffusible materials, which are in relatively high concentration in the leaf, will move into and through the phloem to various regions of the plant. During this movement, material may pass out from the phloem at any level into adjacent cells and so eventually reach all parts of the plant. In this way sugar would be transported, in such a plant as the potato, not only to the roots, but selectively perhaps to the underground branches in some parts of which tuberization is proceeding. In the cells of the developing tuber much of the sugar not used in growth processes is gradually condensed again to starch by the leucoplasts.

Water Balance of Plants. The water content of a plant expressed as percentage of the total weight of the material is a fairly constant quantity, if sampling is uniform. However, when carefully studied, it is found that, even under conditions usually favorable for growth, the water content is at a maximum during the very early morning and that it decreases somewhat toward a minimum in the afternoon. Atmospheric conditions which promote excessive transpiration materially increase this difference in the water content. Likewise, unfavorable conditions for root absorption, such as low water content of the soil, concentration of solutes in the soil solution, and low temperature, may reduce the water content of the plant. The relation between transpiration and absorption is known as the *water balance*. Regarding a close correlation between absorption and transpiration as normal balance, excessive loss of water by transpiration represents a deficit, and the extent to which different species of plants may show a deficit before beginning to wilt varies greatly. Individual plants grown under dissimilar conditions also vary in the water deficit they will endure. It has been found that under the conditions tested a sunflower may endure a deficit of about 28 per cent of its maximum water content, whereas a typical shade-loving plant may wilt with a water loss of only 3 per cent.

CHAPTER IX

GROWTH AND MOVEMENT

Evidences of Growth. Some of the readily observable evidences of growth are increase in size and number of organs. In general, growth involves increasing complexity of form and structure and development of the individual plant. A gardener, thinking in terms of some particular crop, measures growth chiefly by the development of the particular part or parts of the plant yielding the products in which he is interested. A forester measures growth primarily in respect to the height and diameter of his trees. A student of botany may be concerned with the grosser evidences and measurements of growth; but for a broad grasp of the growth concept it is essential also to consider as far as practicable the variety of growth phenomena, the manner in which growth proceeds, the detailed mechanism of certain growth processes, and the environmental factors which influence the rate and character of growth.

Beginning with an active protoplast, assimilation or the making of new protoplasm is a first step in growth, often leading directly to cell division, which results in an increase in cell number. Increase or decrease in weight over short time intervals does not necessarily represent increase or decrease in growth. A maturing seed may lose water and so lose weight, but the loss is not a decrease in growth; on the other hand, a dry seed may take up water, and thus increase in weight, before new growth actually begins. When a potato tuber gives rise, under the soil cover, to new shoots, growth is obviously occurring; but until green shoots are established above ground and are able to photosynthesize, the tuber is losing in dry weight, that is, in total substance. An apple tree, when its flower buds are opening, is for a very short period losing more in substance, through respiration, than it could possibly gain through the limited photosynthesis of the green parts of its flowers. But growth and development are proceeding.

Meristems and Growth. In the discussion of stems and roots in earlier chapters, attention was given to some of the aspects of growth in apical meristems and in the tissues to which these meristems give rise. It was seen that, beginning near the apex, certain growing regions are present: (*a*) a region of cell division, involving for one thing an increase in protoplasm, which suggests a high requirement of nitrogenous foods; (*b*) a region of elongation, representing an increase in cell-wall extent and relatively large additions of water and solutes (chiefly additions to the expanding vacuoles); (*c*) a region of maturation, in which the cells reach their final form and size, and growth subsides. The leaf of a seed plant, as seen in an unfolding bud, has no apical meristem. However, most of its cells undergo a phase of enlargement, which is followed by one of differentiation.

Aside from apical meristems, the cambium is the chief meristem of stems and roots of dicotyledons or of gymnosperms. This region displays through its derivative tissues (phloem and xylem) a sequence of growth phases analogous to that of an apical meristem. Its growth is usually for one period only in annual plants, but in perennials growth activity recurs annually from a persisting cambial layer. So far as the problem has been studied, observations indicate that the activity in growth of all these meristems is conditioned by a supply of auxin and that in general the production of auxin is chiefly the function of young growing organs, especially of the apical regions of stems and of young leaves in their early stages of growth.

Growth Factors. In the study of plants, the expression *growth factors* refers usually to all the internal and external influences which affect growth. Evidently the internal factors must be diverse and complex. In the first place, each species has its own inheritance (Chapter XXXIII)—that is, a complex of possibilities which may be displayed under appropriate conditions. Indeed, the inheritance of a plant may express itself in the operation of almost any other factor that might be mentioned. Water, nutrients, foods, enzymes, and the interrelations of the quantities of these obviously must affect growth rate and vigor. It has been seen, too, that vitamins and auxins apparently condition many phases of metabolism, of growth, and of development.

Relations between similar or dissimilar organs in growth expression constitute a phenomenon of much interest. It has long been observed that the removal of flower buds, as in the tomato, often stimulates leaf development. A tobacco-grower "tops" tobacco plants in the field when they begin to flower, and thus the crop of leaves is improved and increased. Removal of a terminal bud at the time of unfolding in a shrub or tree is usually followed by the development of lateral buds that would otherwise remain dormant. The failure of the lateral buds to grow earlier is interpreted as due to an auxin inhibition, the apex of the terminal bud producing too much auxin to favor the growth of the lateral buds and auxin transport being downward. Numerous instances are known of this type of correlation. Cells, organs, and plants as a whole are characterized by a *grand period* of growth. This is a form of periodicity, which means that the rate of growth is not uniform. It may be illustrated by the growth of a leaf, which is at first slow, then proceeds with increasing rate to a maximum, and finally, at maturity, declines to zero. The grand period includes the entire time of enlargement. If all the leaves produced on the branch of a tree, representing the growth of the current year, are measured, it will be found that there is an orderliness in their sizes. The largest leaves are neither at the base nor at the top but rather in the middle region, so that as the leaves successively developed there was an increase in size to a maximum, followed by a decline. These facts indicate a grand period in leaf development. Changes in external conditions during growth may induce some irregularities in this sequence.

External factors influencing growth are various; they include all climatic and atmospheric conditions, soil properties and composition, diseases and animal depredations, gravity, and mechanical agencies. At this time some of the effects of two of these classes of external factors, namely, light and temperature, will be particularly considered.

Light. The rôle of light as the source of energy in photosynthesis has been discussed. Its effect upon the orientation or growth-bending of the elongating organs of plants will be considered later. For the present, consideration will be given primarily to the influence of light on the form and appearance of a plant. Chief interest attaches to sunlight and to light from such artificial sources as tungsten or fluorescent lamps, which are often used as supplementary sources in greenhouses or in experimental work in the laboratory. The effects of radiant energy in general are of importance; but the present treatment is limited to the effects of the energy represented in the visible spectrum.

Light may influence plant form and behavior in relation to its *intensity*, its *quality*, and its *duration*. By intensity is meant the amount of light energy (measured in any acceptable light units) which strikes a unit surface in unit time. Light meters for use in photographic work measure light intensity, and exposures are timed accordingly. By quality is meant wave length; and this, in the range of the visible spectrum, is apparent to the human eye as colors (Fig. 97). Wave length decreases in the visible spectrum of sunlight from the extreme red (about 760 mμ) through orange, yellow, green, blue, and violet (visible to about 400 mμ). Duration has reference to the length of the light period in the regular cycle of twenty-four hours. Throughout the north temperate zone the "days" of the growing season are essentially long during early and midsummer; they are essentially short during early spring and again during late summer and autumn.

At zero intensity—that is, in darkness—seeds of sunflower or radish, for example, may germinate and the seedlings display marked color and form effects, as compared with seedlings in light. A seedling grown in darkness appears white (stems) or yellowish (leaves). So long as food materials are furnished by the seed, including the food in the embryo, growth in length proceeds, and the tender, succulent seedling, with poorly developed leaves, may attain a length of from three to ten inches or more, depending in part upon moisture and temperature conditions. Such an elongate, spindly structure does not develop adequate supporting tissue; the seedling topples over, ceases to grow, and death soon results. Thus seedlings in darkness promptly display extreme *etiolation*, whereas seedlings grown in light are erect and stocky, with expanded green leaves. By comparison, growth in darkness from such storage organs as bulbs, corms (Fig. 52, *A*), and tubers, with abundant reserve food materials, is much more extensive, although etiolated. The corm of the jack-in-the-pulpit is reported to produce in darkness a whitened plant of more than usual height, with somewhat narrowed leaves, attenuate petioles, and a stalk bearing flowers.

Plants grown in light of low intensity commonly display elongate internodes, leaves smaller than normal, and reduced amounts of supporting tissue. Intense light, on the contrary, is conducive to a stocky development of the plant as a whole, with its leaves relatively thickened. Although conditions vary much with the species, at intermediate light intensities leaves usually become relatively large and somewhat thin, with a characteristic internal structure, including a reduction in the number of layers of palisade cells or in the length of these cells. Certain strains of tobacco raised for cigar wrappers are often grown in partial shade (under cheesecloth tents). In general, species of plants differ widely from one another in their tolerance of shade and likewise in their tolerance of the full sunshine of midsummer.

Changes in the intensity of sunlight due to clouds, dust, or artificial screens effect also some differences in light quality—a fact not always taken into account. Plants grown exclusively under the influence of the longer wave lengths of visible light (the red end of the spectrum) exhibit formative effects similar to those of plants in sunlight of reduced intensity, whereas the short wave lengths of visible light (the blue end of the spectrum) promote a marked stockiness of form. This latter condition has been interpreted as an inhibition of growth, possibly correlated with lessened auxin efficiency or reduced auxin concentration, as a result of the exposure to blue light. It will appear later that the shorter wave lengths notably influence also the orientation of organs and the direction of growth. As might be expected, apparently the full range of the spectrum of sunlight can not be greatly improved upon for an energy distribution favorable to the normal growth of plants.

Photoperiodism, the Response to Light Duration. The duration of the light period of the day varies at the earth's surface chiefly with respect to latitude and season. In the northern hemisphere the longest period of possible sunshine in the daily cycle is on June 21, and the daylight period shortens progressively with the season from this time, forward or backward, to December 21. Definite knowledge of the adjustment of a species to a certain favorable day length, or length of daylight period, called the *photoperiod*, was not at hand until 1920. The observations and information then made available have been greatly extended by many investigators, and it is now recognized that day length is a major factor in the responses of many plants to the environmental complex influencing flowering and fruiting and that it influences also to some extent the development of tubers and bulbs.

In respect to the effects of day length on flowering, three classes of plants are recognized: "long-day" plants, "short-day" plants, and plants that are indeterminate, or neutral to the length of day. In certain cases the particular class to which a given species belongs is not readily apparent, especially in an environment variable except as to day length. In fact, even in a cursory consideration of these classes it is well to bear in mind that certain other environmental factors, particularly temperature and the level of nutrition, have been shown to modify plant reactions, sometimes to an extent such that these factors appear to participate in producing the day-length effects. The total amount of growth is commonly greater the longer the daylight period; the term "photoperiod," therefore, has no implication of favorable day length in respect to total yield of plant substance or, for example, the yield of sugar beets or that of some forage crop.

Long-day plants are those which come into flowering normally above a critical period of day length usually placed at about twelve hours. Below this day length such plants are characteristically vegetative—that is, flowerless. This last statement holds true if any shortening of the period is made at the beginning or at the close of the interval of illumination, since an interval of darkness in the middle of the long-day period has very little effect. Plants typically in the long-day class are such as cereals and certain cultivated grasses, radish and spinach, rocket larkspur, and fringed loosestrife. Among long-day wild species are many of those growing in temperate latitudes and blooming during June and July.

Short-day plants flower more abundantly in day lengths ranging from about seven to twelve hours. Such plants are vegetative in longer periods and typically may be grown economically in continuous illumination, if tolerant of this treatment, only when the goal is some vegetative product. Usually short-day plants are species which characteristically blossom in early spring and in late summer or autumn; violet, aster, chrysanthemum, coleus, cosmos, dahlia, garden balsam, potato, and late varieties of soybean are in this class.

Plants which flower over a considerable range of day lengths are classed as indeterminate, or neutral. Such plants may be expected to respond relatively more easily to the favorableness of several environmental factors. Included among indeterminate species are such cultivated forms as buckwheat, Connecticut broadleaf tobacco, cotton, tomato, and zinnia; dandelion is a weed belonging in this group.

Besides the influences of light referred to in this and the preceding section, there are many other direct and indirect effects, two of which will be briefly mentioned. Light promotes the development of anthocyan, the red pigment which characterizes many attractive "foliage" plants—the same product which appears seasonally (in spring and autumn) in the leaves of many shrubs and trees. The germination of various seeds is affected by light, some, such as bluegrass, favorably, others unfavorably, whereas still others are unaffected. In general, from the germination of a seed to the maturity of the plant, light may exert a many-sided influence on form, appearance, and growth.

Temperature. As the spring advances in temperate regions, vegetation becomes active, the leaves of trees unfold, seeds germinate, and with continuous rise in temperature from day to day—assuming other conditions to be favorable—growth is proportionately accelerated. Roughly stated, these processes continue to an extent and time determined by the inheritance of the species and usually manifested by the attainment of a stage in development which represents a certain degree of maturity (in annual plants) or at least a seasonal advance in stature. Hence temperature is an important factor influencing the early part of the grand period of annual growth. It may also hasten the stage of slowing-up, or maturity. However, all the facts are not so simply stated; the cotton plant, for example, may flower and fruit rather continuously as vigorous growth proceeds until less favorable conditions come into play.

Since growth is the resultant of a variety of processes, such as photosynthesis, absorption, transport of materials, metabolism, and assimilation, and since the character and rate of these processes determine the rate of growth, temperature controls or modifies the rate of growth by influencing the processes in question. In general, a rise in temperature, within limits, accelerates the rate of such processes, and a lowering of temperature depresses their rate. In fact, purely chemical changes in living tissues follow the rule that an increase of 10° C. (18° F.) commonly speeds up reactions two- or threefold, so that at 25° C. a chemical reaction, such as the digestion of starch, has a *temperature coefficient* of 2 to 3, as compared with the velocity of the same reaction at 15° C. Purely physical processes, such as the diffusion of carbon dioxide, may be accelerated only slightly with rise in temperature. Many processes appear to be dominated by chemical reactions, since temperature markedly affects their rates.

For growth as a whole and for all tissue activities there are temperature limits; there is an upper limit (maximum), a lower limit (minimum), and a more particularly favorable (optimum) range of temperature for growth. These are known as *cardinal temperatures*. Cardinal temperatures are not very precisely fixed; rather, they vary more or less depending upon the condition of the plant or organ as influenced by other external factors. For the germination of the seeds of wheat (of a variety not stated) it has been determined that the maximum, minimum, and optimum temperatures are respectively 42.5°, 5°, and 28.5° C. But these values are merely indicative; they are affected somewhat by such variables as the strain or variety of wheat and the maturity and water content of the seeds. The tolerance of either high or low temperatures by seeds increases as the water content decreases, provided the seeds withstand drying. The cardinal temperatures for growing plants also may be approximately determined, but here again the conditions under which the plants are grown will modify the values obtained.

"Hardiness" and "cold resistance" are terms much used in plant production; they refer either specifically to an inherent or induced frost resistance of late spring and early fall or to a general tolerance of winter cold. Both cultivated and wild species of plants display notable differences in cold resistance. Many varieties of cabbage and fall-blooming chrysanthemums are resistant to light frost, whereas tobacco, tomato, and nasturtium are comparatively sensitive. Many evergreen plants in full leaf, such as juniper and spruce, or even rhododendron and holly, withstand severe winter cold. With the gradual onset of the cooler weather of autumn and with the cessation of growth, they no doubt gradually become hardened to cold. However, if taken from rapidly growing conditions and plunged into midwinter temperatures, none would survive. Deciduous native forest trees, and fruit trees such as apple and peach, in northern latitudes usually pass a severe winter successfully, their buds being dormant and hardy. When the buds begin to unfold after successive warm days in spring, they become sensitive; and a sudden drop in temperature with frost may be fatal, or injurious in proportion to growth activity, the still dormant lower buds remaining unharmed. A vegetable- or flower-grower hardens his plants for early spring transplanting by exposing the seedlings for a time in cold frames. Nevertheless, not all species have the capacity to acquire significant hardiness, and such plants as do not harden are planted or transplanted only when the season is definitely favorable.

The internal factors of cold resistance and hardiness are apparently various; the salt concentration, the sugar content, the enzyme activity, and the state of the proteins have in certain cases shown a suggestive degree of correlation with hardiness, but for the most part the problem is undoubtedly a complicated one and one that is relatively little understood. Structural protection, as of leaf buds by leaf scales, is considered important and of value in the survival of the species. This is not because of direct protection against freezing, since with severe cold such buds may freeze repeatedly; but bud scales are regarded rather as a protection against loss of water during freezing and thawing. Most remarkable is the resistance of a few far northern or arctic species which come into flower while the weather is severely cold. It is reported that Cochlearia, a member of the mustard family, may endure temperatures as low as $-46°$ C. while in flower, growth being arrested for a time but development continuing with the return of warmer weather.

As a rule, injury of a growing plant by high temperature is associated with excessive transpiration and is therefore commonly a result of permanent wilting; locally it may result in the phenomenon called "scalding." One effect of an unfavorably high temperature during germination may be mentioned. If bean seeds are germinated at a high temperature, although it is not high enough to coagulate the usual proteins, the seedlings may nevertheless be injuriously affected; the injury is commonly interpreted as a result of the speeding-up of respiration to a rate which induces the formation of toxic by-products or which destroys enzyme systems to such an extent that injurious products are accumulated.

Irritability. The cytoplasm in a leaf cell of Elodea may be in motion at ordinary room temperature (p. 10). If the temperature is gradually raised, movement becomes more rapid, becoming most rapid at an optimum range around 37° C. If the temperature is raised beyond the optimum, movement becomes slower and finally ceases. If, on the other hand, a cell showing streaming at room temperature is cooled, the motion becomes gradually slower, until at about 0° C. it stops. It is evident that this form of cytoplasmic activity is influenced by an external condition, namely, temperature. All other forms of activity of living matter are likewise affected by this and by other external conditions and agencies. Any external condition or change in the quality or intensity of an external agent has been called a "stimulus." This word is rather loosely employed; thus an agency is a stimulus whether it acts more or less directly, as when a chemical substance is injected into a cell, or indirectly, as when a few scraping strokes with a pencil on one side of a tendril evoke a growth or turgor curvature which tends to bend the tendril toward the stimulating agent. The change in rate of movement induced in Elodea cells by temperature or the curvature induced by stroking is a *response*. The ultimate seat of a response is within the cells of the plant involved. Responses include changes of any nature in the activities of cells, of organs, or of the plant as a whole. Responses obviously involve chemical and physical changes; and whatever energy and food materials may be concerned—as in quickened movement or in growth—are the usual ones available to the protoplast. A stimulus is recognizable as a stimulus only if it produces a perceptible response. Practically, therefore, only those stimuli are treated as such which result in a response that can in some way be observed. The capacity to respond to a stimulus is *irritability*. This capacity is considered one of the fundamental characteristics of living protoplasm.

Characteristic Plant Movements. Although seed plants are commonly fixed in the soil and are not motile in the sense that higher animals are, nevertheless the organs of such plants do display movement. In recent years some of the more striking movements of the organs of growing plants have been popularized through motion-picture films, speeded up in presentation in order greatly to magnify the rate of the movements which regularly occur. Most spectacular usually are the movements of opening flowers and the changing positions of the supporting flower stalks. But stems and leaves, if photographed at successive intervals under the changing though favorable conditions of the usual twenty-four-hour daily cycle, display changes in position or in direction of growth which vary in character and extent with the plant or organ observed. In general, these movements or orientation phenomena are in large part induced through the action of external agencies (such as light, gravity, and mechanical shock) upon cell products and materials which in some way effect changes in rate of growth (often a differential in growth rate on the two sides of an organ) or in the state of turgor of the cells. In fact, two classes of movements of living plant organs are differentiated by the characteristics just stated. One of these classes includes all growth movements, or growth curvatures, characterized by the fact that the orientation reached is determined and fixed by growth, being irreversible unless modified by further growth. Movements of the other class, caused by significant changes in the turgor of certain cells or in the turgidity of supporting tissues, result only in the necessity that the organ shall temporarily assume a new position. In the latter case a full recovery of turgidity (involving a reversible change) restores the previous orientation.

Movements of yet another class are induced by the absorption or the loss of water. Alternate water absorption and water loss by the dead awns (hairlike appendages) of the seeds of a species of the grass Spartina cause a twisting and an untwisting of the awns which assist in burying the seeds. Drying-out of maturing organs is sometimes the immediate cause of an explosive type of movement splitting the pods and scattering the seeds, as in certain leguminous plants.

Growth Movements. Growth movements or curvatures may be grouped conveniently in three categories: *nutations*, *nastic movements*, and *tropisms*. Nutations require only brief description. A growing stem tip is not extended in a straight line; rather, it moves in a somewhat irregular spiral. In stems which are radially symmetrical, nutation results apparently from unequal growth rates. The effects are perhaps best accounted for by assuming unequal growth rates in different vertical levels away from the stem apex during any one interval of time or, what amounts to the same explanation, by assuming that successively around the stem each vertical segment grows for an interval at an accelerated rate. The extent of nutation is generally related to the rapidity of growth elongation; the movement is pronounced both in many twining plants and at certain stages in the growth of tendrils.

Nastic growth movements are especially characteristic of dorsiventral organs—organs, that is, with distinct upper and lower surfaces. The environmental agencies inducing the movement may act on all parts of the organ—that is, from all directions; or they may act chiefly from one side. Various external factors such as temperature and light may be concerned, or the factors may be internal. In a growing shoot the early development of a leaf in the bud is characterized by greater growth on and toward the under side, so that the leaf remains for a time within the active bud. Such accelerated growth on the under side is *hyponasty*. More rapid growth in the upper cell layers tending to dispose the leaf at a greater angle to the direction of growth of the axis, as in the stages of bud-unfolding, is *epinasty*. Appropriate treatment of the plant with a certain type of auxin (heteroauxin) usually emphasizes epinasty.

Phototropism. Growing in the open, unshaded by neighboring objects or other plants, an erect herb or tree receives, more or less nearly equally, both direct sunlight and the reflected light of the sky. The growth form of the plant resulting, so far as it is influenced by environmental factors, is essentially well balanced in the distribution of branches and the disposition of leaves. When exposed to unequal or one-sided illumination, not only does the plant as a whole eventually display greater growth on its side toward the source of light; in addition, certain young shoots display growth curvatures which tend to orient their apices in the direction of the incident light. The varying lengths and growth responses of the petioles of leaves are important in the orientation of the leaf blades, generally in such manner that the latter shield one another to a minimum extent. Leaves of a grapevine on a trellis or of ivy on a wall usually form a pattern appropriately called a leaf mosaic. Similar effects characterize many plants with conspicuous leaves. A leaf mosaic in the form of a rosette is shown in Figure 71.

These positions are commonly attained by the unequal growth rates of stems and petioles on opposite sides of each growing organ during this stage of development, the lesser illuminated side growing for the time more rapidly so that the new direction of growth is effected. To some extent, growing parts of leaves participate in the orientation of these organs. The leaves of house plants, such as the geranium, which are growing in a window change their positions so that the upper surface of each blade faces the source of light. That it is the blade rather than the petiole which perceives the light stimulus can be shown by wrapping the petiole of a young leaf of nasturtium or of begonia with tin foil so as to exclude all light and by covering in the same way the blade of a similar leaf whose petiole is left exposed. If the leaves so treated are now illuminated from one side, only the leaf with the exposed blade will respond by a curvature of its petiole.

It will be found that with most light intensities the stem axes of seedlings are with very few exceptions *positively phototropic*, the growth curvature being toward the source of light. Leaves are usually *transversely phototropic*. Some roots, such as those of certain members of the mustard family, are *negatively phototropic*, their curvature being away from the source of light. To determine the regions at which phototropic responses occur, the stems of young plants, as of sunflower or jewel weed, are placed in darkness for twenty-four hours. Then they are marked with India ink at intervals of four millimeters

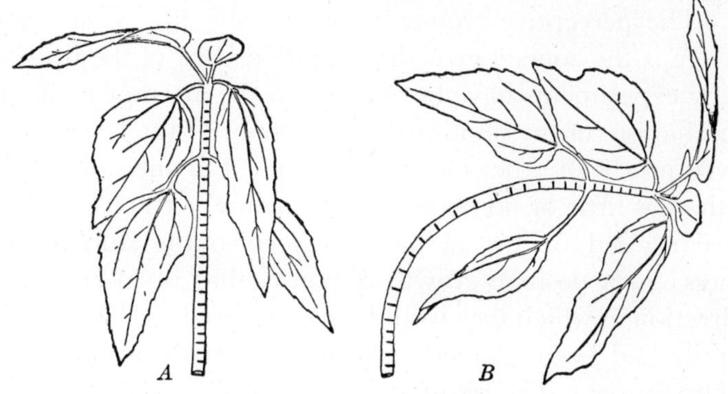

FIG. 129. *A*, part of a sunflower plant with its stem marked at equal intervals. *B*, the same plant after exposure to one-sided illumination. Bending occurs in the region of elongation.

(Fig. 129). Some of the plants are next so placed that they are illuminated from one side, while others are given the usual illumination. In a few hours the stems receiving light from one side only will show phototropic curvature, and by comparison with those receiving ordinary illumination it can be determined (by measuring the intervals between the marks) that the regions of curvature correspond with the regions where the greatest elongation regularly occurs.

Not all organs of plants are phototropically sensitive, and it is of interest that roots and rhizomes, which grow in darkness, usually show no reaction to light. However, sensitivity to light is in no way connected with the presence of chlorophyll, and it may be demonstrated that certain structures in fungi are particularly sensitive. Moreover, the motile forms of certain green algae in a vessel exposed to unilateral illumination orient themselves and *move* in the direction of the incident rays, within the limits of certain intensities and quality of light. Often such algae come to rest and accumulate on the side of the vessel toward the light source.

The classical material for the study of the mechanism of phototropism since the time of Darwin has been the coleoptile of the oat seedling. This structure, enveloping the unexpanded leaves like a sheath, is a conspicuous part of the young seedling. When the coleoptile of a seedling in the upright position is exposed for a requisite time interval (depending upon the light intensity) to one-sided illumination, there is a growth reaction whereby the organ displays a curvature orienting the tip in the direction of the source of light. The perceptive region is the extreme tip. The region of curvature is the zone of growth elongation back of the tip.

Many experiments have been made in the attempt to determine the mechanism of the phototropic reaction. If the coleoptile tip is removed just before the coleoptile is exposed to one-sided illumination, there is little or no phototropic response. Replacement of an exposed excised tip on an unexposed coleoptile stub results—in darkness—in a positive growth response, that is, in curvatures in the direction in which they would have occurred if the entire normal coleoptile had been exposed. An unexposed tip would not cause such curvatures. The results suggest that there is in the coleoptile tip a chemical substance which in unilateral light becomes unequally distributed; and this differential in concentration evokes a difference in growth rate on the two sides of the elongating coleoptile, since through diffusion downward the two sides receive different quantities of the substance.

Proof of the participation of a chemical agent, now known as an *auxin*, in the phototropic reaction was first furnished by very simple procedures. Coleoptile tips were placed on a thin layer of agar gel with the cut surfaces in contact with the agar so that diffusion and trapping of any substance penetrating the agar might occur. The agar was then cut into very small cubes. Each cube was placed on the cut end of a decapitated coleoptile and at one side so as to cover only a segment of the cut surface. After a suitable time interval growth curvatures resulted, the greater growth rate being on the side of the coleoptile capped with the agar cube. Hence the substance which diffused out of the coleoptile tip and was trapped in the agar passed into the tissue of the stub more abundantly on the side on which the agar cube was placed, causing a relatively increased rate of growth on that side and the resulting curvature. Later work has furnished many links in the chain of evidence connecting differential auxin concentration with differences in growth rate. Nevertheless, it does not follow that auxin is the only essential factor in light-growth relations. Light may induce growth-rate stimulation and depression which do not appear to be conditioned primarily by auxin concentration. It may be suggested, also, that the availability of foods and nutrients is among the factors necessarily modifying auxin relations and hence the rate and direction of growth of plant organs.

Effects of Gravity in Tropic Response. Gravity is an environmental factor which acts constantly in the same direction and with the same intensity at any point on the earth's surface. In general, stems tend to grow vertically upward, primary roots vertically downward, and branches of stem or root usually grow transversely or at widely varying angles to the direction of the force of gravity. The ability of plants or of their parts to respond in these various ways to internal changes induced by gravity is *geotropism.* Organs which respond to gravity by growing in the direction of this force—that is, toward the center of the earth—are *positively geotropic;* those which respond by growing away from the center of the earth are *negatively geotropic;* those which grow at right angles or obliquely to the direction of the force of gravity are *transversely geotropic.* To illustrate responses to gravity, seedlings of bean or corn whose roots and stems are a few centimeters long may be placed in a moist chamber, pinned to corks, with the stems and roots displaced from the vertical, hence at various angles to the direction of gravity. In a few hours or more, depending in considerable part upon the rate of growth, the stems will have developed a growth curvature which directs the growing tip upward, whereas a curvature in the opposite direction directs the primary root tip downward.

Geotropic curvatures arise, as do phototropic ones, in consequence of unequal growth rates on the two sides of the organ observed. In the case of geotropism the organs studied are generally displaced from the vertical, and it is the upper and the lower halves of the organ which display different growth rates. Recent results indicate that there is a corresponding differential in the auxin concentration in these tissues, the greater concentration being in the lower half. The unequal distribution of auxin is accordingly regarded as the stimulus which gravity brings into operation. With full understanding that the term "stimulus" may be vague and may seem out of place in referring to concentration relations of a chemical agent such as auxin, it is nevertheless convenient to continue the use of the term in this connection until much more is learned of the mechanism of auxin action. Applying to elongating stem tips in general the knowledge gained from a study of the oat coleoptile, it appears that when such organs are displaced from the vertical the increased auxin concentration on the lower side will induce on that side a more rapid growth rate than on the upper side, as a result of

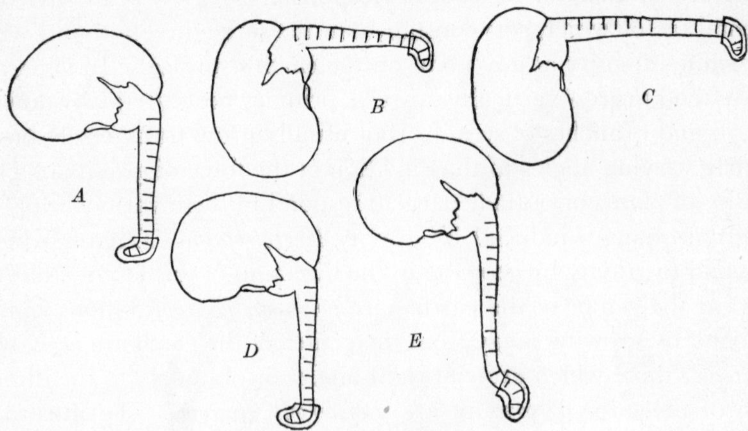

FIG. 130. A method of determining the perceptive region of a root by placing its tip in a glass slipper. *A*, the tip is bent at a right angle. *B*, the same root placed with its tip vertical. *C*, the same root after eighteen to twenty hours. *E*, curvature eighteen to twenty hours after a similar root is placed in position *D* with its tip horizontal.

which the stem tips bend upward. On the contrary, primary roots grow downward, which fact must mean that the more favorable auxin concentration for root growth is in the upper half of the displaced organ. For this apparent paradox the following explanation is considered valid: The root apex is more sensitive to auxin concentration than is the stem. The higher auxin concentration in the lower half of the root, therefore, depresses growth on that side, whereas the relatively lower concentration on the upper side promotes more rapid growth, and hence the curvature is downward.

In most roots ordinarily growing in soil, the part that is necessary for the perception of the effect of gravity appears to be chiefly the root tip, or meristematic region; the region of growth curvature, however, is back from the root tip, that is, in the part which was, during the response, the region of growth elongation. The location of the region of perception may be provisionally determined by cutting off the root tips of several young bean seedlings, which at that time should be growing vertically, at different distances (say 0.5, 1, 2, 3, and 5 mm.) from the extreme tips, then placing the seedlings horizontally in moist chambers for observation after twelve or twenty-four hours. It will be found that removal of what is approximately the major part of the meristematic region renders the root far less capable of carrying out a growth curvature. In this observation interest centers upon the least length of the tip whose removal notably decreases the curvature induced. It is obvious that no response can occur if decapitation of the root includes all the region in which growth elongation is already approaching completion.

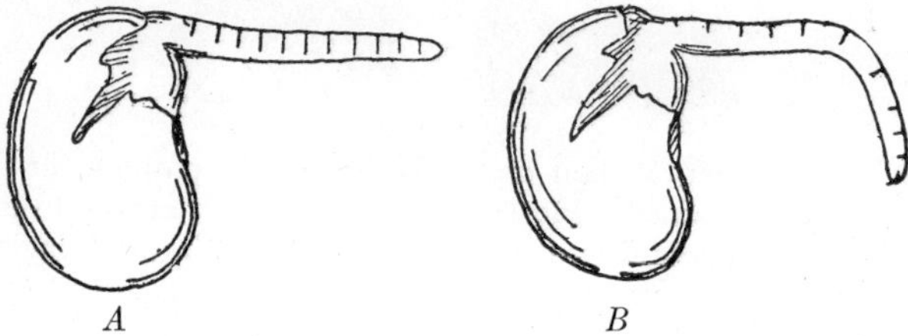

Fig. 131. *A*, bean seedling whose root has been marked at equal intervals and placed in a horizontal position. *B*, the same seedling twenty-four hours later.

The location of the responding portion can be determined by marking with India ink the primary root of a vigorous bean seedling at intervals of one millimeter and placing the seedling in a moist chamber with its root in a horizontal position (Fig. 131). After twenty-four hours it can be determined by measuring the distances between markings that the region of downward curvature corresponds with that of greatest elongation. Various experiments have shown that the region of perception and the region of response are distinct.

In the majority of stems both the perception of the stimulus of gravity and the response to this stimulus characterize the entire region of elongation. The location of the responding portion of a stem may be shown by marking with India ink sunflower or tomato stems at equal intervals and placing the plants parallel to the earth's surface. After a few hours it will be found that an upward curvature has occurred in the elongating internodes; the mature internodes show no response. However, in some stems geotropic response is not localized exclusively in the region of elongation. If a

Fig. 132. At the left, a plant of Iresine in upright position; at the right, a plant which has been turned on its side. The negative response to the stimulus of gravity consists in curvatures at the nodes as well as in the elongating region near the tip.

relatively mature stem of Iresine is placed in a horizontal position (Fig. 132), an upward curvature will occur at each of the younger nodes, as well as in the region near the tip where the internodes are elongating. If a similar experiment is performed with the stem of some grass, such as wheat, curvatures will occur only at the nodes. This is because of the delayed maturation of the nodal tissues.

To determine whether such changes in position of stem and root are geotropic responses, it is necessary to counteract the action of gravity as a stimulus and to observe the direction of growth under the new conditions. This can be done by rotating the plant slowly about a horizontal axis, thus constantly altering the plant's relation to gravity (Fig. 133). Gravity is now no longer operating as a one-sided stimulus. Under such conditions the stem does not grow vertically upward nor the primary root vertically downward, but these organs tend to grow horizontally—that is, in the directions in which they were placed when the experiment began.

Fig. 133. An apparatus (clinostat) for rotating plants slowly about a horizontal axis, constantly changing their relation to the direction of the stimulus of gravity.

In another experiment, first performed by Knight in 1805, the seedlings are placed on the rim of a horizontally revolving wheel (Fig. 134), and the wheel is rapidly rotated. The primary roots of the seedlings now grow diagonally downward and outward;

Fig. 134. Knight's experiment, in which the stimuli of both centrifugal force and gravity are acting upon stems and roots.

the stems grow upward and inward. The stems and roots are responding both to the stimulus of gravity and to that of centrifugal force.

It is impossible as yet to explain geotropic perception, that is, how auxin distribution is affected by gravity, as well as how the distribution of auxin is related to the "transmission of the stimulus" from the perceptive to the responsive portions of a root or stem. A complete explanation of the growth of roots, as in a root system, at all angles with the vertical is not yet available. It is well established, however, that roots grow more freely where the conditions are more favorable, so that the quantity and the direction of root growth may be largely influenced by such factors as moisture (Fig. 135) and

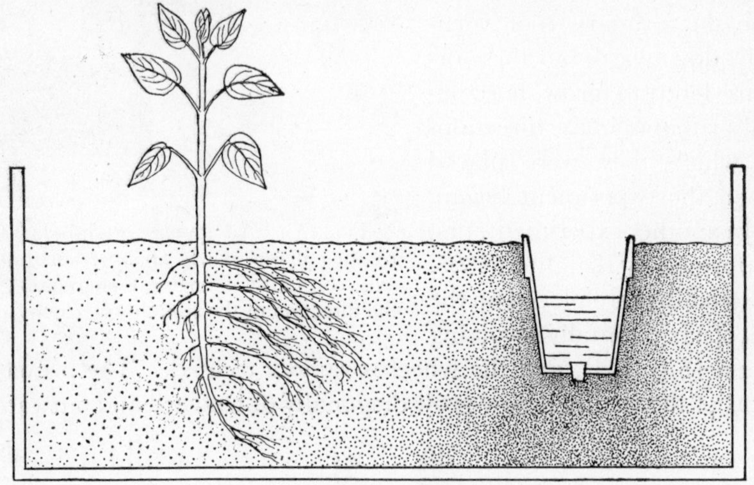

FIG. 135. Section of a box containing sand, with a plant near one end and a porous flower pot containing water near the other. The soil is moister near the pot, as indicated by the darker shading, and the unequal water content of the soil on different sides of the plant affects both the amount of growth and the direction of growth of the roots.

nutrient supply, oxygen tension, temperature, and a complex of conditions recognized as root "competition." Nevertheless, experimental evidence seems to indicate that geotropic curvature is influenced mainly by the production of auxins as growth-regulating substances and by their unequal distribution under the influence of gravity.

Turgor Movements. Growth movements, as indicated previously, are responses which result in lasting changes in the length, size, and number of cells, often in curvatures which persist; and such movements occur only in tissues capable of growth. Turgor movements, on the contrary, represent temporary changes in the turgor of certain cells, involving, therefore, changes in volume arising primarily from loss or gain of water. Since the turgor of the cells in a tissue is often a factor determining the support and the position of

FIG. 136. A sensitive plant (*Mimosa pudica*).

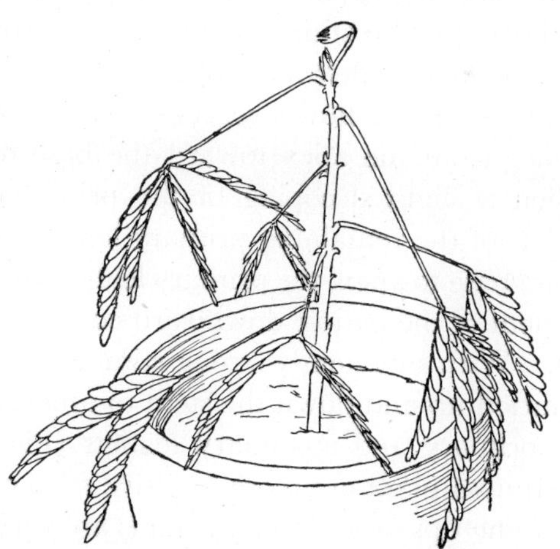

FIG. 137. A Mimosa plant after leaflets and leaves have responded to a contact stimulus.

an organ, it is clear that turgor changes may induce movement. With loss of water from a suitably located tissue, a new position of the organ may be assumed; and if water is again absorbed, the organ may return to its original position.

Among the movements arising through turgor changes are the well-known "sleep movements" of the leaves of species of clover and other plants, the rolling of the leaves of many grasses under conditions of water deficiency, and the very rapid movements which characterize the familiar sensitive plant, *Mimosa pudica*, a native of tropical South America. The reactions of plant organs to effects induced by the various external agencies thus far discussed are ordinarily visible only after the stimulus has been applied for some hours. The sensitive plant, however, is especially suitable for the study of the immediate responses of entire organs to stimulation, particularly by mechanical means such as a touch or a blow. The plant (Fig. 136) has an erect, thorny, more or less branched stem. The leaves have long petioles and are compound, each having two to four primary leaflets, which in turn bear numerous pairs of secondary leaflets.

If a single secondary leaflet of a Mimosa plant, under favorable conditions of light, moisture, and temperature, is touched very lightly, it reacts by a movement which sweeps the apex of this structure upward and slightly toward the tip of the primary leaflet on which it is borne; if the stimulus is somewhat stronger, one or more pairs of secondary leaflets may fold together. If the stimulus is still stronger, there may follow a successive closure of each pair of secondary leaflets from the apex toward the base of the primary leaflet, and then a slight drooping of the primary leaflet. The secondary leaflets of the remaining primary leaflets may then close successively from base to apex, the primary leaflets droop somewhat, and the movement of the petiole downward completes the droop of the whole leaf. With sufficiently strong stimulation, the influence may be transmitted up and down the stem to other leaves and outward to their primary and secondary leaflets (Fig. 137). Some portions of a Mimosa plant are more sensitive than others to a contact stimulus. The tips of secondary leaflets are very sensitive; but nearly all the epidermal cells of aerial organs, except parts of the flower cluster, are likewise sensitive.

Unless a certain pressure is applied when a leaflet is touched, no change occurs in its position—that is, a certain intensity of the stimulus is necessary in order to produce a visible response; the stimulus must be sufficiently intense to bring about whatever chemical or physical effects are essential to induce the changes in turgor later described.

The exact time interval between the application of a stimulus and the visible response can readily be determined. In Mimosa, the stimulus travels at the rate of from 8 to 20 mm. per second. The

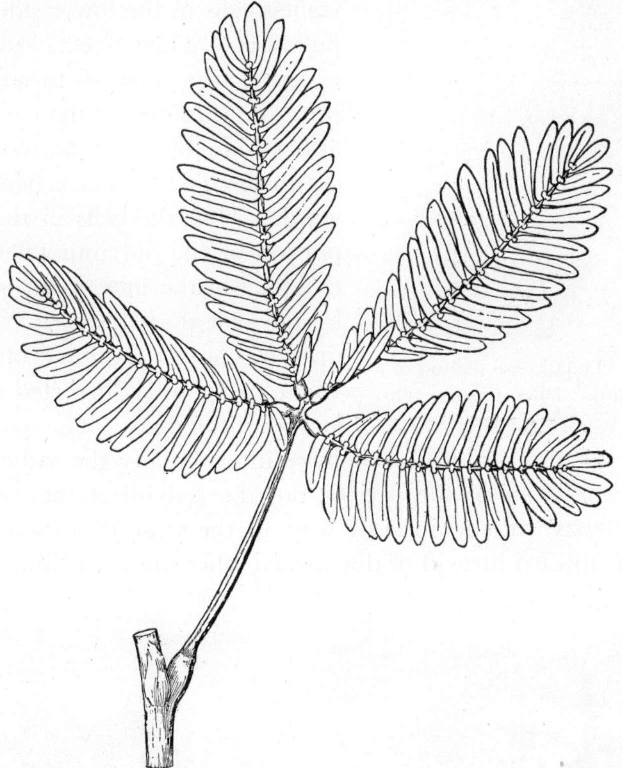

FIG. 138. Leaf of Mimosa, showing the swellings (pulvini) at the bases of the petiole and of each primary and secondary leaflet.

region in which the visible response occurs may be at a considerable distance from the region of perception of the stimulus. This visible response, which consists in a bending of a leaf or of a leaflet, is due to the action of a motor organ, the *pulvinus*. There is a pulvinus at the base of each secondary leaflet, one at the base of each primary leaflet, and one at the base of the petiole (Fig. 138).

Structure and Action of a Pulvinus. A *pulvinus* is an enlargement at the base of a leaflet or of a petiole (Fig. 138). In the center of each pulvinus (Fig. 139) is a strand of vascular tissue, surrounded by a cylinder of living, thin-walled cells; between these cells are fairly large intercellular spaces. When the effect of a stimulus has been transmitted to the pulvinus of the petiole, water exudes into the intercellular spaces from the thin-walled cells in the lower side of the pulvinus. These cells, therefore, experience a loss of turgor; and, since the turgidity of the cells in the upper side of the pulvinus is not diminished, the petiole is bent downward. That the cells in the upper portion of the pulvinus take an active part in the movement is shown by the fact that the petiole is bent upward against the force of gravity when the plant is inverted and the leaf is stimulated. The pulvini at the bases of primary leaflets behave in essentially the same way as does the pulvinus of the petiole, but the pulvini of the secondary leaflets behave in the opposite way, in the sense that these leaflets are bent upward instead of downward when they are stimulated.

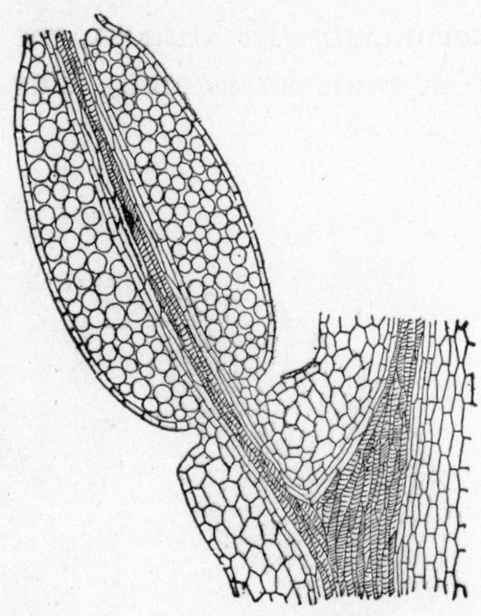

FIG. 139. Lengthwise section of a pulvinus. Diagrammatic.

FIG. 140. Oxalis plants. Leaves in their characteristic positions by day (*left*) and by night (*right*).

It is still uncertain exactly how the changes in permeability are brought about which result in a loss of water into the intercellular spaces from cells of a pulvinus. The stimulus will travel through a killed or girdled stem and is even transmitted through a severed stem if the two portions of the stem are connected by a glass tube filled with water. Some evidence suggests that the reaction is caused by a substance originating in the stimulated cells, which travels in the xylem from the stimulated region to the pulvinus and there brings about changes in permeability.

"Sleep Movements." The same visible responses on the part of leaves and leaflets of Mimosa may be produced by other agencies than contact. The change from light to darkness is a stimulus which causes the leaves and leaflets to change their positions. Leaves of many plants, including Mimosa and its relatives (peas, beans, alfalfa, clover, and other plants of the pea family) as well as some members of other families, change their positions in late afternoon or evening (Fig. 140), thus reacting to variations in the intensity of light. In the morning these leaves return to the expanded position. The changes of position at the approach of night are often called "sleep movements," although they bear no relation to the sleep of animals. Other plant parts may respond to alternations of light and darkness; the flowers of many plants close at night and open in the morning. Such movements of floral parts, al-

FIG. 141. Tulip flowers, open during the day (*left*) and closed at night (*right*).

though induced by changes in illumination, are influenced also by temperature. Tulip and dandelion flowers may remain closed even on bright days if the temperature is sufficiently low. In plant parts possessing pulvini, such as leaves and leaflets, the movements, as has been seen, are due to changes in the turgidity of certain cells. The movements of floral parts, however, often result from inequalities of growth on opposite sides. For example, the opening of the sepals and petals of a tulip (Fig. 141) is due to a greater growth on their inner than on their outer sides. In the closing of these floral parts, growth is greater on their outer than on their inner sides. In this case of the tulip and in other similar cases it would be logical to assume that unequal distribution of auxin is somehow effected.

CHAPTER X

NUCLEAR AND CELL DIVISION

Embryonic Cells. Mention has been made in earlier chapters of the divisions of cells which occur in certain parts of plants. In general, cells that are capable of division are *embryonic* cells. Whatever their later history, all plant cells when first formed are embryonic. As a rule, embryonic cells are substantially alike in structure; mature cells, on the contrary, differ greatly from one another in the respects that characterize fully developed tissues. The power of division is, however, the feature which especially distinguishes embryonic cells. Mature cells do not divide save in response to a special stimulus, such as a wound. A portion of any organ composed of embryonic cells is a *meristem.* In seed plants there is a meristem at the outer extremity of each indefinitely growing organ (stem, branch, or root). In gymnosperms and dicotyledons these regions are connected with one another by a cylindrical meristem, the cambium. Meristems occur in many other portions of plants as well; examples are the cork cambium and the portions of some leaves, such as those of Bryophyllum, that give rise to adventitious buds. The possession of such an extensive series of meristems, making possible an indefinite growth in size and the successive production of organs of a particular type, such as leaves, is one of the points which fundamentally distinguish the more complex plants from the more complex animals.

Significance of Cell Division. Cells increase in number only by the division of pre-existing cells. It follows that all the cells that exist upon the earth today, making up the bodies of plants and animals, have descended through a series of successive cell divisions from the cell or cells that first appeared upon this planet.

All that a cell *inherits* from its parent cell must be received by it in the course of the division of the parent cell. Since all that a plant or animal inherits was derived through the cell or cells that came from the parent, inheritance in many-celled organisms depends, just as does inheritance in individual cells, upon the transmission of substances from parent cell to daughter cell at the time of cell division.

Nuclear Division and Cell Division. The cells thus far discussed contain one nucleus each. Some cells will be described later that contain many nuclei; but the great majority of plants consist chiefly of one-nucleate cells. If a parent cell has one nucleus and if each daughter cell is likewise to possess a nucleus, a nucleus must be provided for each daughter cell. This is accomplished by the division of the nucleus of the parent cell. Nuclei, like cells, increase in number only by division. Always, therefore, in one-nucleate cells, nuclear division precedes, and usually immediately precedes, cell division. Indeed, nuclear and cell division are often brought about in part by the same mechanism, and the impression is likely to be gained that they are parts of a single process. That they are distinct processes, however, is obvious in many-nucleate cells, in which nuclear division and cell division may be far apart in time.

Early Stages in Nuclear Division. A favorable place for the study of nuclear and cell division is the meristem in a root tip (for example, of an onion) that has been killed, sectioned, and stained by the methods outlined in Chapter II.

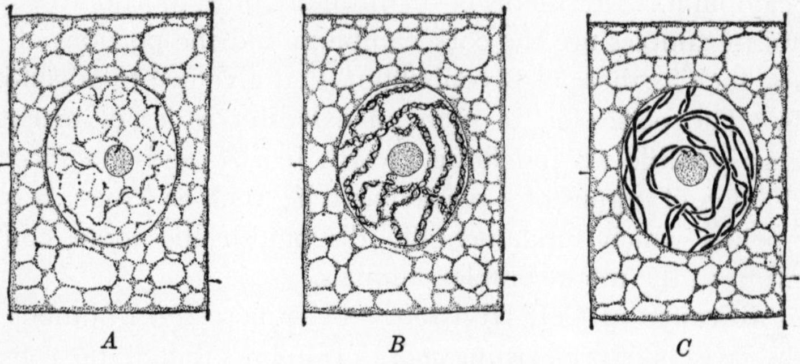

FIG. 142. Early stages in nuclear division. The chromatic strands are beginning to appear as chromosomes, each composed of two chromatids. Semi-diagrammatic.

When a nucleus is to divide, the chromatic strands shorten and thicken. Some of the earliest of these changes are shown in Figure 142, *A*. As the thickening continues, it becomes evident (Fig. 142, *B*) that a definite number of strands (*chromosomes*) are present.

Each chromosome consists essentially of two darkly stained *chromatids* spirally coiled about each other. At some stages the chromatids are surrounded by a more lightly stained matrix. At other stages (Fig. 142, *C*) the matrix is not visible. As each chromosome shortens further, its chromatids gradually uncoil and become more closely appressed (Fig. 143, *A*).

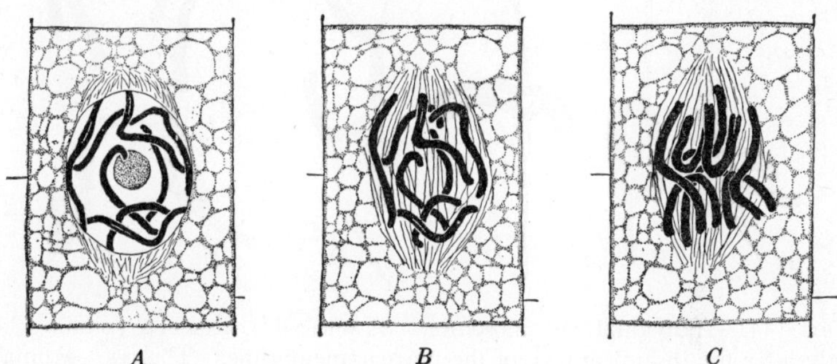

Fig. 143. Succeeding stages in nuclear division, leading (*C*) to the arrangement of the chromosomes in an equatorial plate. Semidiagrammatic.

In any particular kind of plant or animal, the number of chromosomes appearing in the course of nuclear division is constant, except for two special divisions to be described in Chapter XXV and except also as an occasional result of irregularities in the division process. The chromosome number in the common onion is 16; that is, 16 chromosomes regularly appear in a nucleus that is preparing to divide. In the corn the chromosome number is 20; in lilies, 24; in man, 48. Chromosome numbers that have been determined for other organisms vary from 2 to approximately 500.

The Spindle. While the chromosomes are undergoing the changes just described, fibers appear, at first in the cytoplasm (Fig. 143, *A*). The nuclear membrane, and usually the nucleolus or nucleoli, disappear; and the amount of fibrous material increases greatly. The structure constituted by the fibers is called, because of its form, a *spindle*. Some of the fibers run from one end (*pole*) of the spindle to the opposite end. In addition, from a definite point on each chromatid a fiber or group of fibers extends to one spindle pole; and from the corresponding point on the other chromatid of the same chromosome a fiber or group of fibers extends to the opposite spindle pole (Fig. 144, *B*). The movements which the chromosomes and their constituent chromatids are to undergo appear to be caused by contractions of the attached fibers. The spindle now being completed, each chromosome moves so that the points of

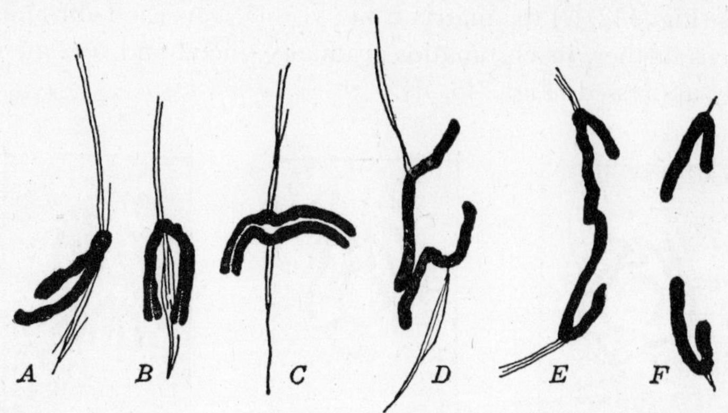

Fig. 144. Individual chromosomes. *A*, one with attached spindle fibers, shortly after the disappearance of the nuclear membrane. The two chromatids are often not apparent at this stage. *B*, chromosome in the equatorial plate. *C*, beginning of the separation of chromatids, from this time on called *daughter chromosomes*. *D*, *E*, later stages in separation. *F*, daughter chromosomes approaching the spindle poles.

spindle-fiber attachment to its chromatids lie about halfway between the poles of the spindle (Fig. 143, *C*). The stage now reached is that of the *equatorial plate*.

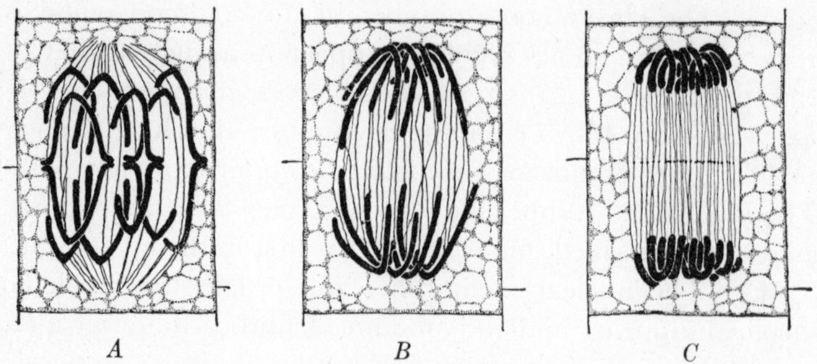

Fig. 145. Completion of nuclear division. A swelling at the midpoint of each spindle fiber (shown in *C*) indicates the beginning of cell-plate formation. Semidiagrammatic.

Separation of Daughter Chromosomes. Next, the two chromatids of each chromosome separate, one moving toward each spindle pole (Figs. 144, 145). The chromatids, finally to be completely separated, are now *daughter chromosomes.* If, as in the onion, there were 16 parent chromosomes, there are now two groups, each of 16 daughter chromosomes. If spindle fibers are attached to the middle of a daughter chromosome, that chromosome as it moves toward the pole becomes V-shaped, the point of the V being directed toward the pole. If fibers are attached near the end of a daughter chromosome, the chromosome becomes J-shaped.

Organization of Daughter Nuclei. The daughter chromosomes ultimately reach the spindle poles. Since the two chromatids of each parent chromosome were exactly alike, the two groups of daughter chromosomes are alike. About each group a nuclear membrane appears; there are now two *daughter nuclei,* each containing nuclear sap and newly formed nucleoli. The chromosomes in each daughter nucleus spread apart and elongate somewhat, and each is now seen to possess two chromatids (Fig. 146, *A*). At some

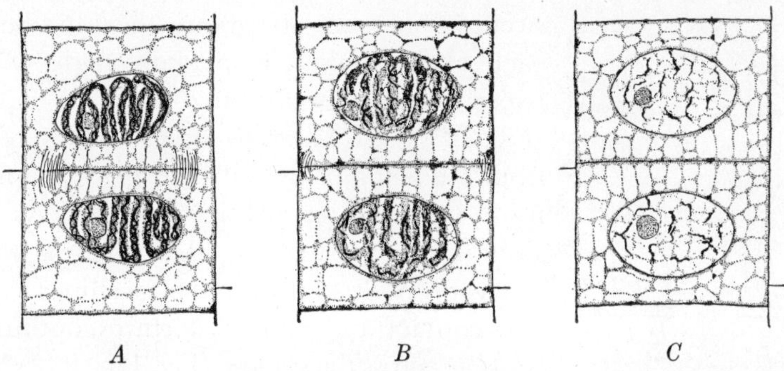

FIG. 146. Organization of daughter nuclei, and completion of cell division. In *C* the nuclei are approaching the resting condition. Semidiagrammatic.

time during the process of nuclear division a duplication of the chromatids has occurred. This duplication has been explained by a lengthwise splitting of each chromatid, but it is questionable whether the process is as simple as a mere splitting.

Since each chromosome is composed of two chromatids at the conclusion of a division and each chromosome is similarly constituted when preparation for the next division begins, it appears that the double condition must persist through the *resting period* that intervenes. The duplication of the chromatids during one division is a preparation for the division of chromosomes that will occur in the next division.

After the appearance of new nuclear membranes, the daughter nuclei grow (Fig. 146, *B*), and eventually each attains about the size that characterized the parent nucleus. During this period of growth, the chromosomes become elongated, their substance stains less deeply, and the distributed condition characteristic of resting nuclei (Fig. 146, *C*) is reached. Either during the organization of daughter nuclei or during the resting stages that follow, the chromosome substance increases in amount. This is evident from the fact that the chromosomes which appear in the division of any nucleus are ordinarily of about the same size as those present in preceding divisions. If there were no increase in their substance, the chromosomes, being halved in each division, would become progressively smaller in successive cell generations.

Cell Division in Higher Plants. At about the time that the groups of daughter chromosomes reach the respective poles, the fibers connecting the poles begin to appear more numerous. A swelling appears at about the middle of each fiber—that is, in a plane midway between the newly forming daughter nuclei (Fig. 145, *C*). These swellings seem to result from a flowing of the substance of each fiber from its ends toward its middle. As the swellings grow, since the fibers bearing them are very close together, the swellings come into contact and unite to form a continuous *cell plate* across the spindle (Fig. 146, *A*). New fibers are formed at the sides of the spindle, beyond the fibers already present; swellings appear on these new fibers, grow, and unite with the cell plate. In this way the plate is extended outward until it reaches entirely across the cell (Fig. 146, *B*). The portions of the spindle fibers which were not used in the formation of the cell plate eventually disappear.

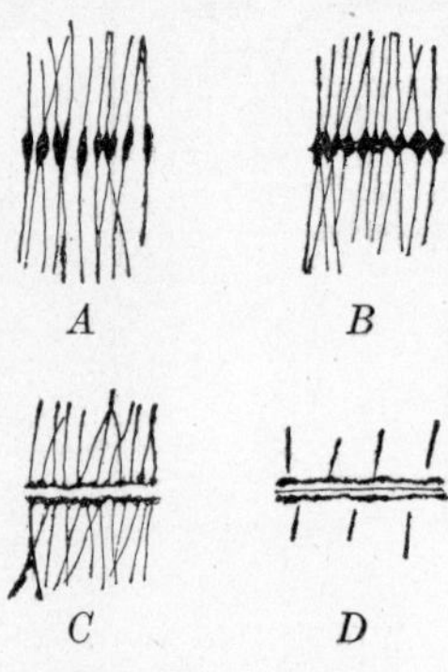

Fig. 147. Much-enlarged views of spindle fibers and of cell-plate formation. *A*, swellings appear on the fibers. *B*, the swellings unite to form a continuous cell plate. *C*, the cell plate splits. *D*, a wall is secreted between the new plasma membranes.

It must be remembered that the cell plate is composed of living matter derived from the fibers of the spindle. After its growth is complete, the cell plate splits into two layers (Fig. 147). Each of these layers, becoming continuous with portions of the old plasma membrane, forms part of the plasma membrane of the corresponding daughter cell. Cell division is now accomplished, for there are two distinct daughter cells, each surrounded by a continuous membrane.

A thin cell wall is next secreted between the newly formed plasma membranes of the daughter cells. In the secretion of the material of the new wall, the living matter of both daughter cells takes part. The new wall, at this time very thin, joins at its outer edges the old wall of the parent cell. It has been seen (p. 13) that if a daughter cell does not divide but instead develops into a mature cell, additional layers of wall material may be deposited upon either side of the original wall, which will then remain as the middle layer of the mature cell wall.

Other Methods of Cell Division. The method of nuclear division that has been described obtains (with some differences in detail) in the cells of all plants and animals that possess nuclei. Nuclei, it is true, occasionally divide by a more direct method, a parent nucleus being simply constricted so as to form two or more daughter nuclei; but divisions of this sort seem to occur only in cells which are

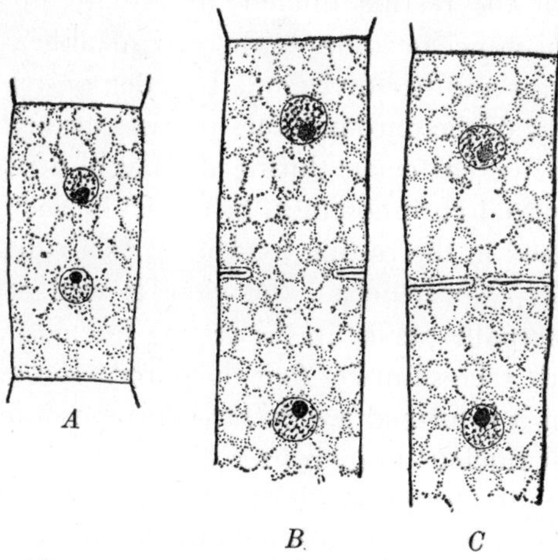

Fig. 148. Cell division by constriction in a fungus. *A*, nuclear division is completed. *B*, a ringlike furrow appears in the plasma membrane; in the furrow a new cell wall is secreted. *C*, cell division is nearly completed. Redrawn from Harper.

destined soon to die or which at any rate are not capable of giving rise to new plants or animals. Cell division, on the other hand, is brought about in different cases by several very different methods.

Division by means of a cell plate occurs almost universally in the more complex plants. The other very common method of cell division is by *constriction* (Fig. 148).

Division by constriction occurs in animals, in many simple plants, and in certain cases (the formation of spores) in some more complex plants. In these cases, cell division (following nuclear division) begins with the development of a furrow or groove in the plasma membrane. This furrow deepens until it has cut entirely through the cell, and finally the furrowing results in the formation of two distinct plasma membranes for the respective daughter cells. If the parent cell is surrounded by a wall, new wall material is secreted within the furrow as the latter deepens. At the conclusion of the process a completed wall lies between the two separate membranes. Two other methods of cell division will be mentioned (pp. 331, 350) in the discussion of the plants of certain groups in which these types of division occur.

Persistence of Chromosomes. The study of nuclear division shows that the chromosomes pass into the distributed condition characteristic of the resting nucleus and that, after a period of growth, their substance becomes again recognizable as chromosomes in preparation for another division. It is demonstrated, therefore, that the *substance* of the chromosomes persists throughout the series of cell generations that occur during the life of a plant. In some cases the individual chromosomes, or a part of each chromosome, can be recognized in the resting nucleus. As a rule, however, this is not the case. Nevertheless, the view is well established that chromosomes actually persist in the resting nucleus, although their form is changed. This implies that the chromosomes that pass into a nucleus when it is formed are *the same* chromosomes that will appear when that nucleus prepares for division. The conception of the persistence of chromosomes as definite structures from cell generation to cell generation throughout the life of a plant (or animal) is based largely upon the following facts:

(*a*) Whatever may be the number of chromosomes passing into a nucleus when it is formed, the same number reappears when that nucleus prepares to divide.

(*b*) The chromosomes which appear in a nucleus in preparation for division are observed to occupy about the same positions that were occupied by the chromosomes which went to form the nucleus.

(*c*) The chromosomes which pass to a daughter nucleus often differ from one another in form and size, and the same differences in form and size appear between the chromosomes of that nucleus when it in turn divides.

Nuclear Division and Inheritance. It has been noted that the inheritance of parental qualities must depend upon the transmission, in the course of cell division, of some definite substance or substances from parent cell to daughter cells. The study of the processes of division shows that, whereas nuclear division brings about with great precision the division of certain structures (chromosomes) into equal parts, the cell division that follows does not divide with any precision the structures in the cytoplasm. This striking difference between the methods by which nucleus and cytoplasm respectively are divided led to the suggestion by Strasburger and by Hertwig, in 1884, that nuclear substances are particularly concerned with the transmission of hereditary characters. The suggestion is supported by the fact that the elaborate and lengthy process of *nuclear division* that has been described is universal or nearly so in nucleated cells that are concerned with hereditary transmission, whereas *cell division* is brought about by very different means in different groups of organisms. Of the structures in the nucleus, only the chromosomes are accurately divided and are persistent; the other nuclear substances—nucleoli and nuclear sap—as well as the nuclear membrane, are temporary, appear at certain times and disappear at others, and are not divided between the daughter nuclei. The conception that chromosomes are the structures chiefly concerned in inheritance has been confirmed by such a mass of evidence, direct and indirect, that it is now generally accepted as fundamental. Much of the same evidence that supports this idea of the function of chromosomes in inheritance indicates also that the individual chromosomes of a nucleus play different rôles. Each chromosome seems to represent a definite fraction of the whole hereditary endowment of the plant or animal. It must be emphasized that the cytoplasm also is important in inheritance, but its function seems to be in general subject to control by substances contained in the chromosomes.

Cell Division, Growth, and Reproduction. The increase in amount of chromosome substance already referred to is one of the processes included under the term *growth.* Evidently the living portions of the cytoplasm must likewise increase in amount in the interval between successive cell divisions; otherwise the amount of living cytoplasm in each cell would steadily diminish from cell generation to cell generation. This growth of the living matter in both cytoplasm and nucleus is a process that especially distinguishes living from nonliving matter. Its occurrence means that living matter has the power of bringing about or inducing the formation of new matter precisely like itself—a power that is not known to be possessed under any conditions by any form of nonliving matter.

Cell division increases the number of cells; that is, it is a process of *reproduction.* Division is the means by which cells reproduce; and all forms of reproduction of many-celled organisms are made possible by cell division. Cell division, and therefore all reproduction, are evidently dependent upon a preceding growth of the living matter within the cell.

At the moment when a cell division is completed, the daughter cells together are no larger than was the parent cell just before its division. Cell division in itself, therefore, does not bring about growth of a plant. But there is a definite relation between cell division and growth, because a cell of any particular tissue can enlarge only to about a certain size. If the plant were composed of a fixed number of cells, therefore, its size would be definitely limited. If, however, some cells remain capable of division, the number of cells may steadily increase and, since each new cell has a certain power of enlargement, the plant as a whole may grow. Hence, growth in size of a many-celled plant depends upon the division (that is, the reproduction) of its cells, which division in turn is dependent upon the growth of the living matter of the cells.

CHAPTER XI

THE CLASSIFICATION OF PLANTS

The Names of Plants. In preceding chapters plants have been considered from the points of view of structure and function. So far as extant records show, the first extensive study of plants from these standpoints was by Theophrastus of Eresus (who lived about 370–285 B.C.), the most important botanist of antiquity. But long before his day it had been recognized that plants were of different kinds, and to each kind (which would now be called a *species*) of familiar plant a name was given. Since the differences between species were sometimes great, sometimes small, it was natural to place similar species together in larger groups such as are now called *genera*. Dioscorides (first century A.D.), a Greek physician, compiled a list of about 500 kinds of plants, chiefly those used in medicine. He placed different kinds together into relatively large groups somewhat like present-day *families*. Among Roman compilers of lists of plants the most influential was Pliny the Elder (23–79 A.D.). Of the 37 books of his "Natural History," 16 deal with plants and their uses.

With the revival of learning in the early Middle Ages, the scholars of western Europe attempted to use the descriptions of Dioscorides and of Pliny in identifying the plants they met with. Although Euricius Cordus (1486–1535) pointed out that the plants of central Europe were not likely to be the same as those described by Greek and Latin writers, and although his greater son Valerius Cordus (1515–1544) discovered and accurately described several hundred new species, their better-known contemporaries, the Herbalists, continued to borrow extensively from the ancient writers.

In general, a genus was given a name which was a single word; as *Pinus* (pine), *Quercus* (oak). The species was designated by an adjective, by two or more adjectives, or by a more lengthy phrase, appended to the generic name. Often the same designation was applied by different persons to the same species, and very frequently the same plant bore different names in different regions. Thus, confusion reigned until the Swedish botanist Linnaeus (1707–1778) prepared careful Latin descriptions for all plants known to him and gave to each a name composed of two words: one (a noun, commonly from a Greek root) for the genus, the other (a descriptive adjective, usually Latin) for the species. This *binomial system* of nomenclature was not new with Linnaeus, but he was the first to apply it systematically and universally. It has been generally used ever since his time, because it provides for each plant a name that is recognized in all parts of the world, however many colloquial terms may be applied to that plant in various localities.

The confusion that has existed in plant nomenclature is illustrated by the names given at different times and in different regions to the species of flax that is cultivated in many parts of the world for its seeds and fibers. This plant, which had been grown in Egypt and southwestern Asia for some thousands of years when Dioscorides wrote, was called by him *Linon.* He cited also the Latinized form of the same word, *Linum*, from which come our words *linen* and *linseed.* Dioscorides quoted also other names used in various localities, such as *Linocalamis*, *Linomyrum*, *Anion*, and *Zeraphis.* Bock in 1552 called it *Linum Germanicum*, noting as other names in use *Linum agreste*, *Linum domesticum*, *Linum urbanum*, and *Linocalamum.* Bauhin in 1620 called it *Linum arvense.* In the Hortus Cliffortianus of 1737 it was designated as *Linum ramis foliisque alternis lineari-lanceolatis, radice annua.* Linnaeus in 1753 gave it the name *Linum usitatissimum* ("the most useful flax"), and this name has since been used by botanists.

Among the common names now in use for this plant in various localities are *lin* and *manouse* in France; *Lein*, *Flachs*, *Ackerlein*, and *Möwenölpflanze* in Germany; *flaechs*, *flas*, *lijn*, and *vlas* in the Netherlands.

Of about 200 species referred to the same genus, one, since it has yellow flowers, is called *Linum flavum;* one is named *Linum grandiflorum* from its large flowers; and another, *Linum perenne* because of its perennial habit of growth.

Systems of Classification. Generally speaking, the earlier attempts at classification were based upon a few arbitrarily selected characters. In one of the earliest of these *artificial* systems plants were grouped according to the nature of their stems and branches as trees, shrubs, and herbs. Theophrastus recognized these groups and distinguished also annual, biennial, and perennial plants. In the artificial "sexual" system devised by Linnaeus, the bases of classification for seed plants were chiefly the numbers and arrangement of floral parts, particularly of stamens and pistils. The *natural* systems devised by later workers, and those used at present, depend upon a comparison of all the conspicuous structures of plants. Such a system attempts to indicate actual relationships.

Those individual plants which are alike in all or most of their structural and functional characters constitute a *species.* Species are the fundamental units. Different species which resemble one another closely are grouped together as a *genus*. Sometimes a genus includes but one species; more commonly it consists of several or many. Just as species are combined into genera, so genera in turn are grouped in a larger unit, a *family*. Families in their turn are grouped in an *order*, orders in a *class*, and classes in a *division.*

Bases for a Natural Classification. All systems attempting to classify plants according to their natural relationships are based upon the view that plants now living on the earth have descended from pre-existing plants. A discussion of the reasons for this view will be found in Chapter XXXIV.

All available evidence indicates that the organisms which first appeared upon the earth were one-celled and that they lived in bodies of water. While these primitive organisms disappeared long ago, there are still many one-celled forms. Some one-celled organisms now living are certainly very different from their early ancestors, but others seem to possess relatively primitive characteristics. The very first organisms, if they still existed, could not be classed as either plants or animals. The same may be said of many simple forms now living. Among one-celled organisms appeared some which, possessing chlorophyll and a cell wall, gave rise to those which are classed as plants. Others, lacking a cell wall and lacking or having lost chlorophyll, became ancestors of what are known as animals.

Many one-celled plantlike organisms formed, and many still form, temporary associations known as *colonies*. Others acquired the habit of remaining together in permanent colonies. In some persistently colonial species, as will appear in later chapters, a division of labor arose between different groups of cells; and these groups of cells became differentiated in ways that better fitted them to perform their particular functions. In this way tissues and organs appeared. In the course of time, the habitation of some plants was changed from water to land. Life on land presented new conditions, the adaptation to which led to greater specialization of structures already present, as well as to the development of new tissues and organs. Hence, speaking very generally, the more complex and more highly specialized plants live on land; the simpler ones, broadly speaking, inhabit the water.

The evolution of plants might be represented by a group of lines which branch early and whose branches themselves branch repeatedly. If all the plants that have lived were fully known, their relationships could perhaps be shown by a set of diagrams each having the form of a much-branched tree. The bases of these genealogical trees would be among the primitive one-celled forms, among which the genealogical trees of animals also arise; their highest branches would represent plants with the greatest complexity of structure. The branches would tend in all directions, including downward, since plants may evolve from a complex to a less complex organization. The information available for the construction of such a diagram concerns chiefly the tips of branches, represented by plants now living. The problem of constructing a complete evolutionary diagram on the basis of branch tips has been compared to that of determining the direction and position of the major branches of a tree so buried in a sand dune that only the tips of its branches are exposed. In reconstructing the genealogical trees of the plant kingdom, four main lines of evidence are used to establish evolutionary relationships. These are: (*a*) evidence from comparison of vegetative structures; (*b*) evidence from comparison of reproductive structures; (*c*) evidence from comparison of present-day plants with ancient (fossil) plants; and (*d*) evidence from the geographic distribution of plants now living. In any such genealogical tree the forkings of the trunk represent the divisions in a natural system of classification; the primary branches represent the classes; the secondary branches, the orders; and the twigs, the families.

Outlines of a Classification. Evaluation of the fundamental importance of characteristic features of major groups of plants is to some extent a matter of opinion. For example, some would place the ferns, other pteridophytes, and seed plants in a single division because all have vascular tissues (xylem and phloem); more would place ferns and other pteridophytes in a division (Pteridophyta) distinct from that of the seed plants (Spermatophyta). In some systems of classification the plants here grouped as Thallophyta are separated into a considerable number of divisions.

According to one widely used system of classification, which will be followed in succeeding chapters, all plants are distributed among the following four divisions:

Thallophyta, plants of relatively simple structure, not having stem, leaves, or roots like those of most ferns and seed plants. Reproductive organs also are simple in structure. The Thallophyta include two subdivisions, *Algae* and *Fungi*. Typically, algae, which include "pond scums" and other mostly small plants of fresh water and many larger "sea weeds" of the oceans, possess chlorophyll and can manufacture carbohydrates. Fungi, including bacteria, molds, and mushrooms, lack chlorophyll and must obtain carbohydrates, and often other foods as well, from external sources.

Bryophyta (Liverworts and Mosses). Members of this division lack vascular tissues. In some, the structure of the plant body is as simple as is that of many thallophytes; others are differentiated into stem and leaves. Bryophytes characteristically have many-celled reproductive organs, the outer layer of cells of each organ being sterile.

Pteridophyta (including Ferns, Horsetails, and Club Mosses). Members of this division possess vascular tissues. Pteridophytes have many-celled reproductive organs similar to those of bryophytes.

Spermatophyta (Seed Plants). Members of this division possess vascular tissues, form pollen tubes, and produce seeds.

In the chapters that follow, one or more representatives of the various classes of each division will be discussed. The representatives selected will be taken up as nearly as possible in their evolutionary order; that is, following the simpler forms, others will be considered in the order of their increasing complexity. Such a selected series of types may show the *general course* of evolution in the plant kingdom, but it can not show the detailed history of the evolution of any one species or genus.

The relationships one to another of the plant groups to be discussed are indicated in the following table. This table must not be considered a complete classification of the plant kingdom, since a few small classes of living plants and some classes of fossil plants are not included.

Division **THALLOPHYTA**
- Subdivision **Algae**
  - Class Chlorophyceae (green algae)
  - Class Myxophyceae (blue-green algae)
  - Class Phaeophyceae (brown algae)
  - Class Bacillariophyceae (diatoms)
  - Class Rhodophyceae (red algae)
- Subdivision **Fungi**
  - Class Schizomycetes (bacteria)
  - Class Myxomycetes (slime molds)
  - Class Phycomycetes (algal fungi)
  - Class Ascomycetes (sac fungi)
  - Class Basidiomycetes (club fungi)
  - Class Lichenes (lichens)

Division **BRYOPHYTA**
  - Class Hepaticae (liverworts)
  - Class Musci (mosses)

Division **PTERIDOPHYTA**
  - Class Psilophytineae (psilophytes)
  - Class Filicineae (ferns)
  - Class Equisetineae (horsetails)
  - Class Lycopodineae (club mosses)

Division **SPERMATOPHYTA**
- Subdivision **Gymnospermae** (gymnosperms)
- Subdivision **Angiospermae** (flowering plants)
  - Class Dicotyledoneae (dicotyledons)
  - Class Monocotyledoneae (monocotyledons)

CHAPTER XII

CHLOROPHYCEAE (GREEN ALGAE)

Nature. The Chlorophyceae are commonly green, their plastids (chloroplasts) containing the pigments chlorophyll *a*, chlorophyll *b*, carotene, and xanthophyll. Their carbohydrate food is usually stored in the form of starch. At some time in their life cycle most of the green algae produce motile cells, whose movement is brought about by slender threadlike structures (*flagella*). Flagellated cells are produced also by brown algae but not by blue-green nor by red algae. The plant body of a green alga may be a single cell or may be many-celled. In the latter case the plant body is usually simpler in construction than is that of a red or a brown alga.

Distribution. Green algae, like other algae, are primarily aquatic and are widely distributed in both fresh and salt waters. Fresh-water members of the Chlorophyceae occur in streams, lakes, and ponds. Some species grow attached to rocks and débris, some to larger plants. Others are unattached and constitute much of the plant portion of the free-floating population of microscopic organisms known as the *plankton*. At times the plankton algae of lakes and ponds are so numerous as to make the water appear colored. Green algae may grow also in places other than permanent bodies of water. They occur, for instance, in temporary ponds, on moist rocky cliffs, and on the shaded sides of trees and rocks. They grow on and in damp soils, where they sometimes develop so luxuriantly as to form a distinct green layer. Certain species can live and multiply under conditions ordinarily thought of as unfavorable for the growth of plants. Examples of this nature are the species of Chlorophyceae living in brine lakes with a salt content of 15 to 30 per cent and the species which grow in semipermanent snow fields of arctic regions or of high mountains. Algae of the latter type may be so abundant as to cause a green or a red coloration of the snow.

Many marine species live chiefly in shallow water along ocean shores, often being attached to rocks at levels that are exposed at low tide. Some attached forms, however, occur where the water is as much as 300 feet in depth.

The motile one-celled green algae are the most nearly primitive of the Chlorophyceae. More advanced forms have immobile cells that are either solitary or united end to end into filaments or side by side into platelike masses. In progressing from the more primitive to the more advanced Chlorophyceae, there is also a greater differentiation of certain reproductive cells (gametes). The Chlorophyceae to be described on succeeding pages are arranged approximately in order of their increasing complexity, either in structure or in methods of reproduction; but it must be borne in mind that the forms selected show only the general course of evolution within the class.

CHLAMYDOMONAS

Structure. *Chlamydomonas* is representative of the more primitive one-celled Chlorophyceae which are motile during a considerable portion of their existence. It occurs in ditches, pools, and lakes, or on moist soil. Sometimes it is found in such quantity that the water appears green.

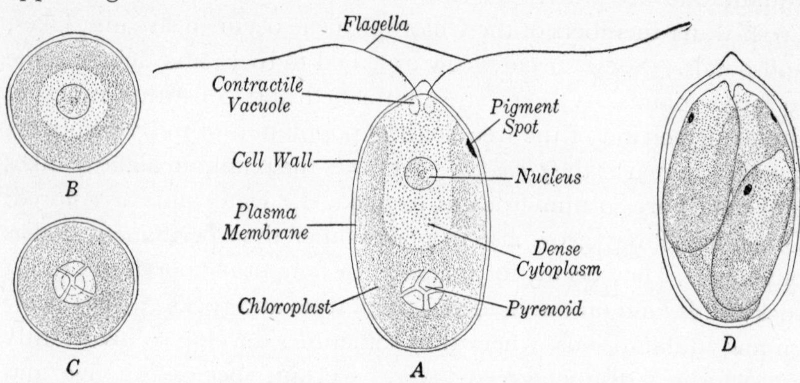

FIG. 149. Chlamydomonas. *A*, motile cell. *B*, cross section of a cell at the level of the nucleus. *C*, cross section at the level of the pyrenoid. *D*, four-celled colony enclosed by the parent-cell wall.

A cell of Chlamydomonas (Fig. 149) is typically egg-shaped. Like other cells that have been studied, it has a wall containing cellulose. The most conspicuous portion of the protoplasm is the chloroplast. Each green cell in a leaf of Elodea or of any other seed plant contains many chloroplasts; a Chlamydomonas cell has but one. This chloroplast, however, is large and very different in shape from the small, rounded chloroplasts that have been described. Its form is that of a cup with a very thick bottom. As in other cells, the film of cytoplasm just within the wall is the plasma membrane. The chloroplast lies next within the plasma membrane. Imbedded in the thicker, posterior portion of the chloroplast is a small, colorless, spherical *pyrenoid*. The pyrenoid is a specialized portion of the chloroplast whose particular function is starch formation. Treatment of the cell with iodine shows the presence of minute, variously shaped starch granules surrounding the pyrenoid. In fact, it is usually the zone of starch granules about the pyrenoid that is seen in a living cell, rather than the pyrenoid itself. The cell has no central vacuole, the region partially enclosed by the cup-shaped chloroplast being occupied by dense cytoplasm in which lies a small nucleus. It is noteworthy that the nucleus of Chlamydomonas is similar, except for size, to a nucleus of one of the more complex plants. It has a membrane, nuclear sap, a nucleolus, and chromatic strands.

At the anterior end of the cell, two fine, threadlike extrusions of cytoplasm called *flagella* extend through the cell wall. Flagella are motile organs which, by lashing backward and forward, propel the cell through the water. The movement of the cell is not haphazard but is a definitely directed response to stimuli. One stimulus largely affecting its movement is light, and the mechanism for the reception of light stimuli is localized in a small orange-red *pigment spot* near the anterior end of the cell. The effect of the light stimulus, received by the pigment spot, is transmitted to the flagella, causing them to move the cell in a definite direction. The response is usually positive, the cell swimming toward the light. If, however, the intensity of the light stimulus passes a certain point, the response is negative—that is, the plant swims away from the light. These responses can be shown by placing a dish containing many Chlamydomonas cells so that it is illuminated from only one side. In light of moderate intensity the cells collect as a green mass on the side of the dish toward the light (a positive response); but when placed in direct sunlight, they frequently collect on the side away from the light (a negative response).

In the dense cytoplasm near the bases of the flagella are a variable number (commonly two) of small, transparent *contractile vacuoles*.

The size of these vacuoles is not constant; they gradually expand to a certain size and then contract, extruding their contents. Their function seems to be that of excretory organs.

Reproduction. Sooner or later a cell ceases to move, the flagella disappear, and sometimes the wall becomes thicker. While the cell is in this quiescent state, the nucleus divides in substantially the manner described in Chapter X. Nuclear division is followed by division of the cell by constriction. The two daughter cells do not form walls but remain within the parent-cell wall. Both daughter cells may divide in the same manner as the parent cell; and in some cases there is a third division, resulting in the formation of eight cells. The final cells, whether two, four, or eight, remain for a time within the parent-cell wall (Fig. 149, *D*). A group of cells so held together may be called a *colony*, but this colony of Chlamydomonas is but a temporary association. Sooner or later each cell of the colony forms a wall of its own, produces flagella, and the parent-cell wall breaks down, allowing the young cells to become free. Each

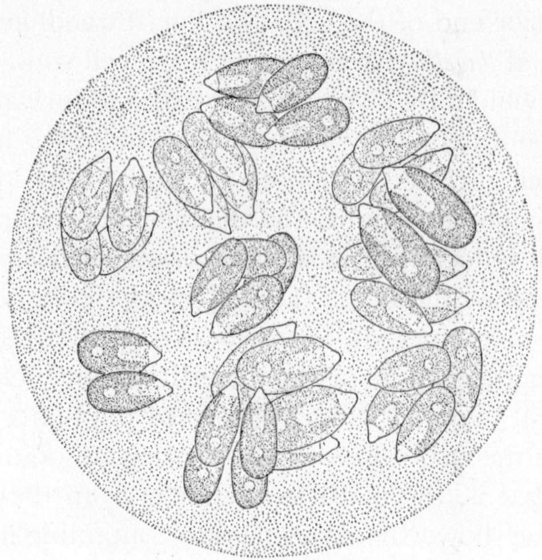

FIG. 150. Many-celled colony of Chlamydomonas enclosed in a gelatinous matrix derived from the parent-cell wall.

young cell is similar to the motile cell first described; and each, as it swims about, grows to approximately the size of the original cell.

Under certain environmental conditions the cells of a colony do not develop flagella and become motile, but remain within a matrix formed by a gelatinization of the parent-cell wall (Fig. 150). Since each of the cells may in turn grow, divide, and form daughter cells, a colony is produced consisting of many cells, sometimes as many as 100 or more, all enclosed within a single gelatinous matrix. Eventually the cells of such a colony form flagella and become free.

Thus, whatever the form of the resultant colony, it is during a quiescent stage in the life history of Chlamydomonas that an increase in the number of cells takes place. This increase in number is brought about by cell division. An increase in number of individuals is commonly spoken of as *reproduction*. In Chlamydomonas, therefore, as in all other one-celled organisms, reproduction and cell division are synonymous terms.

Gametes and Their Union (Fig. 151). Under some conditions the division of a quiescent cell and of its descendants continues until

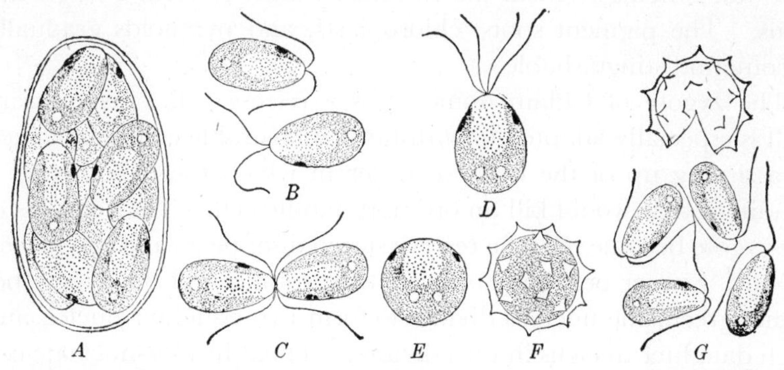

FIG. 151. Chlamydomonas. *A*, gametes before their liberation from the parent-cell wall. *B*, free-swimming gametes. *C*, two gametes preparing to unite. *D*, zygote newly formed by the union of gametes. *E*, zygote, flagella withdrawn. *F*, mature zygote. *G*, germination of a zygote.

16, 32, or 64 daughter cells are formed within the parent-cell wall. Except for their smaller size, these daughter cells are similar to those described above; but their function is different, and they are called *gametes*. The gametes are liberated by a dissolution of the parent-cell wall; and after swimming about for a time they come together in pairs, the cells of each pair meeting at their anterior ends (Fig. 151, *C*). Then they unite to form a single cell. According to the species, uniting gametes are either naked or surrounded by walls. In the latter case the protoplasts escape from the walls, which are left behind and take no part in the process. In most species there is no visible difference between the two uniting gametes. However, in certain species, even though the gametes appear to be exactly similar, union takes place only between two gametes which were produced from different parent cells.

The Zygote. The cell formed by a union of two gametes is a *zygote* (Fig. 151, *D–F*). When first formed, a zygote of Chlamydomonas has no wall; and the two pigment spots, two chloroplasts, and two nuclei derived from the respective gametes are still present. The flagella may disappear during the union; or they may persist, and the young zygote remain motile for a time. A motile zygote is readily distinguished from a motile vegetative cell or from a gamete by its possession of four flagella, as well as of two pigment spots and two chloroplasts. Sooner or later the flagella disappear, and the zygote becomes spherical and begins to secrete a thick wall. While this wall is being formed, the two nuclei unite to form a single nucleus. The pigment spots, chloroplasts, and pyrenoids gradually become indistinguishable.

The zygote of Chlamydomonas is a resting cell. Its resistant wall is especially adapted to withstand unfavorable conditions, such as a drying up of the body of water in which the plant lives—a condition that would kill an ordinary motile cell. The contents of the zygote become red; the reserve starch disappears and is replaced by oil. Sooner or later, however, the protoplast of the zygote becomes green, the nucleus divides to form two daughter nuclei, and each daughter nucleus in turn divides. Then the four-nucleate cell divides into four one-nucleate cells, which, after developing flagella and walls, are freed by a rupture of the old wall of the zygote. These free-swimming daughter cells are similar to the motile cells first described (Fig. 149).

Relationships. Chlamydomonas is one of a great number of one-celled or colonial organisms which during a considerable part of their existence are provided with flagella. Some of these, because of their general similarity, seem to be fairly closely related to Chlamydomonas. Others, more distantly related, differ either in the number of their flagella or in the possession of additional pigments, which, masking the chlorophyll, give to the organisms a color other than green. The green algae to be described on later pages seem to have descended from forms more or less like Chlamydomonas. Some other algae (*e.g.*, the brown algae, Chapter XIV) are probably derived from different types of simple flagellated organisms. As will be noted in later chapters, the higher green plants (including mosses, ferns, and seed plants) seem to have come from green algae.

In addition to the pigmented flagellate organisms mentioned, there are many flagellated forms which lack chlorophyll and other pigments. Some of these nonpigmented types, probably originally derived from pigmented ones, seem to have given rise to various groups of animals and possibly to some of the fungi.

Sexual Differentiation. Many simple algae and other one-celled or colonial organisms form no gametes so far as is known. However, the majority of organisms, both simple and complex, produce gametes which unite in pairs. The establishment of the habit of gametic union so early in evolutionary history and its general persistence suggest that the union of gametes may bear an important relation to the welfare of plant and animal species.

In such comparatively primitive organisms as Chlamydomonas, both gametes of any pair are motile and in most species are alike in size and structure. But in various lines of descent among the Chlorophyceae a differentiation has occurred, resulting in the appearance of gametes of two kinds, *female* and *male*. A beginning of such differentiation appears even in certain species of Chlamydomonas; but, generally speaking, gametic differentiation has accompanied the development of a colonial habit.

The production of a large gamete permits the accumulation of considerable quantities of reserve food for the development of a new colony. But the larger the gamete, the less likely is it to be actively motile. Motility, on the other hand, favors the meeting and union of gametes. Smallness of gametes is favorable to their motility and also makes possible their production in large numbers. The advantages of large size and opportunity for food storage, on the one hand, and of large numbers and motility, on the other, may be secured by a division of labor and a coincidental differentiation in size and structure between gametes. Such a division of labor and differentiation between gametes are illustrated in many of the plants to be studied. The larger gamete, which in most evolutionary lines becomes nonmotile, is *female;* the smaller, more active, is *male.*

These differences between gametes are *sexual* differences. Sex, therefore, implies a differentiation which came about after the habit of gametic union became established. It is not a primitive characteristic of living organisms. The union of the gametes of a colonial plant *leads* to a reproduction of the colony, since the zygote formed by a union of two gametes may develop into a new colony. It is for this reason that the union of gametes, together with the processes that follow the union, is commonly spoken of as *sexual reproduction.* This term is confusing, because a union of gametes, resulting directly in a reduction in number of cells, is itself the reverse of reproduction, which implies an increase in number.

VOLVOX

Structure and Reproduction. Chlamydomonas, it has been seen, may form temporary colonies of irregular shape, in which the cells are imbedded in a gelatinous matrix. While in the colonial condition, the cells are nonflagellate. Some other algae belonging in the same order as Chlamydomonas form colonies that are similarly held together by a gelatinous substance, each cell, however,

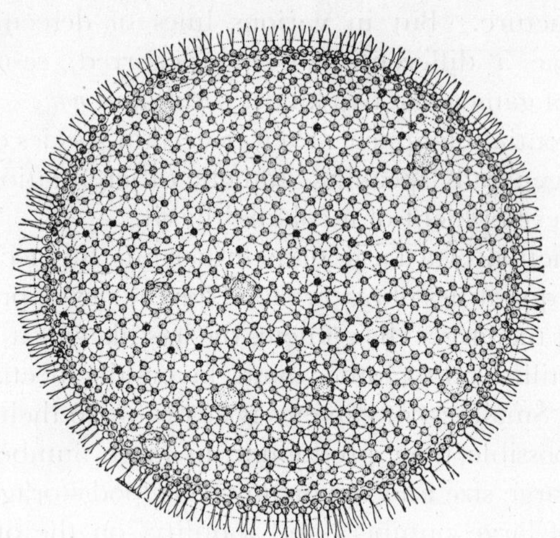

Fig. 152. A colony of Volvox.

retaining its flagella. *Volvox* (Fig. 152) represents the evolutionary culmination of colonies with flagellated cells. It frequently occurs in abundance in semipermanent or permanent pools for a few weeks in late spring or early summer and then disappears until about the same time the next year.

The cells of Volvox, of which there are often a few thousand in a colony, are arranged in the form of a hollow sphere one cell layer in thickness. Each cell of the colony is surrounded by a comparatively thick gelatinous sheath, the sheaths of individual cells being united. Because of the thickness of the sheaths, the protoplasts lie at some distance from one another, imbedded in the hollow spherical matrix formed by the union of the sheaths. In most species of Volvox each cell of a colony is similar in shape and structure to a motile cell of Chlamydomonas. The anterior flagella-bearing end of the cell is toward the surface of the colony, the flagella projecting beyond the colonial matrix. The concerted action of the flagella of all cells propels the colony through the water.

As a colony approaches maturity, certain of its cells, generally from four to ten, become many times larger than other cells of the colony and lose their flagella. Each of these larger cells, by a series of divisions, gives rise to a spherical group of cells which projects into the central cavity of the colony. By further cell division and by the swelling and coalescence of the cell sheaths, each new group so formed develops into a daughter colony, which swims about in the cavity of the parent colony. Here the daughter colonies remain until the rupture or death of the parent colony.

Production and Union of Gametes. Several successive generations of colonies may be produced in the manner just described. Eventually a time comes when gametes are formed instead of daughter colonies. Gamete formation in Volvox (Fig. 153) differs in certain respects from gamete formation in Chlamydomonas. First, while all the cells of a Volvox colony are probably capable of forming gametes, only certain cells, usually but a small percentage of those in the colony, actually do so. Second, the gametes are of two sorts, which differ in size and structure. Development of one kind of gamete begins with the enlargement of a cell and the disappearance of its flagella. Division of this cell and of its descendants produces either a plate or a hollow sphere of small, spindle-shaped, two-flagellate cells. These motile cells are male gametes (*antherozoids*). Gametes of another kind result from the enlargement of other cells of the same or of another colony, whose flagella have disappeared. Such a cell, which does not divide but which grows to many times its original size and remains nonflagellate, is a female gamete or *egg*.

The mature antherozoids escape from a colony, either as free-swimming individuals or as a free-swimming colony that eventually

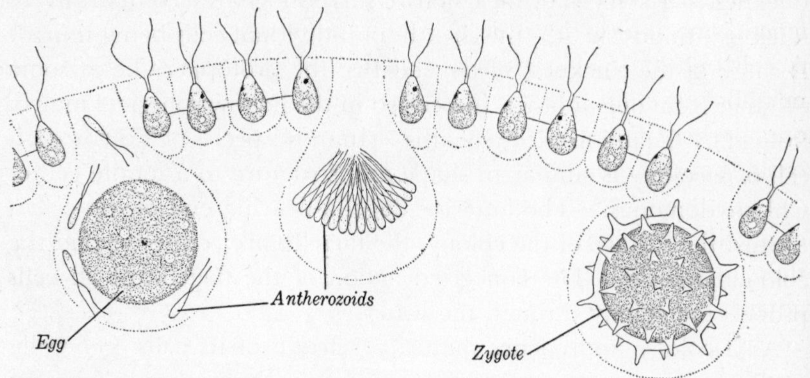

FIG. 153. Volvox. Cross section of a portion of a colony in which eggs and antherozoids are formed and gametic union is occurring. Diagrammatic.

breaks up into individual antherozoids. Antherozoids swimming in the vicinity of an egg are attracted to it, and usually several of them make their way through the gelatinized envelope surrounding the egg. One antherozoid finally unites with the egg, and the zygote formed by this union of a motile antherozoid and a large nonmotile egg develops a thick wall.

The zygotes are retained in the colony until the latter decays or disintegrates. Then they fall to the bottom of the pool, where they remain for several months. Since all colonies in a pool form gametes at about the same time and since the zygotes do not germinate for several months, there is a long period when no free-swimming colonies are present. Finally, however, the zygote wall is broken, and the protoplast becomes free. In some species the protoplast immediately divides and so begins the formation of a free-swimming colony. In other species the extruded protoplast produces á pair of flagella and swims about for a time before dividing.

OTHER SIMPLE GREEN ALGAE

Protococcus. One line of evolution from forms like Chlamydomonas led to the development of permanent colonies of motile cells. This line reached its culmination in Volvox. Evolution in another direction from forms similar to Chlamydomonas led to green algae whose cells, without flagella, live separately, as do those of Chlamydomonas. *Protococcus* (Fig. 154) is a simple representative of this type of evolutionary development.

The green coating often found on the shaded sides of trees, rocks, fences, and buildings commonly consists of masses of Protococcus. A cell of Protococcus is thick-walled and, when not crowded by neighboring cells, spherical. Its protoplast contains a nucleus and one, perhaps sometimes more than one, variously shaped chloroplast.

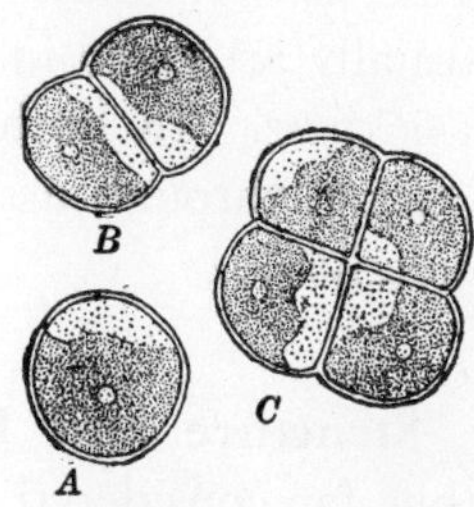

FIG. 154. Protococcus. *A*, solitary cell. *B*, two-celled colony. *C*, four-celled colony.

The daughter cells produced by division of a cell may separate from one another, or they may remain in contact. Division of adjacent cells may result in a platelike or an irregularly formed colony of a variable number of cells which are usually angular in consequence of mutual compression. Cell division and the fragmentation of colonies are the only methods of reproduction in Protococcus. The formation of flagellated cells, either of gametic or of nongametic nature, has never been observed.

Some Simple Colonial Chlorophyceae. Most of the one-celled green algae, like Chlamydomonas and Protococcus, are at times

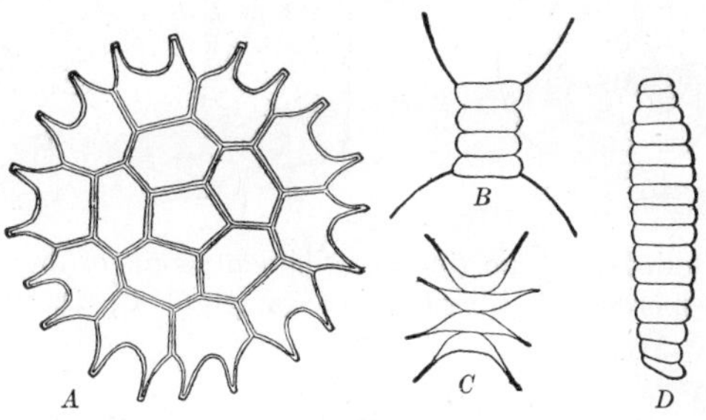

FIG. 155. Colonial green algae. *A*, Pediastrum. *B*, *C*, four-celled colonies of two species of Scenedesmus. *D*, sixteen-celled colony of Scenedesmus.

organized into colonies. In some, as in Chlamydomonas, the colonial phase is of brief duration. From this condition, practically all stages of transition may be found in Chlorophyceae to the condition in which the colony constitutes the dominant phase—that is, the phase of longest duration. Since any many-celled plant is essentially a colony of cells, in a species which has reached the stage of a long-continued adherence of cells the terms *colony* and *plant* may be used interchangeably. Many green algae form colonies the number of whose cells is some power of two. In one of the most widely distributed of these, Scenedesmus (Fig. 155, *B–D*), the somewhat elongated cells lie side by side to form a row of 2, 4, 8, or 16 cells. In another genus, Pediastrum (Fig. 155, *A*), the cells are usually arranged in concentric rings to form a flat plate one cell in thickness. In both Scenedesmus and Pediastrum, any cell of a colony, through a series of divisions, may give rise to a daughter colony.

ULOTHRIX

Structure and Reproduction. The colonial Chlorophyceae thus far considered have been spherical, platelike, or irregular in shape. Many colonial green algae have indefinite numbers of cells attached end to end in an unbranched row or filament. Such an

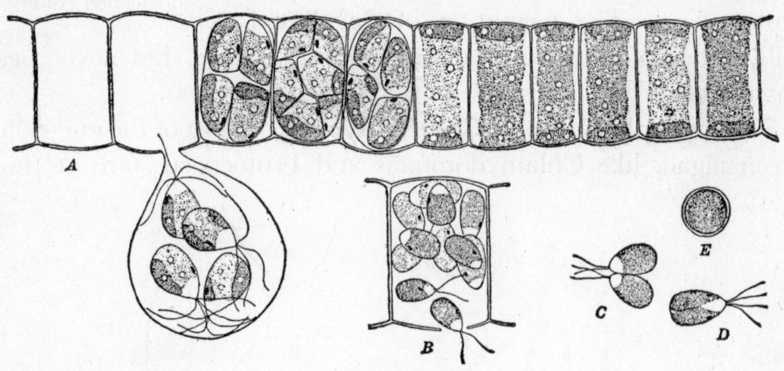

Fig. 156. Ulothrix. *A*, portion of a filament; some of the cells have divided to form swarm-spores. *B*, liberation of gametes. *C*, *D*, union of gametes. *E*, zygote.

alga is *Ulothrix* (Fig. 156), usually found attached to stones, sticks, or other objects in small, cool, swiftly flowing streams or in pools or other bodies of water which do not become warm and stagnant. Each filamentous colony is commonly attached to the substrate by a disklike holdfast developed from the basal cell. Sometimes colonies are free-floating. The cells are short cylinders, each having a single chloroplast in the form of a partial or complete girdle imbedded in the peripheral portion of the dense cytoplasm. The chloroplast contains one, two, or several pyrenoids. Near the center of the cell is a large nucleus.

The cells of Ulothrix divide by constriction. Division increases the number of cells in a colony but not the number of colonies.

Reproduction of the colony (that is, the formation of new colonies) is brought about by the production of motile cells (*swarm-spores*). With the exception of a few cells at the base, any cell of a filament may divide to form 2, 4, 8, 16, or 32 daughter cells. The daughter cells round up, form flagella, and so become swarm-spores, which escape, either singly or enclosed in a vesicle, through a pore in the side of the parent-cell wall (Fig. 156, *A*). The swarm-spores are similar to the motile cells of Chlamydomonas, each being ovoid, with a prominent chloroplast and a conspicuous pigment spot. Unlike the motile cells of Chlamydomonas, each swarm-spore has four flagella instead of two; and there is no cell wall. After swimming for some time, the spore comes to rest on some solid body, withdraws its flagella, forms a wall, and pushes out a protuberance which is the beginning of the formation of a holdfast. The growth and division of this cell, of its daughter cells, and of their offspring—the cells always remaining in contact—give rise to a new filament. A cell of a colony may also, under some conditions, become a rounded spore provided with a wall; or it may first divide to produce two or more such spores. A spore of this type may develop directly into a new filament, or it may be transformed into a swarm-spore which will so develop.

Formation and Union of Gametes. The gametes of Ulothrix are formed in the same manner as are swarm-spores and are similar to the latter except that they are frequently smaller and that each has two instead of four flagella (Fig. 156, *B*). After swimming for a time, the gametes unite in pairs (Fig. 156, *C–E*); and the nuclei of each pair unite. The flagella do not disappear, so that each zygote, having four flagella, continues moving about after its formation. Eventually it comes to rest, withdraws its flagella, secretes a wall, and enters upon a period of rest. Sooner or later the protoplast of a zygote divides to form several (at least four) nonmotile spores, each of which, after liberation from the old zygote wall, may develop into a new filamentous colony.

ULVA

Structure. Some Chlorophyceae with cells more or less like those of Ulothrix form colonies of an entirely different type. One of the most striking of these is *Ulva* (Fig. 157), a marine alga of widespread distribution. This plant, commonly known as the "sea lettuce," usually lives in that zone along the seacoast that is alternately exposed and flooded by tides.

Ulva grows attached to rocks and wharves or to other marine algae. The plant body is an erect, irregularly wrinkled blade that may attain a height of a foot or more but never becomes more than two cells in thickness. Each cell is one-nucleate and has a single chloroplast on the side toward the flat surface of the blade. The plant is anchored at its basal end by an irregularly shaped holdfast composed of interwoven tubular outgrowths from the lowermost cells.

Reproduction. A colony produces either swarm-spores or gametes. Swarm-spores are formed always at the margin of a colony. By a series of divisions 8 or 16 cells, each with 4 flagella, are produced from a single parent cell. These swarm-spores escape through a pore in the side of the parent-cell wall toward the flat surface of the colony. Liberation of swarm-spores usually takes place at the time when a plant is reflooded by an incoming tide, and swarm-spores may be liberated in such quantity that the water appears green. After swimming for an hour or more, a spore comes to rest on some solid body, withdraws its flagella, and forms a wall. From this cell, by a series of divisions, a plant is produced similar to that which formed the swarm-spores.

Production and Union of Gametes. The plant developing from a swarm-spore never forms swarm-spores. Instead, it produces two-flagellate gametes (Fig. 157, *D*, *E*). These are formed and liberated in the same manner as are swarm-spores. Gametic union takes place while the gametes are swimming about in the water; and in all species investigated, union takes place only between two gametes formed by different plants. In most species the two uniting gametes are identical in size, but in at least one species one of a uniting pair is double the size of the other (Fig. 157, *F*).

The flagella do not disappear when two gametes unite, and the zygote may continue to swim for a few hours. Eventually it comes to rest on some firm object, withdraws its flagella, and secretes a thin wall. Within a day or two the zygote divides, and by succeeding divisions a plant is developed similar to that which formed the gametes. This new plant produces swarm-spores, not gametes.

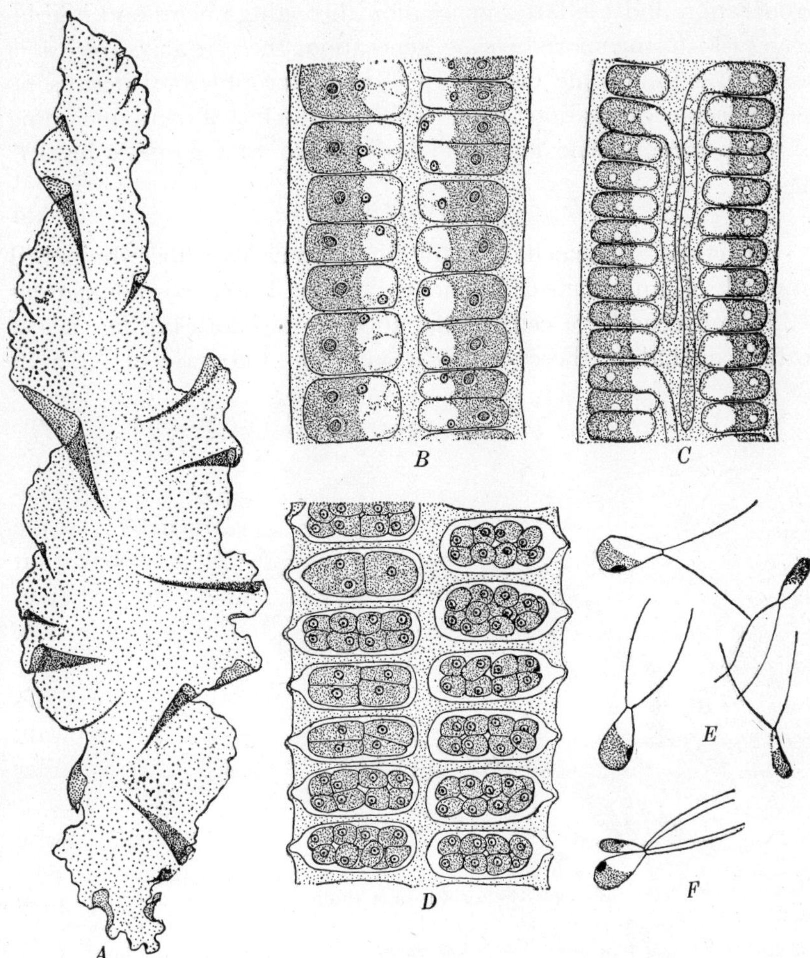

FIG. 157. Ulva. *A*, Thallus of *U. stenophylla*. *B–F*, *U. lobata*. *B*, vertical section through the upper portion of a thallus. *C*, vertical section through the lower portion. *D*, the formation of gametes. *E*, gametes. *F*, gametic union. All from G. M. Smith, *Cryptogamic Botany*, published by the McGraw-Hill Book Company.

Life Cycle. The life cycle of Ulva includes two distinct phases. Swarm-spores develop into plants which produce gametes. Each zygote formed by gametic union immediately develops into a plant similar to that which formed the gametes, but a plant which produces swarm-spores only. Since the spore-bearing plant (or generation) of Ulva gives rise through spores to the gamete-bearing generation and the latter generation through gametes and zygotes gives rise to the spore-bearing generation, there is an *alternation of generations* in the life cycle. In most Chlorophyceae there is no comparable alternation of generations; but a few of them, including some species of the next genus to be described, have a similar history.

CLADOPHORA

Structure. The cells of many filamentous algae form branched instead of unbranched filaments. Some branched filamentous Chlorophyceae have cells similar to those of Ulothrix; the cells of others, including those of *Cladophora* (Fig. 158), are of different

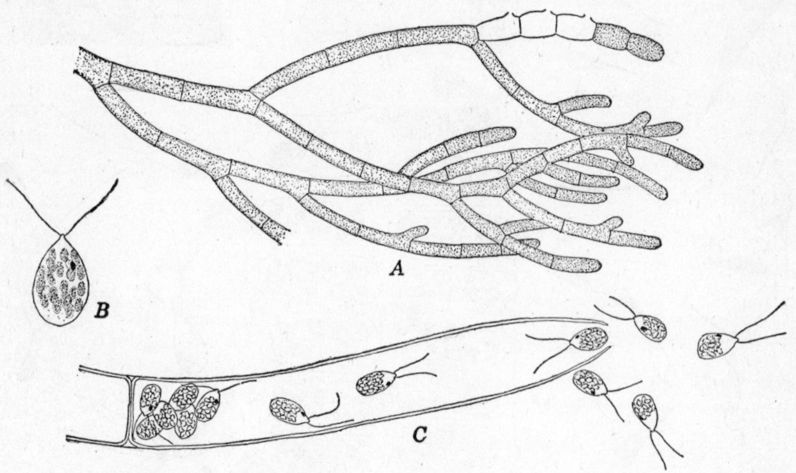

FIG. 158. Cladophora. *A*, portion of a thallus; the empty walls are those from which swarm-spores have escaped. *B*, a gamete. (Both of *C. glomerata.*) *C*, gametes being liberated (in *C. Kuetzingianum*). All from G. M. Smith, *Cryptogamic Botany*, published by the McGraw-Hill Book Company.

structure. Most genera of green algae are found only in fresh or only in salt water. Cladophora is unusual in that certain species live in fresh water whereas others are marine. Fresh-water species usually grow attached to objects in streams and in shallow water along the shores of lakes.

The cells of Cladophora are cylindrical and united end to end in a branching filament. Each cell is surrounded by a thick wall. Within the wall is a layer of dense cytoplasm, in which are imbedded many small disk-shaped chloroplasts. Some chloroplasts contain one pyrenoid each; others lack pyrenoids. In some species the chloroplasts appear to be united in a continuous network. Cladophora differs from algae previously described in that each cell contains many nuclei. These lie imbedded in the dense cytoplasm but farther inward than the chloroplasts.

Cells of Cladophora divide by constriction. New branches are formed usually only by cells near the upper end of a filament. A branch originates as a lateral outgrowth from the upper end of a cell, and the first cell division in the new branch occurs close to the point of origin of the outgrowth.

Reproduction of the Colony. This results from the formation of one-nucleate, four-flagellate swarm-spores. Swarm-spores are produced by cells near the tips of branches, the protoplast of each such cell dividing to form many swarm-spores. The spores are liberated through a small pore near the upper end of a cell, or at its apex if it is a terminal cell of a branch. After swimming for a time, a swarm-spore comes to rest upon some solid object, retracts its flagella, and secretes a wall. Growth and division of this cell, of its daughter cells, and of their descendants result in a new filament identical in appearance with that which produced the swarm-spores.

In some marine species of Cladophora the plant developing from a swarm-spore always produces gametes. They are formed and liberated in the same manner as are swarm-spores and are similar to the latter except that each has two instead of four flagella (Fig. 158, *B*, *C*). After swimming for a time, the gametes unite in pairs to form zygotes. A zygote becomes immobile and secretes a wall. It soon begins development into a filament which eventually produces swarm-spores.

SPIROGYRA

Structure and Reproduction. *Spirogyra*, one of the plants commonly known as "pond scums," is a green alga whose cells form unbranched filamentous colonies. It occurs in pools and other bodies of water, frequently in masses of considerable size. Spirogyra may be distinguished from most other filamentous green algae by the slippery feeling of the filaments.

The cells of Spirogyra (Fig. 159) are cylindrical and attached end to end. This arrangement results from the fact that the planes of all cell divisions are at right angles to the long axis of the cylindrical cells.

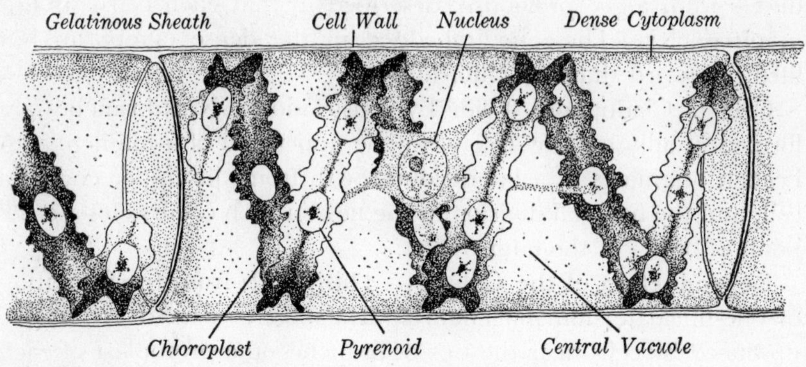

FIG. 159. A cell of Spirogyra.

A thin layer of dense cytoplasm lies just within the wall of each cell. The most conspicuous feature of a cell, and the one from which the name *Spirogyra* is derived, is the chloroplast. Each chloroplast is a trough-shaped ribbon extending spirally from end to end of the cell; it is a part of and is contained in the dense cytoplasm. Each chloroplast contains several pyrenoids. Throughout the length of the chloroplast is a thick central strand connecting and surrounding the pyrenoids, the intervals between successive pyrenoids being approximately equal. A central vacuole occupies the greater portion of the space within the wall. In the center of this vacuole is the nucleus, surrounded by a layer of dense cytoplasm from which numerous strands extend to the dense cytoplasmic layer at the periphery of the cell. Each strand usually joins the peripheral layer just beneath a pyrenoid.

Cell division in Spirogyra, under ordinary conditions, occurs at night. It is preceded by a nuclear division similar to that already described for nuclei of cells in a root tip. The division of the cells increases the number of cells in a colony but not the number of colonies. There is usually no definite means for reproduction of the colony (increase in number of colonies) during the vegetative life of a plant. In most species of Spirogyra new colonies are formed only when a filament is accidentally severed. Since various aquatic animals feed upon the alga, the filaments are frequently cut, so increasing the number of plants. In certain species of Spirogyra, especially in some with small cells, the filaments at times separate into individual cells or short rows of a few cells each, which may then grow into long filaments.

Gametic Union. As a rule, in each species of Spirogyra the union of gametes occurs at a definite time of year, commonly in spring or autumn. In preparation for this process the first step in most species is a pairing of filaments so that the filaments of each pair lie in contact side by side. Next, small dome-shaped protuberances appear at corresponding points in opposite cells of the two filaments (Fig. 160, *A*, *B*). Each protuberance increases in

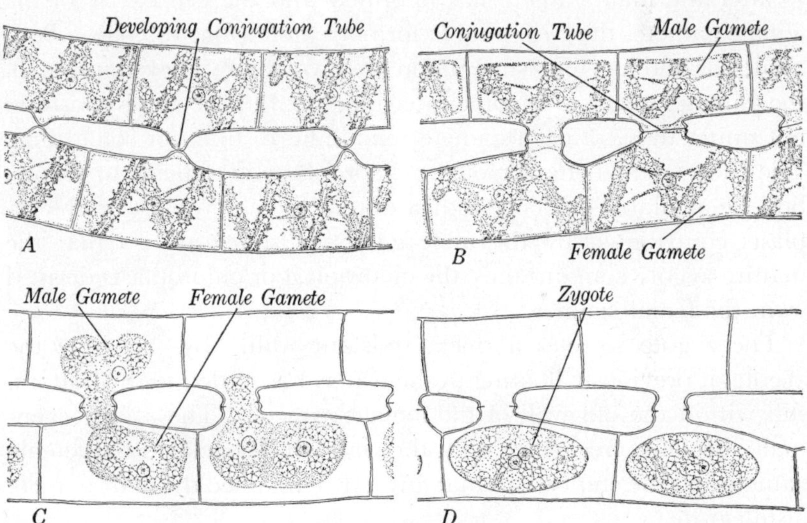

FIG. 160. Spirogyra. Stages in the formation and union of gametes.

length, pushing the paired filaments apart. In the plane of contact of two outgrowths from opposite cells the wall of each is digested, and so a *conjugation tube* is formed. When the formation of the conjugation tube begins, the protoplasts of the conjugating cells (now gametes) are similar in appearance; but as the protuberances grow toward each other, one of each pair of gametes contracts from the wall and becomes rounded. This shrinkage is brought about by a loss of water from the protoplast. The contracted gamete soon migrates through the conjugation tube (Fig. 160, *C*) toward the other gamete, which by this time also has contracted and rounded. The gamete which contracts first and which moves toward the other gamete is spoken of as *male* because of its greater activity; the passive gamete is *female*. Usually all cells of a particular filament become male gametes, or all become female gametes; but at times some become male, and others in the same filament become female gametes.

In certain species of Spirogyra, conjugation takes place between adjacent cells of the same filament rather than between cells of separate filaments. The differentiation into male and female gametes and the formation of a zygote go on, however, in the same way as when cells of different filaments conjugate.

After the male gamete has migrated into the cell cavity of the female gamete, the two unite to form a zygote (Fig. 160, *D*). Both a nuclear and a cytoplasmic union are involved. The cytoplasm of the gametes seems to become intermingled; but the chloroplasts do not unite, those of each gamete remaining distinct for some time. The subsequent behavior of the chloroplasts is difficult to follow; but the available evidence indicates that the chloroplast or chloroplasts contributed by the male gamete disintegrate, so that the mature zygote contains only the chloroplast or chloroplasts derived from the female gamete.

The zygote secretes a thick, resistant wall. By this time the zygote, if previously floating in the water, has settled to the bottom, still within the old wall of the female gamete. The zygote eventually becomes free, since both the wall which enclosed the female gamete and the empty wall that formerly contained the male gamete disintegrate.

When a zygote is newly formed, it contains the nuclei derived from the male and female gametes; these unite to form a single nucleus (Fig. 161, *B*). After a time this nucleus divides to form two daughter nuclei, and each daughter nucleus in turn divides (Fig. 161, *C*, *D*). The four nuclei now present in the zygote are similar when first formed, but three of them soon show signs of disintegration and eventually disappear. The fourth nucleus persists and is the sole nucleus present in the mature zygote (Fig. 161, *F*). The significance of this behavior of nuclei in the zygote will become clear when certain corresponding processes in some of the more complex plants have been discussed (Chapter XXV).

Germination of a Zygote (Fig. 161, *G*, *H*). The interval between the union of gametes and the germination of a zygote may be a few weeks or a few months, or it may extend from one spring until the next. In germination the heavy outer layer of the zygote wall

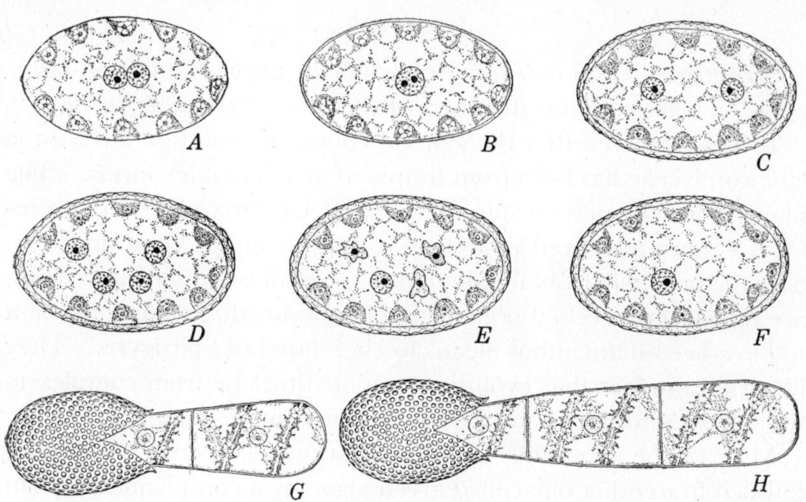

FIG. 161. Spirogyra; *A–F* in section; *G*, *H*, in surface view. *A*, zygote after the union of gametes; gamete nuclei still separate. *B*, gamete nuclei have united. *C*, after the first nuclear division. *D*, after the second nuclear division; four nuclei now present. *E*, three of the nuclei are disintegrating. *F*, after the disappearance of three nuclei. *G*, *H*, stages in the germination of a zygote. All diagrammatic.

is broken; and the cell contents, surrounded by the inner layer of the wall, form a short cylindrical outgrowth. The structures typical of a Spirogyra cell (chloroplast or chloroplasts, nucleus, and dense cytoplasm) are visible in this cell that lies partly within and partly without the broken portion of the zygote wall. A division of the nucleus is followed by a transverse division of the cell. The daughter cell that is now partly within the outer zygote wall layer does not divide; but from the other daughter cell, by repeated cell division and growth, a filament is produced that is similar to the parent filaments.

When from any cause the protoplast of a cell that has prepared to function as a gamete does not unite with another, it not infrequently rounds up, secretes a thick wall, and so becomes, except for its somewhat smaller size, identical in appearance with a zygote. Such a resting cell (*spore*) can germinate in the same manner as a zygote to form a new filament. Thus, it appears that any cell of a Spirogyra filament is capable of functioning cither as a vegetative cell, as a spore which can grow into a new plant, or as a gamete.

DESMIDS

Structure. Almost every collection of algae from fresh-water pools or lakes contains members of the group known as *desmids.*

It has been seen that the general course of evolution among the Chlorophyceae has been from simple to more complex forms. The filamentous colonies of Spirogyra and of Ulothrix represent, therefore, a more advanced as well as a more complex condition than does the one-celled Chlamydomonas. Desmids, on the other hand, are (chiefly) one-celled organisms whose immediate ancestors seem to have been filamentous algae closely related to Spirogyra. They illustrate the fact that evolution may at times be from complex to simpler structure instead of from simple to more complex.

Most of the thousands of known species of desmids are distinguished from other one-celled green algae by a conspicuous median

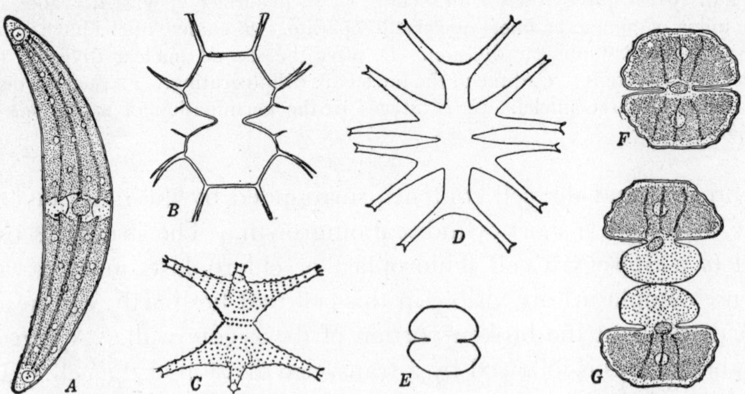

Fig. 162. Desmids. *A*, Closterium. *B*, Xanthidium. *C*, Staurastrum. *D*, Micrasterias. *E*, *F*, Cosmarium. *G*, division of a Cosmarium cell.

constriction, each cell therefore consisting of two symmetrical half-cells (Fig. 162). The cells of various species differ greatly in shape and frequently bear spines or other protuberances. Each half-cell contains at least one chloroplast, often elaborately lobed, and within each chloroplast are one or more pyrenoids. A nucleus lies in the cytoplasm in the region of the median constriction.

Reproduction. New individuals are formed by the division of a parent cell into two daughter cells. Before the cell divides, the nucleus divides, each half-cell receiving a daughter nucleus. Nuclear division is followed by a transverse division of the cell in the plane of the median constriction. Each daughter cell at first consists, therefore, of one half-cell and a portion of the median region of the parent cell. Later, by a growth of the constricted portion, each daughter cell develops a new half-cell (Fig. 162, *G*). In most desmids the daughter cells become separated from each other as the new half-cells are forming, but in a few species the daughter cells remain in contact and by repeated divisions give rise to a filamentous colony which may attain to a considerable length.

Gametic Union. Occasionally, when two mature cells come to lie in contact, their walls break at the median constrictions; and their protoplasts function as gametes (Fig. 163), flowing out and

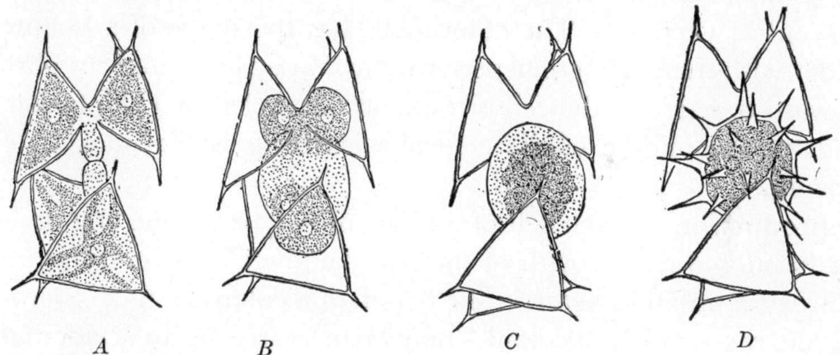

FIG. 163. Staurastrum (a desmid); stages in gametic union. Adapted from De Bary.

uniting to form a zygote. These nonflagellate gametes resemble those of Spirogyra, except that they are not differentiated as male and female. When first formed, the zygote is naked; but soon after its formation it secretes a thick wall. After a considerable period of rest the wall of a zygote breaks or becomes gelatinized; and its contents develop into one, or (by division) into two or four, vegetative cells of the form characteristic of the species.

OEDOGONIUM

Structure. *Oedogonium* is another unbranched, filamentous fresh-water green alga. It is of frequent occurrence in pools and other bodies of water, where the filaments may be attached to submerged objects, including other algae, or may grow in large free-floating masses. The cylindrical cells of Oedogonium (Fig. 164)

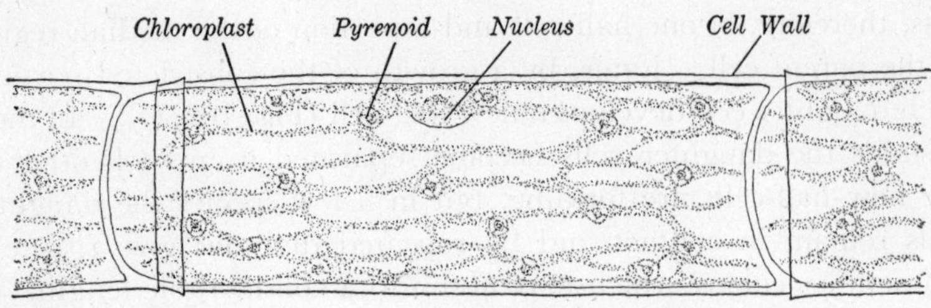

Fig. 164. A vegetative cell of Oedogonium.

are joined end to end. Inside the wall of each cell is a layer of dense cytoplasm containing a single chloroplast, a nucleus, and a large central vacuole. The chloroplast has the shape of a hollow cylinder with many irregular perforations. The large nucleus may lie toward one side of the cell or may be suspended by cytoplasmic strands in the middle of the central vacuole as is the nucleus of Spirogyra.

Reproduction. Each cell of a filament may reproduce by division, the subsequent growth of the two daughter cells resulting, as in Spirogyra, in an increase in the length of a colony. As in Spirogyra, too, the number of colonies may be increased by an accidental breaking of the filament.

Reproduction of a colony occurs also through the formation of swarm-spores (Fig. 165). The protoplast of a cell withdraws somewhat from the wall, becomes rounded, and develops a colorless area at one side. A circle of flagella is developed at the margin of this colorless area. The protoplast has now been metamorphosed into a swarm-spore. After a swarm-spore is mature, the old wall enclosing it splits transversely at onc end; and the spore oozes slowly out through the opening in the wall.

The liberated swarm-spore swims away by means of its flagella and, after swimming for a time, comes to rest with its flagellate end in contact with some solid body, often a filament of Oedogonium. Soon the spore withdraws its flagella and secretes a wall, and its colorless end becomes modified into a disklike or a rootlike holdfast.

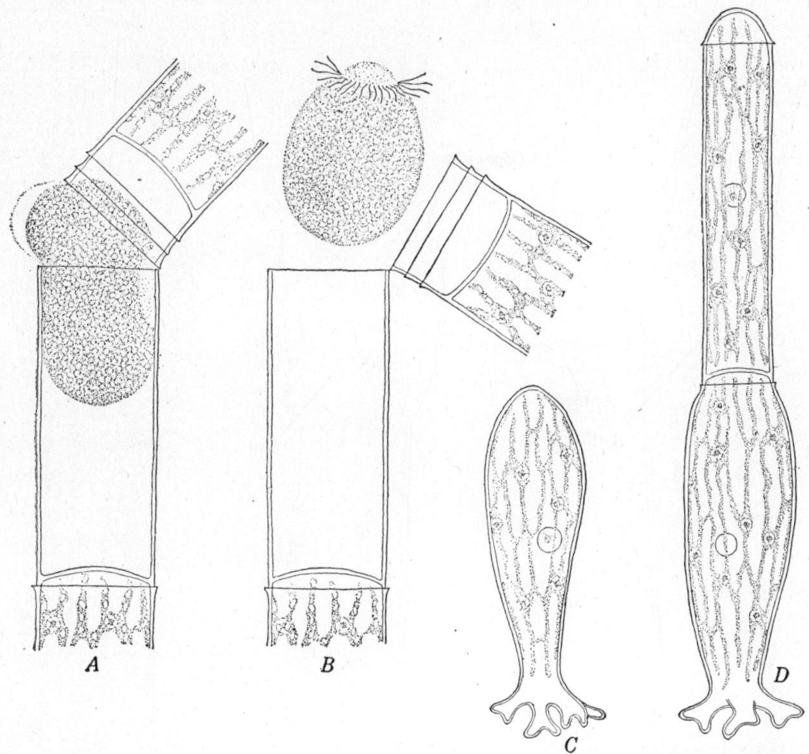

Fig. 165. Oedogonium. *A*, *B*, liberation of a swarm-spore. *C*, beginning of the development of a new filament from a swarm-spore. *D*, two-celled filament.

The cell now increases somewhat in length and then divides transversely into two daughter cells. The lower daughter cell, that with the holdfast, does not divide again; the upper cell, by repeated transverse divisions, gives rise to a long filament, which becomes free-floating if accidentally broken from its attachment.

Formation and Union of Gametes (Fig. 166). Oedogonium forms gametes of two very different sorts. Any cell in a filament, except the basal cell, is capable of dividing into two daughter cells, the upper of which may develop into an *oögonium.* An oögonium becomes somewhat broader than a vegetative cell and spherical or ellipsoid in shape. Its protoplast shrinks somewhat and rounds up to form the female gamete (*egg*), which lies within, and free from, the oögonial wall. A small circular pore may be formed in the

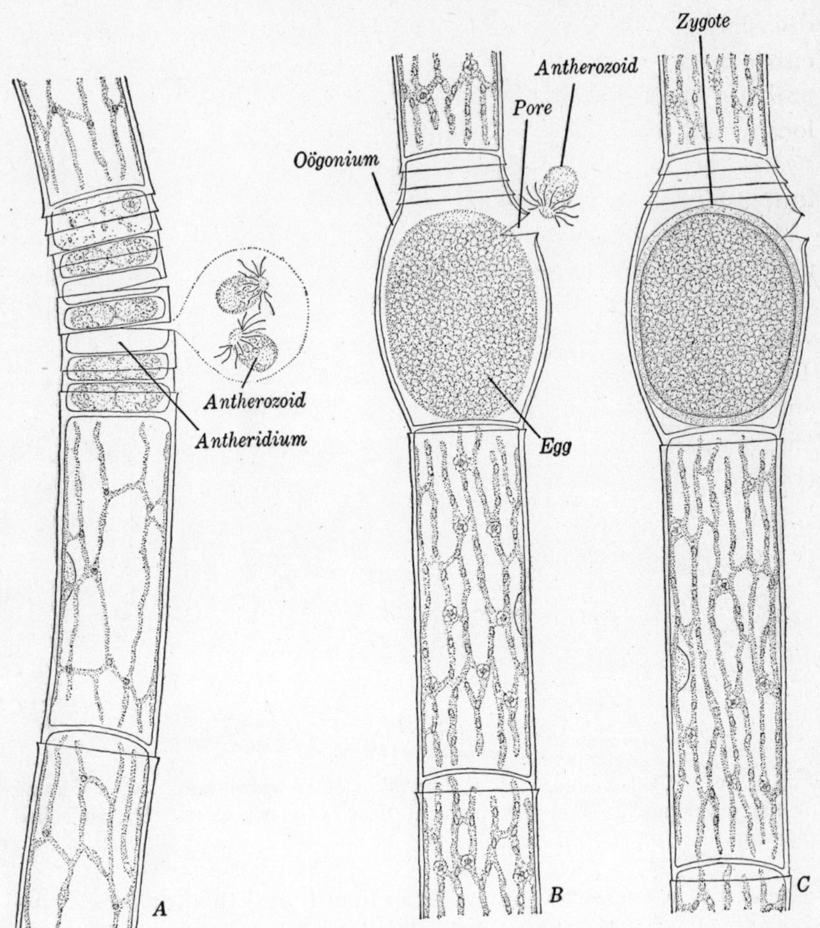

Fig. 166. Oedogonium. *A*, antheridia and antherozoids. *B*, an egg and an antherozoid about to unite. *C*, mature zygote.

oögonial wall as the egg approaches maturity, or the wall may crack transversely instead of opening by a pore. Since the oögonium and the egg are really the same cell, it is hardly necessary to apply both names in Oedogonium. But for the sake of harmonizing the use of terms in this and in some other algae in which an oögonium contains several eggs, it is customary to distinguish the egg of

Oedogonium, which is a protoplast only, from the oögonium, which is the protoplast plus the enclosing wall.

Simultaneously with the development of oögonia, certain other cells of the same or of another filament develop into a short series of disk-shaped cells (*antheridia*). The protoplast of each antheridium either becomes a male gamete (*antherozoid*) or divides to form two antherozoids. Except for their smaller size and their proportionally longer and fewer flagella, antherozoids are similar in structure to swarm-spores. They are liberated from the walls enclosing them in the same manner as are swarm-spores.[1]

An antherozoid swimming near an oögonium responds to a stimulus, exerted probably by a substance diffusing from the oögonium, swims through the pore or crack in the oögonial wall, and unites with the egg. The resultant zygote soon secretes a thick wall. The zygote is eventually liberated by the decay of the oögonial wall and settles to the bottom of the water. Here it usually remains for several months before germinating. When germination takes place (Fig. 167), the wall of the zygote breaks open; and the protoplast,

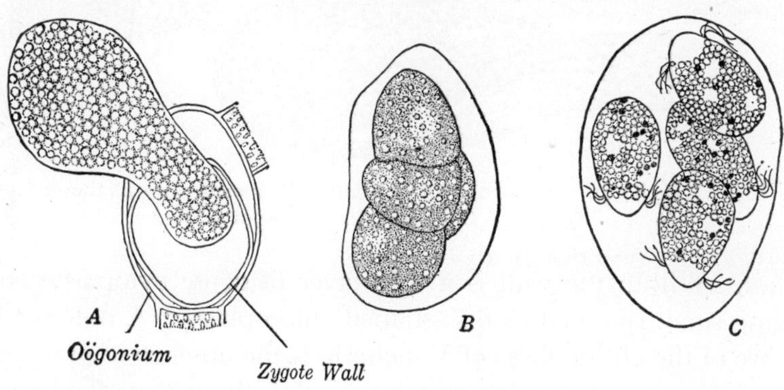

FIG. 167. Germination of the zygote of Oedogonium. After Juranyi.

either before or after escaping from the wall, by division forms four daughter cells, each of which becomes a swarm-spore. These swarm-spores develop into filaments in precisely the same manner as do those produced from vegetative cells.

[1] In a number of species of Oedogonium *dwarf male* plants are formed from motile cells resembling, but smaller than, ordinary swarm-spores. Such a cell, settling on an oögonium or on a cell adjoining the oögonium, develops into a minute plant commonly consisting at maturity of a holdfast and one or two antheridia.

In the organization of its colony Oedogonium represents no advance over Spirogyra or Ulothrix. However, in the differentiation of its gametes it presents a marked advance.

VAUCHERIA

Structure and Reproduction. A large majority of the species of *Vaucheria* live in fresh water or on damp soil; a few species inhabit brackish water. Terrestrial species grow in extensive dense, felt-like masses. Aquatic species live either attached or in free-floating masses.

The vegetative plant body (Fig. 168, *A*) is a single elongate, sparsely branched cylindrical cell that may reach a length of several

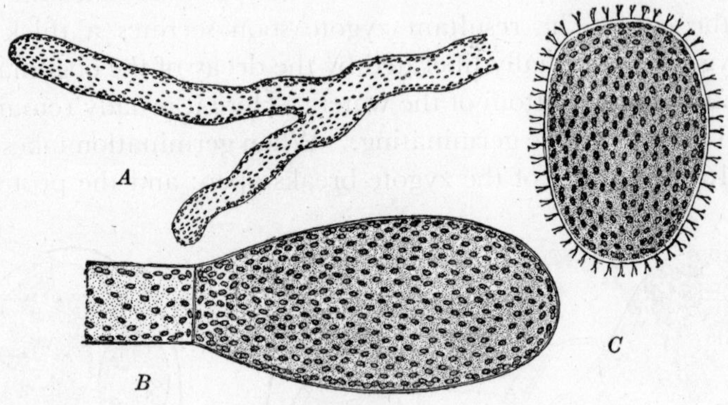

Fig. 168. Vaucheria. *A*, portion of a plant. *B*, sporangium at the end of a branch. *C*, liberated swarm-spore.

inches. Within the wall is a thin layer of dense cytoplasm containing small rounded or disk-shaped chloroplasts. A noteworthy feature of the chloroplasts of Vaucheria is the absence of pyrenoids and of their accompanying starch granules, the reserve food being stored in the form of oil droplets. Many small nuclei are imbedded in the innermost portion of the layer of dense cytoplasm. A central vacuole constitutes the greater part of the volume of the plant.

The cell may divide transversely a short distance back of the tip of any branch. The terminal daughter cell is a spore-producing cell (*sporangium;* Fig. 168, *B*). The protoplast of a sporangium develops into a single large swarm-spore (Fig. 168, *C*) containing many nuclei and chloroplasts and having a pair of flagella just external to each nucleus. The swarm-spore is liberated by a rupture of the tip of the sporangial wall and swims about slowly through the water as the pairs of flagella wave in unison. After swimming for a short time, the spore comes to rest, withdraws its flagella, forms a wall, and begins development into a typical filament by sending out one or more cylindrical outgrowths. Under certain conditions the spore within a sporangium secretes a wall and does not form flagella. When such a nonmotile spore becomes separated from the plant which produced it, it develops into a new plant in the same manner as does a swarm-spore.

Production and Union of Gametes (Fig. 169). The gametes of Vaucheria are differentiated as male and female. The male gam-

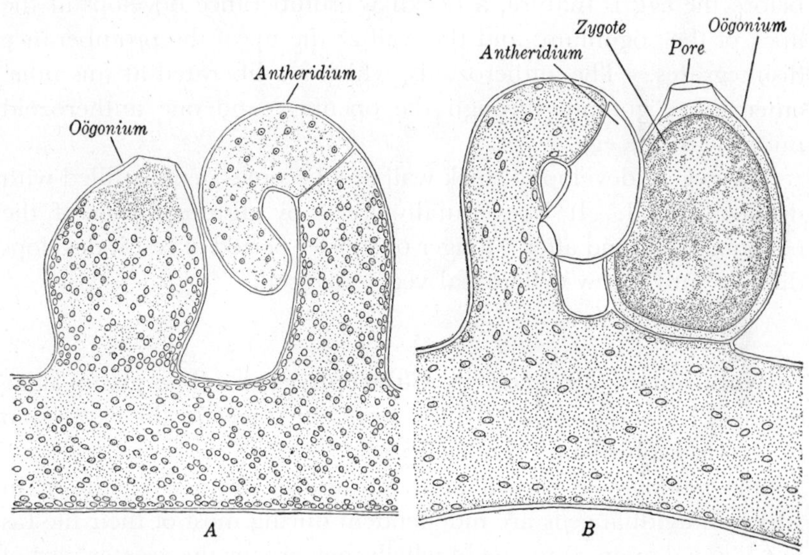

Fig. 169. Vaucheria. *A*, young sex organs. *B*, later stage; the antheridium empty, the oögonium containing a zygote. Both after G. M. Smith, *Cryptogamic Botany*, published by the McGraw-Hill Book Company.

etes (*antherozoids*) are produced within an *antheridium* borne at the end of a short curved branch. A young antheridium is a cell separated from the remainder of the branch by a crosswall. When first formed, it contains many nuclei and chloroplasts; but later the chloroplasts disappear. Eventually the protoplast of the antheridium is divided into a number of one-nucleate cells, each of which becomes metamorphosed into an antherozoid. The antherozoids are liberated by a dissolution of the apical portion of the antheridial wall. Each antherozoid is small and spindle-shaped, lacks a wall, and has two flagella.

The female gametes (*eggs*) are borne in *oögonia.* In some species the oögonia are borne on the same branch that bears an antheridium; the oögonia of other species are borne on separate branches that arise near the antheridial branches. Development of an oögonium begins with an enlargement of the tip of a branch and a cell division that separates the swollen portion (now the oögonium) from the remainder of the branch. At first a young oögonium contains several nuclei, only one of which persists; the protoplast of the oögonium, including the persisting nucleus, is the egg. Shortly before the egg is mature, a beaklike protuberance develops at the apex of the oögonium; and the wall at the tip of the protuberance disintegrates. The antherozoids, which are liberated at this time, enter the oögonium through the opening; and one antherozoid unites with the egg.

The zygote develops a thick wall and becomes densely filled with droplets of oil. It is eventually freed by disintegration of the oögonial wall, and after a longer or shorter period of rest it develops directly into a new cylindrical vegetative cell.

Evolutionary Progress in Chlorophyceae. The green algae discussed in the present chapter represent stages in the expression of several evolutionary tendencies.

One tendency is shown in the transition from a condition in which individual cells are independent during most of their life (as in Chlamydomonas) to one in which they are for the greater part of their existence organized into colonies (as in Volvox and Ulothrix).

A second tendency is toward an increase in complexity of the colony, after the colonial condition has become the dominant phase.

Another tendency is expressed by the appearance of sexual differentiation between gametes, followed by a progressive increase in this differentiation and by a differentiation between the plant parts (organs) in which male and female gametes, respectively, are produced.

A fourth evolutionary tendency is illustrated by the alternation of generations in Ulva and in some species of Cladophora. In most green algae, as in Volvox, Ulothrix, and Oedogonium, there is but one generation. In many other thallophytes, as well as in all divisions of plants above the Thallophyta, there is an alternation of generations fundamentally similar to that of Ulva.

Any of these evolutionary developments may proceed in a parallel way in distinct lines of descent. The habit of a dominant colonial phase, for instance, has appeared in many lines. Volvox, Oedogonium, and Vaucheria, very distantly related, have reached about the same level of sexual differentiation. An alternation of generations likewise has developed in several distinct lines.

Within any given line of descent the expression of different evolutionary tendencies in general proceeds independently. Hence, any particular genus may be relatively primitive in one respect and relatively advanced in another. For example, Oedogonium represents about the same level of colonial development as does Ulothrix, but it is much more advanced than Ulothrix in respect to sexual differentiation. Ulva is more advanced than Oedogonium in colonial development but resembles Ulothrix in having no sexual differentiation between gametes.

CHAPTER XIII

MYXOPHYCEAE (BLUE-GREEN ALGAE)

Nature. In the cells of blue-green algae the photosynthetic pigments are not localized in definite plastids, and the nuclear substances are not organized into definite nuclei. None of the members of this class form flagellated cells, and none of them form gametes. The protoplasm contains a blue pigment (*phycocyanin*) in addition to chlorophyll and the accompanying yellow pigments. The blue, green, and yellow pigments are typically present in such proportions that the protoplast is of a blue-green color, but variations in the proportions of these pigments cause the appearance of many colors and shades other than blue-green.

Although included among the Thallophyta, the Myxophyceae are apparently not closely related to other classes of algae. It is very probable that they arose independently of other algae.

Distribution. Blue-green algae are widely distributed in fresh waters. They are of common occurrence in pools and ditches, especially in those containing stagnant water. Certain blue-green algae found in lakes and reservoirs constitute a portion of the free-floating population of microscopic organisms known as the *plankton*. Plankton Myxophyceae are sometimes present in sufficient quantity to make the water appear colored, and these algae are chief among the organisms whose decay sometimes causes disagreeable odors and tastes in water supplies. Myxophyceae are prominent also among the algae growing on damp soil.

Blue-green algae live in hot springs in various parts of the world, including New Zealand, Iceland, and the United States. They may grow and multiply where the temperature of the water is as high as 187° F. The best-known and most spectacular hot springs are those of Yellowstone National Park. The terraces about these springs result largely from a deposition by the algae of mineral substances dissolved in the water. A coating of Myxophyceae gives the terraces their bright, variegated colors.

Other blue-green algae are found in brackish and salt waters. Most of the marine species are minute one-celled plants that grow upon algae of other classes, but some are filamentous and grow on rocks. A few species float freely; and at times, as in the Red Sea, the water may be colored by the presence of an immense number of free-floating colonies.

Gloeocapsa. The cells of certain genera of blue-green algae are solitary; those of other genera are united in colonies of definite or indefinite form. *Gloeocapsa* (Fig. 170) is a genus of one-celled forms.

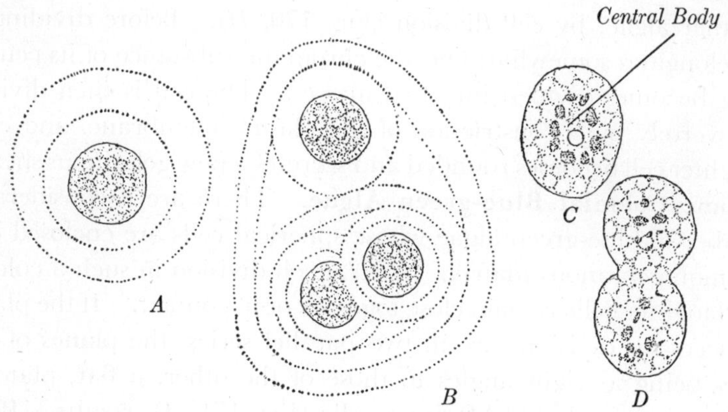

FIG. 170. Gloeocapsa. *A*, single cell. *B*, three-celled colony. *C*, cell fixed and stained, showing the central body. *D*, dividing cell. *C*, *D* redrawn from Olive.

The solitary cells are spherical, each being surrounded by a thick gelatinous sheath, which is often stratified. The sheath lies outside the cell wall proper. Frequently two or more daughter cells of Gloeocapsa remain within the sheath of the parent cell, forming a more or less persistent colony.

Within the thin wall of each cell is a protoplast, differentiated into an outer colored and an inner colorless region. The colored portion of the protoplasm contains the pigments characteristic of the class. The pigments appear to be evenly distributed throughout the peripheral portion of the protoplasm rather than located in definite plastids. In the colored region of the protoplasm also are colorless granules, some of which are reserve foods. Probably many of these are composed of *glycogen*, a carbohydrate somewhat similar to starch. In the central colorless region of the cell is a relatively dense mass of material, the *central body*. This body is described by some observers as consisting in part of substances of the nature of those composing chromosomes, being therefore a nucleus of primitive type but without a nucleolus or a nuclear membrane. Other investigators question this conception and hold that a definite nucleus is lacking. The material of the central body, however, takes the same stains as do chromosomes and is commonly considered to correspond in some measure to the substance of a true nucleus.

An increase in number of cells is brought about in Gloeocapsa, as in other algae, by cell division (Fig. 170, *D*). Before dividing, a cell elongates somewhat; and the chromatic substance of its central body becomes divided into two masses. The cell is then divided transversely by a constriction of the plasma membrane, and each daughter cell becomes rounded and secretes a new gelatinous sheath.

Some Colonial Blue-green Algae. There are a considerable number of blue-green algae whose spherical cells are enclosed in a common gelatinous matrix. After a cell division in such a colony, the daughter cells remain close together or in contact. If the planes of successive divisions are in two parallel series, the planes of one series being at right angles to those of the other, a flat, platelike colony, such as that of Merismopedia (Fig. 171, *A*), results. If the

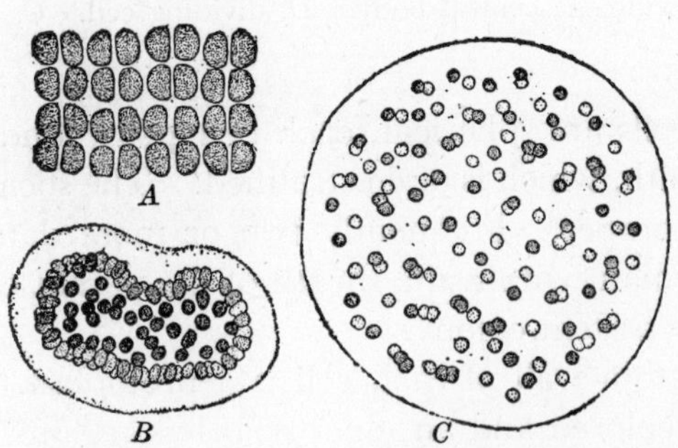

Fig. 171. Colonial blue-green algae. *A*, Merismopedia. *B*, Coelosphaerium. *C*, Aphanocapsa.

division planes are in three series, each set perpendicular to the other two, a more or less massive colony is formed, like that of Coelosphaerium (Fig. 171, *B*) or Aphanocapsa (Fig. 171, *C*). Reproduction of the colony results from an accidental break, or from the occasional freeing of a cell which then by division develops into a new colony.

Oscillatoria. In the majority of colonial blue-green algae, the planes of all cell divisions are parallel. Some of the commonest

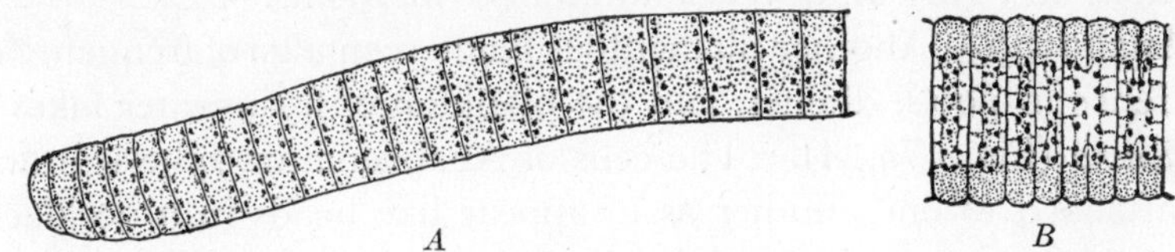

FIG. 172. Oscillatoria. *A*, portion of a living filament. *B*, cells fixed and stained, showing the central body. *B* redrawn from Olive.

forms, whose colonies, produced by such a series of divisions, are simple unbranched filaments, belong to the genus *Oscillatoria* (Fig. 172). Species of this genus are often abundant in temporary pools or on damp soil.

At each end of a filament of Oscillatoria is a hemispherical or conical cell, whose free end is frequently expanded to form a button-like cap. The other cells of the filament are disk-shaped or cylindrical. The protoplast of each cell, as in Gloeocapsa, is differentiated into a colorless central region and a colored outer portion. A feature which distinguishes Oscillatoria from other blue-green algae, and which suggested its name, is its oscillating movement. A filament frequently waves back and forth and occasionally moves longitudinally a short distance. The mechanism of these movements is unknown.

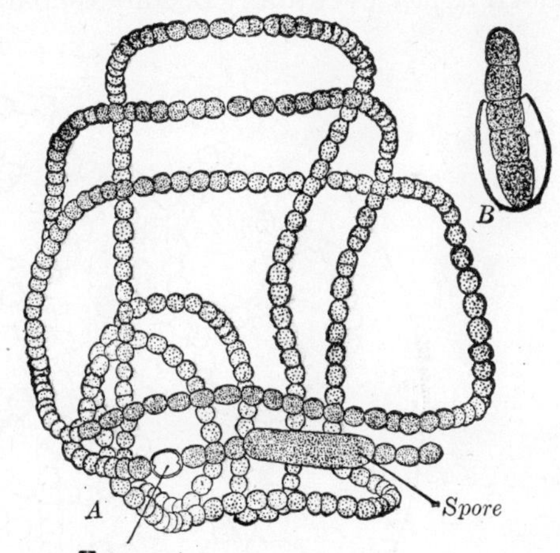

FIG. 173. *A*, filament of Anabaena with a spore and a heterocyst. *B*, a new filament of Cylindrospermum developing from a spore.

As in other filamentous algae the number of cells in a filament is increased by cell division, the central body dividing before or at the same time as the cell divides. Oscillatoria has a definite means also of bringing about reproduction of filaments. Frequently gelatinous disks are formed between adjacent cells at certain points in a filament; later the filament breaks at these points into several short parts, each composed of a few cells, which may then, by division and growth, develop into longer filaments.

Anabaena. Another filamentous blue-green alga of frequent occurrence in pools, ditches, and the plankton of fresh-water lakes is *Anabaena* (Fig. 173, *A*). The cells of Anabaena are spherical and so attached to one another as to appear like beads in a necklace. The filaments may be straight or very much bent and contorted. Surrounding each filament is a thick, very transparent gelatinous sheath. The cells have much the same structure as those of Gloeocapsa or of Oscillatoria.

An occasional cell of an Anabaena filament enlarges greatly, becomes filled with reserve foods, and develops a thicker wall. Such a *spore* eventually becomes separated from the parent filament

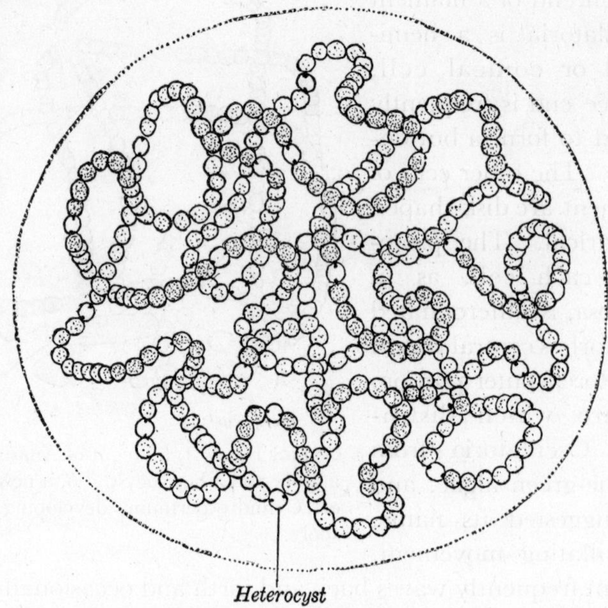

FIG. 174. Colony of Nostoc.

and may develop into a new colony (Fig. 173, *B*). Here and there in a filament are cells with much thicker walls and with transparent contents. These are *heterocysts*. Heterocysts are sporelike in nature, but they are spores whose capacity to develop into new colonies has been almost completely lost. The filaments of some Myxophyceae regularly break into shorter filaments at points next the heterocysts; but this is not so generally the case in Anabaena.

Nostoc. Other filamentous Myxophyceae with heterocysts differ from Anabaena in the shape of the colony or in the arrangement of their cells. *Nostoc* (Fig. 174), which grows both on damp soil and in water, resembles Anabaena in cell and colonial structure and in spore formation. A Nostoc colony is surrounded by a gelatinous sheath much firmer and tougher than that of Anabaena.

A colony of Nostoc may become separated into daughter colonies, which remain within the original tough sheath. By the growth and breaking up of the daughter colonies, a mass of considerable size is often formed. Such a mass, containing separate filaments imbedded in a gelatinous matrix, is a compound colony.

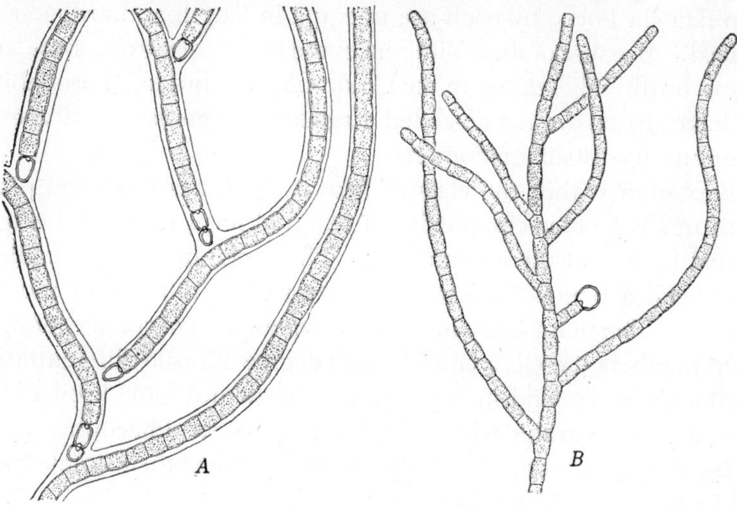

Fig. 175. *A*, Tolypothrix, showing false branching. *B*, true branching in Nostochopsis.

Branching Filamentous Colonies. The filaments of some blue-green algae undergo a "false branching" (Fig. 175, *A*). This occurs when, in consequence of growth and cell division, a series of a few cells within a filament pushes outward and to the side of an adjoining cell; further growth and divisions may follow. In a few genera true branching (Fig. 175, *B*) occurs essentially as in Cladophora, described in the preceding chapter.

CHAPTER XIV

PHAEOPHYCEAE (BROWN ALGAE) AND BACILLARIOPHYCEAE (DIATOMS)

PHAEOPHYCEAE (BROWN ALGAE)

Nature. The Phaeophyceae are distinguished from other algae by the fact that their plastids are of a golden-brown color. This color is due to a pigment (*fucoxanthin*), chemically similar to xanthophyll, that masks the chlorophyll which is also present. Swarm-spores and motile gametes differ from those of other algae in that the two flagella borne by each are unequal in length and are laterally placed. Because of these differences the brown algae are considered not to be directly related to the Chlorophyceae but in all probability to have arisen from one-celled flagellated organisms different in structure from Chlamydomonas.

Evolution within the class of brown algae has produced plants with much greater complexity of external form than has been attained by any of the green algae. The range in size varies all the way from a plant of microscopic size to one 150 feet or more in length. The plant body in some brown algae is of simple construction; in others there is a considerable degree of tissue differentiation. Although in size and in complexity of structure some brown algae are fairly comparable with many seed plants, the Phaeophyceae are to be included among the Thallophyta because of their simple spore- and gamete-producing organs.

Distribution. Except for two or three species, all the brown algae are marine. Most of them live along rocky shores where the water is less than 50 feet in depth. Many occur only in colder portions of the oceans, but certain genera live only in tropical and subtropical waters.

Brown algae are extremely diverse in form, structure, and method of reproduction. The first of the three genera here described is representative of the simpler Phaeophyceae; the other two are among the more complex members of the class.

ECTOCARPUS

Structure. *Ectocarpus* (Fig. 176) is a marine alga whose much-branched, filamentous plant body grows attached to larger algae, or to rocks and other objects. Along the Atlantic coast of North America it is very common, especially in the intertidal belt. It is not found in so great abundance along the Pacific coast.

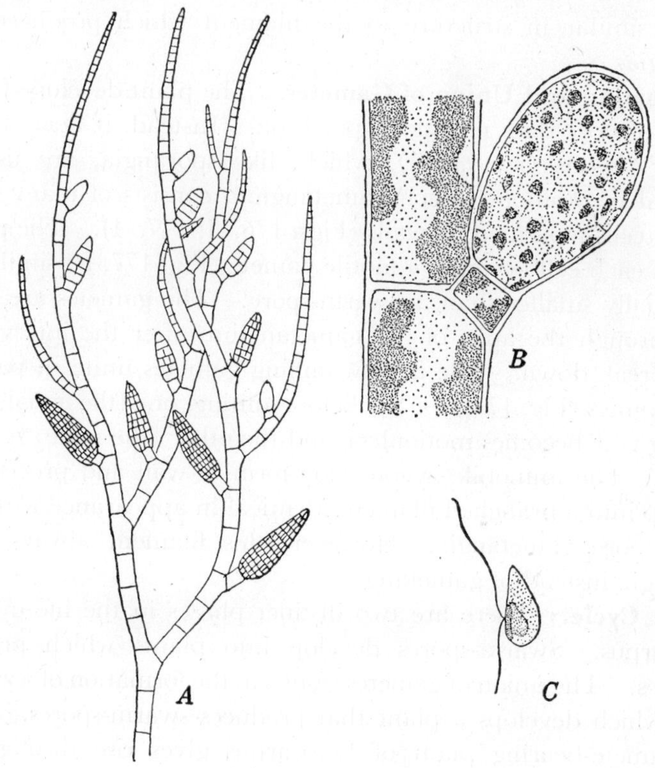

FIG. 176. Ectocarpus. *A,* portion of a thallus bearing sex organs. *B,* sporangium. *C,* swarm-spore.

The cells are cylindrical and have relatively thick walls. Each cell is one-nucleate and contains many small disk-shaped or ribbon-like golden-brown plastids.

Spore Formation. In some plants, terminal cells of the main branches, or the terminal cells of short lateral branches, develop into *sporangia.* A sporangium begins its development as a one-nucleate cell. After a series of nuclear divisions, its protoplast is divided into a number of swarm-spores (usually 64 or 128), which are liberated by a breaking down of the apex of the sporangial wall. A swarm-spore (Fig. 176, *C*) is pear-shaped, has one nucleus and one plastid, and bears two lateral unequal flagella. After swimming for a time, the spore comes to rest on some solid body, withdraws its flagella, and forms a wall. From this cell, by successive transverse divisions and growth, a branched filament is developed that is similar in structure to the filament which produced the sporangia.

Formation and Union of Gametes. The plant developed from a swarm-spore does not form sporangia. Instead, it bears multicellular organs (*gametangia*), which, like sporangia, are usually terminal in position. Each gametangium consists of many small cubical cells separated by walls (Figs. 176, *A*; 177, *A*). The protoplast of each cell becomes a motile gamete (Fig. 177, *B*) similar to, but usually smaller than, a swarm-spore. The gametes are liberated through the apex of the gametangium after the intervening walls break down. The free-swimming gametes unite in pairs to form zygotes (Fig. 177, *C–F*). Before uniting, one (the female) of a uniting pair becomes motionless, and the other (the male) remains motile. The immobile zygote soon forms a wall and proceeds to develop into a branched filament identical in appearance with that which bore gametangia. However, this filament always bears sporangia instead of gametangia.

Life Cycle. There are two distinct phases in the life cycle of Ectocarpus. Swarm-spores develop into plants which produce gametes. The union of gametes results in the formation of a zygote, from which develops a plant that produces swarm-spores. Since the gamete-bearing plant of Ectocarpus gives rise through the zygote to the spore-bearing plant, and this through its spores to the gamete-bearing plant, there is an *alternation of generations*.

Under certain conditions the regular alternation of generations in Ectocarpus may be modified. A spore-producing plant may form many-celled sporangia similar in structure to gametangia. The swarm-spores from such a sporangium give rise to spore-producing plants. On the other hand, the gametes from a gamete-producing plant, if conditions do not favor gametic union, may function as spores which develop into new gamete-bearing plants.

An alternation of generations essentially similar to that in Ectocarpus characterizes most other genera of brown algae. But in many genera, including the next to be described, the two generations differ greatly in size and structure.

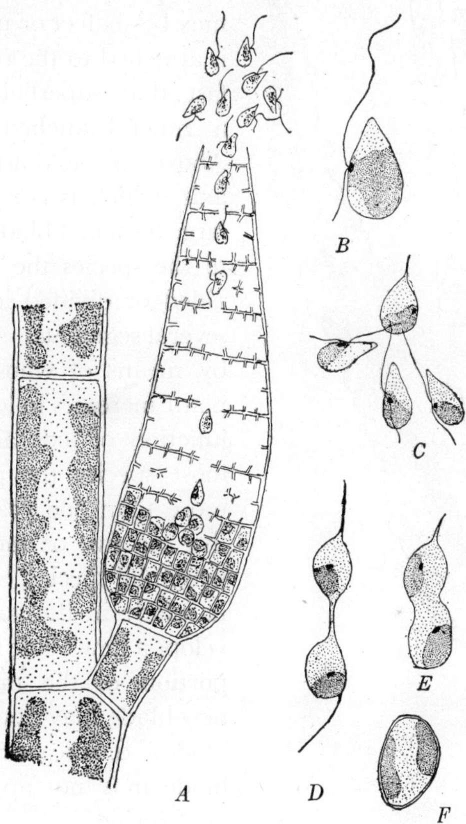

FIG. 177. Ectocarpus. *A*, sex organ, gametes being liberated. *B*, gamete. *C*, female gamete (above) whose flagella have been withdrawn; below, three male gametes. *D*, *E*, stages in the union of gametes. *F*, zygote. *B–F* redrawn from Berthold.

LAMINARIA

Structure. The common kelp, *Laminaria*, lives in comparatively shallow water along rocky shores but just below the low-tide level. It is widespread along those portions of the Atlantic and Pacific coasts of North America where the water is relatively cool. At one time kelps and rockweeds (p. 286) were of considerable importance as sources of potassium and iodine. The discovery of mineral deposits containing these elements has, however, made their recovery from algae unprofitable under ordinary conditions.

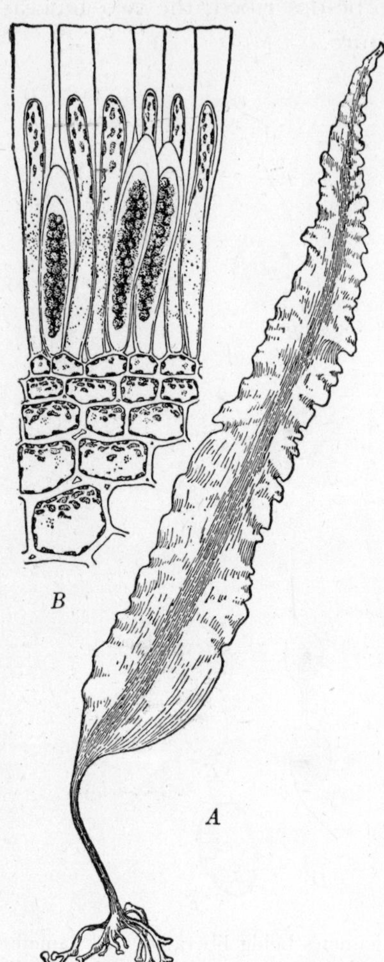

FIG. 178. Laminaria. *A*, thallus. *B*, cross section of a portion of a thallus bearing sporangia. *B* after Oltmanns.

A plant (Fig. 178, *A*), which may be six feet or more in length, is attached to the rock by a holdfast that superficially resembles a much-branched root system. Above the holdfast is a stemlike axis, which is continuous with a large flattened blade. According to the species the blade is undivided or divided lengthwise into several segments. The meristem, by means of whose activity the plant increases in length, is at the junction of axis and blade. In most species the plant lives for more than one year, and it may live for five or more years. In perennial species, each plant loses its blade in the autumn and develops a new blade from the upper portion of the meristem. The new blade may develop as the old blade is disintegrating, or the new blade may not appear until the next spring.

The axis is differentiated into two tissues. In the outer part is a region of approximately cubical cells containing plastids. In the center is a region composed of interwoven cylindrical cells without plastids. Some evidence indicates that the central part may be a conducting tissue. The blade likewise has compactly arranged cells next the surface and loosely arranged elongate cells in its interior.

Spore Formation. In late summer or early autumn some of the surface cells of the blade of Laminaria develop into sporangia (Fig. 178, *B*), which are very similar in structure and development to those of Ectocarpus. The sporangia of Laminaria occur in closely packed groups on the blade and are intermingled with elongate hairlike cells. The swarm-spores, similar in appearance to those of Ectocarpus, are liberated by a breaking of the sporangial walls. A swarm-spore develops, not into a plant similar to that which formed it, but into a very small filamentous plant.

Formation and Union of Gametes. The plants developing from swarm-spores are of two sorts, producing, respectively, male and female sex organs. The male plants (Fig. 179, *A*) bear small an-

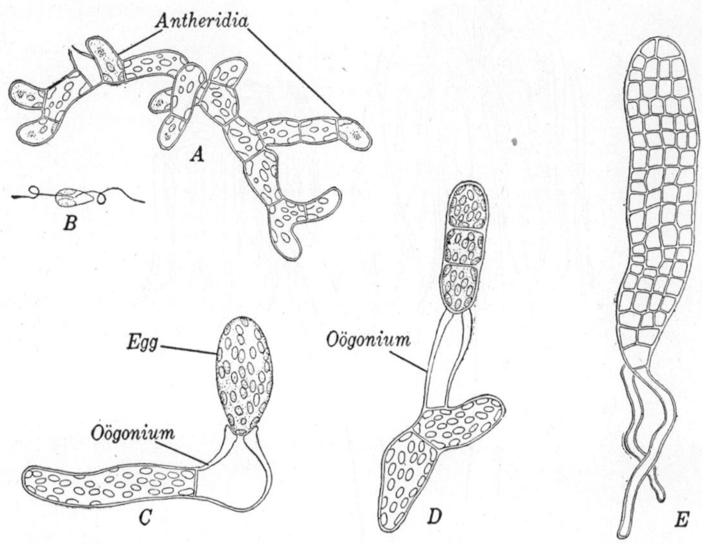

FIG. 179. Laminaria. *A*, male plant. *B*, antherozoid. *C*, *D*, female plants; in *D*, the egg has united with an antherozoid, and the zygote has begun to develop into a young spore-bearing plant. *E*, somewhat later stage in the development of a spore-bearing plant. All after Kanda.

theridia near the tips of their branches. The protoplast of each antheridium becomes a single motile antherozoid. The female plants (Fig. 179, *C*, *D*) bear oögonia, which are usually but not invariably terminal cells of branches. An oögonium is longer and thicker than other cells of the female plant. Its protoplast becomes an egg containing many plastids. The mature egg is extruded through, but remains attached to, the apex of the oögonial wall.

An antherozoid swims to and unites with an egg. The resultant zygote divides transversely, and further transverse divisions produce a short erect filament of six to ten cells that remains attached to the apex of the oögonial wall (Fig. 179, *D*). This filament, by further transverse and vertical divisions (Fig. 179, *E*), develops into an erect sheet one cell in thickness but composed of hundreds of cells. Several of the lowermost cells of the sheet send out tubular outgrowths (*rhizoids*) that help anchor the developing plant to the underlying rock. Later cell divisions in the basal portion of the sheet are in three planes. Continued cell division and growth in this region lead to the development of a plant like that first de-

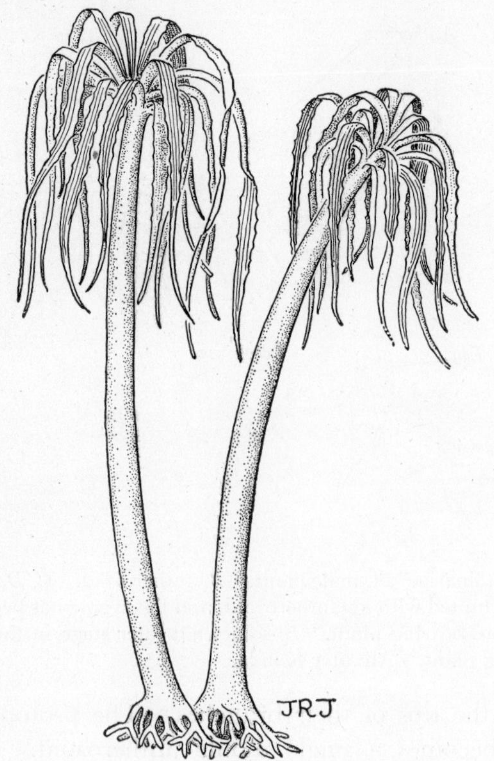

Fig. 180. The "sea palm," *Postelsia palmaeformis*.

scribed, which in time produces sporangia. Under certain conditions an egg may develop into a new plant even if it does not unite with an antherozoid.

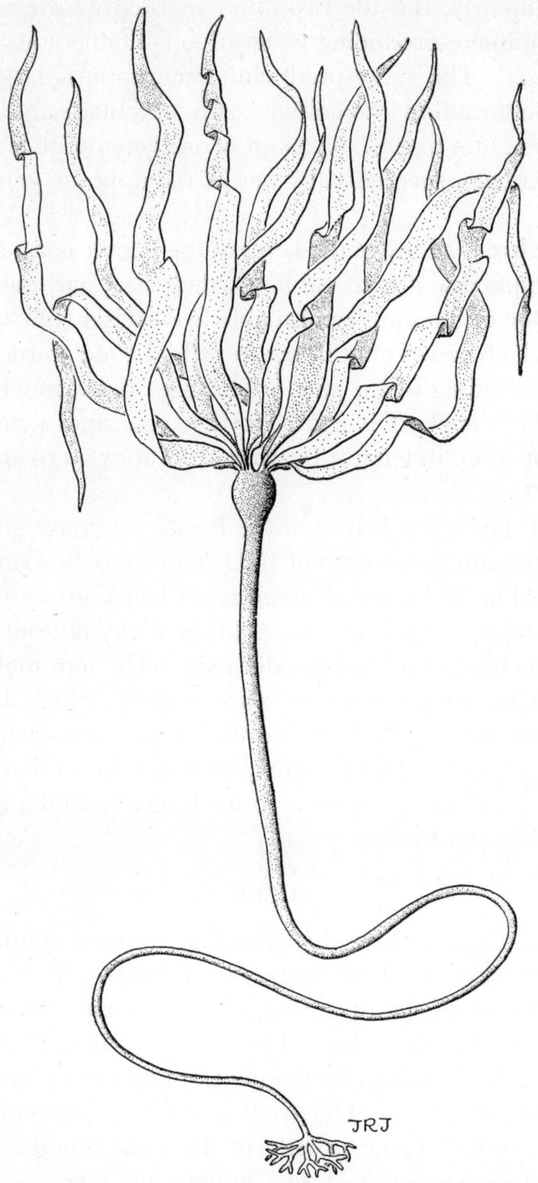

Fig. 181. Nereocystis, a giant kelp.

Life Cycle. There are two alternating generations in the life cycle of Laminaria, but the two differ markedly in size and structure. The gamete-producing generation is filamentous and of microscopic size. The spore-producing generation is large, with an external differentiation into holdfast, axis, and blade and an internal differentiation into tissues. A plant of one generation is invariably, so far as is known, succeeded by one of the opposite generation.

Other Kelps. Many of the kelps of the Pacific coast are notable for their complexity of external form, their size, and their habits of growth. One of the most remarkable is Postelsia (the "sea palm," Fig. 180), which grows only in the intertidal zone on rocks exposed to the full pounding of the surf. This alga has a much-branched holdfast, which anchors it firmly to the rock, and a stout flexible axis a foot or more in length, bearing at its apex a crown of leaflike blades.

Several of the "giant kelps" of the Pacific coast are annuals, and some of them grow to a length of 100 feet or more in a single season. Nereocystis (Fig. 181), one of these giant kelps, grows in water 20 to 40 feet in depth. It is anchored to the rocky bottom by a holdfast from which arises a long, slender axis. The terminal portion of the axis is expanded to constitute a gas bladder, which floats on the surface of the water and bears several long, strap-shaped leaves. Another giant kelp (Macrocystis), growing in similar locations, bears many small blades along its branching axis and a gas bladder at the base of each blade.

FUCUS

Structure. The rockweed (*Fucus*, Fig. 182) is a common inhabitant of the seacoasts of all temperate regions. This alga grows most abundantly in the upper limits of the areas that are temporarily exposed by the tides. The leathery, flat, ribbon-shaped thallus is attached to rocks by the development of its basal end into a disk-shaped holdfast. The thallus forks at intervals, the two prongs of each fork being usually of the same length. Here and there in certain species are large, hollow, bladder-like expansions containing gases, chiefly carbon dioxide, that help buoy the plant when it is submerged. Growth occurs at the free end of each branch. Fucus does not show as marked a differentiation into tissues as does Laminaria; but in mature portions of the plant the cells of the outer part are compactly, those in the interior more loosely, arranged.

Formation and Union of Gametes. The free ends of branches are often somewhat swollen; and in the swollen portions are many

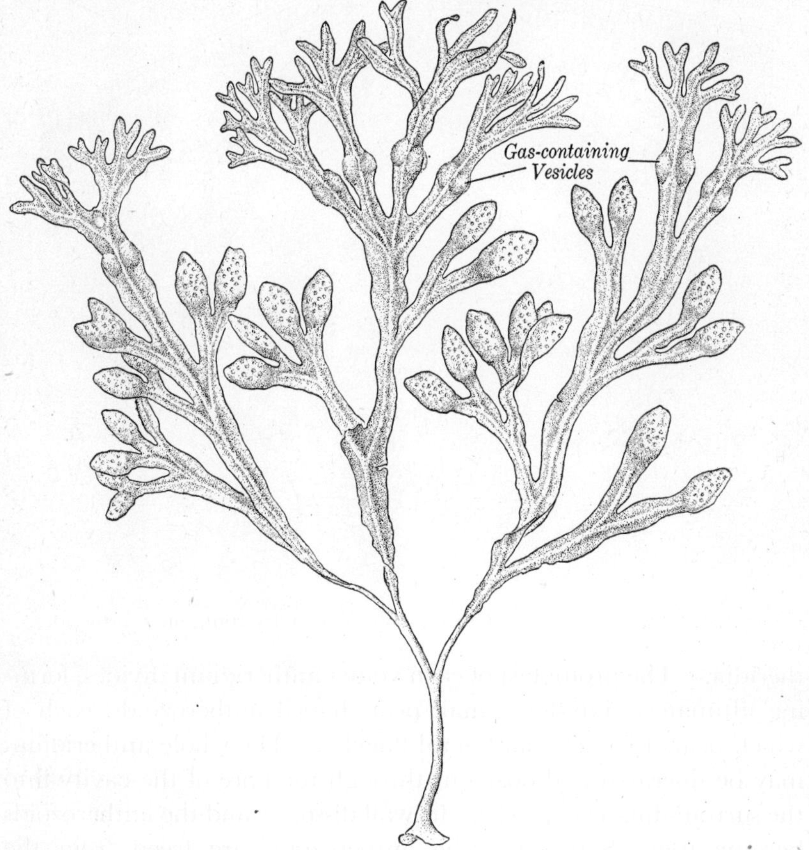

FIG. 182. A thallus (plant) of *Fucus vesiculosus*. In the swollen ends of branches are cavities (their position marked by dotlike pores) in which sex organs are produced.

approximately spherical cavities, each with a porelike opening at its apex. It is in these cavities that the sex organs (oögonia and antheridia) are produced. In some species of Fucus, oögonia and antheridia are borne in the same cavity; in other species, the two kinds of organs are produced in separate cavities; in still others, they are borne on separate plants. The cavities in which antheridia are produced (Fig. 183) are lined with branching many-celled hairs, the terminal cells of whose lateral branches become an-

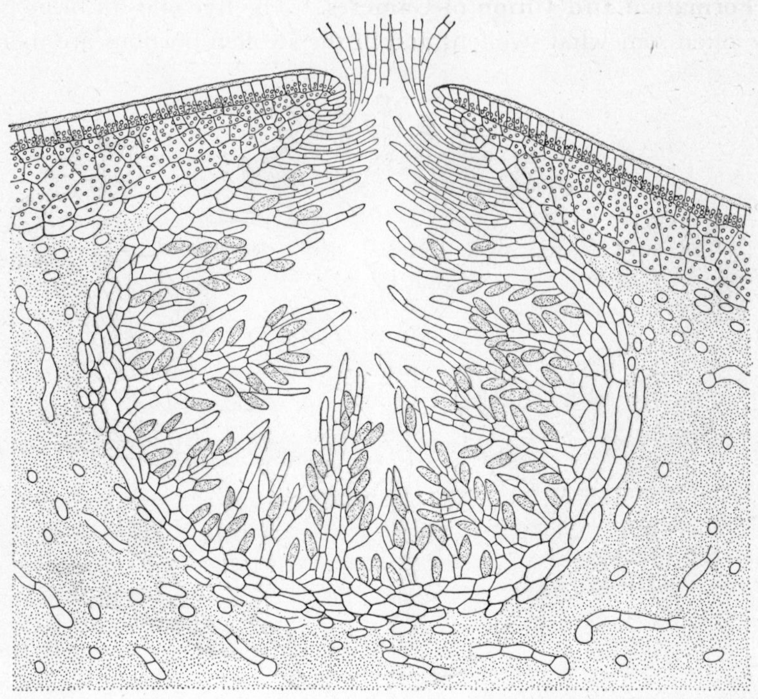

FIG. 183. *Fucus vesiculosus.* Cross section of a cavity containing antheridia.

theridia. The protoplast of each young antheridium divides, forming ultimately sixty-four small pear-shaped antherozoids, each of which bears two unequal lateral flagella. The whole antheridium may be liberated and ooze out through the pore of the cavity into the surrounding water, where its wall dissolves and the antherozoids become free. Sometimes the antherozoids are freed from the antheridium while the latter is still in place on the branch that produced it (Fig. 185, *B*).

The oögonia (Fig. 184) are borne at the ends of short stalks. A young oögonium is one-nucleate. During its development three nuclear divisions occur. Then the eight-nucleate protoplast divides into eight one-nucleate eggs, which are angular because of mutual pressure (Fig. 185, *C*). The wall of an oögonium has three layers. After the eggs are mature, the outermost wall layer breaks; and the eggs, still surrounded by the two inner wall layers, are discharged. The enclosed mass of eggs floats out through the pore of the cavity into the surrounding water (Fig. 185, *D*, *E*). Here the eggs are

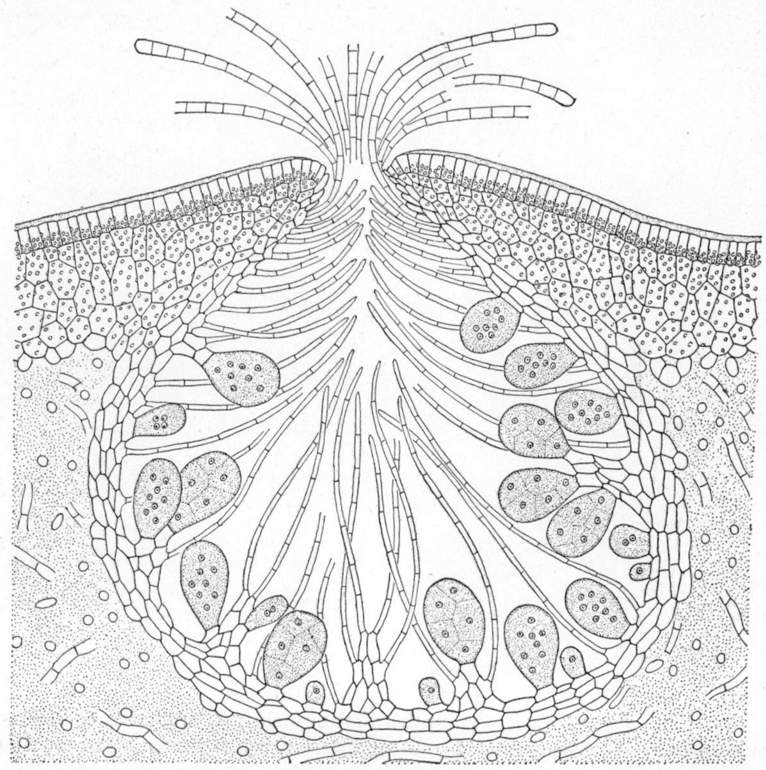

FIG. 184. *Fucus vesiculosus.* Cross section of a cavity containing oögonia.

freed by the rupture and dissolution of the remaining oögonial wall layers. The eggs become spherical as soon as they are free. Antherozoids that come into the neighborhood of an egg swim toward it (Fig. 185, *F*), apparently in response to a chemical stimulus; and many antherozoids become attached by their flagella to the egg. Eventually one antherozoid makes its way into the egg, the cytoplasm of the egg and that of the antherozoid unite, and their nuclei unite.

The zygote soon settles to the bottom of the water, secretes a wall, and becomes attached to some solid object. Within a few hours it divides to form two daughter cells, one of which sends out a short rhizoid that attaches the young two-celled plant more firmly to the substrate (Fig. 186). Both daughter cells divide, other divisions follow in rapid succession, and within three or four days the young

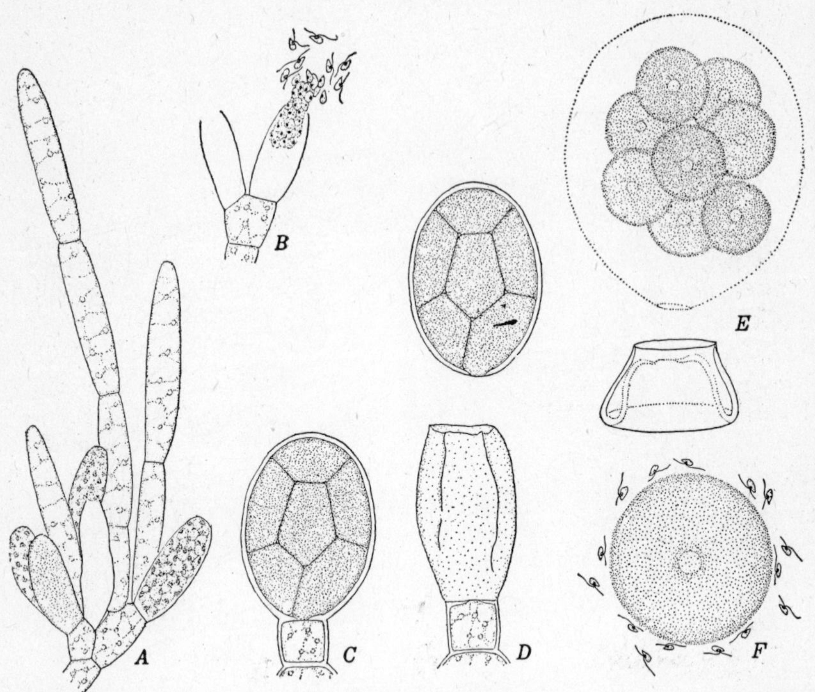

Fig. 185. *Fucus furcatus*. *A*, antheridial branch. *B*, antheridium liberating antherozoids. *C*, oögonium. *D*, oögonium from which the group of eight eggs is escaping. *E*, a later stage; eggs are separating. *F*, egg surrounded by antherozoids.

plant consists of a hundred or more cells. This plant is approximately spherical; but as growth continues, it becomes flattened and resembles a branch tip of a mature plant.

Sargassum. Among other brown algae which, like Fucus, form small motile antherozoids and large nonmotile eggs is the "gulf weed" (*Sargassum*, Fig. 187). Unlike most other brown algae it is found chiefly in warmer portions of the oceans. Sargassum has essentially the same type of flat, branching thallus as Fucus; but most species show a more marked differentiation into stemlike and leaflike branches. Many branches terminate in gas bladders; and if a plant becomes detached, it floats freely. Certain species of Sargassum never grow attached to a substrate. Two of these occur in abundance in the so-called "Sargasso Sea," an area of about a

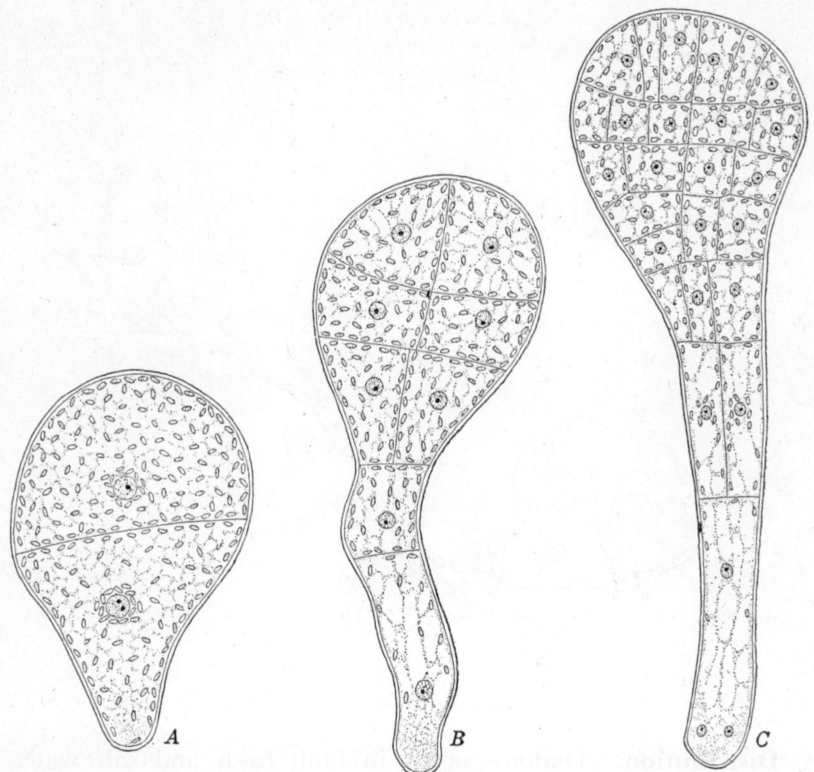

FIG. 186. Young plants of *Fucus furcatus* produced by the germination of a zygote. *A*, one day old. *B*, two days old. *C*, four days old.

quarter million square miles, east of Florida and the West Indies. These free-floating species multiply continuously by means of the fragmentation of the thallus; they never produce gametes.

BACILLARIOPHYCEAE (DIATOMS)

Nature. On the basis of the color of their plastids the diatoms seem to be brown algae, but they are considered to constitute a distinct class. They differ from other algae in that each cell has a silicified wall consisting of two overlapping halves. They form also rejuvenescent cells of a special type not found in other algae. Their plastids contain a brown pigment, somewhat different from the fucoxanthin of brown algae, that masks the chlorophyll which also is present.

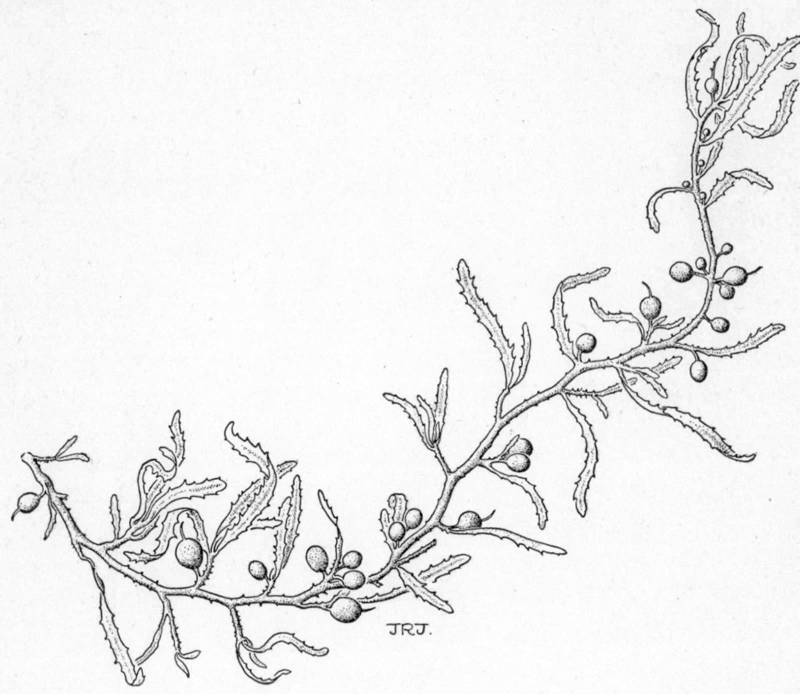

FIG. 187. Portion of a thallus of *Sargassum natans*. From the "Sargasso Sea."

Distribution. Diatoms occur in both fresh and salt water. They compose an important part of the plankton of the oceans, and in early spring and late fall they make up the major portion of the plankton of fresh-water lakes. Other diatoms of both fresh and salt water grow intermingled with, and attached to, algae of other classes, or upon rocks and other solid bodies in the water.

The siliceous wall of a diatom does not decay after the death of the cell, and great numbers of the walls accumulate at the bottom of any body of water in which diatoms live. Layers of fossil diatom walls deposited in former arms of the ocean are known as "diatomaceous earth." Some deposits of this nature in the western United States are over 1,000 feet in thickness. Diatomaceous earth is of considerable economic importance as a heat-insulating substance, as a source of fine abrasives, and as a filtering material. The abrasive qualities of some silver polishes and tooth pastes are due to fossil diatom walls.

Structure. Diatoms are usually one-celled, but in some species the cells are united into filamentous or branching colonies. The shape of the cell differs greatly in various species, but in all cases the wall consists of two overlapping halves that fit together as do the two parts of a candy box. The wall is strongly impregnated with silica. Cell walls of diatoms are characteristically marked by minute pores or short lines. The markings either are radially arranged with reference to a central point (Fig. 188), or their ar-

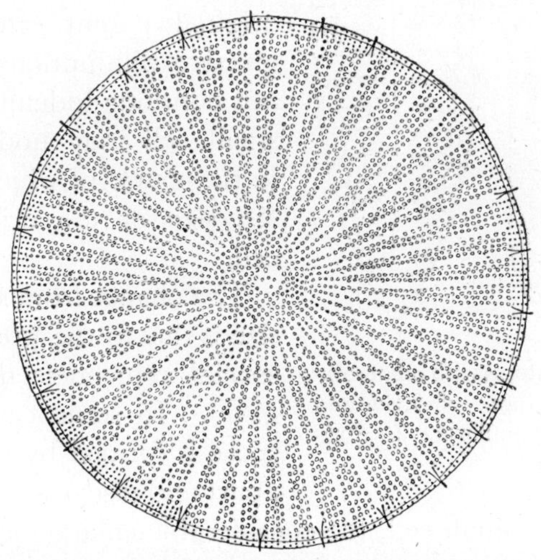

FIG. 188. A diatom (Stephanodiscus) whose wall markings are radially arranged. After G. M. Smith, *The Fresh-Water Algae of the United States*, published by the McGraw-Hill Book Company.

rangement is bilaterally symmetrical with respect to the long axis of the cell (Fig. 189). There is a layer of dense cytoplasm just within the wall; within this layer is a central vacuole. Included in the dense cytoplasm are one, two, or several brown plastids. The single nucleus is imbedded either in the outer dense cytoplasmic layer or in a strand of dense cytoplasm that cuts across the central vacuole.

Reproduction. Nuclear division is followed by a division of the whole protoplast, each of the two daughter protoplasts remaining within one of the closely fitting halves of the parent-cell wall. The development of a half-wall over the naked face of each daughter protoplast completes the enclosure of the daughter cell by a typical two-parted wall. The daughter cells in most species separate; but in some species they remain attached. Of the daughter cells formed by division, one is of the same size as the parent cell, the other slightly smaller. In consequence of reproduction by cell division, most of the cells in time are appreciably smaller than the original parent cell. The progressive diminution in size does not continue indefinitely, since a small cell may undergo change in the course of which it grows to the size of the original parent cell.

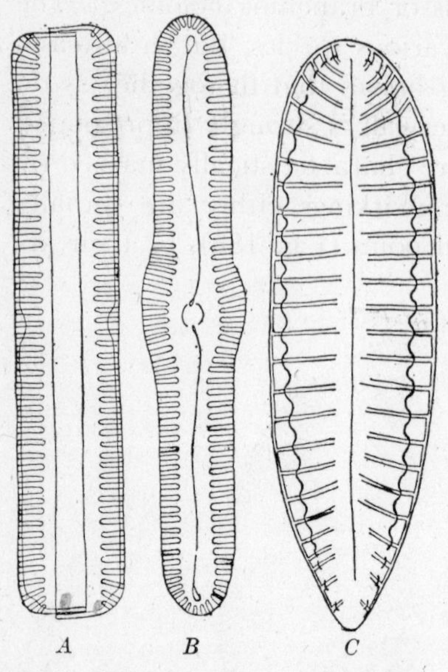

FIG. 189. Diatoms with bilaterally symmetrical markings. *A*, *B*, side and top views of a Pinnularia. *C*, Surirella in side view.

The change from small to large size is due to the production of a special rejuvenescent cell (*auxospore*). In some cases an auxospore is formed by the spreading apart and discarding of the halves of the wall of a small cell, the considerable enlargement of its protoplast, and the formation of new half-walls about the enlarged protoplast. In other cases the auxospore is a zygote formed by the union of two protoplasts. An auxospore, no matter how formed, divides longitudinally to form two vegetative cells.

CHAPTER XV

RHODOPHYCEAE (RED ALGAE)

Nature. The characteristic color of red algae is due to the presence in their plastids of a red pigment (*phycoerythrin*) which masks the chlorophyll. Color, however, is not a certain criterion, since the thalli of certain species of Rhodophyceae are olive-green, golden-brown, olive-black, or purplish-black. Among the structural features which distinguish the red algae are the occurrence of nonflagellate male as well as female gametes and, in most species, the presence of broad cytoplasmic connections between adjoining cells of the plant body.

The union of nonmotile gametes of different sizes, characteristic of the red algae, is so unlike gametic union in other algae that the Rhodophyceae appear to have arisen entirely independently. Primitive one-celled organisms from which they may have been derived are, however, unknown; and the origin of the class is obscure.

Distribution and Structure. Rhodophyceae, like Phaeophyceae, are chiefly marine. They are most abundant in the warmer waters of the oceans, but they are by no means absent in cooler regions. They always grow attached to some solid object and frequently below the levels exposed by tides. In cooler waters the lowest depths at which algae, chiefly reds, occur are 150 to 180 feet. In regions somewhat nearer the equator, such as the Mediterranean, where a larger proportion of the days are sunny and where, because of the sun's position, its rays penetrate the water for a considerable distance during a greater part of the year, red algae have been dredged from depths of 300 to 600 feet A few Rhodophyceae, including members of the widespread genus Batrachospermum, live in fresh water.

Although none of them attain to so great a size as do some brown algae, the numerous species of red algae show much variation in both size and form (Fig. 190). In some, the thallus is a much-branched feathery structure; in others, it is flat and leaflike, thin and delicate, or tough, leathery, and compact. The thalli of those red algae known as Corallines are heavily impregnated with lime. The coralline algae are especially abundant in tropical waters and are of great importance in the formation of "coral" reefs and atolls.

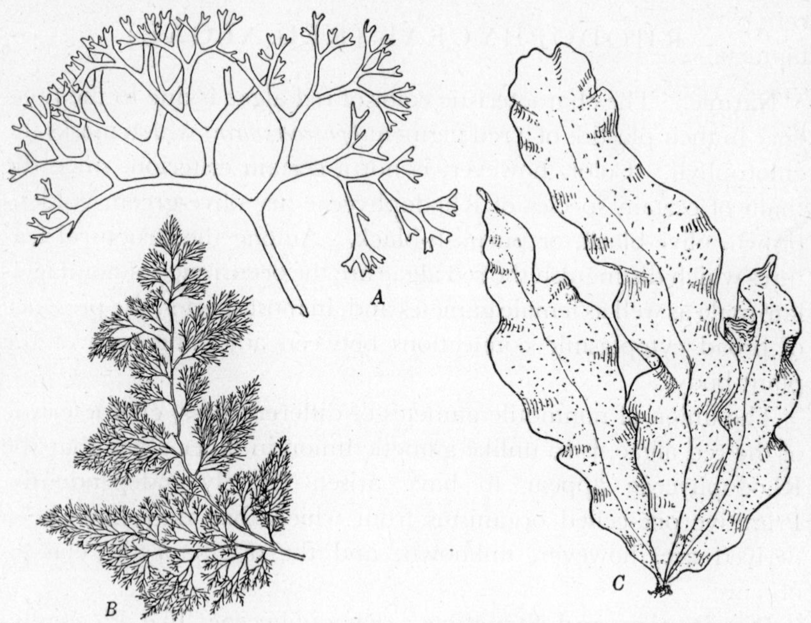

FIG. 190. Types of red algae. *A*, thick, branching thallus of Chondrus. *B*, feathery thallus of Polysiphonia. *C*, thin, leaflike thallus of Grinnellia.

Of the two genera discussed in this chapter, one is typical of the Rhodophyceae whose reproductive organs and life cycle are relatively simple; the other is representative of those with more elaborate reproductive organs and a more complicated history.

NEMALION

Structure. *Nemalion* is a marine alga of widespread distribution, which grows attached to rocks in the intertidal zone. The thallus (Fig. 191, *A*) is a sparingly branched cylinder 1/32 to 1/4 inch in diameter and up to 2 feet in length. The central portion of a cylindrical branch consists of an interwoven mass of filaments which run lengthwise. The outer portion of the branch consists of many short, branched filaments, whose arrangement is in general perpendicular to that of the central filaments. Intervening spaces between both lateral and longitudinal filaments are filled with a firm, colorless gelatinous substance. Adjacent cells in a filament are not completely separated by walls; their protoplasts are in contact by means of a coarse strand of cytoplasm which extends through a central pore in the crosswall between each two adjoining cells. All cells are one-nucleate. The cells of the longitudinal filaments are colorless; each cell of the lateral filaments contains a single reddish-brown, star-shaped plastid, within which is a pyrenoid.

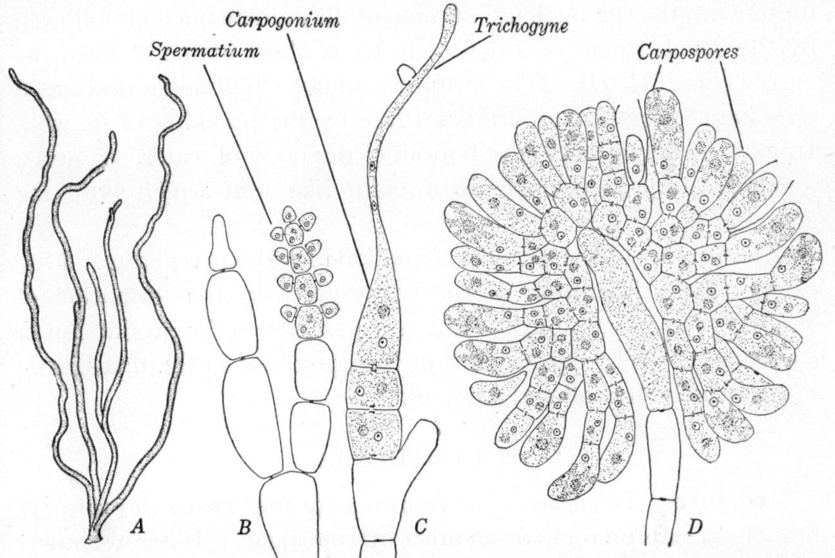

Fig. 191. Nemalion. *A*, thallus. *B*, portion of a branch bearing spermatia. *C*, portion of a branch bearing a carpogonium; a spermatium has united with the trichogyne. *D*, cluster of carpospores borne on branches that have developed from the zygote. All after G. M. Smith, *Cryptogamic Botany*, published by the McGraw-Hill Book Company.

Formation and Union of Gametes. The male gametes (*spermatia*) are borne laterally and terminally toward the outer ends of lateral filaments of the thallus (Fig. 191, *B*). Each spermatium is a small, nonmotile cell. They are liberated by a rupture of the enclosing walls and are carried in all directions by currents of water. As they float about in the water they form new walls.

A female sex organ (*carpogonium*) is the terminal cell of an unbranched three- or four-celled filament borne on a lateral filament of the thallus (Fig. 191, *C*). The free end of the carpogonium is prolonged into a long hairlike outgrowth, the *trichogyne*. The basal portion of the protoplast of the carpogonium, including its nucleus, is the egg. Spermatia carried by water currents may lodge against and become attached to the trichogyne. The walls of one spermatium and of the trichogyne break down at the point of contact, and the protoplast of the spermatium moves into the trichogyne. The nucleus of the spermatium divides shortly after entering the trichogyne; the two daughter nuclei move toward the base of the carpogonium, and one of them, reaching the enlarged basal portion, unites with the egg nucleus. Union of the gamete nuclei is followed by the development of a dense cluster of short filaments from the zygote (Fig. 191, *D*). The terminal cell of each filament becomes a *carpospore*. The carpospore is set free by the breaking of its wall. It floats away, settles to the bottom of the body of water, secretes a new wall, and develops into a plant like that which bore the gametes.

Life Cycle. The history of Nemalion includes two phases. One extends from liberation of the carpospores to the formation of gametes; the other, from the union of gametes to the production of carpospores. The carpospores in turn give rise to the first phase, the plant which produces gametes.

POLYSIPHONIA

Structure. *Polysiphonia* is a marine alga that grows in profusely branching tufts on rocks or on other marine algae. It has a slender, cylindrical, branching axis (Fig. 192). The axis and each of its main branches consist of several superimposed tiers of cells which are elongated in the direction of the length of the branch. Each tier includes a central cell which is surrounded by a single layer of jacket cells. At each end of the central cell is a thick cytoplasmic strand connecting it with the central cell of the adjoining tier. The jacket cells of each tier are similarly connected with the central cell of the same tier. The final small lateral branches are simple filaments whose cells are connected by cytoplasmic strands. All cells are one-nucleate, and each contains many small, disk-shaped, reddish plastids.

Formation and Union of Gametes. Male and female gametes are borne on separate plants. The spermatia (male gametes) are densely crowded on filaments borne laterally on the axis and on its main branches (Fig. 192, *B*). The spermatia become separated from the filaments and are carried in all directions by water currents.

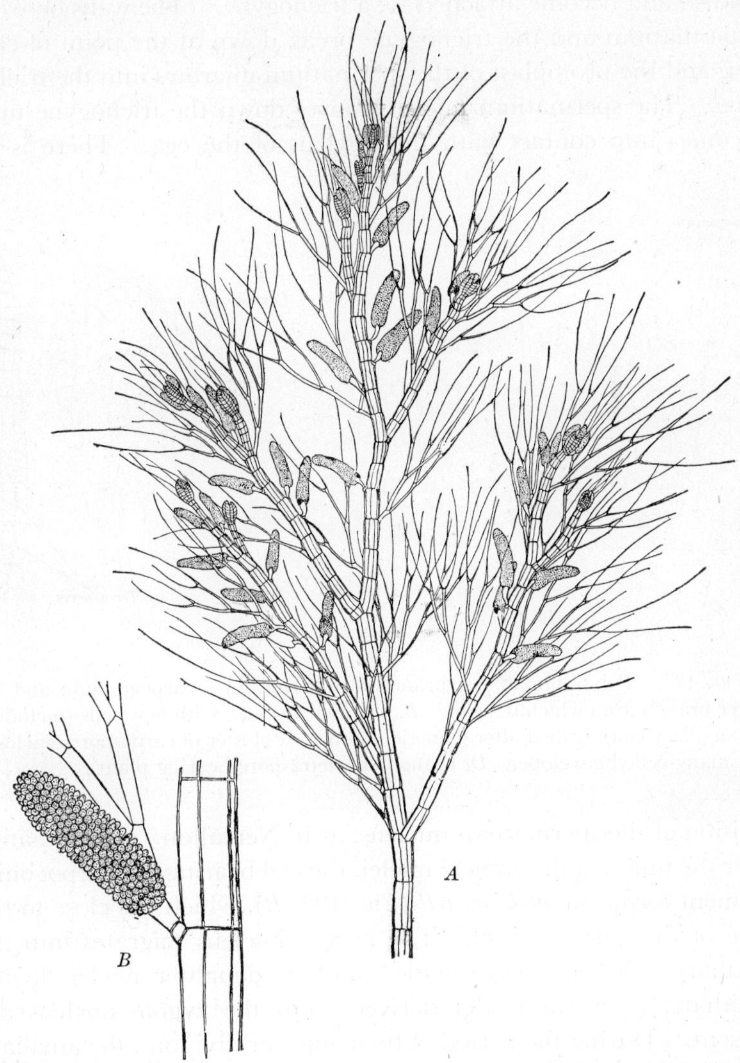

FIG. 192. Polysiphonia. *A*, portion of a thallus with spermatium-bearing branches. *B*, portion of a branch bearing spermatia. Both redrawn from Thuret.

A carpogonium (Fig. 193, *A*) is the terminal member of a short, lateral, four-celled filament. It is similar to a carpogonium of

Nemalion, consisting of a hairlike terminal trichogyne and an enlarged basal portion.

As in Nemalion, spermatia carried by water currents may lodge against, and become attached to, a trichogyne. The walls between a spermatium and the trichogyne break down at the point of contact, and the protoplast of the spermatium migrates into the trichogyne. The spermatium nucleus moves down the trichogyne until it comes into contact with the nucleus of the egg. There is no

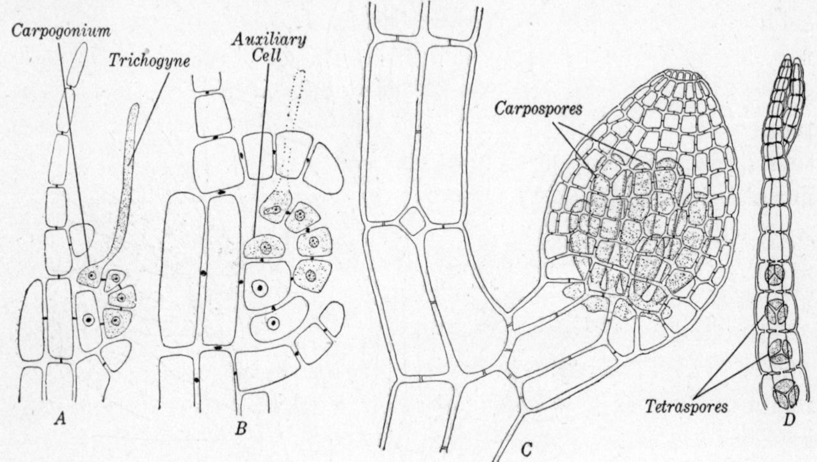

FIG. 193. Polysiphonia. *A*, branch terminating in a carpogonium, and the larger branch from which it arose. *B*, a similar branch, with new cells (including the auxiliary cell) formed after gametic union. *C*, cluster of carpospores enclosed in a many-celled envelope. *D*, branch of a tetraspore-bearing plant.

division of the spermatium nucleus, as in Nemalion. Immediately after the union of the gamete nuclei, the cell bearing the carpogonial filament forms an *auxiliary cell* (Fig. 193, *B*), which lies close to the base of the carpogonium. The zygote nucleus migrates into the auxiliary cell and there divides, and its daughter nuclei divide. Ultimately, several nuclei derived from the zygote nucleus are present. During the period of these nuclear divisions, the auxiliary cell has become large and irregular in shape, because of fusion with adjoining cells. Many short filaments, containing nuclei descended from the zygote nucleus, grow from the auxiliary cell; and a carpospore is formed at the tip of each filament. In Polysiphonia the cluster of carpospores is not freely exposed but is enclosed by a flask-shaped, many-celled envelope, developed from neighboring cells of the thallus. The envelope is open at its apex (Fig. 193, *C*).

The carpospores become free, float out through the apical opening of the surrounding envelope, and then are carried about by water currents. Such of them as come to rest upon a solid object may develop into plants exactly similar in appearance, so far as their vegetative structure is concerned, to the plants that bore spermatia and carpogonia. The plants developed from carpospores do not, however, bear gametes. Instead, they produce *spore mother cells*, each of which divides to form four spores. These spores, because they are formed in groups of four, are called *tetraspores*. The tetraspores (Fig. 193, *D*) are formed within the branching axis of the plant body. Each of several successive tiers of an axis contains a single group of tetraspores that lies between the central cell and the jacket layer. The tetraspores become free and are dispersed by water currents. Those which settle to the bottom of the water may germinate. A plant produced by the germination of a tetraspore always bears gametes instead of tetraspores.

Life Cycle. The history of Polysiphonia includes three distinct phases, which follow one another in regular succession. One phase includes the plant which develops from a tetraspore and produces gametes. The next phase extends from the union of gamete nuclei to the production of carpospores. The third phase is represented by the plant which develops from a carpospore and produces tetraspores. A tetraspore in turn gives rise to a gamete-bearing plant.

CHAPTER XVI

SCHIZOMYCETES (BACTERIA)

Occurrence and Distribution. Antoni van Leeuwenhoek (1632–1723) of Delft, Holland, was probably the first person to see bacteria; certainly he was the first to describe them. He became interested in minute structures because he used the crude lenses of his day to study the threads used in the making of linens. He became interested also in the development of microscope lenses; and with the improvements which he made, he could see objects not previously observed. Using magnifications of about 150 diameters, he was able to distinguish living objects in a drop of saliva. In a letter to the Royal Society of London in September, 1683, he wrote:

> . . . and then to my great surprize perceived that the aforesaid matter contained very many small living Animals, which moved themselves very extravagantly. the biggest sort had the shape of *A*. their motion was strong and nimble, and they darted themselves thro the water or spittle, as a Jack or Pike does thro the water. These were generally not many in number. The *2d* sort had the shape of *B*. these spun about like a Top, and took a course sometimes on one side, as is shown at *C*. and *D*. they were more in number than the first. In the *3d*. sort I could not well distinguish the Figure, for sometimes it seem'd to be an Oval, and other times a Circle. These were so small that they seem'd no bigger than *E*. and therewithal so swift, that I can compare them to nothing better than a swarm of Flies or Gnats, flying and turning among one another in a small space.

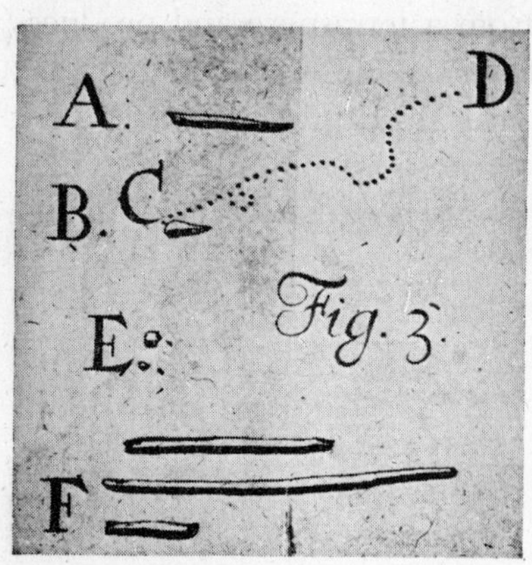

Fig. 194. Leeuwenhoek's figures of bacteria, published in 1683.

From his drawings (Fig. 194) there is no doubt that the "small living Animals" were bacteria.

In 1876, Pasteur, as a result of his extensive studies on fermentation and decay, first gave to the world some notion of the great importance of bacteria. In the same year, Koch demonstrated that anthrax, a disease of cattle, is due to a specific bacterium; and, in 1882, he showed that human tuberculosis and Asiatic cholera likewise are caused by bacteria.

Bacteria occur everywhere and under all conditions that are not absolutely fatal to living matter. They have been found in undisturbed soil to a depth of more than 16 feet, although the great majority of soil bacteria occur within the upper 6 inches. They are present in both fresh and salt waters, often at great depths. The ice and snow of glaciers and icebergs contain bacteria, though never in great numbers. In the lower layers of the atmosphere they are very abundant; they are present also at higher levels, as is shown by their occurrence in hailstones. The cells of many bacteria, in a dormant state or as spores, may be cooled to the temperature of liquid air (about 190° C. below the freezing point) or may be kept at the temperature of boiling water for long periods without being killed. Most of them, however, can grow and multiply only at the temperatures at which other organisms thrive; in fact, bacteria of certain species are active only within a temperature range of a very few degrees.

A Bacterial Cell. Bacteria are the most minute of one-celled plants; some of the smallest are less than 1/125,000 inch in diameter, and the largest are not more than 1/5,000 inch in diameter and 1/320 inch in length. On the basis of their shape, bacteria are referred to three general types (Fig. 195). A bacterium of spherical form is called a *coccus;* one that is rod-shaped, a *bacillus;* and one of spiral form, a *spirillum*. Under certain conditions some bacteria become very irregular in shape and sometimes unusually large. These modified cells are "involution forms." Their appearance is thought to be due to growth under unfavorable conditions; but some bacteria, such as the nitrogen-fixing species to be discussed later, take on at least three distinct forms during a complete life cycle.

The protoplast of a bacterial cell is surrounded by a rigid wall. In most cases this wall probably contains *chitin*, a substance that is characteristic of the hard outer coverings of the bodies of insects; in a very few instances bacterial cell walls have been reported to contain a substance allied to cellulose. Outside the wall in many cases is a slimy gelatinous sheath. The protoplasm is always dense, containing very small vacuoles and granules of varying sizes. There are no plastids; and true chlorophyll is never present, although some

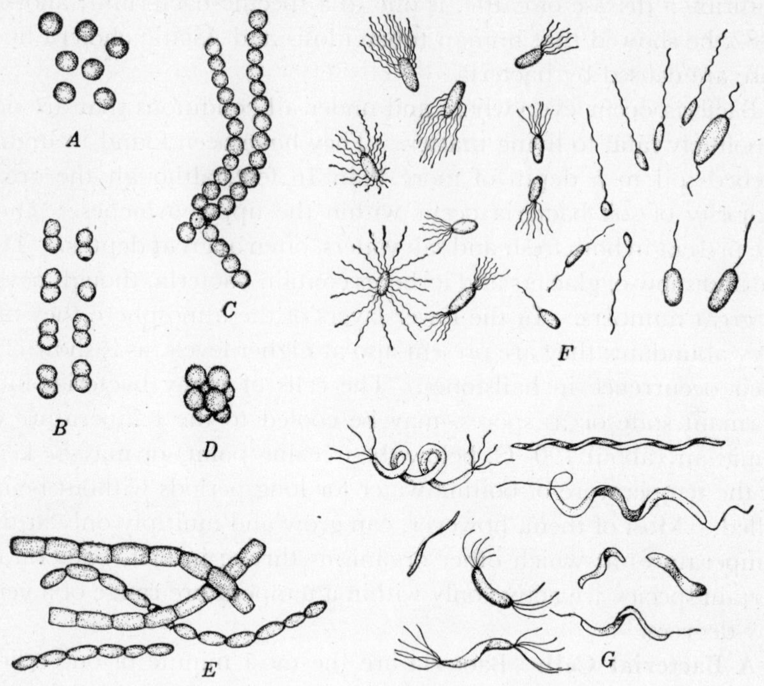

Fig. 195. Types of bacterial cells. *A–D*, species of cocci. *E*, species of bacilli. *F*, flagellated bacilli of various species. *G*, spirilla.

bacteria produce pigments of various colors, which are contained either in the protoplasm or in the enveloping sheath. Some of the granules are composed of glycogen; some, of proteins; and some, of fats. Other granules are present, which take up the same dyes as do chromosomes; these are ordinarily distributed throughout the protoplasm, but in a few species they are aggregated in a central mass in each cell. Many investigators have thought that these stainable granules in bacterial cells represent nuclear material; others have suggested that the whole cell is in effect a nucleus.

Many bacteria move by means of flagella (Fig. 195, *F*, *G*). In some, there is a single flagellum at one end of the cell; in others, there are several flagella at one or at each end; and still others bear many flagella at various points. Most cocci are without flagella;

the greater number of bacilli and spirilla are flagellated. The rate of movement varies greatly. Bacteria of a few species can travel a distance of 2,000 times their own length in an hour; the spirillum of Asiatic cholera has been seen to move for a short time at a rate of 7 inches, or 80,000 times its own length, per hour.

Reproduction. The cell divides by a process of constriction (p. 232), which cuts it into two equal daughter cells. In some species the parent cell elongates just before division. Most bacteria, however, divide first; and the daughter cells later grow in length. Cell division in many bacteria occurs about once every half hour; a few divide even more rapidly. At the rate of one division each half hour, the descendants of a single individual at the end of 24 hours would number 281,474,976,710,656. Numbers of this order, however, are never approached because environmental conditions, such as the limits of food supply, soon check growth and division.

Another method of division is described in certain species; at one stage in the life of the organism its protoplast breaks up, and each of the many fragments becomes reorganized into an independent cell.

Colony Formation. After the division of a cell, its daughter cells may separate or may remain in contact; in the latter case a colony of characteristic type results. The cells of nearly all spirilla ordinarily separate at once after division (Fig. 195, *G*). Bacilli often remain attached in pairs or in long chains (Fig. 195, *E*). Cocci occur in the form of a four-celled plate, of a cube of eight cells, or (the commonest type) of a large mass of cells like a cluster of grapes (Fig. 195, *A–D*). In one order of bacteria (Actinomycetes), the cells remain attached in branched filaments.

When bacteria are living in a liquid medium, the gelatinous sheath outside the wall, if one is present, commonly swells greatly. Individual cells or colonies then adhere by means of their swollen sheaths in large masses of irregular shape. The result is the formation of the scum (zoögloea) so often present on the surface of a liquid in which bacteria are abundant.

Dormant Stages. Under various conditions unfavorable to growth and reproduction, such as the drying out of the substrate, some bacterial cells pass into a dormant state. Such a cell loses water, and its protoplast may become separated from the wall; but more often the entire cell shrinks slightly and in this condition may remain unchanged for a very long time. When conditions are again favorable for development, the cell absorbs water and resumes its ordinary activities.

Fig. 196. Bacterial colonies on an agar plate after several days' growth. Each colony has developed, through repeated divisions, from a single cell.

In certain species the dormant cell takes the form of a *spore* (Fig. 197), the protoplast shrinking, rounding up within the old cell wall, and secreting a new, thicker wall. The spores of bacteria are especially resistant to drought, starvation, and extreme temperatures. In some species a spore, though shorter, is of greater diameter than the old wall; and consequently the whole structure has the shape of a spindle or of a drumstick. Spores remain dormant until conditions are again suitable for growth, when they absorb water and resume the typical form (Fig. 197, *C*, *D*). Spores of the anthrax bacillus have been found capable of such return to an active condition after 18 years in dried-up cultures. In the cases of a few bacilli, a spore retains its wall when it returns to the ordinary condition;

but more commonly the spore wall is broken at this time by the enlargement of the protoplast, and a new wall is formed.

Metabolism. Since bacteria lack chlorophyll, they can not manufacture carbohydrates (with certain possible exceptions, to be mentioned later) and therefore are dependent, at least for their

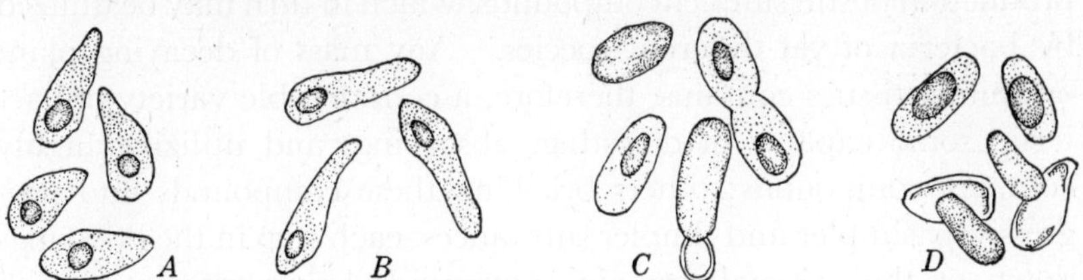

FIG. 197. The formation and germination of bacterial spores. *A*, spore formation in *Bacillus fusiformis*. *B*, spore formation in *Bacillus polymorpha*. *C*, spores and their return to activity in *Bacillus megatherium*. *D*, spores and their return to activity in *Bacillus mycoides*. All after de Soriano.

carbohydrate foods, upon the products of other organisms. The majority of species require proteins also, but some can use certain compounds of ammonium in the manufacture of proteins. Some bacteria obtain foods from dead bodies of plants or animals or from substances that have been made by plants or animals. Plants that secure foods in this manner are *saprophytes*. Other bacteria obtain foods from living plants or animals (*hosts*); such bacteria are *parasites*, and many of these cause diseases of their hosts. Both saprophytic and parasitic methods of nutrition are dependent upon the action of a variety of enzymes secreted by the bacteria concerned.

Most bacteria utilize in respiration free oxygen obtained from the air. Such bacteria are *aerobes*. Other bacteria can respire without a supply of free oxygen, and they therefore live and thrive in conditions under which air is excluded. These are *anaerobes*. Most anaerobic bacteria can live only in the presence of organic substances containing oxygen in combination; and it is probable that the oxygen-containing compounds are broken down by enzymes, the energy so released being utilized by the bacteria.

The destruction of organic substances, including the dead bodies of plants and animals, by saprophytic bacteria is of vital importance to more complex organisms. The processes involved in this destruction, commonly known as *putrefaction* and *decay*, release energy which is utilized by the bacteria. Proteins, fats, and other substances contained in the cells of plants and animals may be used by bacteria as foods. Some bacteria can utilize these directly. The metabolic activities of such bacteria result in the production of simpler compounds, which may then be used as foods by bacteria of other species. The activity of these latter bacteria results in the production of still simpler compounds, which in turn may be utilized by bacteria of yet different species. Any mass of decaying plant or animal tissues contains, therefore, a considerable variety of bacteria: some capable of digesting, absorbing, and utilizing highly complex compounds; others breaking these compounds into progressively simpler and simpler substances, each step in the breaking-down of the original organic compounds being associated with enzymes produced by bacteria of particular species. Some of the compounds formed during bacterial decomposition are responsible for the disagreeable odors associated with decaying organic matter. Especially is this true if decay takes place in the presence of much water.

Some Economic Aspects of Bacterial Action. Among the substances produced in the course of the metabolic processes carried on by bacteria are many that are useful or beneficial in connection with human activity. Many industries, indeed, are wholly or largely dependent upon the results of bacterial action. This is true, for example, in very large measure, of dairying.

Fresh milk consists of 85 to 90 per cent water, three to four per cent proteins (chiefly casein), about four per cent each carbohydrates (especially milk sugar) and fats, and small amounts of inorganic substances. Milk is an emulsion in which the fats are distributed through the watery solution as minute droplets, each surrounded by a thin film of casein. Many bacteria fall into the container as the milk is drawn from the cows; these bacteria, together with those already present in the milk and in the container, at once begin to utilize as foods various substances present in the milk and consequently increase in number. Prominent among the results of their metabolic activities are the conversion of milk sugar into lactic acid, which sours the milk, and the coagulation of casein, which causes curdling.

The activities of bacteria can be checked by rapidly heating milk to a temperature of 60° to 65° C. for 20 to 30 minutes and then quickly cooling it. This simple method may be used when small quantities of milk are to be treated. In larger dairies, however, where thousands of gallons are handled each day, special complicated machinery is in use; and the heating and cooling are carried on as a continuous process while the milk passes through pipes to the place where it is to be bottled and sealed. This process of *pasteurization* (so called because it was devised by Pasteur) kills most of the active bacteria but not those which are in the spore condition.

In making cheese, the casein of milk is coagulated by suitable reagents, and the coagulated mass (cheese) is allowed to ripen. In the processes involved in the ripening of cheese, bacteria play important rôles. Some cause chemical changes in the coagulated casein, which result in a softening of the cheese. The spongy texture of Swiss and other cheeses is due to the presence of gas-forming bacteria. Other bacteria, together with some of the larger fungi, produce substances that give to various cheeses their characteristic odors and flavors.

The minute droplets of fat present in milk tend to run together and rise when lactic-acid bacteria and certain other species destroy the casein film that surrounds each droplet. Churning of this floating mass of droplets (cream) results in a further aggregation of the fat globules into butter. The amount of butter obtained in the churning of cream depends upon the extent to which the casein films have been destroyed and may therefore be increased by the use of cultures of appropriate species of bacteria. The flavor of butter also is affected favorably or otherwise by the activities of certain bacteria.

An anaerobic bacterium (Clostridium) is used extensively in the manufacture of butyl alcohol and acetone from sugar. Butyl alcohol and acetone are used as solvents in many industrial procedures. Molasses is the source of sugar in most instances, but any starchy grain may be used.

In the processes that tobacco leaves undergo after being harvested, various bacteria take an important part. While the leaves are hanging in sheds where moisture is partly controlled, changes are brought about by bacterial action; these changes, which constitute the "curing" of the leaves, include a partial decomposition of proteins and carbohydrates present. Later, the leaves are packed under carefully controlled conditions in large bins or in barrels, where bacteria, often during a period of many months, bring about a further series of changes known as "ripening." The changes involved in curing and ripening affect the flavor of the tobacco and hence its value in the preparation of pipe tobacco, cigars, and cigarettes.

Each of the varied steps preparatory to the tanning of skins of animals into leather may be completed by bacterial activity, although many tanneries now substitute chemicals for bacteria at certain stages. Most of the bacteria here concerned are of the putrefactive type, but their processes are controlled and limited. Their activity results successively in the destruction of fats and tissues adhering to the skin, in the loosening of hair from the skin, and in certain chemical changes in the skin itself. Tanning, the final step in the series, brings about a combination of proteins in the skin with tannin or some other reagent. This last process is purely chemical.

The final disposition of sewage is dependent upon the work of a host of bacteria. In the septic tank which may dispose of the sewage of a single home, bacteria (mostly anaerobic) break down the solid matter and decompose the organic substances present into very simple compounds, including water, which may without harm be allowed to seep into the soil or to flow into bodies of water.

The sewage of cities is commonly allowed to pass very slowly over beds where much of the solid matter, somewhat changed, settles. This may be dried and used as fertilizer. The more liquid portion of the sewage continues to be acted upon by putrefactive bacteria until it is completely decomposed and the disease-producing bacteria that may be present are destroyed. In some disposal plants the entire sewage is kept in continual motion until bacterial action is completed. In order to hasten the process, the sewage may be forced through sprays (Fig. 198), thus bringing its particles into contact with the air and supplying an abundance of oxygen for the aerobic bacteria which perform most of the work of decomposition.

Nitrification. The decay-producing bacteria and fungi, by their activities, prevent the continued accumulation of organic matter and so make it possible for other bacteria to free certain elements in the soil that may again become available for plant growth. In the process of decomposition most of the nitrogen formerly present in plant and animal proteins takes part in the formation of compounds of ammonium. The ammonium compounds reaching the soil are utilized in the metabolic processes of soil-inhabiting bacteria belonging to the genus Nitrosomonas. In the course of the activities of these bacteria, the ammonium compounds are oxidized into

FIG. 198. A sewage-disposal bed in which the sewage is forced through sprays to hasten decomposition. Photograph courtesy of B. P. Domogalla.

nitrites. The nitrites, in turn, are utilized by bacteria of another genus (Nitrobacter), which by further oxidation change the nitrites to nitrates. The value to these *nitrifying* bacteria (Nitrosomonas and Nitrobacter) of the oxidative processes seems to be that these processes replace ordinary respiration, liberating energy which the bacteria can utilize in the manufacture of foods. The nitrates formed by the action of nitrifying bacteria can be absorbed by green plants and used by them in building up new proteins and other nitrogenous compounds.

Denitrification. If the soil contains an excess of nitrogenous compounds, or if there is a lack of oxygen as in wet or waterlogged soils, nitrifying bacteria are unable to carry on their usual metabolic processes. Such conditions are favorable, however, for bacteria of another group (*denitrifying* bacteria) which are capable of reversing the nitrifying process. Some of the denitrifying bacteria reduce nitrates to nitrites and ammonium compounds; other species reduce nitrites to free nitrogen. Since both types of denitrifying bacteria are usually present in the soil, there is rarely any considerable accumulation of nitrates. An accumulation of nitrites may, however, occur; if so, this condition is unfavorable for the growth of green plants, since nitrites in soils have a toxic effect. In contrast with nitrifying organisms, the presence of denitrifying bacteria affects green plants adversely by reducing the supply of available nitrogenous material in the soil.

Nitrogen Fixation. It has long been known that leguminous plants (clover, peas, beans, and their relatives) in some way increase the nitrogenous content of the soil, but it was not until bacteria were found living in the nodules on the roots of such plants (Fig. 199) that the relation of bacteria to this increase was recognized. The bacteria in the root nodules do not harm the host plant, the association being of mutual benefit. The bacteria invade the host by penetrating the wall of a root hair (Fig. 200, *B*) and reproduce very rapidly. The result of their repeated division is the formation of long strands of bacterial cells, which ultimately extend into the cortical regions of the root. Each strand is surrounded by a rigid sheath of carbohydrate material. The presence of the bacteria in the cortical cells of the host supplies a stimulus to certain neighboring cells, in consequence of which the latter divide. The increase in number of cells in a localized region of the host plant results in the formation of a swelling or nodule (Fig. 200, *A*). The newly formed host cells also are invaded, until finally a large proportion of the cells of the nodule are filled with bacteria. The bacteria utilize some of the free nitrogen of the air that penetrates

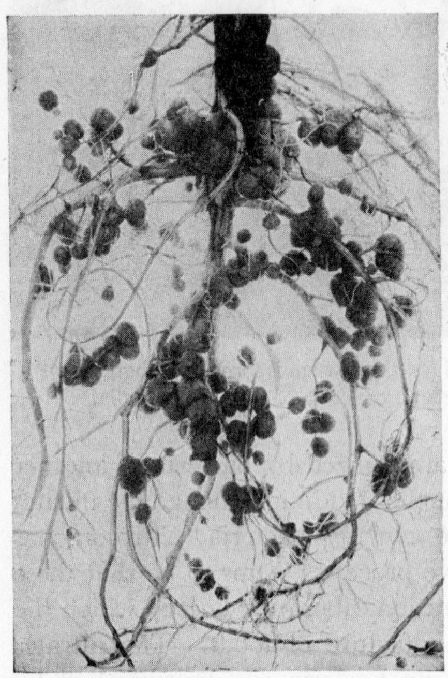

Fig. 199. Nodules on the roots of a soybean. Photograph courtesy of E. B. Fred.

the interstices of the soil, building it up ("fixing" it) into complex compounds. The bacterial cells, at first short and rod-shaped, in time become elongated; and many of them become thickened and often lobed and branched. The protoplasm of each cell becomes granular and organized into one or more distinct bodies. The

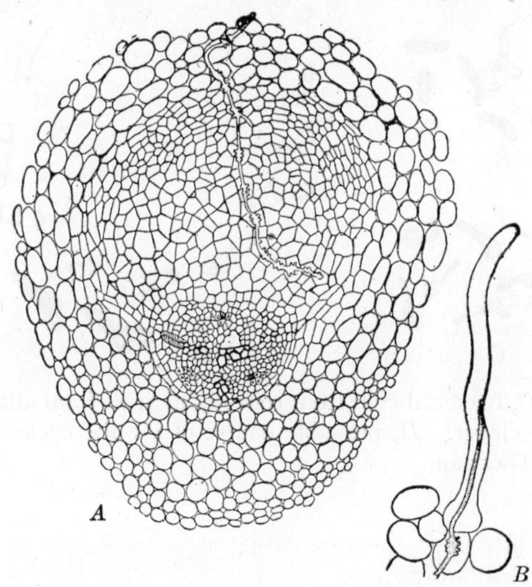

FIG. 200. *A*, cross section of a nodule on a root of a vetch. The root hair through which the bacteria entered the root has been sloughed off with the other epidermal cells; the infection strand is visible. *B*, entrance of nodule-producing bacteria through a root hair. Redrawn from Atkinson.

further history of these cells is still uncertain. As these changes begin within a nodule, some of the nitrogenous compounds previously formed pass from the bacteria in the nodule through the vascular bundles to all parts of the host plant and are used by the host. A considerable amount of nitrogenous material, however, remains in the nodule; and as the host dies and decays, its nodules also decay, so increasing the nitrogenous content of the soil. The host plant supplies the bacteria with sugars and other foods and in turn utilizes the nitrogenous compounds manufactured (fixed) by the bacteria.

Certain bacteria living independently in the soil are able, as are those living in root nodules, to fix the nitrogen of the air. One genus of these soil bacteria (Azotobacter) is of some importance, its members being capable in the course of a year of fixing from 15 to

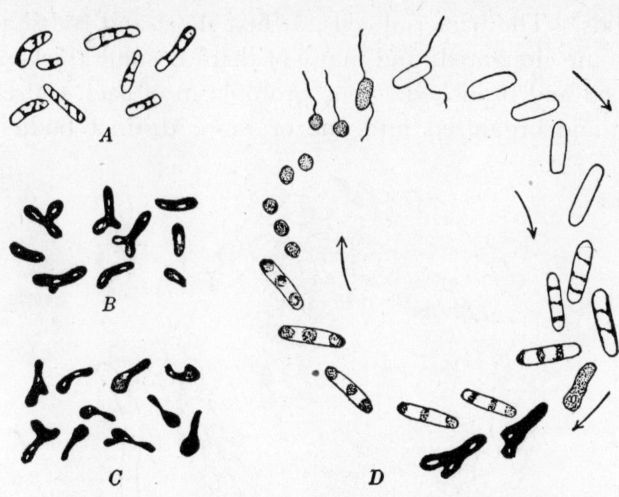

Fig. 201. *A–C*, bacterial cells from root nodules: *A*, from alfalfa; *B*, from the pea; *C*, from red clover. *D*, probable course of the life cycle of a root-nodule bacterium; after Thornton.

Fig. 202. Alfalfa plants grown in a sandy soil poor in mineral nutrients. The soil in the pot at the left was inoculated with nodule-forming bacteria, that in the right-hand pot was not inoculated. Photograph courtesy of E. B. Fred.

40 pounds of atmospheric nitrogen per acre. Some other bacteria and a blue-green alga (Nostoc) are able to fix some nitrogen, but the quantities fixed by other organisms than Azotobacter and the nodule bacteria are very small.

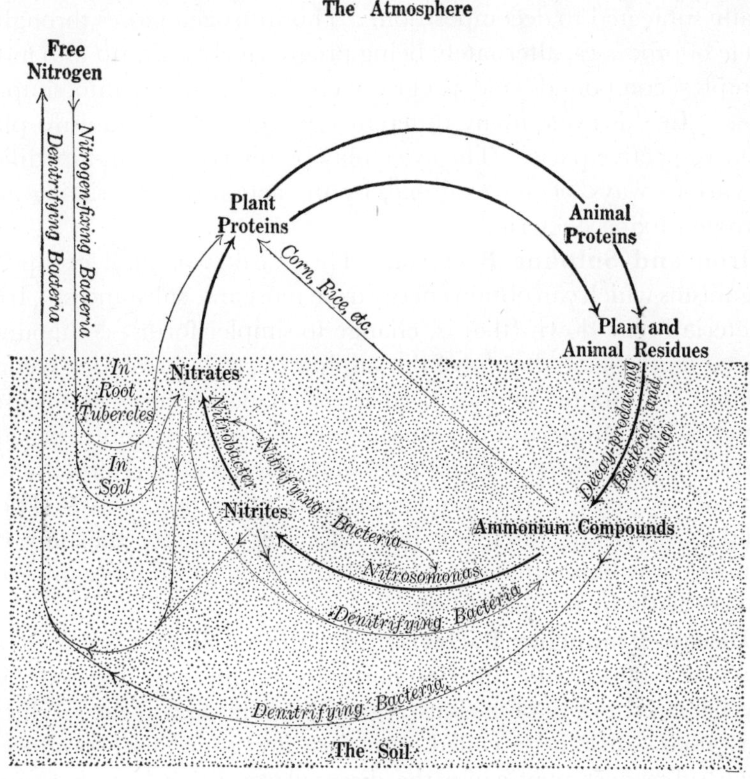

FIG. 203. Diagram illustrating the nitrogen cycle. The chemical compounds involved in the cycle are shown in **bold-faced** type; the organisms causing the changes, in *italics*. The ordinary course of the cycle is shown by heavy lines; light lines indicate variations from this course.

The Nitrogen Cycle (Fig. 203). The series of changes through which nitrogen passes in consequence of the activities of bacteria and of other organisms is the *nitrogen cycle*. The complex compounds making up the dead bodies of plants and animals are, as already described, converted into simpler compounds by the activities of decay-producing bacteria and other fungi. The nitrifying bacteria, acting upon these simpler compounds, convert them finally to nitrates, which may be absorbed by a green plant. Through the metabolic activities of the green plant, these nitrates are again built up into proteins and other very complex compounds. In turn, the green plant dies, and its substance undergoes decomposition; or the plant may serve as food for an animal, whose tissues are eventually subjected to decomposition. Thus nitrogen passes through a cycle of processes, alternately being progressively built up into more complex compounds and progressively broken down into simpler ones. In this cycle many different types of living organisms play their respective parts. The cycle may be interrupted and modified in various ways, as, for example, by the action of denitrifying and nitrogen-fixing bacteria.

Iron and Sulphur Bacteria. These are two small groups of organisms which can obtain energy from inorganic substances. Iron bacteria break down (that is, change to simpler forms) compounds containing iron, and some of the sulphur bacteria break down compounds containing sulphur. In these changes energy is released which is used in part in the building up of foods—possibly, in some cases, carbohydrates. These particular bacteria, therefore, are not dependent upon foods manufactured by other organisms. These (and possibly the nitrifying bacteria) are probably the only organisms now living that can manufacture foods from inorganic substances without the aid of light.

Disease-Producing Bacteria. A plant or animal, some or all of whose tissues do not function normally, is said to be diseased. In the bacterial decay of various vegetable, milk, and meat products, poisonous substances called *ptomaines* are sometimes produced. Such substances may cause the diseased condition known as ptomaine poisoning, although most cases of so-called ptomaine poisoning seem to be due to poisons produced by bacteria within the digestive tract of the person or animal affected. Botulism is caused by the presence in canned foods of a bacterium (*Clostridium botulinum*) which produces a virulent poison. The death rate from botulism is much higher than that from ptomaine poisoning, reaching in some poisoned groups as high as 70 per cent of the number of individuals affected.

Ptomaine poisoning and botulism are caused by saprophytic bacteria. A very large proportion of the diseases of both plants and animals result from the presence of parasitic organisms, including a great number of bacteria. The symptoms of a disease are the responses of the host to stimuli of various sorts resulting from the presence of the parasite. Prominent among such stimuli are those supplied by substances known as *toxins*, which are produced by many parasitic bacteria. The nature of bacterial toxins is not fully understood, but they are among the most poisonous substances known. The toxin of lockjaw is more than 200 times as poisonous as arsenic, 150 times as virulent as strychnine, and 40 times as poisonous as the venom of a rattlesnake. Many toxins, including those of lockjaw and diphtheria, are given off by the bacterial cells during their life and cause the serious symptoms associated with these diseases. Toxins of typhoid and of some other diseases remain within the bacterial cells until they die and decay, when the toxins are absorbed by the host.

The recovery of the host from a diseased condition is due to the development within his body of substances (*antitoxins*) which counteract the poisonous effects of toxins. Individuals differ greatly in their susceptibility to diseases caused by parasitic bacteria. Some are entirely immune to such a disease as diphtheria, whereas others are highly susceptible. A person may be immune because he has recovered from the disease and therefore has the antitoxins in his blood; or he may have been made immune by injections of "toxin-antitoxin," prepared by means of a toxin which is obtained in quantity by growing the diphtheria organism in culture. A healthy horse is inoculated with a minute amount of the toxin, then every few days with increased doses, until at the end of five or six months the quantity of toxin used is several hundred times that first used. When tests show that a satisfactory amount of antitoxin has developed, blood is taken from the horse and allowed to clot; the blood serum which contains the antitoxin is standardized, to this is added a definite quantity of the toxin, and the combined toxin-antitoxin is used in immunizing persons susceptible to diphtheria.

Viruses. In many cases the study of a disease of a plant or animal, including man, has failed to disclose the presence of bacteria or other organisms that might be responsible. An extract from the tissues of the diseased organism may be passed through a filter too fine to permit the passage of the smallest bacteria; yet the extract, after filtering, will produce disease when it is inoculated into a healthy individual. Even if the extract is greatly diluted, in some cases to the extent of one part in a million, it can cause disease. The extract contains a substance called a *virus* that brings about the diseased condition in the host. Some students of disease-producing viruses hold that they consist of or contain living organisms of ultramicroscopic size, which are able to grow and multiply.

Certain very important virus diseases of plants will be referred to in Chapter XXI.

Smallpox is a human virus disease that has been known for centuries. Immunity to smallpox is produced by inoculation (vaccination) with the virus of a similar but milder disease of cattle (cowpox). Many bacteriologists consider that cowpox is caused by a weakened form of the same virus that produces smallpox.

Yellow fever is caused by a virus transmitted through a mosquito which has previously bitten a victim of the fever. Apparently the virus undergoes some change in the body of the mosquito, because yellow fever will result from a bite only if some days have elapsed since the mosquito has bitten a diseased person. Parrot fever (psittacosis) is similarly caused by contact with certain birds. Little is yet known as to the details of the transmission of these diseases. The virus of epidemic infantile paralysis enters the body either by way of the nasal passages, thence finding its way into the brain cavity, or by way of the mouth and alimentary tract; in either case it affects the spinal cord.

Hydrophobia, influenza, and chicken pox are other human diseases that are ascribed to viruses. There are still differences of opinion, however, as to the real causal agents. Typhus or eruptive fever, trench fever, and Rocky Mountain spotted fever are usually listed as virus diseases but differ from most of these in that the bodies of insects which transmit them contain very minute bacterium-like structures, and that similar bodies may be found in the diseased individual.

Bacteriophages. In 1896, it was found that filtered water from the Ganges could check the growth of bacteria and that this power was lost if the water was boiled. Later it was observed that in certain cultures of bacteria many colonies died. The bacterial cells in these colonies had actually disintegrated. If material from such cultures was added to healthy bacterial cultures, these also soon died and the cells disintegrated. In 1917, d'Herelle passed cultures of dysentery bacilli through extremely fine filters and found that the filtrate checked the growth of bacteria. Microscopic examination showed that the bacteria had been destroyed. Material from colonies killed in this manner, when brought into contact with healthy colonies, caused their death. D'Herelle concluded that a substance was present which was in some way capable of increasing in amount. This substance he called a *bacteriophage.*

Bacteriophages are now known to be widespread in nature. They are present in the digestive tracts of man and other animals, in river waters, in soil, and in sewage. Since they may be considered as causing virus diseases of bacteria, it is hoped by some that they will in time assist in the control of diseases caused by bacteria.

Relationships. The most widely accepted view regarding the origin of bacteria is that they have descended from blue-green algae which, becoming adapted to a saprophytic or parasitic existence, lost their chlorophyll. This idea is supported by the simple cell structure common to blue-green algae and bacteria, by the fact that gametic union is not known to occur in either group, by the tendency of blue-green algae to live in liquids or on substrates containing considerable proportions of organic matter, and by the fact that some algae of other classes have become adapted to a saprophytic or to a partially or entirely parasitic mode of life and that a few such species have lost the power of forming chlorophyll.

On the other hand, the possession of flagella by many bacteria suggests their derivation directly from simple flagellated organisms, possibly distantly related to those from which green and brown algae seem to have independently descended.

A third possibility is suggested by the ability of iron and sulphur bacteria to manufacture foods from inorganic substances. It is conceivable that bacteria more or less like these might have existed before chlorophyll-containing organisms appeared and that these or similar bacteria may therefore have been more primitive than any of the algae. It has been argued that other bacteria may have been derived from such primitive forms after the appearance of green plants, upon which all present-day bacteria except such as the iron- and sulphur-oxidizers are directly or indirectly dependent.

It is not out of the question that two or all three of the explanations just suggested may be correct, different groups of bacteria having descended from independent sources.

CHAPTER XVII

MYXOMYCETES (SLIME MOLDS)

Nature. Slime molds, like bacteria, lack chlorophyll and are therefore commonly included among the plants known as *fungi.* They differ from other fungi particularly in passing through a stage in which the whole plant is a naked many-nucleate cell of indefinite form. A few slime molds are parasitic on seed plants; the greater number are saprophytes, most commonly found on moist, rotting

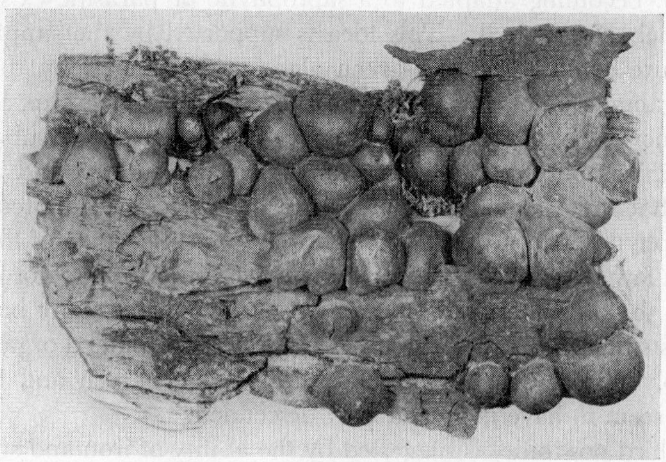

FIG. 204. Fruiting bodies of Lycogala.

wood. Recent studies have shown that many of these latter slime molds are actually dependent on bacteria and fungi, and in some cases on one-celled animals present in and on the rotting wood. A large number of species of slime molds are of world-wide distribution.

Lycogala. During late spring and throughout the summer the small fruiting bodies of *Lycogala* (Fig. 204), one of the commonest slime molds, occur singly or in small clusters on moist, decaying wood in shaded places. These fruiting bodies, averaging about a half inch in diameter, are almost spherical, except when they are pressed against one another. They are pink when young, later turning to a glistening gray or bronze. Each fruiting body contains an immense number of minute spores, which escape in a dust-like cloud when the mature structure is broken open.

The spores are easily carried by air currents, often to great distances. When a spore falls upon a moist surface, it absorbs water, its wall breaks, and the one-nucleate protoplast emerges. The immediate behavior of this small naked cell is probably in large part dependent upon the environment. It may develop at once into an amoeboid, pear-shaped swarm-spore, with a single flagellum at its pointed end (Fig. 205, *A*). But more often it divides to form two or four such swarm-spores (Fig. 205, *B*). The spores may grow

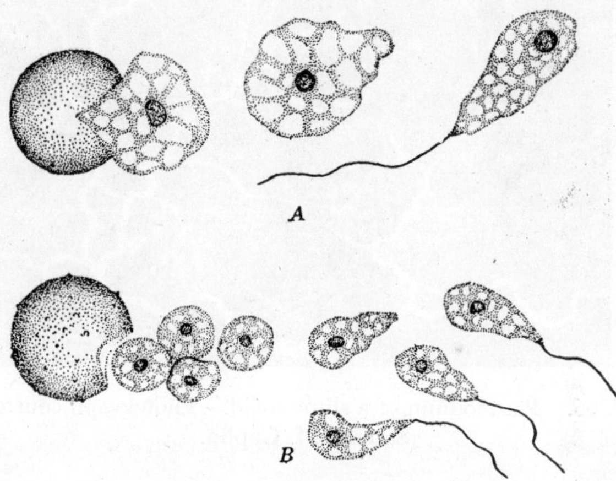

FIG. 205. Germination of the spores of slime molds; *A*, of Lycogala; *B*, of Physarum.

and divide to form other swarm-spores, and this process may be repeated; but eventually the swarm-spores, or at least some of them, function as gametes. The zygote formed by the union of two gametes absorbs food and grows, soon becoming many-nucleate. A naked cell containing more than one nucleus is a *plasmodium* (Fig. 206). The plasmodium further increases in size by the absorption and assimilation of food, and repeated nuclear divisions occur within it. It may unite with similar plasmodia. If food and moisture are abundant, growth and nuclear divisions may continue for weeks and even for months. A single plasmodium sometimes becomes several inches in diameter and a half inch in thickness and contains thousands of nuclei. Such a large plasmodium moves in the same amoeboid fashion as does a smaller one.

When the food supply or the moisture is lessened, the plasmodium becomes rounded, thicker, and less transparent and often turns to a scarlet color. If the plasmodium is in the interior of a decayed log

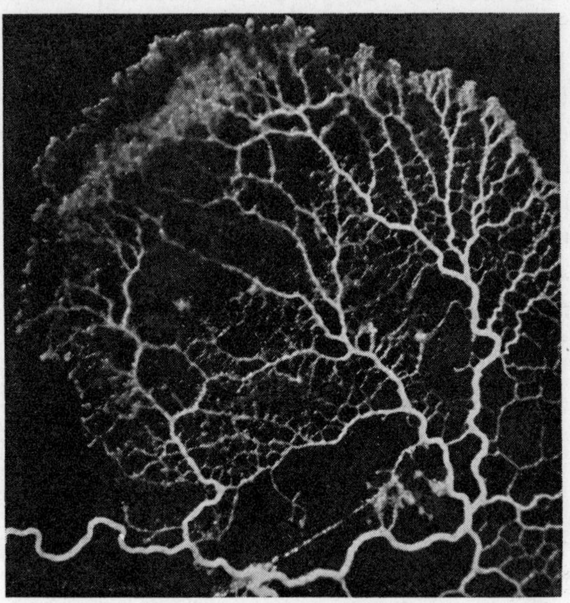

FIG. 206. Plasmodium of a slime mold. Photograph courtesy of Samuel M. Caplin.

or stem, it now creeps out to a drier and more exposed surface. During this movement, portions of the plasmodium are often separated from the main body. These smaller plasmodia, as well as the main plasmodium, come to rest and begin to round and heap up at a number of points.

The rounding up at each point is the beginning of the formation of a fruiting body. The plasmodium changes from scarlet to pink and at the same time extrudes considerable water and solid material. As the water evaporates, the dry waste material forms the outer layer of the wall of the fruiting body. This wall is at first thin, but it gradually becomes thicker by the accumulation of material on its inner side. In some cases a translucent second wall layer is deposited inside the first layer.

During the deposition of the wall the many nuclei become uniformly distributed throughout the dense cytoplasm. The plasma membrane now becomes furrowed at various places on the surface of the cytoplasm. The furrows become deeper, then branch and rebranch (Fig. 207), finally cutting the entire protoplasm into small one-nucleate cells. This method of division by means of furrows which progressively divide a many-nucleate cell into smaller and

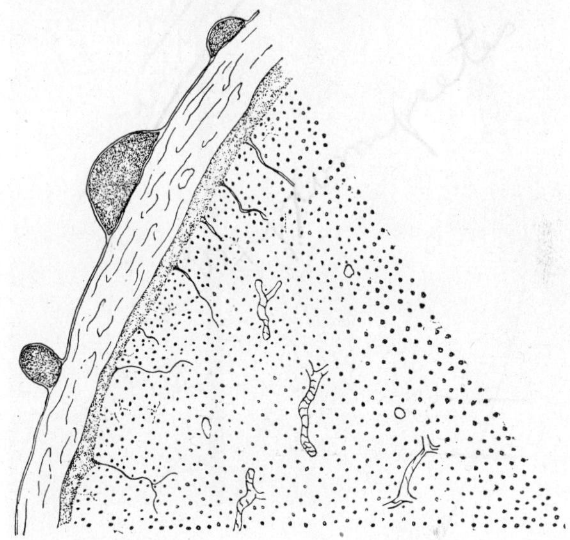

FIG. 207. An early stage of cell division in a fruiting body of Lycogala, leading to the formation of spores. The minute dark bodies are nuclei.

smaller cells occurs also in some other fungi, as well as in a few algae. The small cells (spores) contract slightly, and each secretes a wall. Within some of the growing furrows there is secreted a firm substance which forms a much-branched tubular structure, the *capillitium*. The capillitium constitutes a network within whose meshes lie the spores. By the time the spores are mature, the wall of the fruiting body has become firm; and unless mechanically injured, it may remain intact for a long period.

When the plasmodia of Lycogala, as well as those of many other slime molds, are suddenly dried, they often pass into a hard, brittle condition. The organism in this condition is spoken of as a *sclerotium*. When moisture is restored, a sclerotium may return to the plasmodial form.

Other Slime Molds. The spherical fruiting body of Lycogala is simple as compared with the fruiting bodies of other slime molds. That of *Stemonitis* (Fig. 208) has a broadened base, from which rises

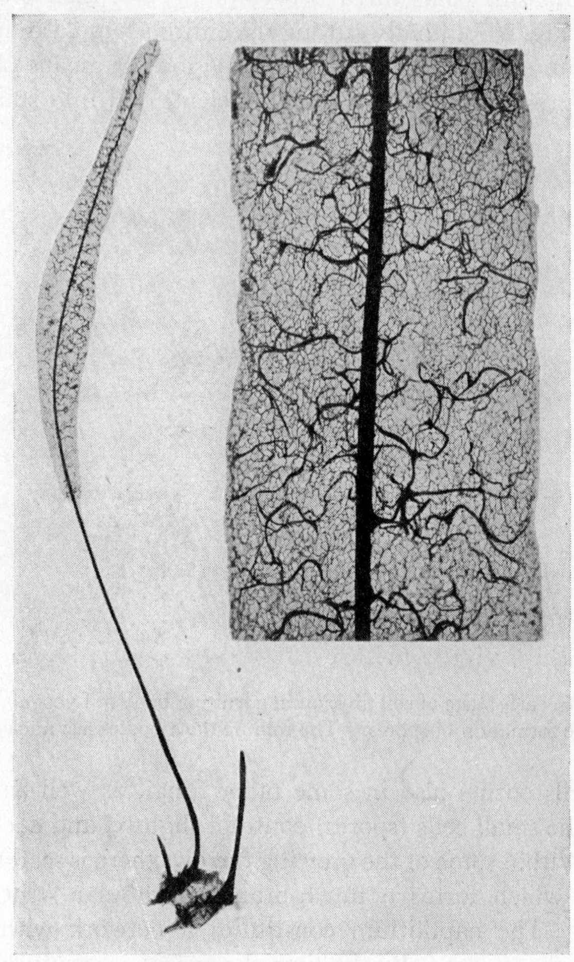

FIG. 208. *Left*, the stalked sporangium of Stemonitis. *Right*, a portion of the sporangium, highly magnified.

a slender, tapering stalk that bears at its upper end a cylindrical, chocolate-colored sporangium. The stalk continues into and through the sporangium to its tip and gives rise within the sporangium to many branches, which form a delicate capillitial network. The wall of the sporangium is so frail that it disappears as soon as the spores are mature. The sporangia of the stalked fruiting bodies of other slime molds are of various forms. Some are club-shaped, some spherical, hemispherical, or cone-shaped. Their colors are equally varied.

Fuligo, one of the largest slime molds, is often found on rotting leaves, on tanbark, and on the refuse of sawmills and lumber yards. Its plasmodium is transformed into a single large fruiting body (Fig. 209), which is a rounded and flattened mass, often five or six

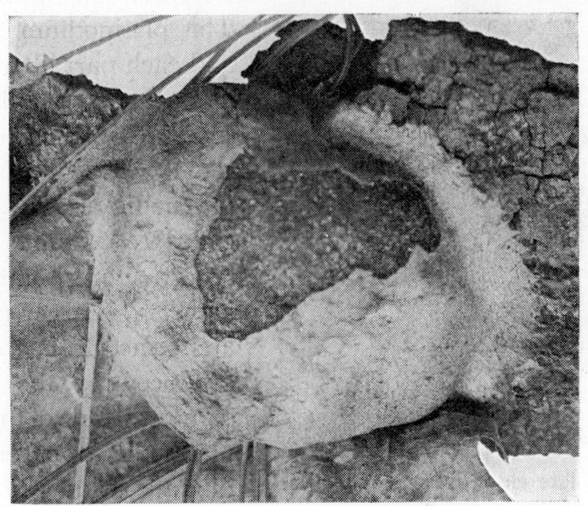

Fig. 209. Fruiting body of Fuligo.

inches in diameter and an inch in thickness. The wall of the fruiting body is not layered as in Lycogala but is crustlike, spongy, and of various shades of yellow or brown. The interior is divided into many irregular connecting chambers by the platelike branches of the capillitium.

In a few slime molds, including *Dictyostelium*, which is usually found on barnyard refuse, the amoeboid cells do not unite to form a plasmodium but merely remain in contact. This fungus is unusual in that individual cells lose water and become cemented to one another to form the stalk as well as the wall of the sporangium. The cells within the sporangium shrink slightly; and each, secreting a cell wall, becomes a spore.

Parasitic Slime Molds. The species that parasitize seed plants do not produce fruiting bodies. A plasmodium of one of these species divides within the host tissue into masses of spores, the masses being either irregular or of a characteristic form. One of the best known of the parasitic slime molds (*Plasmodiophora*) causes a disease (*clubroot*) of the cabbage and related plants (Fig. 210). A swarm-spore of Plasmodiophora enters a root of the host plant, where it forms a small plasmodium. This plasmodium fragments and each part liberates from four to six small swarm-spores that migrate deeper into the cortical tissues. The plasmodia are always intracellular. Some of the swarm-spores function as gametes. Larger plasmodia are formed from the zygotes produced by the union of gametes. One of these larger plasmodia apparently may migrate as a whole, or it may divide into parts which become distributed throughout the parenchymatous tissues of the root (Fig. 211). An invaded host cell increases greatly in size. It finally dies when it is almost completely filled by the many-nucleate plasmodium. This plasmodium eventually divides into one-nucleate spores, which are liberated as the host tissue breaks down and which may in turn bring about the infection of another host plant.

Fig. 210. Clubroot of the cabbage, caused by Plasmodiophora.

Relationships. There has been much discussion as to whether slime molds should be treated as plants or as animals. The distinctions made by the popular mind between plants and animals are based upon an acquaintance with the more complex organisms of both "kingdoms." The slime molds are one of several groups of simple organisms which can with more or less plausibility be classed in either way. Whether they are called plants or animals is therefore a matter of little consequence.

The various forms assumed by the uninucleate cells, including the walled spore, the amoeboid, and the flagellate conditions, are all to be found among the groups of simple organisms known as

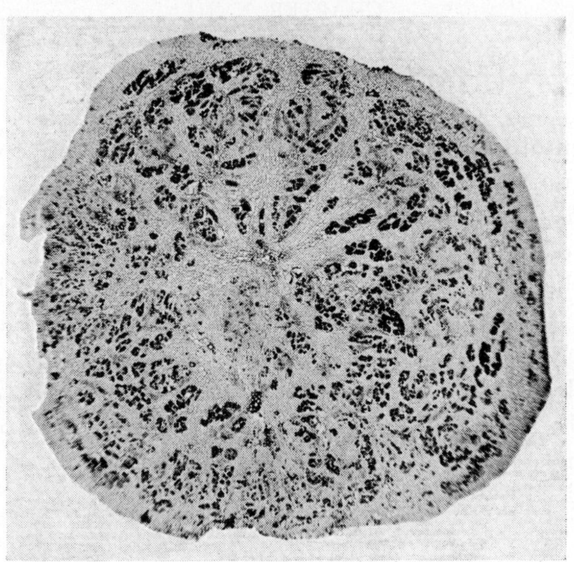

Fig. 211. Cross section of a cabbage root infected by Plasmodiophora. The dark masses are plasmodia.

flagellates and rhizopods. The rhizopods (including Amoeba), usually classed as animals, seem to have come from flagellates. It is probable, therefore, that slime molds have descended from flagellate ancestors, either directly or through the rhizopods.

Plasmodia are produced also by some flagellates and some rhizopods. The formation of a fruiting body, however, within which spores are borne, is a distinctly plantlike character and is suggestive of types of fruiting bodies produced by many fungi. It is particularly because of their fruiting bodies that slime molds are classed with fungi, although there seems to be no reason for thinking that they are directly related to any of the other fungi.

CHAPTER XVIII

PHYCOMYCETES (ALGAL FUNGI)

Filamentous Fungi. There are many simple plants which, like bacteria, do not contain chlorophyll; all these plants are classed together as *fungi*. The bacteria are the simplest fungi. The great majority of fungi are more complex than bacteria in that their bodies, whether one- or many-celled, are composed of branching filaments. One large class of (chiefly) filamentous fungi which, particularly in their methods of formation and union of gametes, are more or less like certain algae, are known as *Phycomycetes* (algal fungi). In some phycomycetes there occurs a union of gametes that are nearly or quite alike in size and structure. Others are characterized by the union of very unlike gametes.

RHIZOPUS

Structure. Among phycomycetes with like gametes is included an order known as "black molds." One of these is the common bread mold (*Rhizopus nigricans*), which forms an abundant soft, white, cottony growth on moist bread. The plant body is a filamentous, much-branched structure, each branch (*hypha*) being a slender thread. The whole complex of hyphae is a *mycelium*.

The dark-colored spores produced by the bread mold are variable in size and shape, though usually ovoid (Fig. 212, *A*). When a spore comes in contact with water, it enlarges and becomes spherical; its wall, formerly wrinkled, becomes smooth. These changes result from the fact that the protoplasm absorbs water, swells, and exerts pressure on the wall. A little later, if the temperature is favorable, the outer layer of the wall breaks (Fig. 212, *B–D*); and a short hypha, surrounded by the innermost layer of the wall, protrudes. This hypha elongates rapidly, branches, and so gives rise to a young mycelium. If a spore is sown in water, the mycelium growing from it soon dies, because the only available food is the small amount present in the spore. On the other hand, if a spore germinates in a nutrient liquid or on a piece of moist bread or other similar source of food, growth continues until a much-branched mycelium is formed.

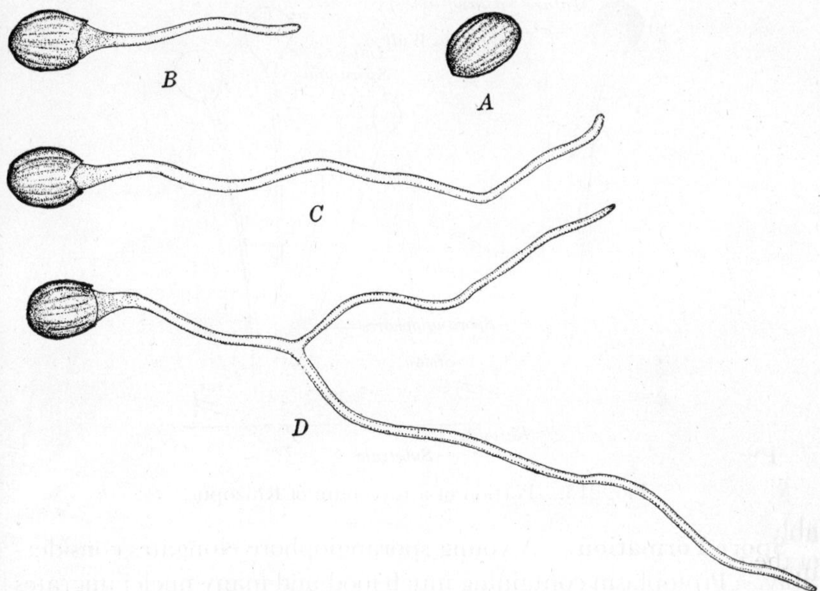

FIG. 212. A spore of Rhizopus (*A*), its germination (*B*), and stages in the development of a mycelium.

A young hypha has a cell wall, within which is a granular cytoplasm; this contains many vacuoles of varying sizes, droplets of oil, and glycogen (a carbohydrate similar to starch) and includes many small nuclei. The protoplasm is in continuous movement, chiefly toward the tips of the various branches. The entire mycelium is as yet but a single undivided cell. An older plant (Fig. 213) is composed under ordinary conditions of hyphae of at least three types. Those of one sort (*rhizoids*) anchor the plant and penetrate the substrate. The rhizoids, and a few other hyphae that come into contact with the bread or other substrate, secrete enzymes which digest the foods there present. The digested foods are absorbed by the mycelium and used in its growth. Certain other hyphae (*stolons*), usually larger than the rhizoids, grow approximately parallel to and above the substrate for a distance; and then, bending downward, each stolon develops another group of rhizoids. Hyphae of a third type grow upward from the stolons at points where the rhizoids are formed. Each of these erect hyphae (*sporangiophores*) bears a *sporangium*.

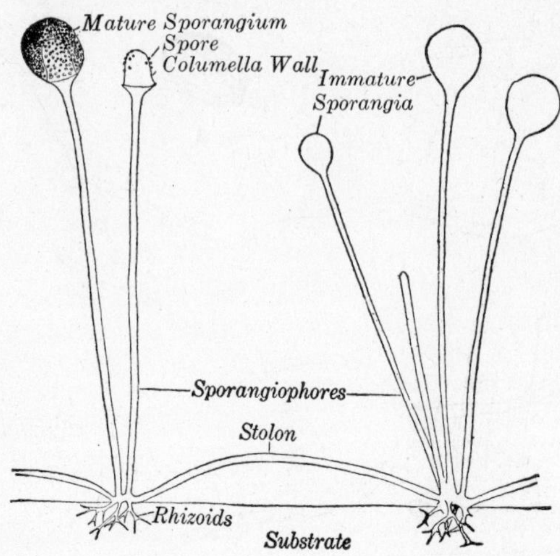

FIG. 213. Portion of a mycelium of Rhizopus.

Spore Formation. A young sporangiophore elongates considerably. Protoplasm containing much food and many nuclei migrates into its enlarging tip, the sporangium (Fig. 214, *A*). The portion of the protoplasm containing most of the nuclei and food aggregates in the outer part of the enlarging sporangium, leaving the center occupied by protoplasm with many large vacuoles and a few nuclei. Some of the vacuoles become arranged in a dome-shaped layer between the outer, denser and the inner, less dense protoplasm (Fig. 214, *B*). These vacuoles soon become flattened; and as they come into contact with one another, they unite into larger vacuoles until finally their union forms a cleft separating the outer from the inner part of the sporangium. The united vacuolar membranes form a plasma membrane on each side of the cleft. The cleft is completed by a furrowing of the original plasma membrane about the base of the sporangium (Fig. 214, *C*). Between the two new plasma membranes a wall is secreted, which separates the dome-shaped central part of the sporangium (the *columella*) from the outer part, the spore sac proper. The latter is now a separate cell provided with a continuous plasma membrane. This membrane becomes furrowed at various points, both on the side next the outer wall and on that next the columella wall. The furrows cut into the protoplasm, branching, and dividing the contents of the spore sac into smaller and smaller protoplasts of irregular shape. The small cells ultimately produced by this process of *progressive cleavage* are the spores, each containing a variable number (2–10) of nuclei. This method of division by means of furrows which progressively divide a many-nucleate cell into smaller and smaller cells occurs also in some other

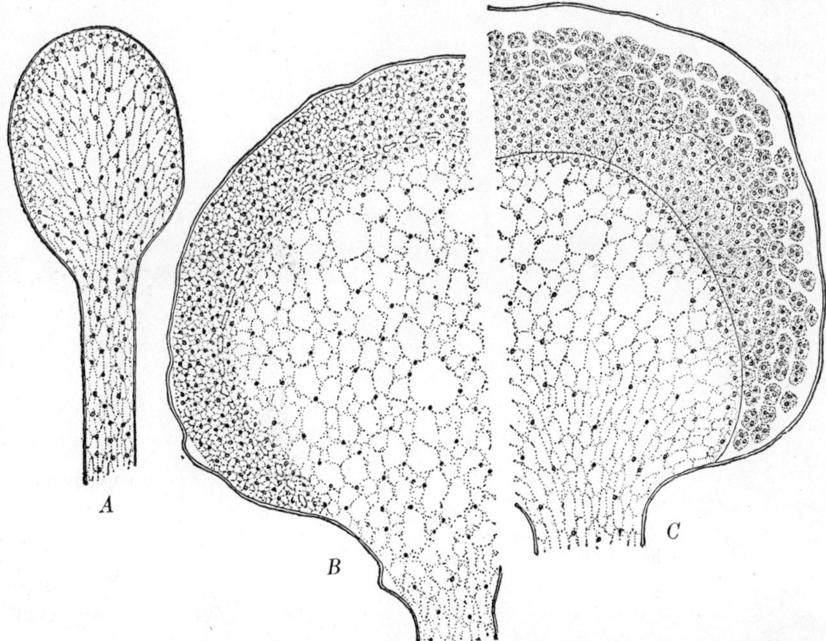

FIG. 214. Rhizopus. *A*, young sporangium at the apex of a sporangiophore. *B*, sporangium with a dome-shaped layer of vacuoles. *C*, the columella wall has been formed, and the protoplasm of the spore sac is dividing by progressive cleavage to form spores. All from G. M. Smith, *Cryptogamic Botany*, published by the McGraw-Hill Book Company.

fungi (including slime molds, Chapter XVII), as well as in a few algae. It is very different from division by means of a cell plate or by constriction.

Finally the newly formed spores become rounded, and each secretes a wall. The outer wall of the spore sac dries and becomes fragile when the spores are mature; and any slight disturbance breaks it, liberating the spores. The columella persists as a dome-shaped structure at the end of the sporangiophore (Fig. 213). A mycelium usually remains one-celled until columella formation takes place in the sporangia, but after this time cell divisions by constriction may occur and crosswalls be formed in various portions of the mycelium. At any stage of development, however, under unfavorable environmental conditions, divisions may occur in the hyphae. Even after such divisions, each of the cells that constitute the plant, except the spores, is comparatively large and many-nucleate.

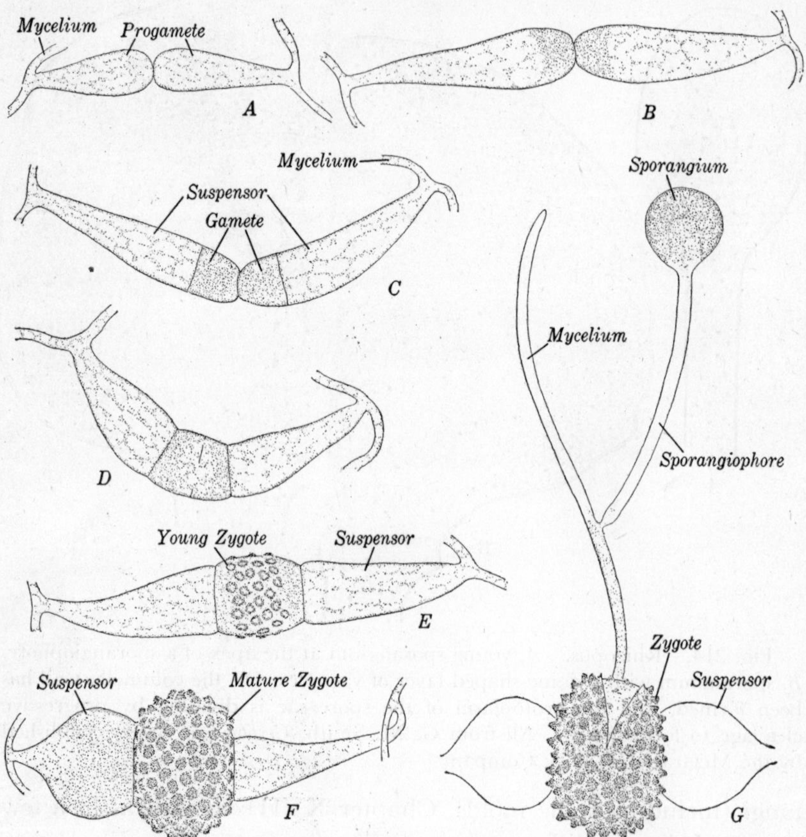

FIG. 215. Rhizopus. Stages in the formation of gametes (*A–C*), their union (*D*) to form a zygote (*E*, *F*), and the germination of the zygote (*G*).

Formation and Union of Gametes (Fig. 215). Gametic union in Rhizopus resembles the corresponding process in Spirogyra in that the two gametes are alike in size and are without flagella. When two hyphae of separate Rhizopus plants of distinct strains (see the next paragraph) come into contact, a short side branch (*progamete*) may be produced by each hypha at the point of contact. The terminal portion of each progamete becomes swollen. Within this swollen portion a transverse division occurs; and a crosswall is secreted, the many-nucleate end cell so formed being a gamete. The basal portion of each *progamete*, which connects the gamete with the mycelium, is the suspensor. In time the walls between the two gametes, where they are in contact, dissolve; and the gametes unite to form a zygote. The zygote wall becomes very thick and black and has a rough outer surface. The thick-walled resting zygote contains an abundance of reserve foods, largely in the form of fats, as well as many nuclei derived from each of the gametes. The subsequent history of the nuclei in the zygote is not fully known, but it is probable that some of them at least unite in pairs. After a period of rest the zygote germinates (Fig. 215, *G*), giving rise to a hypha, which soon forms a sporangiophore and a sporangium. This sporangium, except for its smaller size, is similar to the sporangia produced on the ordinary mycelium.

The plants of Rhizopus belong to strains of two different sorts, referred to as *plus* and *minus*. No gametes are formed unless a hypha of a plus mycelium comes into contact with one of a minus mycelium. In Spirogyra, the two uniting gametes are conspicuously different in behavior, so that they may be designated as male and female. In Rhizopus the two gametes are often different in size; but such differences are too variable to make it certain that they represent a sexual differentiation. A few black molds, however, have distinctly different male and female gametes.

Relatives of Rhizopus. While Rhizopus is the one most commonly found in the household, several other black molds are widespread. One of these (Phycomyces) has sporangiophores which often reach a height of several inches. Pilobolus (Figs. 216, 217), frequently found in barnyard refuse, has a mechanism for throwing the entire sporangium to a distance of more than six feet. Although the majority of black molds are saprophytic, a few are parasitic on other fungi; and some cause important diseases of both plants and animals. Many of the saprophytic black molds are very active in the early stages of decay, in many instances being much more active than are the bacteria. Some are used in the manufacture of alcohol the molds converting starch into sugar.

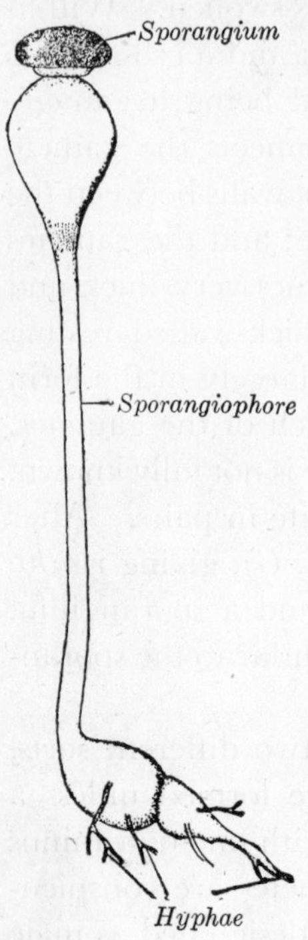

FIG. 216. Portion of the mycelium of Pilobolus, a black mold, with sporangiophore and sporangium.

Among other phycomycetes with like gametes, which are possibly related to the black molds, the best known are species of Empusa. One member of this genus is a parasite of the common housefly, which it kills in great numbers. Its mycelium is composed of many short cells, each containing one to several large nuclei.

SAPROLEGNIA

Nature and Structure. *Saprolegnia* (Fig. 218) is one of the commonest of those phycomycetes that produce sharply differentiated male and female gametes. Its species and those of other members of the same order are commonly found in water, growing on the living or dead bodies of insects and fishes and often on other animal and plant substances. For this reason these fungi are called "water molds." However, many if not all of them are abundant in surface soils. Saprolegnia and its immediate relatives are usually saprophytic; but under some conditions they become parasitic upon fish, probably gaining entrance to the bodies of the hosts through wounds, and produce a destructive epidemic disease. Root diseases of many plants also are caused by fungi closely related to Saprolegnia.

The mycelium consists of hyphae, some of which are short and penetrate the substrate; others are long and extend in all directions from the material upon which the fungus is growing. Like that of Rhizopus, the mycelium is, while young, a single much-branched, many-nucleate cell.

Spore Formation (Fig. 218, *A*, *B*). The protoplasm of the long external hyphae, at first vacuolate, gradually becomes denser and finally granular, especially at the tips. The tip of each hypha, becoming separated by cell division, forms a terminal many-nucleate sporangium. By progressive cleavage the protoplasm of the sporangium is divided into many small, spherical, one-nucleate spores. The tip of the sporangium breaks, and through the opening

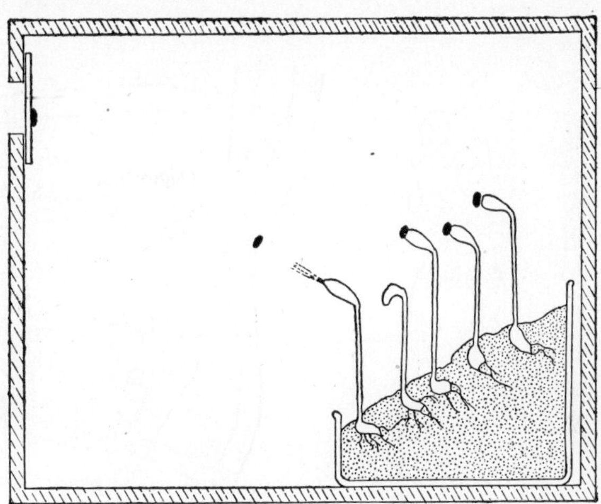

FIG. 217. A culture of Pilobolus placed in a dark box. The sporangiophores bend toward the small window through which light is admitted, and the sporangia are discharged toward the window.

so formed the spores emerge; each spore develops two flagella and finally swims away. After the swarm-spores have escaped, the basal wall of the sporangium becomes softened and is pushed up by the protoplasm below into the cavity of the old sporangium, where a new sporangium is formed. By a repetition of this process as many as three or four sporangia may be formed successively, each within the wall of the next older one. A swarm-spore may swim about until it comes into contact with a source of food, when it comes to rest, withdraws its flagella, secretes a cell wall, and develops into a slender hypha. This hypha penetrates the substrate, where it branches and develops into a mycelium.

Formation and Union of Gametes (Fig. 218, *C*, *D*). Under some conditions certain hyphae produce sex organs instead of sporangia. The many-nucleate tip of a hypha enlarges greatly, becomes cut off as a separate cell, and develops into an oögonium. The protoplast of the oögonium becomes divided into a variable number (4–32) of one-nucleate female gametes (eggs).

Slender branches arising—some just beneath the oögonium, others on neighboring hyphae—grow toward, and become closely applied to, the oögonium. The slightly enlarged terminal portion of each of these hyphae is cut off as a many-nucleate antheridium. From the antheridium grows a slender *fertilization tube*, which pene-

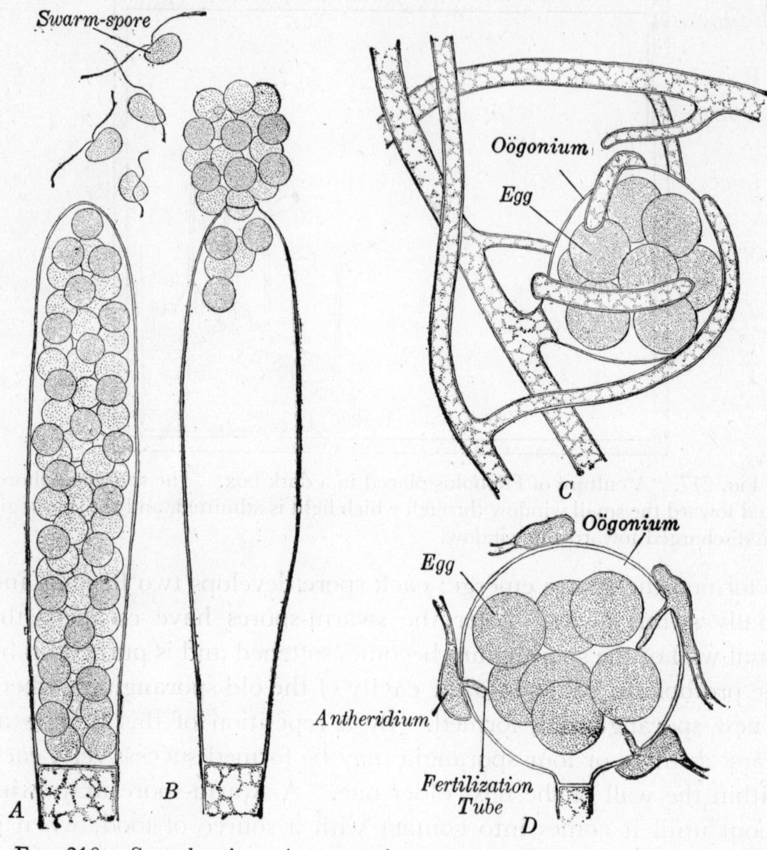

Fig. 218. Saprolegnia. *A*, sporangium containing spores. *B*, sporangium from which spores are emerging. *C*, oögonium surrounded by antheridial branches. *D*, after the formation of antheridia by the antheridial branches and the development of fertilization tubes.

trates the oögonium and comes into contact with one or more eggs. In some species of Saprolegnia a nucleus and some cytoplasm, together constituting a small male gamete, pass from the antheridium through the fertilization tube into each egg. The zygote formed by union of the gametes secretes a thick wall. In other species, antheridia and fertilization tubes are not produced or, if produced, do not function. Even in such cases, however, the eggs become thick-walled and have the appearance of zygotes. Under these conditions an egg functions as a spore, just as a gamete of Spirogyra sometimes does. The zygote or thick-walled spore usually enters upon a period of rest and may retain its vitality for many months. The method of its germination is not well known.

Relatives of Saprolegnia. The immediate relatives of Saprolegnia, members of the same order, resemble it in structure and in the general course of their life history. There are important differences between members of the order, however, in the structure of sporangia and in the methods of liberation and germination of swarm-spores.

ALBUGO

Nature and Structure. All species of *Albugo* are parasitic on seed plants. A very common one infects the radish, cress, mustard,

FIG. 219. *Left*, a healthy flower cluster of the radish. *Right*, a single flower of a radish plant infected by Albugo. The white patches are masses of spores.

shepherd's purse, and related plants. The portions of the host plant containing the fungus, which may be leaves, stems, branches, flowers, or fruits, are often discolored or enlarged and markedly distorted (Fig. 219). In time white, mealy patches develop on the infected parts. Because of the appearance of these spots the disease is often called the "white rust." The mycelium of Albugo, like that of phycomycetes previously mentioned, is one-celled when young, many-nucleate, and composed of many hyphae, which grow between the cells of the host. Foods are obtained by means of short, knoblike lateral branches that penetrate the walls of the host cells.

Spore Formation. A time comes when, in consequence of an especially rapid branching of the mycelium, dense masses of hyphae are formed at various places beneath the epidermis of the host. Each hyphal mass gives rise to a layer of parallel, stocky, thick-walled cells, whose long axes are perpendicular to the epidermis

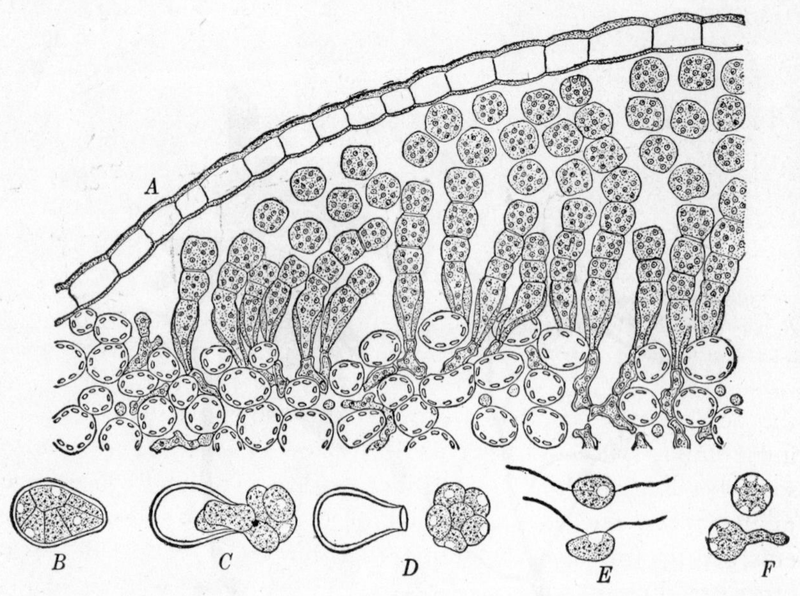

FIG. 220. Albugo. *A*, Portion of a cross section of an infected leaf; conidia are being formed beneath the epidermis of the host. *B–D*, germination of conidia. *E*, swarm-spores. *F*, germination of a swarm-spore. All from G. M. Smith, *Cryptogamic Botany*, published by the McGraw-Hill Book Company.

(Fig. 220, *A*). Each cell of this layer elongates at its tip; and cell division cuts off a small, many-nucleate spore (*conidium*). The cell just below the spore elongates, and a second conidium is formed beneath the first. A repetition of this process produces a chain of conidia. The pressure caused by the elongation of numerous parallel spore chains finally breaks the epidermis of the host. It is the exposure of a mass of conidia that causes the mealy appearance characteristic of the fungus. The conidia are now easily detached from one another and scattered. When they germinate, each divides to form six or more two-flagellate swarm-spores, which in turn can infect a new host plant. The disease is spread throughout the growing season of the host by the production of successive crops of conidia.

Formation and Union of Gametes (Fig. 221). After the production of conidia, certain hyphae penetrate the deeper tissues of

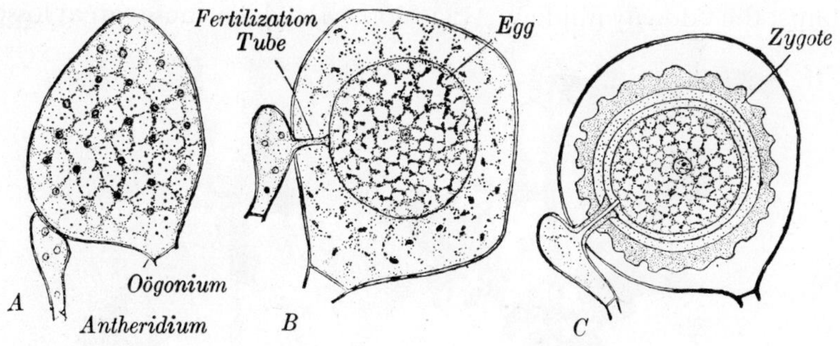

FIG. 221. Gametic union in Albugo. *A*, young oögonium and antheridium. *B*, oögonium in which the egg has been delimited; the antheridium has developed a fertilization tube. *C*, old oögonium containing a zygote.

the host plant, especially those of the petioles or stem. In the intercellular spaces of these tissues the tips of the hyphae enlarge, some becoming spherical and filled with a dense cytoplasm containing many nuclei. A cell division occurs, which separates the enlarged tip (now an oögonium) from the rest of the hypha. Another cell division within the oögonium in time separates a single, usually one-nucleate, central egg from the surrounding many-nucleate protoplasm. The egg is bounded by a plasma membrane, but no wall is formed between it and the peripheral cell. By this time the slightly enlarged tips of other hyphae have come into contact with the oögonium; the tips of these hyphae, set apart by cell division, become antheridia. A slender fertilization tube from one antheridium pierces the wall of the oögonium and grows until it reaches the egg. A male gamete passes from the antheridium through the fertilization tube, enters the egg, and the male and female nuclei unite. The zygote formed by this union becomes surrounded by a thick wall. The cytoplasm and nuclei of the peripheral cell gradually disintegrate. Repeated nuclear divisions occur in the zygote, which at maturity contains typically 32 nuclei. After several weeks' rest the zygote may germinate. In germination, water is absorbed, and cell and nuclear divisions occur, so that finally more than 100 two-flagellate, one-nucleate swarm-spores escape, each capable of infecting a host.

Relatives of Albugo. The "damping-off" fungus (Pythium), which causes wilting and decay in seed beds of various cultivated plants, the "downy mildew" (Plasmopara), which causes great losses

Fig. 222. Early and late stages in the late blight of potato, caused by Phytophthora. Photograph courtesy of I. E. Melhus.

to the grape industry in the United States and Europe, and Phytophthora, which causes the destructive "late blight" of the potato (Fig. 222), are closely related to Albugo, differing from it chiefly in the manner of production of their spores.

Relationships of Phycomycetes. The members of this class show considerable resemblances to certain algae. Rhizopus and the other black molds are thought by some to have arisen from algae more or less like Spirogyra, because of the presence of similar or not greatly differentiated gametes and because of resemblances in methods of gamete-formation. The many-nucleate, undivided mycelium of the black molds renders this hypothesis questionable. It has been suggested, however, that there may be a connection through Empusa and some of its relatives, whose mycelia are made up largely or entirely of short cells, each often containing one large, centrally placed nucleus similar in position and structure to a nucleus of Spirogyra.

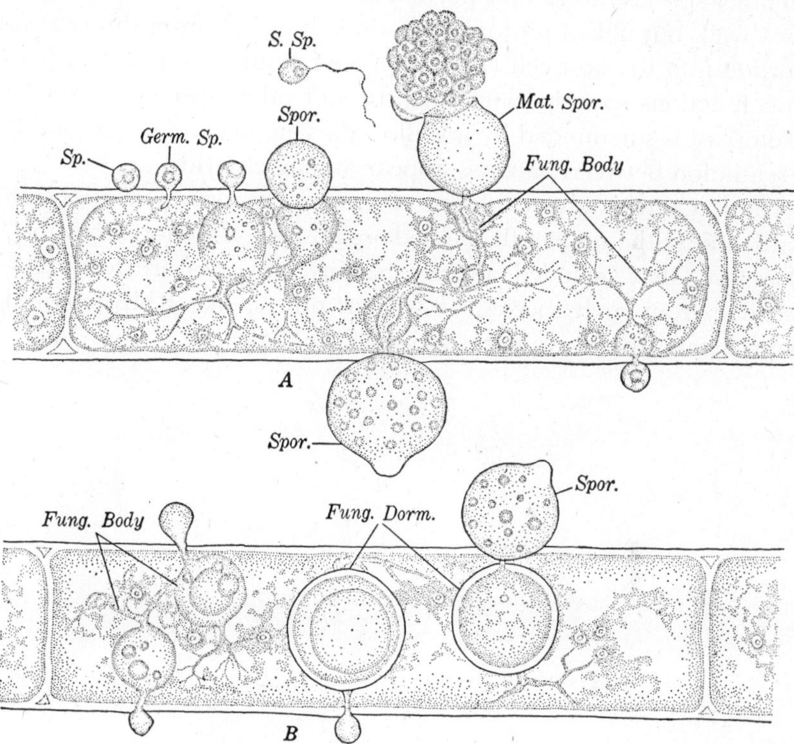

FIG. 223. A chytrid (Chytridium) parasitic upon a green alga (Rhizoclonium). *A*, stages in the history of the fungus under ordinary environmental conditions. *B*, stages in its history under adverse conditions. *S. Sp.*, swarm-spore; *Sp.*, spore attached to host; *Germ. Sp.*, germinating spore; *Fung. Body*, body of fungus within the host; *Spor.*, developing sporangia; *Mat. Spor.*, mature sporangium, spores being liberated; *Fung. Dorm.*, dormant stage of fungus. After a drawing by A. F. Bartsch.

Saprolegnia and its immediate relatives may have come from algal ancestors similar to Vaucheria. Vaucheria and Saprolegnia are alike in their undivided thalli with many small nuclei; in possessing motile spores; and in the differentiation between oögonium and antheridium, and between male and female gametes.

A large order of fungi (Chytrids), mostly aquatic and in large part parasitic, and very much simpler than either Rhizopus or Saprolegnia, should be mentioned here because they are usually listed with the phycomycetes. Some chytrids have naked many-nucleate protoplasts that give rise by progressive cleavage to spores. In other species the greater portion of the plant body is surrounded by a wall, but naked protoplasmic threads extend from this central portion into the host cell (Fig. 223). At maturity the walled portion functions as a sporangium. In still other species the entire protoplast is surrounded by a wall. Varying degrees of sexual differentiation between gametes appear among chytrids.

Many chytrids give evidence of a not very remote relationship with some of the simpler flagellated organisms. It is not impossible, therefore, that included among the phycomycetes are forms descended from such species, as well as others, like Rhizopus and Saprolegnia, that have been derived from algae.

CHAPTER XIX

ASCOMYCETES (SAC FUNGI)

Nature. Members of this, the largest class of fungi, vary greatly in form and structure. Some are saprophytic, some parasitic. All ascomycetes at some time in their history produce spore sacs (*asci*), within which are formed *ascospores*. The number of ascospores in an ascus is variable; in a large majority of species the number is eight. In addition to ascospores, various ascomycetes produce spores of one or more other types, some species having, including ascospores, as many as four spore forms.

YEASTS

Structure and Reproduction. A yeast is a fungus consisting of a single ovoid cell or of a colony of two or more such cells. The most conspicuous feature of a yeast cell (Fig. 224, *A*) is a large

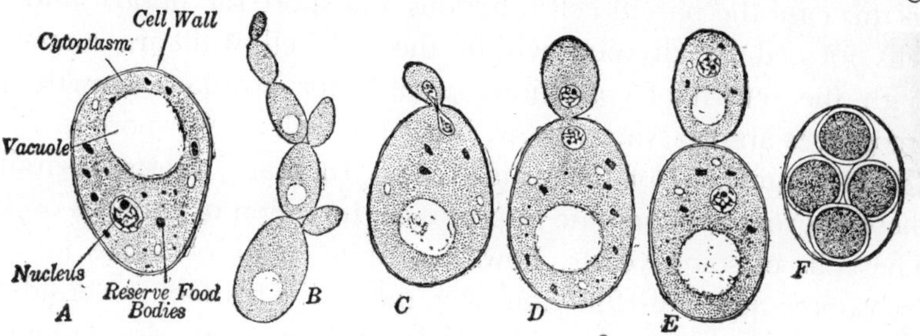

FIG. 224. Yeasts. *A*, mature cell. *B*, colony formed by repeated cell division. *C–E*, stages in cell division. *F*, ascospores. *A*, *C–E*, from stained preparations. *B*, *F*, from living material.

vacuole lying in a finely granular dense cytoplasm. In the dense cytoplasm also are reserve food particles of varied shapes and sizes. Some of these are rounded masses of glycogen or globules of fat; others, more or less angular, consist of proteins. In specially stained cells it is possible to distinguish a nucleus with chromatic strands and a nucleolus. A cell wall which probably consists, in part at least, of chitin encloses the cell.

In a culture containing actively growing yeasts, cells of varying sizes often occur in colonies (Fig. 224, *B*). The cells composing each colony have been derived from a single cell as a result of division and growth (Fig. 224, *C–E*). In the reproduction of a yeast under ordinary conditions, the nucleus divides in essentially the same manner as do the nuclei of more complex plants. A small localized area of the wall, usually at or near one end of the cell, becomes softened, probably as a result of enzymatic action. The wall bulges in the region of softening, a swelling, or bud, thus being produced. As this bud is forming, some of the cytoplasm and one daughter nucleus pass into it. A constriction of the plasma membrane in the plane of origin of the bud brings about a division of the cell into two daughter cells of very unequal size. The smaller of these daughter cells (the former bud) grows rapidly, and soon it also may produce a bud and divide in the same manner as the parent cell. The cells may remain attached or may separate.

Under conditions unfavorable for the ordinary development just described, such as a scarcity of food or water, a yeast cell often divides to produce a limited number, typically four, of one-nucleate cells which remain within the wall of the parent cell (Fig. 224, *F*). In this case the parent cell functions as a spore sac (*ascus*), and the cells formed by division within the old cell wall are *ascospores*. With the return of conditions suitable for ordinary growth, the ascospores absorb water, grow, burst the wall of the spore sac, and develop into cells of the usual type. In many yeasts, including those of greatest economic importance, no union of gametes occurs. The cells of some yeasts, however, unite in pairs before forming ascospores and thus function as gametes. This fact is considered by some investigators as evidence that the yeasts are descendants of ascomycetes that had a more complex life cycle.

Fermentation. It was known to the ancients that if a mixture of flour and water (dough) was allowed to stand, it would make a leavened bread very different from the unleavened bread baked immediately after the dough had been prepared, and that leavening would proceed more rapidly if sugar was added. It has long been a matter of general knowledge, too, that if fruit juices are exposed to the air and left undisturbed for a time, the liquid becomes cloudy, gases are given off, and, as the sugar disappears, the liquid becomes alcoholic. But not until European wine-makers and brewers became interested in an effort to control the flavors of wines and beers was something definite learned regarding the agencies concerned in the fermenting of fruit juices and in the making of bread. Pasteur showed that these processes are due to the activities of yeasts and other microörganisms.

Most yeasts can live and grow only in a solution containing a sugar or substances that may readily be changed to sugars. Yeasts can not grow and multiply, however, unless other substances are present, because the carbon, hydrogen, and oxygen of a sugar are not the only elements necessary for the building up of living matter.

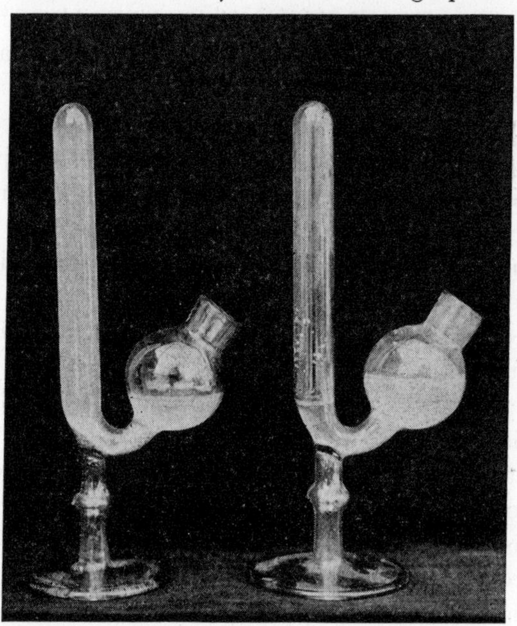

FIG. 225. Evolution of carbon dioxide during fermentation. The closed arm of the tube at the left is filled with a sugar solution containing yeast; the tube at the right shows the effect, after a few hours, of the production of carbon dioxide, which has forced the liquid out of the closed arm.

If the solution containing the necessary food substances is in a thin layer, so permitting access to an abundant supply of air, the yeast cells will grow and divide rapidly, using a considerable portion of the sugar as a source of both building materials and energy. If, on the other hand, little oxygen is available, as when the yeast cells are so deeply immersed in the solution that most of them are cut off from the air, the majority of the cells settle to the bottom and there live as anaerobes. Under this condition the cells secrete an enzyme (*zymase*) which breaks down the sugar into alcohol and carbon dioxide, and the yeast makes use of some of the energy so released. Hence *alcoholic fermentation* is a type of respiration, which, in the absence of free oxygen, replaces ordinary respiration as a source of energy for the yeast. A single species of yeast can apparently break down only a certain sugar or certain sugars, and some few rare yeasts are not known to cause alcoholic fermentation under any conditions.

The yeasts which bring about the fermentation of fruit juices in the making of wines and ciders are largely *wild* species. These yeasts live in or on the soil of vineyards and orchards and are carried with dust to the skins of the fruits. When the fruits are crushed, the yeasts are brought into contact with the fruit juices, and fermentation ensues. The yeasts that ferment grape juice are of various species, and the characteristic flavors of different wines are due in large part to differences in the yeasts as well as in other organisms present, which cause, in addition to alcoholic fermentation, the formation of substances that modify the flavor of the wine.

Yeasts used in brewing and in bread-making are *cultivated* yeasts. Cultures of these yeasts are grown and kept pure with the greatest care in order to prevent their contamination by wild yeasts and other organisms.

Some bacteria and several fungi other than yeasts are capable of inducing alcoholic fermentation. The production of alcohol by these organisms is encouraged by growing the bacteria and fungi under anaerobic conditions. A few black molds closely related to Rhizopus, as well as some species of Penicillium and Aspergillus (p. 350), readily form alcohol; and the commercial production of alcohol on a large scale is due in considerable measure to the activities of such fungi.

POWDERY MILDEWS

Structure and Reproduction. These parasitic fungi appear during the summer and fall, giving to the leaves or young stems of their various host plants a whitish mealy or powdery appearance (Fig. 226). The mycelium, composed of short one-nucleate cells, grows on the surface of a leaf or stem. Short branches from some of the cells of the mycelium, which act as absorbing organs, pierce the

FIG. 226. A powdery mildew on leaves of phlox.

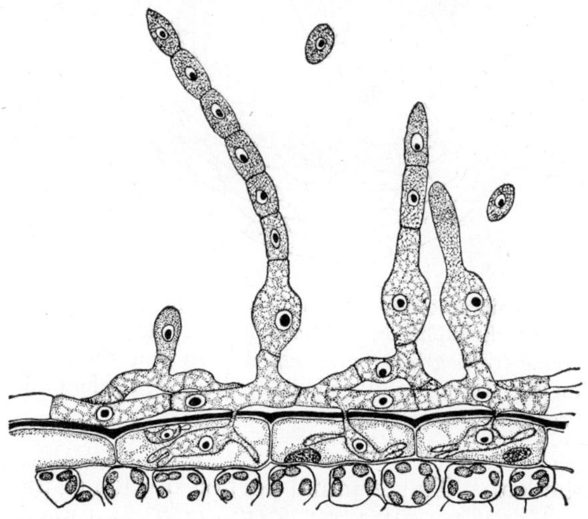

FIG. 227. Microsphaera. Mycelium growing on the surface of a leaf. Short absorbing cells penetrate the epidermis of the host. Upright branches produce conidia.

walls of the epidermal cells of the host or, growing through stomata, penetrate the walls of the layer of cells next beneath the epidermis.

A common powdery mildew (*Microsphaera*) lives on the leaves of the lilac. As soon as the mycelium has become well established on the host, some of its cells grow outward, perpendicularly to the

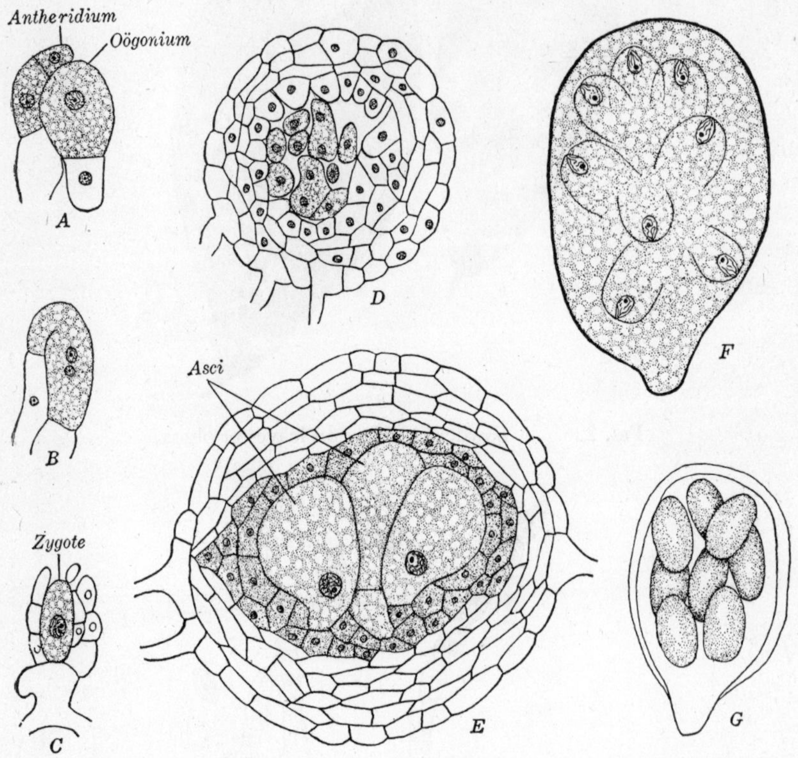

FIG. 228. Gametic union and ascus development in powdery mildews; *A–C*, Sphaerotheca; *D*, *E*, Erysiphe; *F*, *G*, Microsphaera. *A*, *B*, union of gametes. *C*, zygote. *D*, young fruiting body; the cells derived from the zygote are shaded. *E*, cross section of a fruiting body containing asci. *F*, *G*, the formation of ascospores. *A–E* redrawn from Harper.

surface of the leaf. The terminal portion of each of these elongate cells is separated by a cell division (Fig. 227) and becomes a short cylindrical spore (*conidium*). Other divisions occur successively below the first, so that a row of conidia is produced. The conidia are easily detached and separated from one another and, since they can germinate immediately, are responsible for the rapid spread of the fungus to other leaves throughout the growing season.

Formation and Union of Gametes. Sex organs are formed at the ends of special branches of the mycelium which grow so as to come into contact in pairs (Fig. 228, *A*, *B*). The slightly enlarged terminal cell of one branch of each pair is an antheridium; the much more enlarged terminal cell of the other branch is an oögonium. The one-nucleate protoplast of the oögonium functions as an egg; that of the antheridium, as a male gamete. The walls at the point of contact between oögonium and antheridium are dissolved, and through the opening so formed the male gamete passes into the oögonium. The nucleus of the male gamete and that of the egg unite, and the opening between antheridium and oögonium is later closed. The zygote formed by the union of egg and male gamete now divides, giving rise to a row of three to five cells. Branches arise from some of the cells of this row (Fig. 228, *D*). Certain cells of these branches, containing two nuclei each, develop

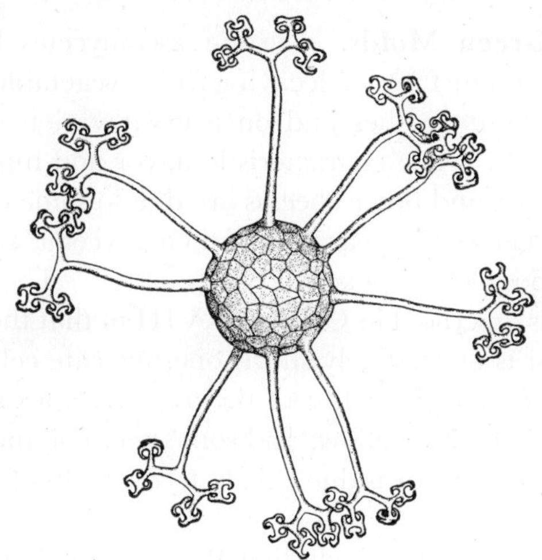

Fig. 229. A mature fruiting body of Microsphaera.

into asci. The two nuclei in each young ascus unite (Fig. 228, *E*), and the ascus enlarges rapidly. During its growth the single nucleus now present divides, its daughter nuclei divide, and their daughter nuclei divide, so that the ascus contains eight nuclei distributed throughout its cytoplasm. By a process of cell division peculiar to the ascomycetes (*free-cell formation*), in which not all the cytoplasm of the parent cell (the ascus) is included within the daughter cells, eight or fewer one-nucleate cells are formed inside the ascus (Fig. 228, *F*, *G*). These cells are ascospores.

After the union of egg and male gamete, the zygote becomes surrounded by hyphae which grow from the cells immediately beneath. While the asci are enlarging, the surrounding hyphae form a structure, black and almost spherical, in whose central portion the asci are enclosed (Fig. 229). Certain superficial cells of this fruiting body develop into greatly elongated appendages, which (in Microsphaera) fork repeatedly toward their outer ends. The many fruiting bodies formed on an infected leaf become detached as the mycelium decays, and are scattered by winds. In the spring the outer layers of each fruiting body break down, exposing the asci, from which the ascospores escape. An ascospore falling on a lilac leaf may grow into a new mycelium.

OTHER ASCOMYCETES

Blue and Green Molds. Certain ascomycetes form tangled mycelial masses on surfaces of decaying fruits, vegetables, and meats, as well as on damp leather and on a great variety of plant and animal substances. The characteristic flavor and mottled appearance of Roquefort and other cheeses are due to some of these fungi. Because of the general appearance of their mycelia, ascomycetes of this type are popularly spoken of as "molds." They differ from the black molds described in Chapter XVIII in that their branching mycelium consists of relatively short, one-nucleate cells and also in their production of asci. Most of the ascomycetous molds appear blue or green; some are yellow, and some very common species are almost black. The color is due chiefly to the walls of the abundant conidia.

In some of these molds, including Penicillium (Fig. 230, *B*), conidia are borne in chains at the ends of much-branched hyphae. In others, including Aspergillus (Fig. 230, *A*), a spore-bearing hypha ends in a large swelling from which develop many approximately cylindrical outgrowths; each of the latter produces a chain of conidia. Under ordinary conditions conidia are the only spores produced by these fungi; but at times certain of them form fruiting bodies containing asci and ascospores.

Many of the blue and green molds are used in various commercial processes. Some of them are able to change starch to sugar and so are used as "starters" in alcoholic fermentation. Others are

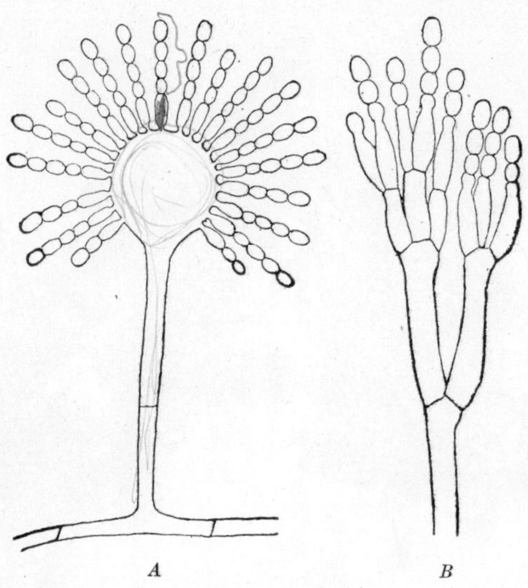

FIG. 230. *A*, lengthwise section of a conidium-bearing branch of Aspergillus. *B*, conidium-bearing branch of Penicillium. Both diagrammatic.

used in the tanning of leather; the enzyme takadiastase is supplied by one of these molds; another is used in the making of sake, the national Japanese alcoholic beverage. Some produce oxalic, citric, and gluconic acids; from several ascomycetous molds vitamins are obtained on a commercial scale. All of them probably play an important part in the early stages of the decay of plant and animal substances.

A very large group of ascomycetes, whose spherical or flask-shaped fruiting bodies open to the outside by a narrow pore through which the asci and ascospores escape, are among the most important disease-producing fungi. The chestnut blight, which has almost destroyed the American chestnut, and the Dutch elm disease, which is now threatening the American elm, are two diseases caused by such ascomycetes. The national government is coöperating with several states in an effort to check the spread of the elm disease.

Cup Fungi. These ascomycetes, some of the best-known species of which belong to the genus Peziza, grow usually on decaying wood or on soils rich in humus. Some of them are parasitic. The vegetative body of any one of them is an extensive, much-branched mycelium composed of many short, one-nucleate cells. The mycelium gives rise, at the surface of the substrate in which it grows,

FIG. 231. Fruiting bodies of a cup fungus (Sclerotinia) which causes the brown rot of the peach. Photograph courtesy of E. E. Honey.

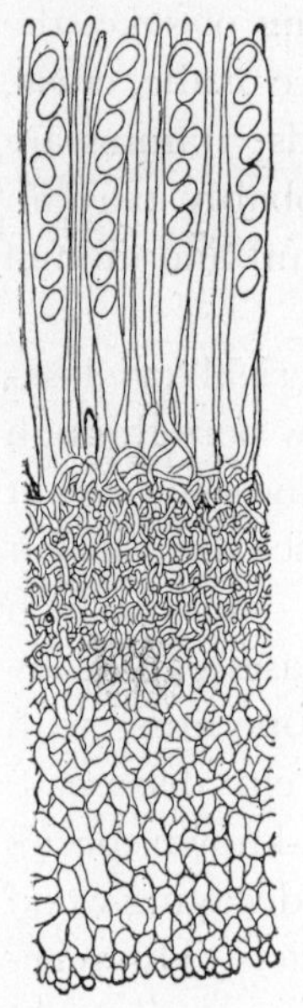

to one or many cup- or saucer-shaped fruiting bodies (Fig. 231). Each of these bodies corresponds to a fruiting body of a powdery mildew, in that its formation is the result of the union of one or more pairs of gametes. The fruiting body proper is usually borne on a stalk of varying length. At first it is almost spherical, with a small apical opening. As it grows, it opens more widely to form the characteristic cup. The interior of the cup is lined with a layer of cylindrical asci intermingled with sterile hyphae (Fig. 232). The outer portion of the cup is composed of a dense mass of interwoven hyphae. The fruiting bodies of different species range in size from almost invisible

FIG. 232. Cross section of a portion of a fruiting body of Peziza, showing asci intermingled with sterile hyphae, and the hyphae making up the part of the cup below the asci.

specks to structures several inches in diameter. A few of the cup fungi are important parasites, although the great majority of them are saprophytic.

Morels. These fungi, members of the genus Morchella, grow on rich, moist soil. The fruiting bodies, which appear following late spring rains, are considered by many to be the most delicious of the edible fungi. The many-celled, much-branched mycelium penetrates the soil for several inches and, after a period of very rapid growth, develops compact masses of hyphae a short distance below the surface of the soil. If abundant moisture and food are available, each of these hyphal masses grows into a fruiting body (Fig. 233) composed of densely interwoven hyphae, which pushes through the soil and completes its growth to mature size within a few hours.

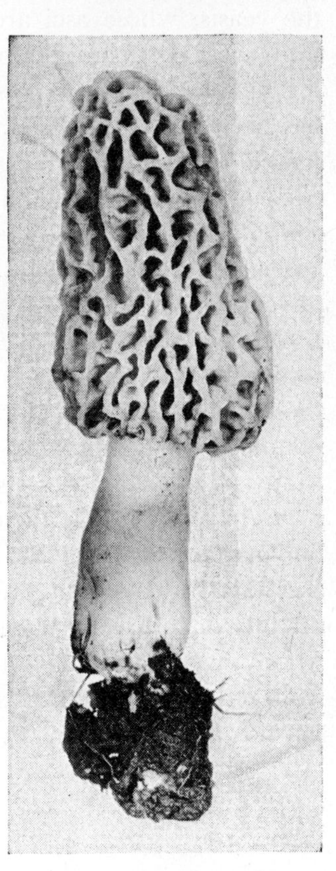

Fig. 233. A morel.

The mature fruiting bodies of various morels differ greatly in size, the more common forms having a cream-colored, thick, hollow, fleshy or waxy stalk one and one half to three inches long and one half to one inch in diameter. At the top of the stalk is a more or less conical hollow cap of about the same length as the stalk but somewhat broader at or near its base. When the fruiting body emerges from the soil, the cap is fairly smooth; but on its surface soon appears a network of ridges, the depressions between which vary in size and shape. The color of the ridges is that of the stalk; the depressions are usually of some shade of brown. Lining the depressions are numerous elongate cylindrical asci containing ascospores. Intermingled with and at times overtopping the asci are many slender hyphae. When the spores are mature, the asci elongate slightly, their tips break, and the ascospores are shot out.

Relationships. With the exception of some relatively simple forms, the development of asci and the method of ascospore formation are remarkably uniform throughout the large class of ascomycetes. The common possession of so highly specialized a structure as the ascus seems to demonstrate the close relationship of all or nearly all the members of the class. Among possible exceptions are the yeasts, whose asci are perhaps essentially different in nature from those of such undoubted ascomycetes as the powdery mildews.

The question of the possible origin of the ascomycetes as a group has been much discussed. The asci of certain simpler species resemble the sporangia of some phycomycetes. The conidia of powdery mildews and of many other ascomycetes are very like the conidia of some phycomycetes. These similarities, with others of lesser importance, suggest a possible descent from some ancient phycomycetes.

On the other hand, there are striking resemblances between ascomycetes and red algae. Certain ascomycetes, including some of those concerned in the formation of lichens (Chapter XXII), have nonmotile male gametes similar to the spermatia of red algae. Many ascomycetes possess trichogynes; their oögonia with trichogynes hence resemble the carpogonia of red algae. Hyphae growing, in many ascomycetes, from the zygote and ultimately producing asci have been compared with the branches which in red algae arise directly or indirectly from the zygote and give rise to carpospores. Many investigators have thought that the ascomycetes are derived from red algae which, becoming saprophytic or parasitic, lost their plastids and pigments.

CHAPTER XX

BASIDIOMYCETES (CLUB FUNGI)

Nature. These constitute another large and varied group of fungi, including both parasitic and saprophytic species. All are characterized by the production of spores on a special structure, the *basidium*. In addition to these *basidiospores*, many basidiomycetes produce spores of one or more other types.

SMUTS

Corn Smut: Mycelium and Winter Spores. The smuts are parasitic basidiomycetes which live and produce dark-colored masses of spores within various organs and tissues of their host plants. The term "smut" was suggested by the appearance of these spore masses. Smuts attack many wild plants and also cause some of the most important diseases of the cereal grains, including corn, and of some other cultivated plants. In general, each particular species of smut is parasitic upon a single host species. The species attacking the corn produces swellings, often as large as a man's fist, upon the stem, leaves, or prop roots, as well as in the ears or tassels (Fig. 234). The black, powdery masses contained in these swellings include immense numbers of thick-walled *winter spores*.

The vegetative body of the corn smut (Fig. 235, *A*) is a branching mycelium composed of many one- or two-nucleate cells. It grows largely in the intercellular spaces of the host and sends short absorbing branches into the host cells. The cells of the host that are invaded by the fungus are not killed at once; on the contrary, as a result of the stimulus supplied by the presence of the fungus, these host cells grow and divide rapidly, some of them reaching a remarkable size. In this way a swelling of the infected organ is caused. Eventually, however, the cells in the diseased tissues of the host are killed. The diseased portion of the corn plant now consists of a tangled mass of hyphae intermingled with the remains of the walls of the host cells, the whole being covered by the epidermis of the host. Repeated cell division occurs within the hyphae, forming a great number of short, two-nucleate cells. These cells are young spores. The protoplast of each spore becomes rounded and se-

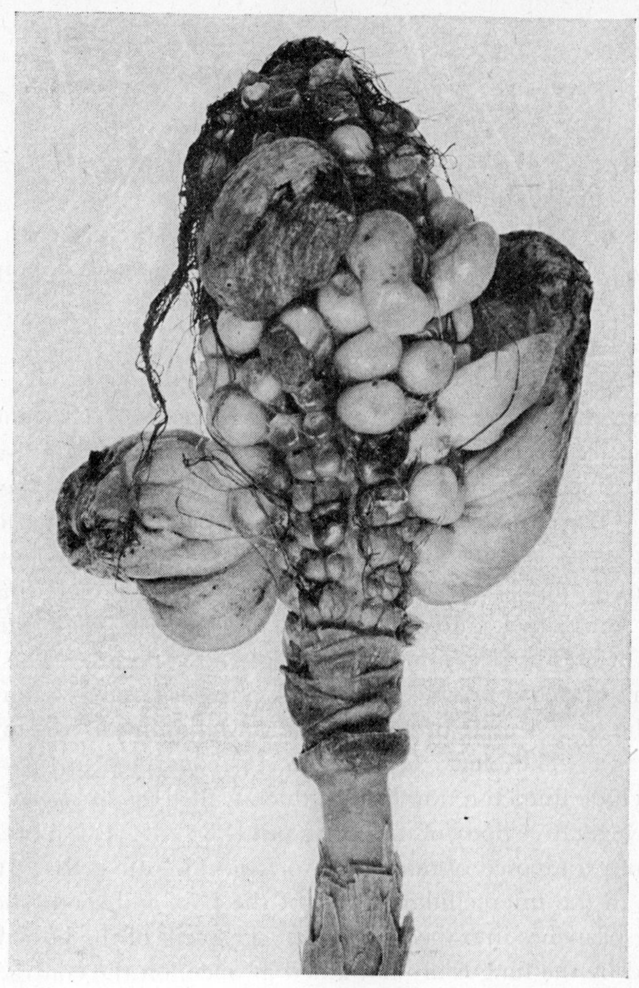

FIG. 234. An ear of corn infected with smut.

cretes a thick, dark wall. Meanwhile the hyphal walls surrounding the spores so formed soften and disappear. The two nuclei in each spore finally unite, so that a mature winter spore contains a single nucleus.

Basidiospores. The swelling containing the mass of winter spores may break open at any time after the spores are mature. The spores may germinate immediately if sufficient moisture is present, but in the majority of cases they do not germinate until

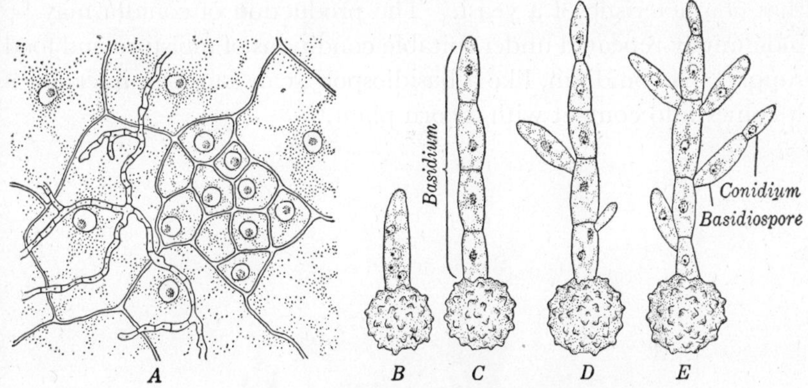

FIG. 235. Corn smut. *A*, mycelium growing through the tissues of the host. *B–E*, germination of a winter spore and formation of a basidium and basidiospores; in *E*, one basidiospore has produced a conidium by budding.

the spring following their formation. In germination, a spore sends out a short outgrowth; while this is being formed, the nucleus of the spore divides, the daughter nuclei divide, and further nuclear divisions may follow. The nuclei migrate into the outgrowth from the spore, and cell divisions occur between them. The outgrowth, a *basidium*, is usually four-celled (Fig. 235, *C*, *D*). Each cell of the basidium may give rise to one or more projections, which in time are separated as thin-walled *basidiospores*. The formation of each basidiospore is preceded by a nuclear division; one daughter nucleus migrates into the spore. If a basidiospore is carried by any means to a corn plant, it may bring about a new infection and develop into a mycelium. Infection is possible in any portion of the plant where young growing tissues are present and probably also at any place at which internal tissues are exposed by a wound. The mycelium developed from a single spore penetrates only a short distance; its cells are one-nucleate, and seldom if ever does it reach the spore-producing stage. If, however, the mycelium comes into contact with a mycelium from a basidiospore of another strain, there is a union of cells but not of nuclei; from each two-nucleate cell so formed, a mycelium develops, which ramifies through the host tissues and ultimately gives rise to winter spores.

A basidiospore, either attached to the basidium or freed from the latter, if not conveyed to a corn plant, can produce a spore of another type (*conidium*) by a process of budding (Fig. 235, *E*) very like that characteristic of a yeast. The production of conidia may be indefinitely repeated under suitable conditions of moisture and food supply. A conidium, like a basidiospore, can cause an infection if it comes into contact with a corn plant.

Fig. 236. Loose smut of the oat; *left*, an uninfected head; *right*, an infected head.

Other Smuts. The corn smut can produce an infection at any time during the growing period of the corn, but its mycelium grows only a short distance from the place of infection. Many other smuts, on the contrary, usually produce infection during only a limited portion of the life of the host; but their mycelia may penetrate to all parts of the host plant.

A familiar example of the latter type is the "loose smut" of oats (Fig. 236). Infection of an oat plant takes place chiefly in the flowers and in very young seedlings. In the former case the winter spores germinate in the flower, giving rise to basidiospores of two types (*plus* and *minus*). Spores of the two types, coming in contact, unite; and from the cell so formed is developed a hypha which penetrates the outer layers of the developing oat kernel (grain) as well as the surrounding chaffy structures. In these host tissues the mycelium becomes dormant and remains in this condition until the kernel germinates, when the mycelium again becomes active and spreads throughout the young seedling.

In other cases, spores may germinate in the vicinity of a young seedling. If two of the resultant basidiospores unite, a short hypha is developed which can infect a seedling. Further development is similar to that following infection of the flower. An infection of the seedling by a mycelium from either source probably can not take place after the seedling is more than three days old. A mycelium established by either method in the seedling penetrates all parts of the developing oat plant. The infected plant is somewhat stunted. When it forms flowers, the mycelium penetrates the floral structures and for a time grows very rapidly, so that almost all the cells of each flower and of its neighboring structures are invaded. Winter spores are formed by the mycelium in essentially the same way as in the case of the corn smut. The mass of winter spores occupies the place of the kernel and involves also some of the surrounding chaffy structures. In consequence of the breaking down of the mass of winter spores, these spores are liberated and may be carried by winds and other agencies to healthy flowers, which become infected as already described. In some varieties of oat this latter period of infection is not limited to the time of flowering; further infection may occur during the later development of the kernels and even at the time of threshing.

The loose smut of barley and the "closed smuts" of oats and barley seem to have a history essentially similar to that of the loose smut of oats. The closed smuts are so called because their winter spores are produced only in the kernels of the host, each kernel remaining enclosed by healthy chafflike structures.

Smuts differ greatly in the time and manner of origin of the two-nucleate condition. The majority of them are similar to the corn smut in that the mycelium becomes two-nucleate as soon as two basidiospores or two conidia or two cells of mycelia of opposite strains have united. In the onion smut, a basidiospore may give rise to a mycelium which often lives in the soil as a saprophyte before invading the tissues of the young onion plant. During this entire development the cells remain one-nucleate, and it is not yet known just when the two-nucleate condition arises.

Fig. 237. Stems of wheat infected with stem rust, bearing uredosori (*A*, *B*) and teleutosori (*C*).

RUSTS

Stem Rust of Wheat. The rusts constitute a group of parasitic basidiomycetes including almost 3,000 known species, one or more of which lives upon almost every species of seed plant as well as upon some of the ferns. Every rust produces spores of at least two distinct types; and some have three, four, or even five different kinds of spores.

The best-known rust, and the one that causes the greatest economic loss, is the stem rust of wheat (Fig. 237). The presence of the fungal mycelium within its tissues affects the wheat plant in various ways. First, the fungus kills many of the cells of the host and uses their contents for its own growth; second, the fungus robs the host of foods which would otherwise be used for growth in parts other than those in which the fungus occurs; third, as a result of the killing of host cells containing chloroplasts, the photosynthetic activity of the wheat plant is greatly reduced. In consequence of these effects produced by the fungus, the diseased plant is stunted and pale green. It ripens prematurely, and its small, shrunken kernels contain very little reserve food.

Phase of the Rust in the Wheat. Stems and leaves of wheat plants infected by this fungus often bear powdery masses, whose reddish color suggested the name "rust." Such a mass consists of innumerable small orange-red, two-nucleate *uredospores* (Fig. 238, *A*). These spores appear first in late spring, and their production continues until the plant matures. They may be carried by various means, especially by winds, to other wheat plants. When a uredospore falls on a growing wheat plant, it germinates, sending out a hypha (Fig. 238, *B*) which, on reaching a stoma, pushes through it into the intercellular spaces of the host. Here the hypha grows into a much-branched mycelium composed of many short cells, each, like the uredospore, containing two nuclei. The cells of the mycelium produce short branches which penetrate, and absorb food from, the cells of the host. As the mycelium develops, the growth and repeated branching of some of its hyphae give rise to compact masses of cells at certain spots immediately beneath the epidermis. The hyphae that make up each such mass finally grow outward to form a layer of parallel *basal cells*, which press directly against the epidermis.

Each basal cell (Fig. 238, *A*) elongates and divides transversely; the lower daughter cell formed by this division is now the basal cell. The upper daughter cell divides in its turn to form a terminal uredospore and a stalk cell. Like other cells of the mycelium, the basal cell, the stalk cell, and the uredospore are two-nucleate. Since

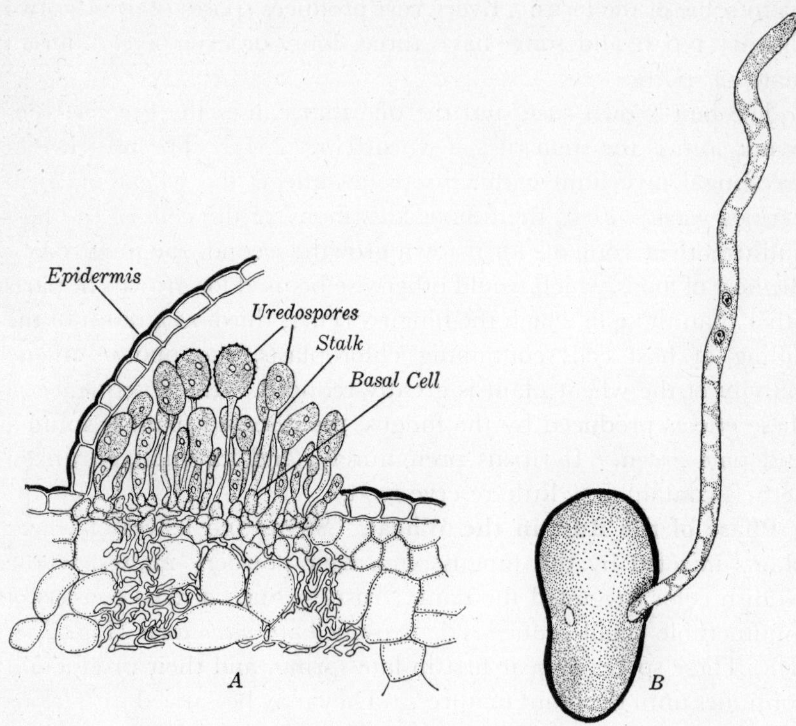

FIG. 238. *A*, portion of a uredosorus of the stem rust; stages in development of uredospores. *B*, germinating uredospore.

each basal cell may repeat this history, chains, each composed of uredospores alternating with stalk cells, are formed which press against the epidermis of the host. Finally the epidermis is ruptured in a more or less slitlike fashion, exposing the mass of spores. Such a mass of spores is a *sorus* (plural, *sori*). The uredospores, with or without their stalk cells, are easily detached from the basal cells. If a detached uredospore falls upon the same or upon another wheat plant, it may germinate and produce an infection like that already described. Only 10 or 12 days after such an infection are required for the development of a mycelium and the production of a new crop of uredospores. A sorus may produce successive crops of uredospores, and a succession of new sori may appear on the same host plant; hence, a single mycelium may during a season produce innumerable thousands of uredospores through whose agency the disease becomes more widespread.

The spread of the rust is dependent upon atmospheric conditions. It is favored by warm, moist, cloudy weather. Hot, dry, clear weather, on the other hand, checks its spread, because the spores require considerable moisture for germination and because hyphae growing from the spores will not long withstand the heat of the sun's rays.

As the host plant approaches maturity, the mycelium, which up to this time has borne uredospores, produces spores of another type, *teleutospores* (Fig. 239). A teleutospore is formed in the same man-

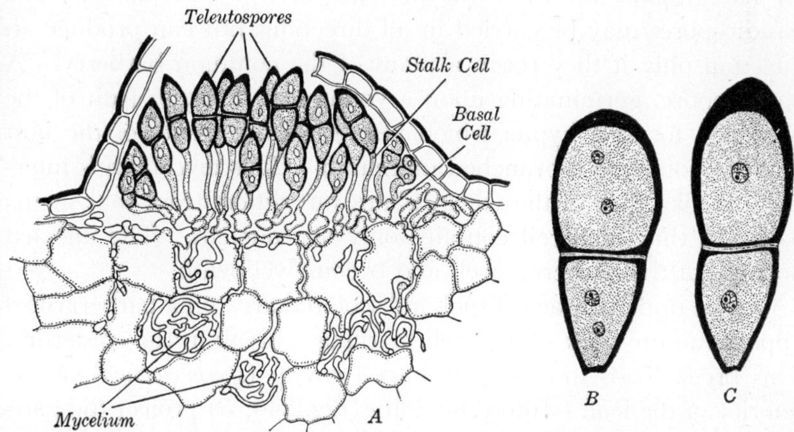

FIG. 239. *A*, portion of a cross section of a wheat stem with a teleutosorus. *B*, *C*, teleutospores before and after the union of the nuclei in each cell.

ner as a uredospore, except that the upward projection cut off from a basal cell divides into a row of three cells, the upper two of which become enlarged to form the teleutopsore. The first teleutospores may appear in the same sori with uredospores; later-developed sori may contain only teleutospores.

Teleutospores have much thicker cell walls than uredospores, are darker, and usually do not germinate until the spring following their production. Each cell of a young teleutospore, like other cells of the mycelium, has two nuclei. As the spore matures, however, the two nuclei in each cell unite, so that the cells are finally one-nucleate.

Each cell of a teleutospore behaves in germination as if it were itself a spore. Under suitable conditions of temperature and moisture, either one or both cells may germinate. The nucleus of the germinating cell divides, and its daughter nuclei divide, the cell now containing four nuclei. The germinating cell pushes out a short hypha, the *basidium*, which divides transversely into four cells (Fig. 240, *A*), each containing one of the four nuclei of the parent cell. Each cell of the basidium produces a small projection into which pass the nucleus and most of the cytoplasm. The enlarged end of this projection, containing the nucleus, becomes a separate *basidiospore*.

Phase of the Rust in the Barberry. The wheat rust requires for its complete life cycle the presence of two host plants. The basidiospores may be carried in all directions but can produce an infection only if they reach a plant of the common barberry. A basidiospore, germinating upon a young leaf, twig, or fruit of the barberry, forms a hypha which penetrates the tissues of the host and develops into a branched mycelium. This mycelium is intercellular, like that in the wheat plant, but differs from that in the wheat in that each cell contains only one nucleus. The infected portions of the barberry swell and become yellowish.

On the upper surface of such a discolored area on a barberry leaf appear minute dark spots, each marking a break in the epidermis. This break leads into a flask-shaped cavity (*spermogonium*) in the interior of the leaf. Into this cavity (Fig. 240, *B*) project the hair-like terminal cells of many hyphae; at the ends of these hyphae, very small, one-nucleate, sporelike cells (*spermatia*) are formed by constriction. The spermatia, in a liquid given off from other cells within the spermogonium, exude to the outer surface of the leaf.

While spermogonia are being formed in the upper portion of the infected region of the leaf, masses of hyphae (*aecidial initials*) develop at various points just within the lower epidermis of the infected region. From these initials hyphae grow out in several directions; some grow upward through the spermogonia, others grow to the outside through the epidermis or through a stoma. If a spermatium from a different strain comes into contact with such a hyphal tip, the protoplast of the spermatium unites with a cell of the hypha.

Probably there is a migration of nuclei through the hypha to an aecidial initial, which is stimulated to further growth. Certain cells of the initial become two-nucleate, and a layer of basal cells is formed very much as in the formation of a sorus (producing uredo- or teleutospores) in the wheat. Each two-nucleate basal cell of this *aecidium* gives rise by repeated nuclear and cell divisions to a row or chain of two-nucleate cells (Fig. 240, *C*), alternately large and small.

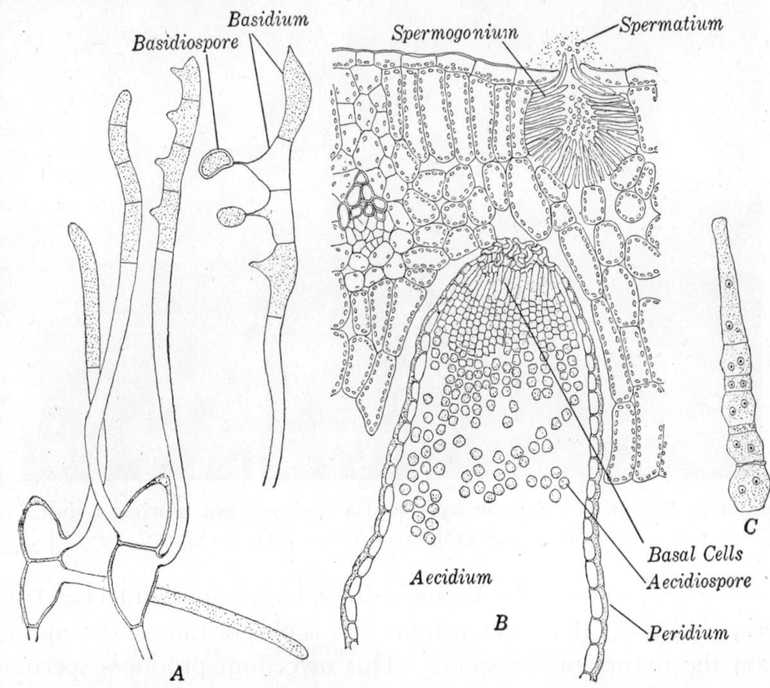

FIG. 240. Stem rust of wheat. *A*, germination of teleutospores. *B*, portion of a cross section of a barberry leaf with a spermogonium and an aecidium. *C*, a single chain consisting of a basal cell, aecidiospores, and alternating disintegrating cells. After G. M. Smith, *Cryptogamic Botany*, published by the McGraw-Hill Book Company.

The larger cells of the chain become *aecidiospores;* the smaller cells disintegrate. Thus, from a group of basal cells a corresponding number of chains of aecidiospores is formed. The group of chains is surrounded by a continuous layer of fungal cells known as a *peridium*, the whole structure (the aecidium) being distinctly cup-shaped. Commonly, aecidia of the wheat rust appear in clusters (Fig. 241).

Just how the two-nucleate condition, characterizing the basal cells of an aecidium, arises is still not fully settled. Different answers have been given to this question by different investigators, and it may well be that the method varies as between different species of rust. It is established that certain rusts, including the wheat rust, produce two kinds of basidiospores, referred to respectively as *plus* and *minus*. When a single basidiospore infects a barberry leaf, it develops a mycelium that is plus or minus, depending upon the nature of the spore. This mycelium produces spermogonia and spermatia but only incompletely developed aecidial initials whose basal cells are one-nucleate. If, on the other hand, mycelia are present derived from both plus and minus basidiospores, an aecidium is developed with two-nucleate basal cells; and these basal cells produce chains of aecidiospores.

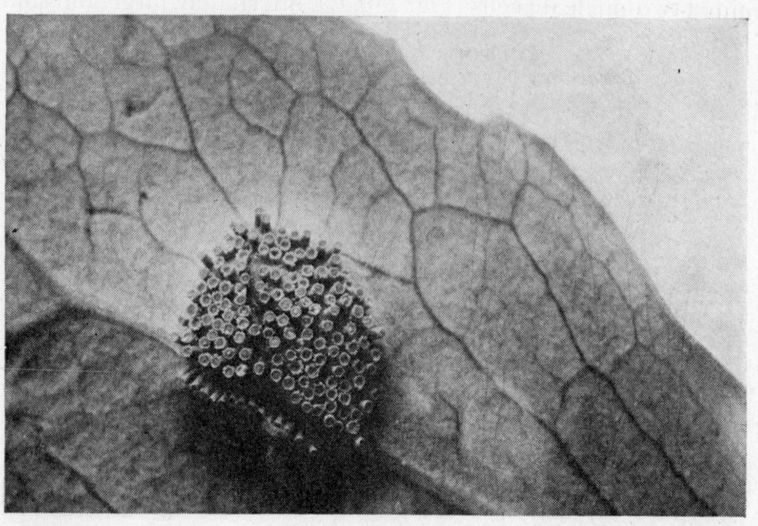

FIG. 241. Portion of the lower surface of a barberry leaf bearing a cluster of aecidia. Photograph courtesy of J. G. Dickson.

In some rusts, again including the wheat rust, it has been found that, if spermatia from a plus mycelium are transferred to a spermogonium borne by a minus mycelium or vice versa, two-nucleate basal cells appear in the young aecidia and the aecidia continue development. In some way, therefore, a mixture of plus and minus spermatia or of plus and minus mycelia causes the appearance of two-nucleate basal cells.

When fully mature the aecidiospores are shed from the aecidia. They can not infect the barberry; but if one of them is carried by any agency, such as the wind, to a wheat plant, it germinates, forming a hypha which penetrates a stoma and grows within the tissues of the wheat into a branching mycelium composed of two-nucleate cells. It is this mycelium that produces uredospores and eventually teleutospores.

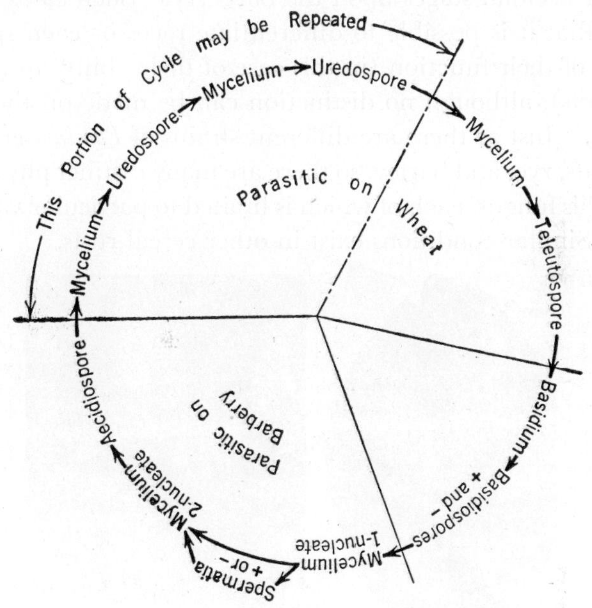

FIG. 242. Life cycle of the stem rust of wheat.

Overwintering of the Wheat Rust. Epidemics of wheat rust occur frequently in regions where no barberries are found. Such epidemics are due in part to the survival of uredospores over exceptionally mild winters. In wheat-growing regions with relatively moderate climates, such an overwintering of uredospores may be of regular occurrence. Some rust epidemics in the wheat-growing regions of the Dakotas, Montana, and western Canada are caused by uredospores that have been carried by winds from states farther south. Teleutospores, therefore, although regularly produced, are not always essential to the overwintering of the rust.

Different Strains of *Puccinia graminis*. The wheat rust occurs also on some wild grasses, including the quack grass. There are rusts on rye, oats, barley, and several common grasses which are very similar to the stem rust on the wheat and which are for convenience called by the same name (*Puccinia graminis*). But the uredospores of the stem rust of wheat will infect the oat only with difficulty and will not produce on the oat a serious disease. Likewise, uredospores from *Puccinia graminis* on oats, rye, or barley will not readily infect wheat. Both the rust on wheat and that on oats pass their aecidial stages upon the barberry. Such cases illustrate the fact that it is possible to differentiate races or even species on the basis of their function (in this case of their ability to infect different hosts), although no distinction can be made on the basis of structure. Just as there are different strains of *Puccinia graminis* on wheat, oats, rye, and barley, so there are many distinct physiological races of this fungus, each of which is limited to particular varieties of wheat. Similar conditions exist in other cereal rusts.

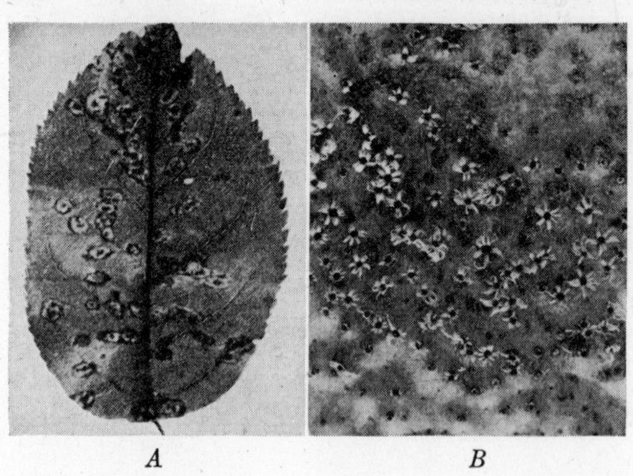

A *B*

FIG. 243. Apple rust. *A*, apple leaf, with groups of aecidia on its lower surface. *B*, enlarged view of an area bearing aecidia.

Other Rusts. The apple rust forms spermatia and aecidiospores on leaves and fruits of the apple (Fig. 243) and of some of its relatives. On the red cedar it produces swellings of the branches (so-called "cedar apples," Fig. 244), in which teleutospores are formed. A teleutospore, still attached to the host, germinates, producing a basidium and basidiospores. The basidiospores infect the apple. This rust forms no uredospores.

Some rusts, in contrast to the wheat and apple rusts, complete their life cycles on a single host. Examples of this sort are the rose rust, the asparagus rust, the hollyhock rust, and the orange leaf rust of blackberries and raspberries. Many rusts have a shorter life cycle than the wheat rust. For example, the apple rust just mentioned produces no uredospores. The hollyhock rust repre-

FIG. 244. Apple rust. *A*, "cedar apples" on the red cedar. *B*, a cedar apple producing hornlike gelatinous projections on which teleutospores are formed.

sents the shortest known type of life cycle among the rusts; it produces only teleutospores and basidiospores. Although various rusts omit the formation of aecidiospores, spermatia, or uredospores, no rust is known which does not produce both teleutospores and basidiospores.

OTHER BASIDIOMYCETES

Field Mushroom. Numerous basidiomycetes, including many of the most conspicuous ones, are saprophytic. One of the commonest saprophytic basidiomycetes is the field mushroom (*Psalliota campestris*), which often grows in the rich soils of fields and open woods. A strain of this species is the one mushroom that is extensively cultivated. Its vegetative body consists of colorless or whitish branching, short-celled hyphae, which live for the most part underground. The cells of this mycelium are at first one-nucleate; but after a certain stage two-nucleate cells are formed, probably in consequence of a union of one-nucleate cells which therefore function as gametes. Some of the hyphae are interwoven into thicker strands; but these strands, as well as the separate hyphae, are easily broken when the soil is disturbed. After the mycelium has been developing for some time, compact, rounded masses of interwoven hyphae appear here and there on the underground strands.

FIG. 245. Young fruiting bodies of the field mushroom (Psalliota) arising from the mycelium.

At first such a mass is almost microscopic; as it matures, it develops into the fruiting body commonly called a "mushroom" (Fig. 245). This body becomes differentiated into a stalk and a cap. The margin of the cap is attached to the stalk by a thin membrane, which is broken as the cap enlarges. A portion of the membrane remains attached to the stalk in the form of a ring. Before the breaking of the membrane, the lower portion of the cap, extending from the stalk to the outer edge, has become transformed into many thin plates (*gills*), each free at its lower edge but attached above to the more compact portion of the cap. As the cap grows, it becomes much flattened, so that the gills are fully exposed. The mature cap

FIG. 246. Mature fruiting body of the field mushroom.

Fig. 246) is two to five inches in diameter; its top is white, cream-colored, or brownish; it bears many fine, silky hairs and often some brownish scales. The flesh is white, turning to pink if broken.

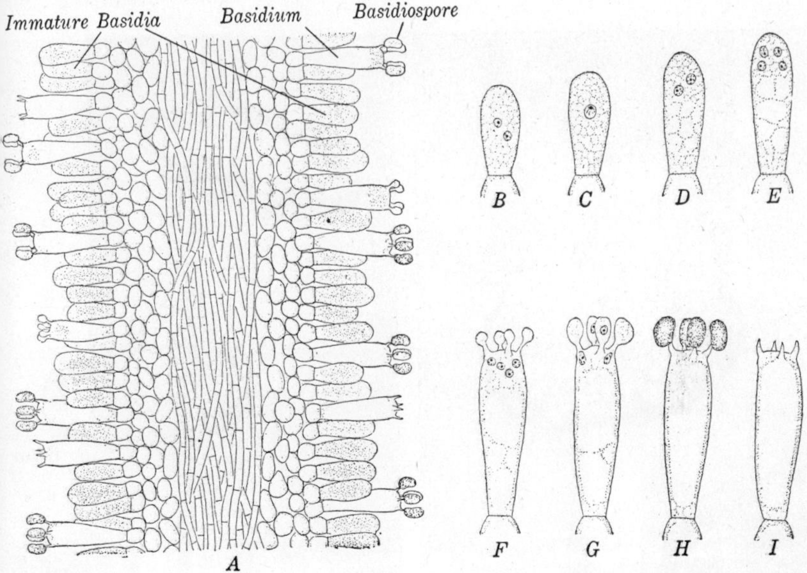

FIG. 247. *A*, diagram of a cross section of a portion of a gill of Psalliota. *B*, young two-nucleate basidium. *C*, after the union of the two nuclei. *D*, *E*, after the division of the zygote nucleus to form two nuclei (*D*), and of the daughter nuclei to form four (*E*). *F–I*, stages in spore formation.

The gills are at first flesh-colored or pink, gradually changing, as the fruiting body grows older, to dark brown. The terminal cells of many of the hyphae which compose a gill form a layer on each side of the gill (Fig. 247). The cells of this layer are parallel to one another and perpendicular to the surface of the gill. Most of the cells of the surface layer become much-enlarged basidia. Each basidium is at first, like other cells of the mycelium, two-nucleate. The two nuclei in a basidium unite; this union is followed by two nuclear divisions, so that the basidium contains four nuclei. From the free end of each basidium grow two or four slender projections; the outer end of each projection swells, into it pass one or two of the nuclei of the basidium, and the enlarged end is cut off as a basidiospore. In this way each basidium produces four (or in some strains, particularly in the strain which is commonly cultivated, two) basidia. When a basidiospore germinates, it gives rise to a mycelium which may in time produce fruiting bodies.

Other Mushrooms. The shaggy mane (Fig. 248), which grows singly or in clusters on soil rich in humus, has a structure much like

FIG. 248. The shaggy mane (Coprinus). *Left*, a young fruiting body. *Right*, older, disintegrating fruiting bodies.

that of the field mushroom. The cap is long and narrow, and its upper surface bears numerous patches of hyphae interwoven in the form of strands and plates. As basidia and spores mature, the cap darkens; its lower edge and eventually the whole cap soften and break down into black, slimy droplets. The shaggy mane and the closely related inky cap are edible.

Among the most beautiful, as well as the most dangerous, mushrooms are the deadly Amanita (Fig. 249) and the fly mushroom, also an Amanita. At the base of the stalk of each of these mushrooms is a cup or bulb, from whose center arises the stalk with its conspicuous ring. The deadly Amanita has a pure white cap; that of the fly mushroom is reddish or orange-colored. Scattered over the upper surface of the fly mushroom are sometimes white wartlike elevations. The gills and the spores of both species are white.

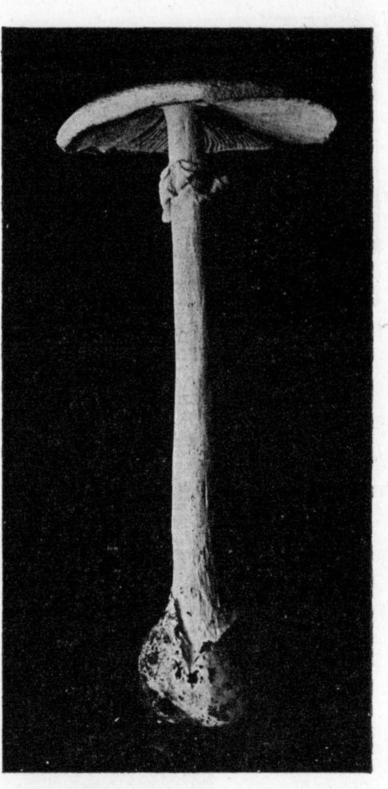

FIG. 249. The deadly Amanita.

The honey mushroom commonly occurs in clusters about trees or stumps during late summer and autumn. Both stalk and cap are yellow or brownish. The stalk is tough and commonly bears a definite ring. Near the center of the cap are usually a number of erect dark scales. The oyster mushroom forms large clusters on trunks of dead or dying trees. The stalk is short and very thick and bears a large cap, often six inches in diameter. The stalk and cap are white. The name "oyster mushroom" was suggested by the shape of the cap, which is commonly much more developed on one side than on the other. Both the honey mushroom and the oyster mushroom are edible.

There are no general rules for distinguishing between edible mushrooms and those which are unfit for food or poisonous. The one safe rule is to eat only mushrooms identified by an expert.

Bracket Fungi. Basidiomycetes belonging to another considerable group live as saprophytes or parasites on various trees and shrubs. The mycelium penetrates the wood, and on the external surface of the tree or shrub it produces fruiting bodies of various forms. One of the simplest types of these fruiting bodies is composed merely of a crustlike layer of hyphae bearing basidia. The fruiting bodies of another type grow erect and are variously branched. In a third type, the branches of the fruiting body are covered with teeth or spines which project downward and whose outer surfaces bear basidia. The fruiting bodies of a fourth type are the so-called "brackets" (Fig. 250) that appear on stems and branches. Some of these brackets are soft, expanded outgrowths in whose lower surfaces are innumerable fine pores lined with basidia. Most of such fleshy forms live for but a single season. The fruiting bodies of other bracket fungi are firm, hard, sometimes almost woody in texture, and grow in size from year to year, forming each year a new pore-containing layer below, and extending beyond, that of the previous year (Fig. 251). The fruiting bodies of *Fomes applanatus*, one of the commonest bracket fungi, are often 12 inches or more in diameter and may live for 10 years or longer.

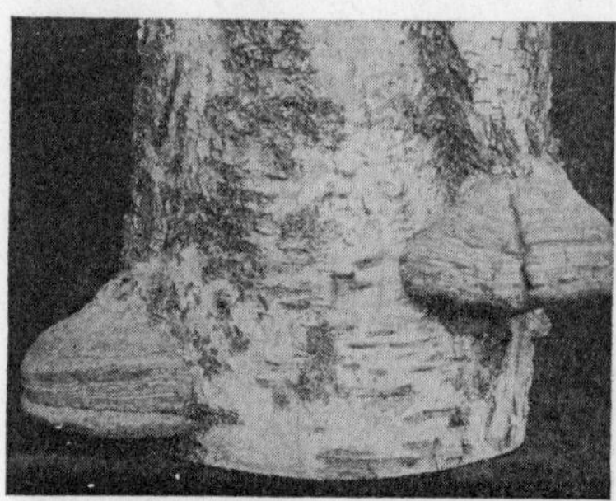

Fig. 250. Bracket fungi (Fomes) on the trunk of a birch.

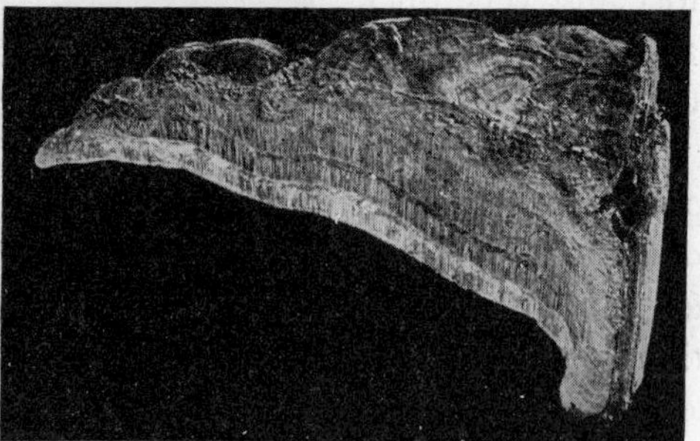

Fig. 251. Lengthwise section of a bracket fungus.

The bracket fungi and their close relatives cause immense losses through the decay of the wood of living trees, as well as of logs and timber in lumber yards and of lumber in factories and warehouses. It is estimated that these "wood-destroyers" cause each year more damage than forest fires.

Puffballs. The basidia and spores of another group of basidiomycetes are enclosed, often in special chambers, within the fruiting body. The spores of some species escape through special pores; those of others are set free only when the fruiting body decays or is accidentally broken. The best-known members of this group are the common "puffballs" of pastures and woods (Fig. 253). The mycelium of a puffball grows in the soil or in rotting wood; on it

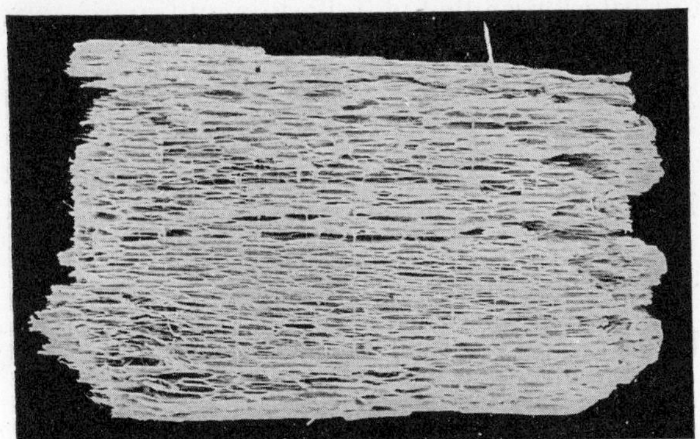

Fig. 252. Disintegration of wood caused by a bracket fungus.

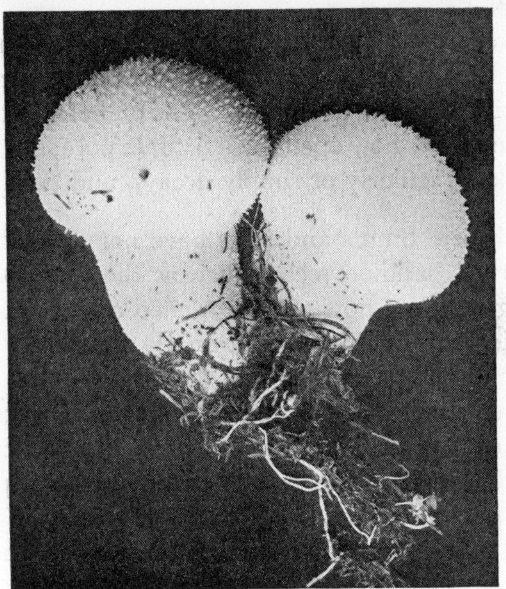

Fig. 253. Puffballs.

are developed spherical bodies, comparable at first to an early stage of the field mushroom. These bodies grow, those of some of the giant puffballs reaching a diameter of 20 to 30 inches and a weight of several pounds. The interior of a puffball remains white until its full size is reached, when numerous scattered areas in the upper portion darken. This color change occurs at a time when the ends of some hyphae have formed basidia. Other darkened areas appear successively within the fruiting body, until finally the greater portion of its interior is filled with basidia and spores. Some of the

Fig. 254. The earth star (Geaster), a puffball.

hyphae surrounding the masses of spores disintegrate; other hyphae, whose walls become thickened, form a spongy network or serve as the boundaries of special chambers. The outer layer of the fruiting body in some species now opens by a definite pore; but in most puffballs it breaks irregularly or simply decays, and the spores escape.

Relationships. Smuts and rusts have not always been classed with the "true" basidiomycetes, such as the mushrooms. While these three groups are now usually treated as constituting a single class, of which the smuts are most nearly primitive, some writers still consider the smuts unrelated to the others.

There is no group of algae from which the basidiomycetes can readily be imagined to have been derived. The basidiospores have been likened to conidia, and some basidiomycetes produce true conidia that resemble those of some phycomycetes. The spermatia of rusts are similar to those of some ascomycetes. Basidiomycetes resemble ascomycetes also in possessing a mycelium composed at different stages of one- and two-nucleate cells. In other respects the mycelia are similar enough in the two classes to render plausible the conception of a relationship, perhaps through a remote common ancestry, between basidiomycetes and ascomycetes.

CHAPTER XXI

PLANT DISEASES

Causes of Disease. When, as a result of external conditions, the ordinary or "normal" functions of a plant or of its parts are interfered with or deranged, the plant is said to be *diseased*. The various ways in which the structure and functions of the plant are thus caused to deviate from the normal condition are spoken of as *symptoms*. A very large proportion of plant, as well as of animal, diseases result from the attacks of other organisms. In such a case it is the parasitic organism that causes the disease and not infrequently the death of the host.

Many parasitic animals are capable of entering and living in the tissues of plants; among the most common of these are species of nematodes, or "eel worms." Nematodes are often root parasites, their presence in roots resulting in the formation of galls. The wheat nematode and some others of the group can invade all portions of the host plant and entirely check the formation of normal fruits.

Among parasitic plants are some that contain chlorophyll. Certain algae, for example, live in the tissues of more complex plants, sometimes doing no injury to the host but at other times causing disease. Of parasitic seed plants the best known are the mistletoes and dodders.

Virus Diseases. There are a considerable number of plant diseases for which, as for such human diseases as scarlet fever and cancer, no causal organism has been found. Among the more common of these are the virus or mosaic diseases of potato (Fig. 255), tobacco, and cucumber. Each of these hosts may be attacked by several virus diseases. The mosaics of these and of some other plants can readily be transmitted from plant to plant. The virus diseases of the peach, including "yellows," are transmitted under natural conditions in a manner not yet fully understood. Artificially, peach yellows can be transmitted only by means of grafting or budding. Some virus diseases, like aster yellows and curly top of the sugar beet, are transferred only by specific insects. As in the cases of certain animal viruses, the active agent of such a plant dis-

FIG. 255. Mosaic disease of potato. *Left*, an uninfected leaf; *right*, an infected leaf. Photograph courtesy of James Johnson.

ease must have spent some time in the body of the insect carrier. The virus diseases of certain members of the pea family differ from most diseases of this class in that they may be transmitted through seeds.

The symptoms of virus diseases are variable; in most cases the leaves of the host are malformed, stunted, and wrinkled; often they are mottled in appearance—hence the term "mosaic." In a few cases the entire plant is badly stunted or blighted; in others the number of leaves is greatly increased, but they are abnormal in size and color.

Diseases Caused by Bacteria. One of the commonest bacterial plant diseases is the fire blight, or pear blight (Fig. 256), which occurs on the apple, crab apple, pear, and related plants. The bacterium causing this disease gains entrance to the host through wounds, or more often through the floral nectaries, and multiplies very rapidly, killing the host cells so quickly that the affected portion appears scorched. After the close of the growing season, the bacteria remain dormant at the edges of the diseased portion; when the host plant resumes growth the following spring, the bacteria again multiply rapidly and are often exuded in a viscous liquid. Insects visit this exudate and carry the bacteria to other plants.

Soft rot, caused by bacteria that enter the host through wounds, is responsible for the rotting of many vegetables in the field and for still further losses if the diseased vegetables are stored in warm moist places.

Cabbage is attacked by a black rot caused by bacteria that enter the leaves of the host, usually through water pores. The bacteria travel through the conducting elements of the xylem, multiplying

Fig. 256. Fire blight of pear.

so greatly as to clog these elements. The water supply is thus cut off from the tissues of the plant, and if the main stem is invaded the whole plant may die.

Crown gall, so called because of the large galls formed on stems and roots at the surface of the soil, is a serious disease of apples (Fig. 257) and is abundant also on many other plants, including raspberries, grapes, and walnuts. The bacteria enter through wounds; the stimulus supplied by their presence causes a rapid division of the host cells in their vicinity, as well as a marked enlargement of many of these cells.

Fig. 257. Crown gall of apple.

Diseases Caused by Slime Molds. Most slime molds are saprophytic, but a few are parasitic in the tissues of higher plants. The strictly parasitic slime molds do not produce fruiting bodies as the saprophytic species do. A plasmodium of one of these species divides within the host tissue into masses of spores, which masses may be irregular or may take on a characteristic form. One of the best known of these parasitic slime molds (Plasmodiophora) causes the clubroot disease of cabbage and related plants (see page 326).

Closely related to Plasmodiophora is an organism causing the powdery scab of potatoes. This disease has long been known in Europe, and in some localities it is very destructive. It appeared in the extensive potato-growing areas of southeastern Canada and adjacent parts of the United States about 1910; here it has been practically eliminated by the sterilization of tubers before they are planted and by the growing of resistant varieties. The slime mold causes the formation of blister-like spots on developing tubers; the spots increase greatly in size and become filled with a brownish powdery substance composed of broken-down tissues together with the spores of the fungus.

Diseases Caused by Phycomycetes. The serious diseases due to Albugo (Fig. 219), Pythium, Plasmopara, and Phytophthora (Fig. 222) were mentioned in Chapter XVIII. The damage done by the downy mildew of the grape (Plasmopara) and the late blight of potato (Phytophthora) has been greatly checked in the United States by systematic spraying of the host plants. Another phycomycete (a chytrid, Urophlyctis) attacks alfalfa in the irrigated regions of the West. The fungus invades the young alfalfa buds at the surface of the soil, checks their development, and causes the formation of numerous galls. Aphanomyces, related to Saprolegnia, attacks the roots of many leguminous plants and sometimes causes serious losses through the breaking down of the tissues of the roots, so preventing the transportation of water.

Diseases Caused by Ascomycetes. Besides the powdery mildew of the lilac (Chapter XIX), a number of powdery mildews cause plant diseases some of which result in considerable damage.

One of the simpler ascomycetes (Taphrina) causes plum pocket. The younger branches, leaves, and fruits of the plum, invaded by

FIG. 258. American chestnut trees killed by the chestnut blight. Photograph by Ernest L. Crandall, received through the courtesy of the American Forestry Association.

this fungus, are stimulated to excessive growth. The fruit often becomes hollow, the pit being absent. After a period of rapid vegetative growth, the fungal hyphae grow to the outside of the part affected and on its surface form many asci. Peach leaf curl at one time caused losses of several millions of dollars each year, but this disease is now not serious when control measures are employed. Poplar, alder, hazel, and other hosts are attacked by various species of Taphrina.

The apple and pear are often injured by species of Venturia, which produce a dark-colored mycelial growth on the leaves and fruits. The mycelium penetrates only the cuticle, but the growth of the epidermal and immediately underlying cells of the host is checked. Infected fruits are often very irregular in shape and sometimes display large cracks. Conidia, formed at the ends of protruding hyphae, spread the disease during the growing season. After the leaves fall, the fungus penetrates them and continues to grow as a saprophyte. In the dead leaves, small rounded fruiting bodies containing asci are developed; the fruiting bodies and asci mature the next spring and liberate ascospores that can infect new hosts.

Fig. 259. Brown rot of plum.

About 1904, a disease was discovered on chestnut trees in the vicinity of New York City; during succeeding years it spread throughout the chestnut forests of New York and neighboring states. So serious was the disease and so rapid its spread that all efforts made by state and national governments failed to check it, and the chestnut forests of the United States have been almost entirely destroyed (Fig. 258). The disease is caused by an ascomycete, probably introduced from Japan, where it has long been known but does little damage.

In 1930 a disease of the American elm was found at Cincinnati and Cleveland. This disease has been called the "Dutch elm disease" because it was first described in the Netherlands. It was soon found to be widely distributed in the vicinity of New York City. Strenuous control measures, including the complete destruction of diseased trees, seem to have brought the disease under control; but much remains to be done before it is finally entirely eradicated.

Fig. 260. Branch of a white pine infected with the blister rust, as seen in spring. The white spots are blisters through which aecidiospores are extruded.

Cherries, plums, and related plants are attacked by species of Sclerotinia (Figs. 231, 259); infected fruits decay and turn dark brown. Many conidia are produced by the aerial hyphae on the surfaces of the decaying fruits; and if there is ample moisture, the disease is spread by the conidia from tree to tree. The brown-rot fungus remains alive in fruits that fall to the ground and resumes growth the next spring, forming saucer-shaped fruiting bodies containing many asci. The ascospores, liberated during spring rains, communicate the disease to the newly forming fruits.

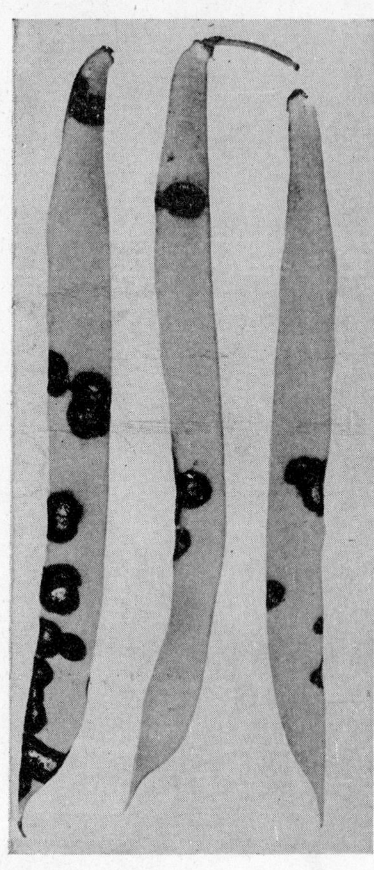

Fig. 261. Anthracnose of the bean.

Diseases Caused by Basidiomycetes. All cereal grains and many wild grasses are attacked by one or another of the smuts (Chapter XX). Serious diseases of the onion, of rice, and of many leguminous plants also are caused by smuts.

In addition to those discussed in the preceding chapter, various species of rusts are parasitic upon the great majority of seed plants, both cultivated and wild. Some attack ferns as well. The white pine blister rust (Fig. 260), which threatens the existence of all five-needle pines in the United States and Canada, was imported from Europe on pine seedlings. The rust was first noted in 1906 at Geneva, New York. It spread very rapidly and at the present time has extended across the continent. Its most recent and most rapid progress has been in the states of Washington, Oregon, and Idaho, and into adjacent parts of Canada.

The stage of this rust that produces uredo- and teleutospores is passed on currants and gooseberries. One means being used in the attempt to control the disease is the extermination of cultivated and wild currants and gooseberries in the neighborhood of the forests of five-needle pines. There is a hope also that resistant strains of pines may be found.

Diseases Caused by Imperfect Fungi. Imperfect fungi are so called because they or many of them are thought to be ascomycetes or basidiomycetes whose life cycles are only partly known. The part of the cycle which is known in each case produces spores of varied types but does not include the ascospore- or basidiospore-forming stage. Each year the study of these fungi reveals the unknown stages in the life cycles of some of them, which are then transferred to the appropriate class (ascomycetes or basidiomycetes). Many thousands of species of imperfect fungi are known, a large proportion of them being parasitic and causing diseases of bryophytes, pteridophytes, and especially of seed plants. Among diseases that they produce are the early blight of potato, the leaf spot of beets, anthracnose of beans (Fig. 261), and cabbage yellows.

CHAPTER XXII

LICHENES (LICHENS)

Nature and Forms. A lichen is peculiar in being formed by the intimate association of two very different plants, one of which is a filamentous fungus, the other in almost all instances an alga. The two organisms seem in most cases to derive mutual advantage from their association, the alga making carbohydrate foods and the fungus absorbing and retaining moisture for the partnership. In temperate regions, the fungal component is always an ascomycete; in a few lichens of warmer regions it is a basidiomycete. In the majority of lichens the other component is a one-celled green alga; in

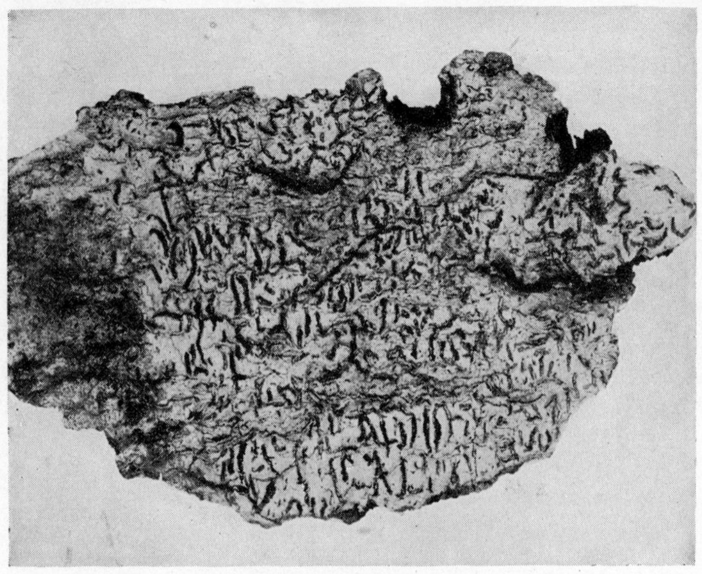

Fig. 262. A crustose lichen (*Graphis scripta*). The dark linear and curved structures are fruiting bodies.

many, however, it is a blue-green alga. One lichen has been reported in which a filamentous fungus is associated with a bacterium rather than with an alga. The bacterium is of a species that produces a pigment which gives the lichen a reddish appearance. Lichens may be divided according to their forms into three principal types (Figs. 262–266): *crustose*, forming crusts on trees, rocks, or soil; *foliose*, with leaflike thalli whose upper and lower surfaces are different; and *fruticose*, which are pendent or erect.

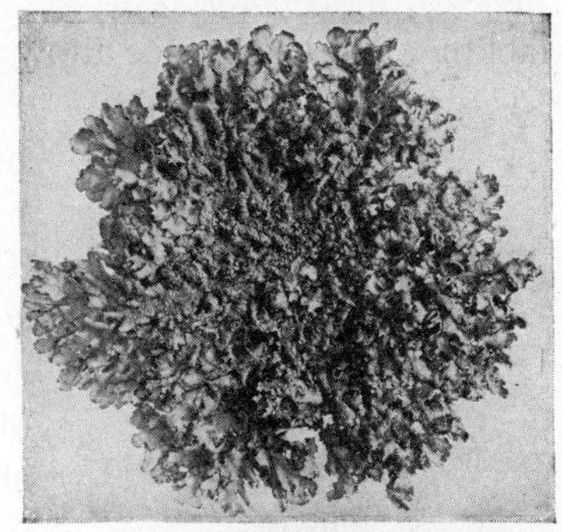

Fig. 263. Parmelia, a foliose lichen.

Crustose species vary greatly in form, color, and thickness. The body of such a lichen (Fig. 267, *A*) usually consists of an upper layer of closely packed and interwoven fungal hyphae, beneath this a layer of algal cells intermixed with hyphae, and finally a region of loosely woven hyphae which are intimately intermingled with the substrate. An additional lower, closely packed layer is present in some species, especially in those which develop free lobes at the margin of the thallus. The bodies of some crustose lichens are partly or wholly imbedded in the bark, disintegrating rock, or soil upon which they grow. In the latter case, all that appears above the surface of the substrate may be the fruiting bodies of the lichen. *Graphis scripta* (Fig. 262) is a crustose lichen growing upon and partly imbedded within the smooth bark of some trees. Superficially it appears as an ashy or whitish crust on the surface of the bark, marked by black linear, curved, or branched fruiting bodies. Because of the resemblance of the fruiting bodies to hieroglyphic writing, this lichen has been observed and recorded since very ancient times.

Fig. 264. Gyrophora, a foliose lichen.

A foliose lichen consists of one or more flat lobes, some parts of which usually adhere more or less firmly to the substrate by means of strands of hyphae. The structure of the thallus is similar to that of a crustose lichen except that there is in all cases a well-developed lower, closely packed layer from which grow holdfasts—strands of hyphae which attach the thallus to the substrate. Some foliose lichens, such as Gyrophora (Fig. 264), are attached by small central holdfasts. On the lower sides of certain large foliose lichens are depressed, light-colored areas. In these areas the lowermost layer is lacking, and its absence allows a free passage of air to the algal layer.

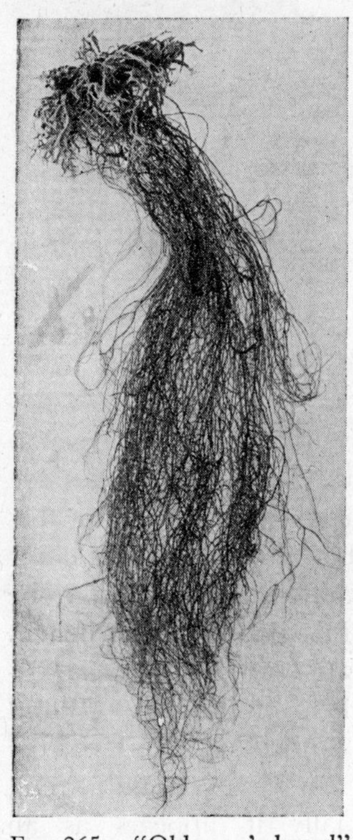

Fig. 265. "Old man's beard" (Usnea), a fruticose lichen.

The body of a fruticose lichen varies in shape from flat to cylindrical. Commonly it is much branched (Fig. 265). There is a central region of hyphae, surrounded by a zone containing algal cells, and this in turn by an outer zone of compact hyphae. There are no clearly differentiated upper and lower surfaces. The lichen is attached to the substrate by a definite basal portion composed of strands of densely packed hyphae. In some lichens, such as Cladonia (Fig. 269), the body is a combination of a crustose or foliose part with erect (fruticose) stalks.

Vegetative Multiplication. Any separated portion of the body of a lichen may, under suitable conditions, develop independently. The commonest method of vegetative multiplication, and one found in most lichens, is by the development on the upper surface of minute budlike outgrowths (*soredia*, Fig. 267, *B*). A soredium is composed of one or more algal cells surrounded by fungal hyphae. Soredia are formed at points at which the outermost layer of the thallus is interrupted and are sometimes so abundant as to appear like dust on the surface of the thallus. Each soredium is pushed outward by the elongation of the hyphae to which it is attached; other soredia are formed below it, and later they too are pushed out. In certain species of lichens this is the only known method of reproduction of the thallus. Many lichens bear on their surfaces also larger branching outgrowths, which likewise are composed of both fungal and algal elements. These outgrowths are easily broken off when dry, and under suitable conditions they may develop into independent lichens.

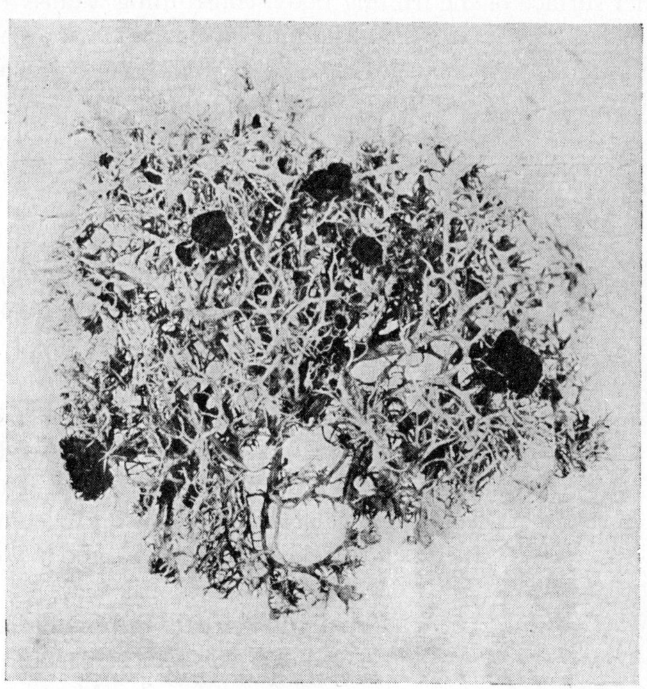

FIG. 266. A fruticose lichen (Evernia), with saucer-shaped fruiting bodies containing asci.

Spore Production. Minute dark pores appear on the surfaces of many lichens. Each such pore opens into a small cavity (*pycnidium*). At the tips of hyphae lining the cavity, spores (*pycnidiospores*) are formed. The spores are extruded and, if they germinate, produce new fungal hyphae. Experiments indicate that when these hyphae are grown in association with the appropriate algal cells, a lichen thallus results. In some lichens pycnidia are the only spore-forming organs known.

In case the fungal component is an ascomycete, asci are borne either in saucer-shaped (Fig. 268) or elongated (Fig. 262) organs on the surface of the lichen or in approximately spherical structures that are partly or entirely imbedded in the thallus. In a few lichens, the formation of asci has been shown to be preceded by a gametic union. Whatever the form of fruiting body, the included asci are intermingled with slender sterile hyphae (Fig. 267, *C*). Both asci and sterile hyphae grow approximately at right angles to the inner surface of the fruiting body, constituting a fairly definite lining layer. Each ascus, in most lichens, contains eight ascospores. The spores are one-, two-, several-, or many-celled, their shapes varying with the genus and species.

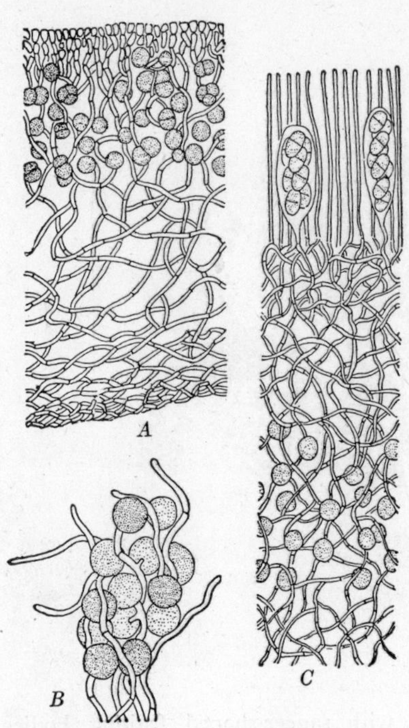

Fig. 267. *A*, cross section of a lichen thallus. *B*, a vegetative bud (soredium). *C*, cross section of a small portion of a fruiting body; asci are intermingled with sterile hyphae.

An ascospore, or each cell of an ascospore, may develop into a hypha which branches and elongates until its food supply is exhausted. If the hypha does not come into contact with algae of the species with which it is ordinarily associated, it dies; but if the appropriate algae are encountered, the fungus grows about the algal cells to form a lichen.

Practical Importance. Lichens play a large part in the formation of soil. Many crustose lichens gradually dissolve and disintegrate rocks to which they are attached. Lichens may be almost wholly imbedded in such rocks, the rock particles being held together by the gelatinized walls of the hyphae. When the lichens die they form, together with the disintegrated rock, a substrate for the growth of other lichens or for that of mosses, ferns, and seed plants.

The "reindeer moss" (*Cladonia rangiferina*, Fig. 269) is of considerable value as a food for reindeer and cattle. It forms dense tufts, sometimes 12 inches in height, and is abundant in extremely cold regions, where other vegetation is practically nonexistent and where it may be buried in snow for long periods without injury. It grows equally well on sand, moist turf, or soils otherwise barren.

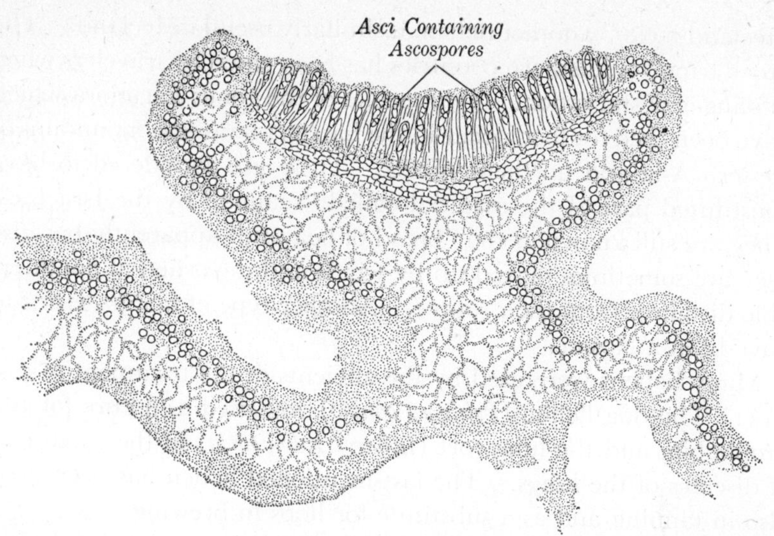

FIG. 268. Cross section of a fruiting body of a lichen.

FIG. 269. The reindeer moss (*Cladonia rangiferina*).

"Iceland moss," another lichen, is similarly useful in Iceland. The "rock tripe" of northern countries has been eaten by travelers when in danger of starvation. Two species of the genus Lecanora which have been used for food occur in the barren plains and mountains of western Asia and northern Africa. These are considered to have constituted part of the material called "manna" by the Israelites. They are still known as the "bread of heaven," apparently because they are sometimes picked up by winds and deposited at considerable distances from their source. Another type of manna seems to have been a Nostoc.

Many lichens were used by the ancients in the treatment of disease. The dog lichen (*Peltigera canina*) was used as a cure for hydrophobia, and the lungwort (*Lobaria pulmonaria*) in the treatment of diseases of the lungs. The last-mentioned lichen has been used also in tanning and as a substitute for hops in brewing.

The cell walls of the fungi in a number of lichens contain coloring substances. The most important of these coloring matters is orchil, or cudbear, which is obtained from species of Roccella and Lecanora. In extracting this pigment, the lichen is soaked in an alkaline solution until the latter attains a purple color. Orchil was formerly extensively used in the dyeing of woolen and silken fabrics. Orcein, a purified extract of orchil, serves as a stain for microscopic preparations. Litmus, used as an indicator for acidity or alkalinity, is derived from the same lichens as orchil.

CHAPTER XXIII

BRYOPHYTA: HEPATICAE (LIVERWORTS)

Nature. Liverworts are green plants, constituting one of the two classes of bryophytes. Most of them grow prostrate upon the surface of the substrate, although many produce branches or other organs that tend to grow upright. Some are strictly thallose; in others the plant body is differentiated into stem (and branches) and leaves, which organs, however, are almost or quite without distinction of tissues. Growth of the thallus or of a stem or branch is chiefly at one end—the anterior end, or apex. Bryophytes, including the liverworts, are sharply distinguished from thallophytes by the nature of their sex organs. These organs are always many-celled; some of their cells, at least those of an outer layer, are sterile —that is, they do not develop into gametes.

The remote ancestors of the group must have been green algae; but whatever species may have constituted links between algae and liverworts have long since disappeared. Most liverworts are terrestrial, living on soil, rocks, decaying wood, or the bark of trees. A few live in or on water, but these are clearly descended from terrestrial species. Since algae are characteristically aquatic, many of the features that distinguish liverworts from green algae are to be considered adaptations to a land habit. However, liverworts are still dependent upon an abundant supply of water, although some, such as certain species living on tree trunks, can withstand long periods of desiccation.

RICCIA

Gametophyte. Members of the genus *Riccia* are among the simplest liverworts. Most of the 100 or more species of this genus live on moist soil or, rarely, on rocks. Two of the most common, however, *Riccia natans* and *Riccia fluitans*, often occur floating in pools, ponds, and lakes. If the body of water in which they are living partly or entirely disappears, the plants left stranded upon the mud continue to live and grow. A thallus, especially one of *Riccia natans* (Fig. 270), growing on soil displays a different habit of growth from that which characterized it on the water. *Riccia natans*

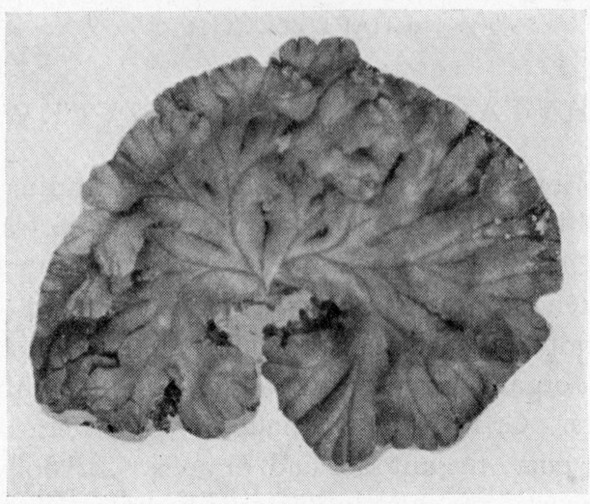

Fig. 270. A gametophyte of *Riccia natans* growing on soil. Natural size.

will be particularly described in the following paragraphs.

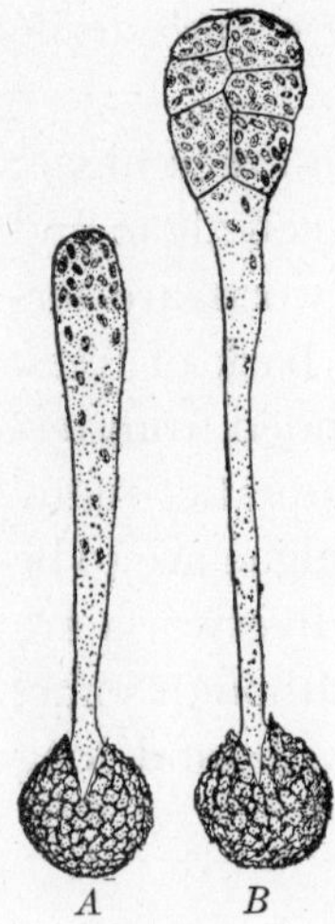

Fig. 271. *A*, germination of a spore of Riccia. *B*, early stage in the development of a thallus from a spore. Modified from Campbell.

A spore of Riccia, under favorable conditions, germinates by swelling and pushing out at one side a filamentous outgrowth (Fig. 271). In this process, the outer layers of the spore wall are broken, and the protruding filament is surrounded by an extension of the innermost layer of the wall. The dense cytoplasm and chloroplasts of the spore aggregate chiefly in the outer end of the filament; at this end, by a series of cell divisions, a small group of cells is formed. At the tip of this cellular mass a horizontal row of three to five *initial cells* is soon differentiated. All further growth is due to the division of these initial cells and to the growth and division of their derivatives. The apical region of the plant, therefore, marked by a notch in which are the initial cells, is the region of growth.

When living on land, the thallus is flat and at first ribbon-shaped; it is thickest in the middle and gradually thinner toward the margins. While it is still short, one or more cells in the center of the apical row of initial cells fail to divide. The row thus becomes divided into two groups of initial cells. In consequence of the formation of daughter cells which lie between these two groups, the two initial regions gradually diverge; and ultimately the thallus forks, each fork or branch now having its own row of initial cells. In time each branch forks, and the process is indefinitely repeated. The result of this method of branching is the formation of a rosette-like plant When it grows on water, the thallus is thicker; and each branch grows but little in length before it in turn branches. The water form, consequently, is more compact than the land form. On the upper surface of each branch is a median longitudinal furrow. The apical portion of a branch can live through the winter and resume growth the following spring.

In time the older parts of the thallus begin to undergo progressive death and decay. When decay reaches a point at which branching occurred, the surviving parts constitute two separate plants. Therefore, as a result of apical growth, branching, and the progressive death of older portions, the number of plants is from time to time increased. New plants are sometimes formed also by the separation of adventitious buds produced on the lower surface of the thallus. Apparently, too, any cell or group of cells can, in response to an effective stimulus such as that supplied by a wound, develop a branch that may become a new thallus.

In a mature part of the thallus (Fig. 272) the upper surface is formed by a single-layered epidermis. Below this, and occupying the greater portion of the thickness of the thallus, are many air chambers, separated from one another by partitions one cell in thickness. The uppermost air chambers open externally through small pores in the epidermis, each pore being surrounded by a ring of five or six cells. The deeper-lying chambers are sometimes connected with one another and with the uppermost chambers by pores in the intervening partitions. The cells of the epidermis, as well as those constituting the partitions between chambers, contain many small chloroplasts; these cells, having access through air chambers and pores to the gases of the atmosphere, can carry on photosynthesis. The part of the thallus below the air chambers varies in thickness from one layer of cells at the margins to several layers in the median portion; indeed, in the median region air chambers may be entirely lacking. The cells of this lower tissue contain few or no chloroplasts; some of the cells contain masses of oil mixed with other substances. From the lower surface of the thallus grow many narrow scales, each a single layer of cells. Some cells of the lower surface grow out into long, slender rhizoids which attach the plant to the soil or extend into the water. Some rhizoids are smooth-walled; the walls of others have peglike internal thickenings. The rhizoids, in their mode of origin and in their functions, resemble the

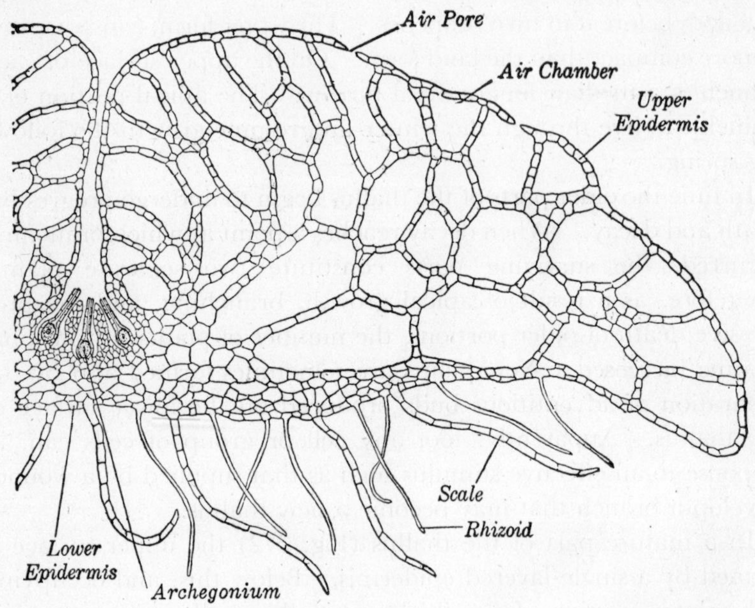

FIG. 272. Portion of a cross section of a thallus of Riccia bearing archegonia.

root hairs of a seed plant. Scales are more abundant on the water form, rhizoids on the land form.

Sex Organs. The female gamete (egg) is produced in an *archegonium*, the male gamete (antherozoid) in an *antheridium*. The archegonium of a liverwort is very different from any structure found among the thallophytes. The antheridium differs from organs of the same name borne by some algae and fungi in that it possesses an outer layer of sterile cells—cells, that is, which never develop into male gametes. These sex organs may appear on plants of Riccia living either on the water or on land. Both archegonia and antheridia may be borne by the same plant and even by the same branch. They are produced in three to five rows on the upper surface in the median furrow (Fig. 272) and when mature, in consequence of the division and growth of neighboring cells, are nearly or quite imbedded in the thallus.

Antheridia appear first on young plants; after a varying number of antheridia have been formed, the development of archegonia begins. Each sex organ originates in the apical region of the thallus; hence, in a branch bearing organs of both kinds, the antheridia are on the older portion, and the archegonia are nearer the apex.

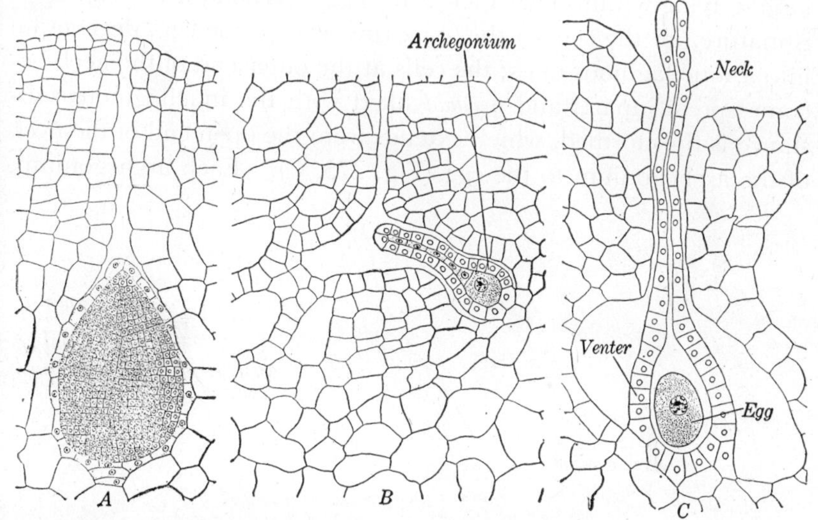

FIG. 273. Sex organs of Riccia. *A*, antheridium with surrounding tissue. *B*, nearly mature archegonium with surrounding tissue. *C*, mature archegonium.

An antheridium (Fig. 273, *A*) consists of a short, few-celled stalk and an ovoid body; the latter is composed of an outer layer or jacket of sterile cells and many internal cells which, while the antheridium is growing, undergo division. After division of the internal cells ceases, each of the hundreds now present develops into an antherozoid. An antherozoid (resembling that of Marchantia, shown in Fig. 282, *B*) has a slender, somewhat coiled body and two long flagella attached near its anterior end. The mature antheridium is enclosed within a cavity of the thallus; this cavity opens by a narrow pore at its upper end. After antherozoids are formed, if water penetrates the cavity, the sterile cells constituting the upper end of the antheridial jacket become softened and disintegrate; and a viscous fluid containing the antherozoids oozes out of the antheridium and through the neck of the cavity to the upper surface of the thallus. Here, if sufficient water is present, the antherozoids swim freely.

An archegonium (Fig. 273, *B*) also has a short stalk; its body is composed of an enlarged basal *venter* and a slender *neck*. The body, including neck and venter, consists of an outer layer of jacket cells and an inner axial row typically of six cells, of which the lowest and largest, lying within the venter, is the egg. When the archegonium is mature, all the cells of the axial row, except the egg, degenerate into a mucilaginous mass; the cells at the outer end of the neck become spread apart; and a *canal* filled with the mucilaginous substance is thus formed, which extends from the open end of the neck of the archegonium to the egg (Fig. 273, *C*). Each archegonium,

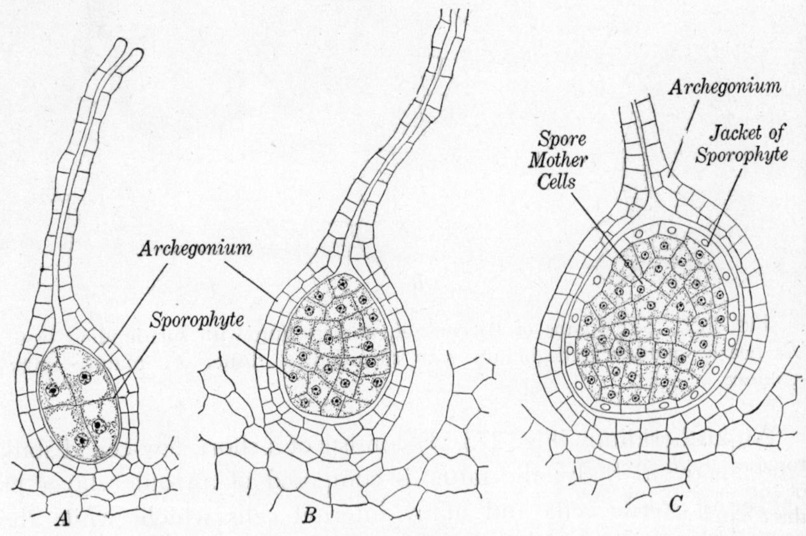

FIG. 274. Riccia. Stages in the development of a sporophyte within the venter of an archegonium.

like an antheridium, is enclosed in a cavity, but the end of its neck protrudes slightly above the surface of the thallus and into the median furrow.

Gametic Union. When the plant is floating, some of the freely swimming antherozoids are sure to come into the immediate vicinity of mature archegonia. If the plant is on land, a film of water must be present on its upper surface, as at the time of a rain or of a heavy dew, in order to make possible the approach of an antherozoid to an archegonium. In either case the antherozoid, coming near the mouth of an archegonium, responds to a stimulus, probably of a chemical nature, by swimming directly toward and into the archegonium and down its neck toward the egg. Several or many antherozoids may enter an archegonium. One of them (and usually, at least, only one) unites with the egg.

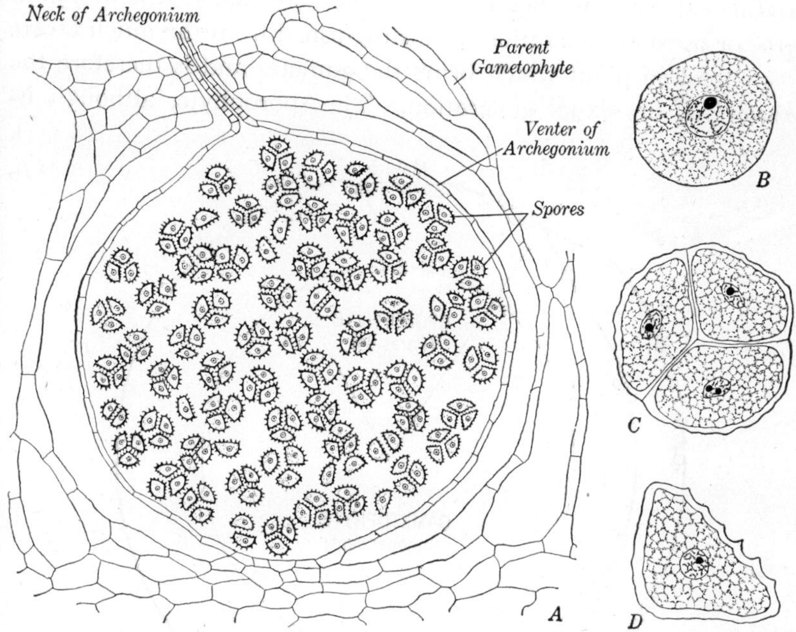

FIG. 275. *A*, Mature sporophyte of Riccia. The mass of spores is still surrounded by the inner cell layer of the venter, which is enclosed within the tissue of the gametophyte. *B*, spore mother cell (of *Riccia Austini*). *C*, spores (only three of the four visible) formed by the division of a spore mother cell. *D*, mature spore.

Sporophyte. The zygote formed by the union of egg and antherozoid secretes a new wall and begins to grow almost immediately. Soon it divides in an approximately horizontal plane. As a result of succeeding divisions and further growth (Fig. 274), a spherical mass of cells is developed from the zygote; the cells of the outer layer of this mass, becoming large and flat, constitute a sterile jacket. These outer cells contain chloroplasts and carry on some photosynthesis. Divisions of the cells within the jacket continue until there are present a large number of *spore mother cells.* These become more or less separated and rounded; then follow two divisions, forming from each mother cell four spores (Fig. 275). The spores in turn become separated, and each secretes a thick wall. The simple spherical structure developed from the zygote, although very small and entirely different from the plant that bore the gametes, is nevertheless a distinct plant. Since this small plant produces spores and therefore reproduces asexually, it is the *sporophyte*, or asexual generation, as distinguished from the much larger green thallose plant which bears the gametes and is therefore the *gametophyte*, or sexual generation. The sporophyte, although its

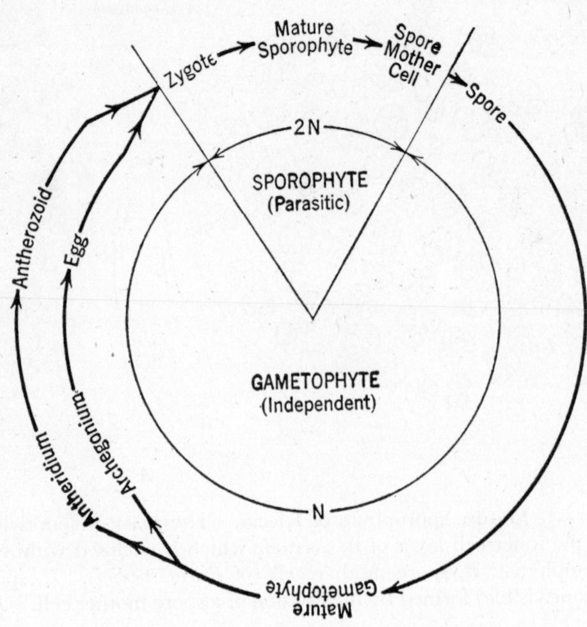

FIG. 276. Life cycle of Riccia (or other liverwort).

cells carry on a limited amount of photosynthesis, is largely parasitic upon the gametophyte; that is, it depends upon the gametophyte for water and for some nutrient substances.

The development of the zygote into a sporophyte goes on within the venter of the archegonium. As the sporophyte grows, the venter also grows, continuing to enclose the sporophyte, while the neck of the archegonium withers. Soon after the union of the gametes, the venter in consequence of cell divisions becomes two cells in thickness. After spores are formed, the cells of the inner layer of the venter, as well as those of the jacket of the sporophyte, disintegrate. The rounded mass of spores, now surrounded only by the outer cell layer of the venter, remains imbedded in the gametophyte until the spores are liberated by the death and decay of that part of the thallus. Each spore may then develop into a gametophyte.

Alternation of Generations. The life cycle of Riccia includes two distinct phases or *generations* (Fig. 276). The germinating spore develops into a gametophyte, which bears sex organs in which gametes are produced. The union of gametes forms a zygote. The zygote develops into a sporophyte, whose characteristic function is the production of spores. Each spore produced by a sporophyte may in turn develop into a gametophyte. These facts can be expressed in the following formula: Gametophyte—Gametes—Zygote—Sporophyte—Spores—Gametophyte—Gametes, etc. Each generation produces by means of its reproductive cells the other generation; hence, there is an *alternation* of the two generations.

MARCHANTIA

Gametophyte. From a condition, somewhat like that in Riccia, of a simple thallose gametophyte and a very simple sporophyte, evolution among liverworts seems to have proceeded in several divergent directions. In one line of descent, beginning with forms more or less like Riccia and culminating in *Marchantia*, both gametophyte and sporophyte became progressively larger and more complex. The gametophyte of Marchantia presents, so far as we now know, the highest degree of complexity (though not the greatest size) ever attained by a thallose plant.

The gametophyte of *Marchantia polymorpha* (Fig. 277), one of the most widely distributed liverworts, grows on moist rocks or soil. It resembles that of Riccia in general form, as well as in its method of development from a spore, in apical growth by means of a group of initial cells, and in method of branching. It is, however, broader and thicker than the thallus of Riccia and has a rather conspicuous midrib, marked above by a shallow groove and below by a projecting ridge. The upper surface of the thallus is divided into small

FIG. 277. Plants of *Marchantia polymorpha* bearing cupules in which gemmae are produced.

diamond-shaped areas (Fig. 278, *A*), each area indicating the position of an air chamber just beneath the uppermost layer of cells. The air chambers are in a single layer (Fig. 278, *B*); each chamber opens externally by a pore, which is surrounded by a chimney-like structure composed of four vertical rows of cells. In each chamber are branching filaments of cells, growing upward from the layer of cells that compose the floor of the chamber. The cells of these filaments contain chlorophyll and constitute the chief photosynthetic tissue of the plant, but there are many chloroplasts also in the cells of the layers bounding each chamber above and below and in those of the partitions between the chambers. The portion of the thallus below the air chambers consists of several layers of cells possessing few or no chloroplasts. Many of these cells contain leucoplasts, which form storage starch; in some of them are oil bodies like those of Riccia; a few large cells contain mucilage. The cells of this part

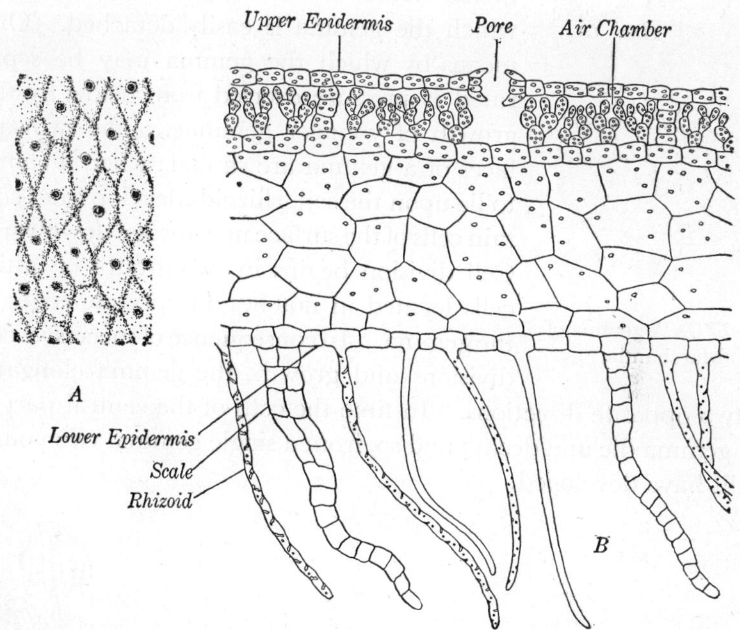

FIG. 278. Marchantia. *A*, surface view of a portion of a thallus; each rhomboidal area marks the position of an air chamber. *B*, cross section of a portion of a thallus.

of the thallus are parenchymatous, except that in the midrib are elongated cells with locally thickened walls, constituting probably a rudimentary conductive tissue. From the lower surface of the thallus grow scales and rhizoids. Some rhizoids are smooth-walled; the inner surfaces of the walls of others are marked by localized thickenings of varied form.

Vegetative Multiplication. In consequence of apical growth and branching and of the progressive death of the older parts of the thallus, the number of plants is increased, just as is the case in Riccia. Adventitious branches also may develop from almost any part of the thallus in consequence of wounds or possibly of other stimuli; and these branches, if separated by any means, become new plants. In addition, Marchantia has a means of vegetative multiplication by the formation of lens-shaped structures (*gemmae*) which are produced in great numbers in shallow cups (*cupules*, Fig. 277) on the upper surface of the thallus. Each gemma (Fig. 279) is attached to the thallus by a single-celled stalk, from which the gemma is easily detached. One means by which the gemma may be separated is pressure exerted from below by the growth of younger gemmae. The two surfaces of a gemma are similar; when it comes to lie upon the soil, rhizoids develop from certain cells of the surface now turned downward. Cell division begins in two groups of initial cells located in notches on opposite edges of the gemma. In consequence of successive cell divisions and growth, the gemma elongates in two opposite directions. In time the cells of the central part of the gemma die and decay; and so, from a single gemma, two young thalli have developed.

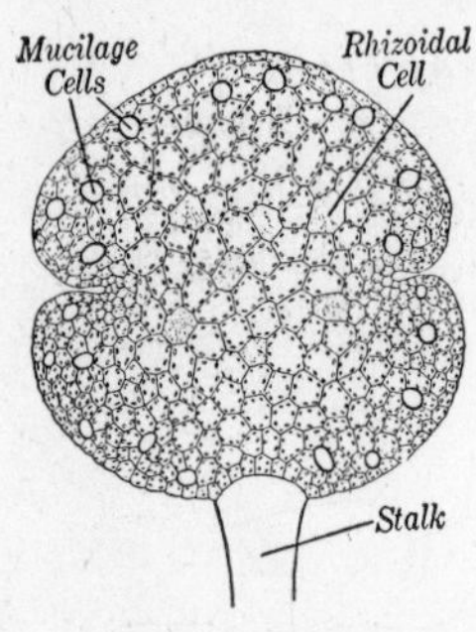

Fig. 279. A gemma of Marchantia.

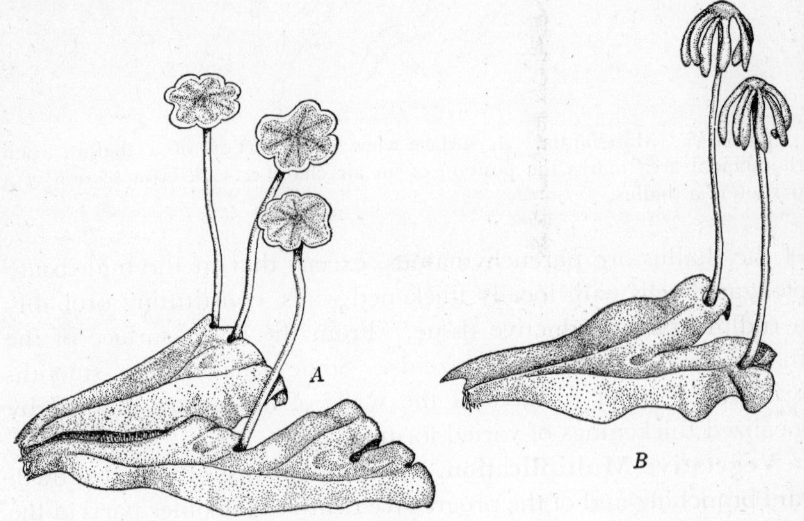

Fig. 280. Plants of Marchantia bearing sexual branches. *A*, male. *B*, female.

Sexual Branches. The sex organs of Marchantia are borne on special upright branches (Fig. 280), each composed of a stalk and a terminal horizontal disk. Male and female branches (in *Marchantia* *polymorpha*, though not in some other species of Marchantia) are borne on distinct plants. The sexual distinction between plants of this species is so sharply fixed that gemmae from a male plant give rise always to male plants and those from a female plant develop always into female plants. The upright sexual branches are direct continuations of the horizontal branches of the thallus, and a cross section of the stalk of a male or female branch shows the presence of tissues corresponding respectively to those of the upper and lower surfaces of an ordinary branch of the thallus.

The disk borne by a male branch (Fig. 281) is typically eight-lobed; and imbedded in the upper surface of each lobe are many

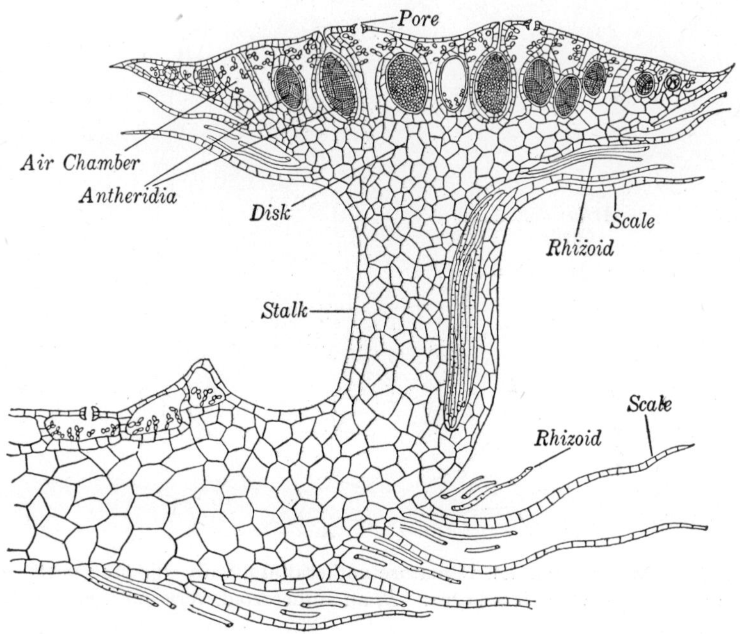

Fig. 281. Marchantia. Vertical section of a male branch and of a portion of the thallus.

antheridia (Fig. 282, *A*), the oldest nearest the center, the youngest toward the outer extremity of the lobe. Between the cavities containing antheridia are air chambers with pores. When an antheridium is mature, contact with a drop of water causes some of the sterile cells in the upper part of its jacket to disintegrate; and the mass of antherozoids (Fig. 282, *B*) oozes out to the surface.

A female disk (Fig. 283, *A*) also is typically but inconspicuously eight-lobed, a group of archegonia being borne in an inverted position, not imbedded, on the lower surface of each lobe. However,

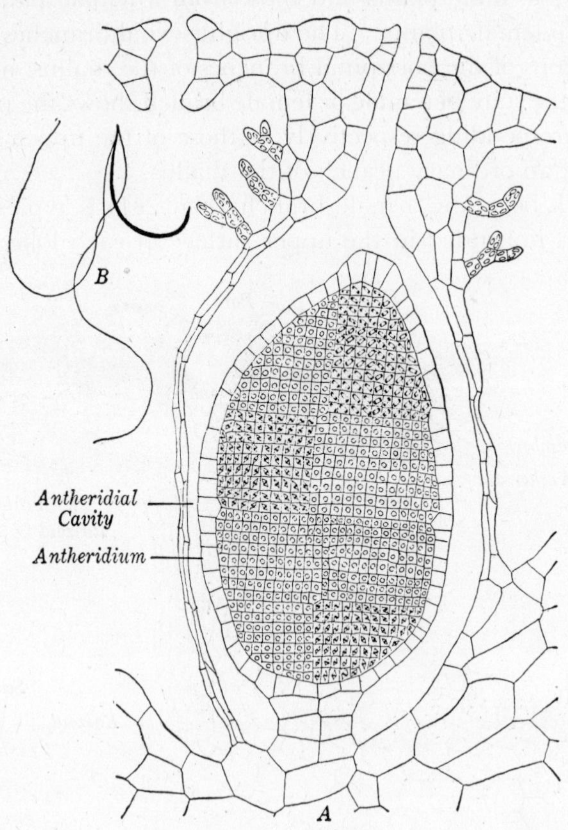

Fig. 282. Marchantia. *A*, immature antheridium, with adjoining parts of the male disk in which it is borne. *B*, an antherozoid, very much enlarged.

the first-formed archegonia appear on the *upper* surface of the lobe and, with the apical region of the lobe, are pushed over to the lower surface in consequence of growth in the central part of the upper side of the disk. After this change in position of the apical region, it continues for a time to produce new archegonia. The group of archegonia borne on each lobe is surrounded by a fringed curtain-like outgrowth. From the upper surface of the female disk, green rays, typically nine in number (see Fig. 280), grow outward beyond the disk and curve downward, somewhat resembling the ribs of an umbrella. The stalk of the female branch is very short when the gametes unite; later it elongates considerably, so that the sporophytes, developing within the venters of the archegonia, are carried

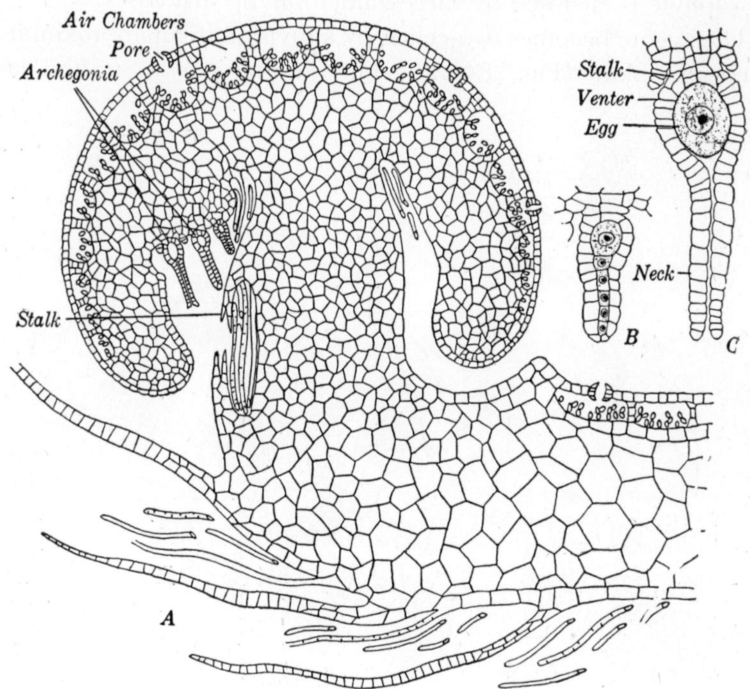

FIG. 283. Marchantia. *A*, vertical section of a female branch showing its attachment to the thallus. (Rays do not show in the section.) *B*, a young archegonium. *C*, a mature archegonium.

upward. The elongation of the stalk and the position of archegonia on the lower side of the disk are favorable to the distribution of spores produced by the sporophytes.

The union of gametes is dependent upon the presence of water. Probably antherozoids are carried from male to female plants at times when the plants are partly or entirely submerged, as by spring rains. Possibly the splashing of rain drops from the surfaces of male disks may suffice, if female plants are in the immediate vicinity of the male plants.

Sporophyte. A zygote develops into a sporophyte within the venter of the archegonium (Fig. 284). The cells of the venter divide and grow, so that the sporophyte remains enclosed. A ring of cells at the base of the archegonium develops into a sheath which loosely surrounds the archegonium with the enclosed sporophyte. The curtain about the group of archegonia persists, so that the sporophyte is enclosed by three gametophytic structures.

The zygote becomes two-celled by a division in an approximately horizontal plane (Fig. 284, *A*). Further divisions occur, and early

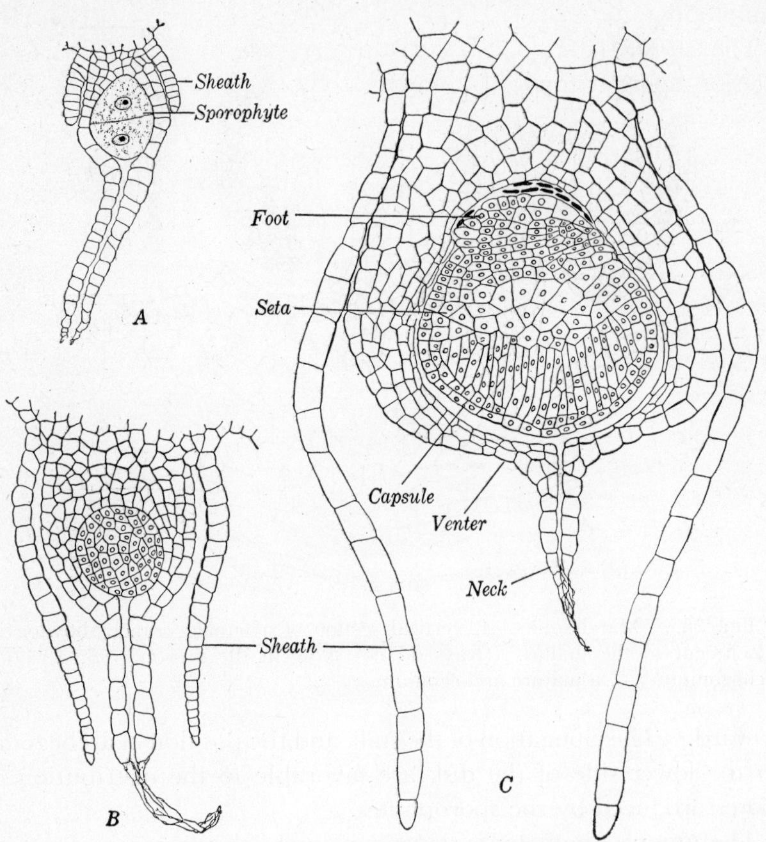

FIG. 284. Marchantia. *A*, two-celled sporophyte within the venter of the archegonium. *B*, somewhat older sporophyte. *C*, considerably older sporophyte. All drawn to the same scale as *B* and *C*, Figure 283.

in its history tne sporophyte becomes differentiated into three distinct parts (Fig. 284, *C*). These are:

(*a*) A broad basal *foot*, which grows in among the cells of the female disk at the base of the archegonium and which absorbs water and nutrient substances from the gametophyte;

(*b*) A terminal, nearly spherical *capsule*, considerably larger than the foot, in which spores are ultimately formed; and

(*c*) A stalk (*seta*) connecting foot and capsule, which is very short while the sporophyte is developing. When the spores are mature, the cells of the seta elongate; the greatly lengthened seta pushes the capsule out through the three enclosing layers developed from the gametophyte.

The capsule (Fig. 285) has a jacket one cell in thickness. In its interior, spores are formed by the division of spore mother cells.

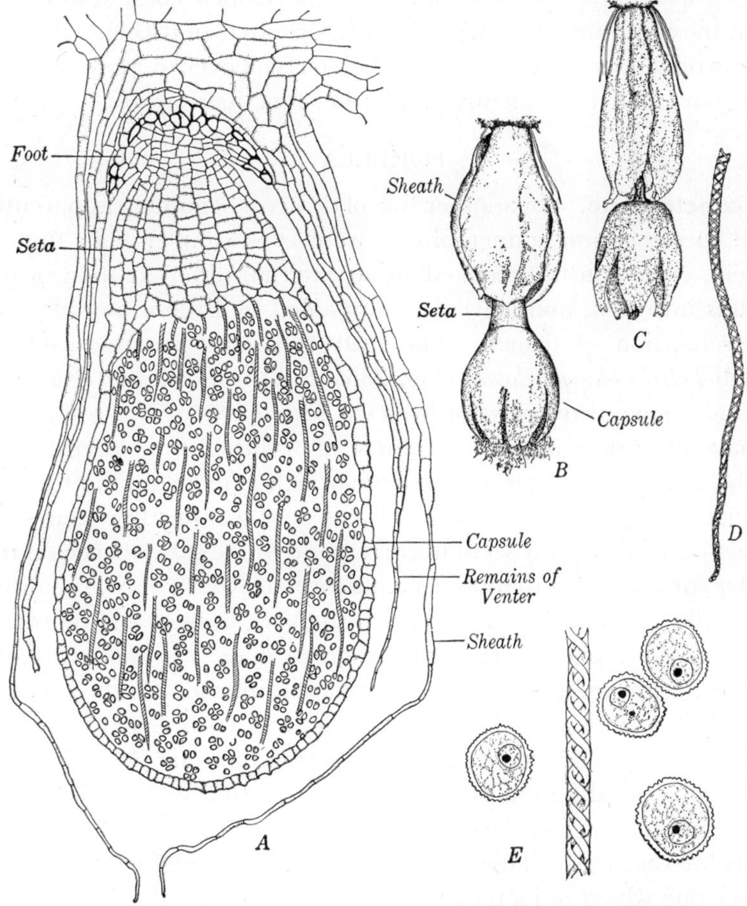

Fig. 285. Marchantia. *A*, nearly mature sporophyte in lengthwise section. *B*, mature sporophyte in external view. *C*, the same later, after spores and elaters are shed. *D*, portion of an elater. *E*, a few spores and small part of an elater, highly magnified.

Intermingled with the spores are long, slender cells (*elaters*) with pointed ends and spirally thickened walls. The elaters curl and uncurl as they become alternately dry and moist, and by virtue of these changes in form they play a part in the distribution of the spores. When, after the spores are mature, the elongation of the seta of the sporophyte pushes the capsule beyond the sheath, the capsule wall splits into a variable number of lobes; and the spores so liberated are readily caught up and distributed by air currents. Each spore may develop into a new gametophyte.

The sporophyte of Marchantia has developed considerably beyond the condition of the very simple sporophyte of Riccia. A large proportion of its tissues, instead of being given over to spore production, have taken on nutritive and other functions.

PORELLA

Gametophyte. In another line of descent, beginning apparently with species whose gametophytes were even simpler than that of Riccia, evolution has resulted in an external differentiation of the thallus into stem and leaves, accompanied by little if any internal differentiation of tissues. The leafy liverworts so produced, of which *Porella platyphylloidea* (Fig. 286, *A*, *B*) is a common example, typically have three rows of leaves. The leaves of two rows seem to have been developed in the course of evolution from lateral lobes of the thallus, the divisions between which extended almost to the median line, leaving as a central axis only a midrib or stem; the leaves of the third row seem to correspond to the scales borne on the under surface of the thallus of such a form as Riccia or Marchantia.

Porella grows most commonly on the bark of trees and on rocks, the branching plants forming close green mats. It can withstand drying for several months without apparent injury. At the growing end of the stem is a single *apical cell* (Fig. 286, *C*) instead of a row of initial cells such as occurs in Riccia or Marchantia. An apical cell of Porella has the form of a triangular pyramid whose base is the free (anterior) face of the cell. It divides in a plane parallel to one of its lateral faces. This division forms a flat daughter cell and a larger one which in its turn behaves as an apical cell. This apical cell divides in a plane parallel to a second lateral face; the next division parallels the third lateral face. By a regular succession of such divisions alternately in three planes, three series of flat daughter cells are formed (*X*, *Y*, *Z*, etc., Fig. 286, *C*). Each of these series of cells gives rise, by further cell divisions and growth, to a portion of the stem and to one of the three rows of leaves. The stem from time to time produces lateral branches. Each branch has an apical

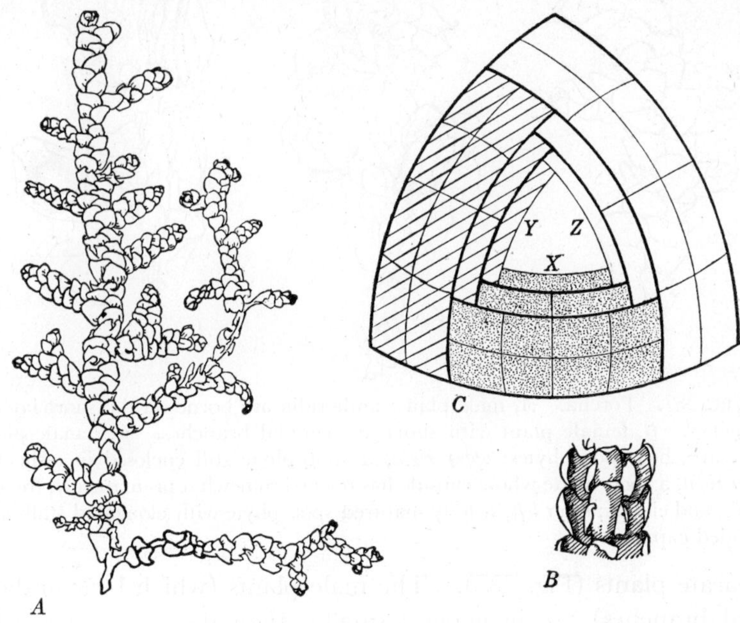

FIG. 286. Porella. *A*, gametophyte viewed from above. *B*, small portion seen from below, showing three rows of leaves and the lower lobes of the leaves of the lateral rows. *C*, diagram of an apical cell with three lateral faces (*X*, *Y*, *Z*) and the cells that have been derived from each face.

cell, and its development (including the production of leaves and sometimes of secondary branches) repeats the development of the main stem. Scattered smooth-walled rhizoids, which attach the plant to the substrate, grow from the lower surfaces of stem and branches.

Each lateral leaf has a large upper lobe and a smaller lower one; the lower lobe appears like a flap attached to the stem and to the posterior edge of the upper lobe and turned forward under the latter. Each lobe consists of one layer of cells. When a branch is formed, it replaces the lower lobe of a leaf. On the lower side of the stem is a row of smaller leaves, also one cell in thickness There is virtually no differentiation of tissues in stem, branches, or leaves.

Sex Organs. These arise on special lateral branches, antheridial and archegonial branches being borne (in *Porella platyphylloidea*) on

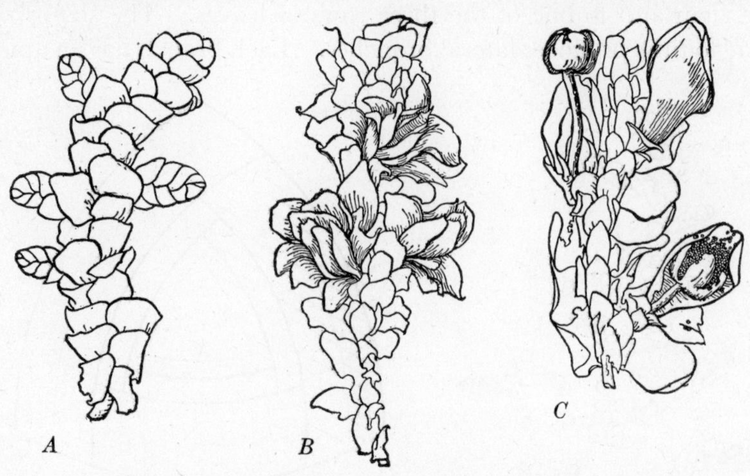

Fig. 287. Porella. *A*, male plant; antheridia are borne on the short lateral branches. *B*, female plant with short archegonial branches. *C*, female plant with attached sporophytes; *upper right*, a sporophyte still enclosed in a sheath; *lower right*, a sporophyte whose capsule has opened somewhat prematurely, freeing spores and elaters; *upper left*, a fully matured sporophyte with elongated stalk and emptied capsule.

separate plants (Fig. 287). The male plants (which bear antheridial branches) are in general smaller than the female (bearing archegonial branches), but the difference is not great enough to make it easy always to determine the sex of a plant that is not producing sexual branches.

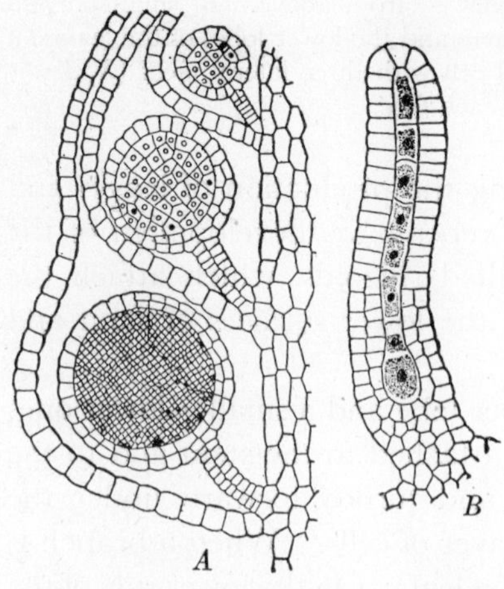

Fig. 288. Porella. *A*, portion of a branch bearing antheridia. *B*, an archegonium.

An antheridial branch is comparatively short, and its leaves are very close together. In the axil of each leaf is an antheridium (Fig. 288, *A*), differing from an antheridium of Riccia or Marchantia only in that it has a long stalk and that its jacket, except at the outer end, is composed of more than one layer of cells. It is not enclosed in a cavity. The antherozoids are like those of Marchantia and, as in that plant, gametic union depends upon the presence of sufficient water to enable a swimming antherozoid to be carried to the neighborhood of an archegonium.

An archegonial branch is shorter than an antheridial branch; it bears only two or three leaves and, at its end, a group of a few archegonia. One of the archegonia is developed from the apical cell of the branch, and thus further growth of the branch is pre-

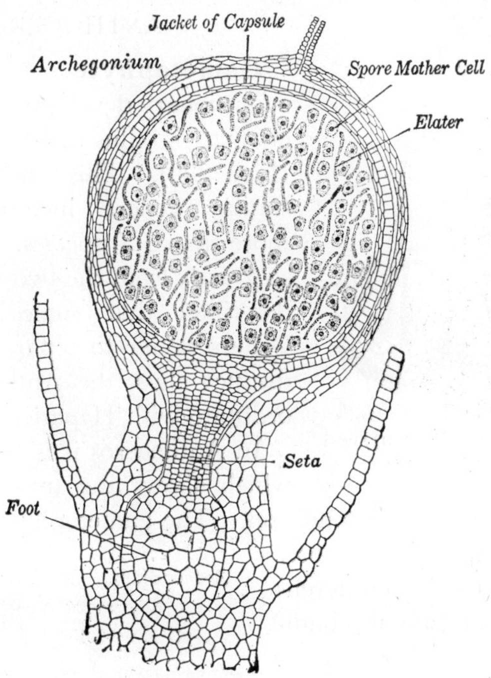

FIG. 289. Porella. Lengthwise section of a developing sporophyte, with adjacent parts of the parent gametophyte.

vented. Each archegonium (Fig. 288, *B*) resembles one of Riccia or Marchantia except that the venter is little broader than the neck. When the archegonia are mature, the group is surrounded by a thin sheath developed from the archegonial branch below the archegonia.

Sporophyte. The sporophyte of Porella (Fig. 289) is similar to that of Marchantia in being composed of foot, seta, and capsule. As in Marchantia, the seta elongates when the spores are mature, pushing the capsule well out beyond the enclosing sheath.

The jacket of the capsule consists of two or more layers of cells. In the interior of the capsule are produced, as in Marchantia, spores and elaters. When the elongating seta has pushed the capsule beyond the sheath, the jacket splits from its apex to near its base into four parts, liberating the spores. Each spore may develop into a new gametophyte.

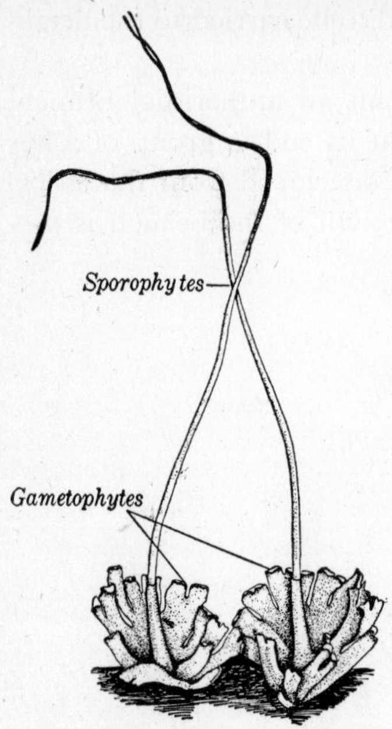

FIG. 290. Plants of *Anthoceros fusiformis*. Magnified about three times.

ANTHOCEROS

Gametophyte. A third type of evolutionary development among liverworts is illustrated by *Anthoceros* (Fig. 290). This and a few very similar genera include somewhat more than 300 species. These differ so greatly from the liverworts already described that some present-day writers prefer to separate them as a distinct class, the Anthocerotae, coördinate with Hepaticae and Musci.

In Anthoceros it is the sporophyte which shows the most marked advance over a primitive condition. The gametophyte is small and irregularly and inconspicuously branched. It has no differentiated tissues and no air chambers but has intercellular spaces opening to the lower surface of the thallus. Some of these spaces are filled with a mucilage-like substance; in others are colonies of a blue-green alga (Nostoc.) Antheridia (Fig. 291) develop in small clusters, each cluster within an internal cavity beneath the upper surface of the thallus. When the antheridia are mature, the layers of cells forming the roof of the cavity disintegrate. Archegonia (Fig. 292)

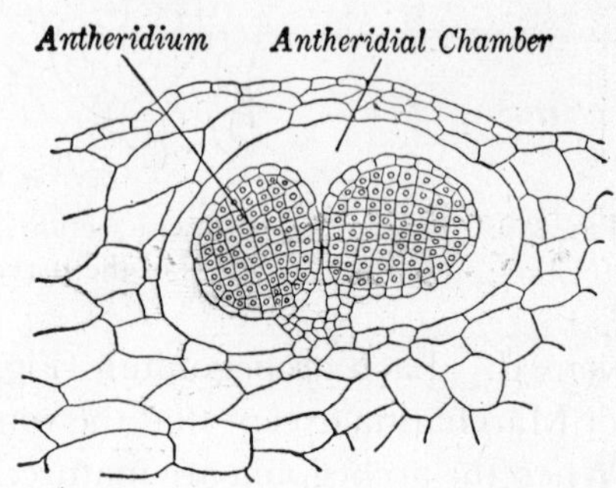

FIG. 291. Anthoceros. Portion of a thallus in vertical section with two enclosed antheridia.

develop separately rather than in groups and are closely imbedded in the upper surface of the thallus, only the extreme ends of their necks protruding. The venter and neck of each archegonium are continuous with the surrounding cells of the thallus. As in other liverworts, gametic union is brought about by antherozoids which swim down the canal in the neck of an archegonium.

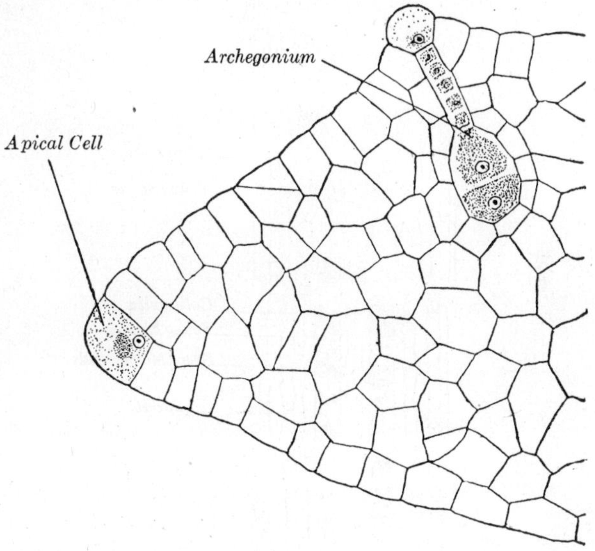

Fig. 292. Anthoceros. Vertical section of a portion of a thallus with an imbedded archegonium.

Sporophyte. A young sporophyte consists of a foot and a capsule. At the base of the capsule is a meristem, in which cell division continues for a long time. Consequently, the capsule grows into a slender cylindrical structure which may project an inch, or in some species two to six inches, above the surface of the gametophyte. In the center of the capsule (Fig. 293) is a *columella* of sterile tissue with somewhat elongated cells; at the outside is a jacket of several cell layers; and between the jacket and the columella, extending over the top of the latter, is a cylindrical zone in which spores and elaters are produced. The outer cells of the capsule contain chloroplasts; the surface layer contains stomata very like those of seed plants. The sporophyte is therefore able to carry on photosynthesis to a considerable extent. All water and food materials derived

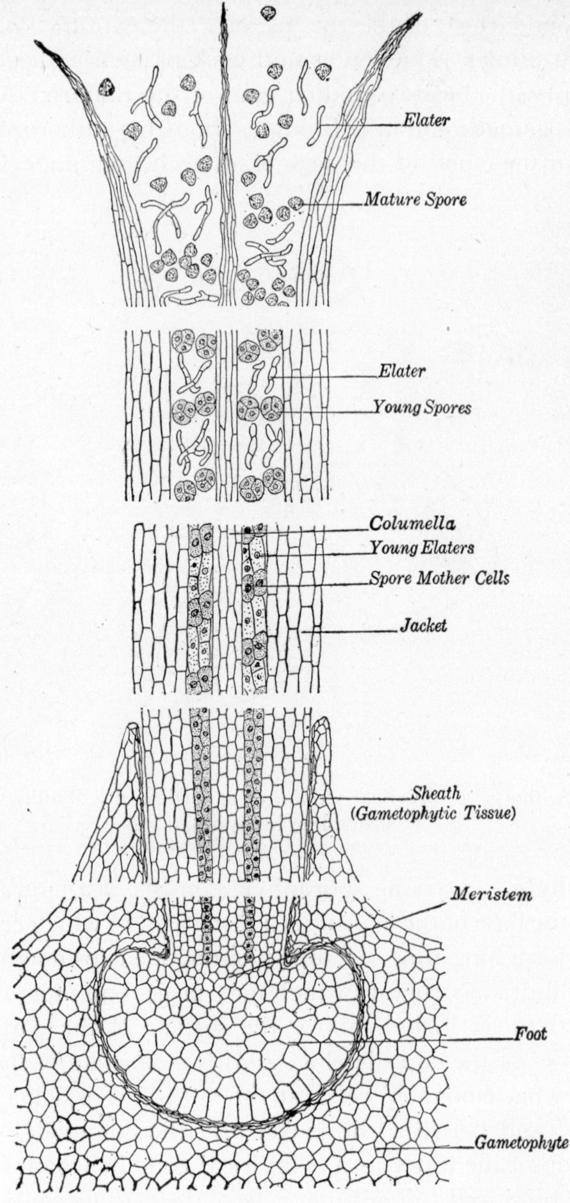

FIG. 293. Lengthwise sections at different levels of a sporophyte of Anthoceros, surrounded at its base by gametophytic tissue. Diagrammatic.

from the soil must, however, still come to the sporophyte through the gametophyte.

Spores are formed first in the upper end of the capsule by the division of spore mother cells; as the capsule grows from below, new spore mother cells and spores are produced at successively lower and lower levels. Elaters are formed in groups alternating with groups of spores. The jacket splits, beginning at its top, into two parts as the first-formed spores mature; the split is continued downward to keep pace with the successive formation and maturation of spores.

In the early stages of development of the sporophyte, the jacket of the archegonial venter and neck and the neighboring cell layers of the gametophyte develop into a sheath which lengthens as the capsule grows upward. Finally the sheath ceases to grow; and the still elongating capsule breaks through the sheath, which remains about the base of the capsule.

CHAPTER XXIV

BRYOPHYTA: MUSCI (MOSSES)

Nature and Distribution. Mosses, constituting the second class of bryophytes, resemble in some respects the leafy liverworts. They differ from these, however: (*a*) in that the gametophyte begins as a very simple filamentous or thallose plant (the *protonema*) from which the leaf-bearing stem arises; (*b*) in a greater degree of tissue differentiation in stem and leaf than is to be found in any leafy liverwort; (*c*) in that a smaller proportion of the sporophyte is devoted to spore production, and a larger proportion to nutritive tissues.

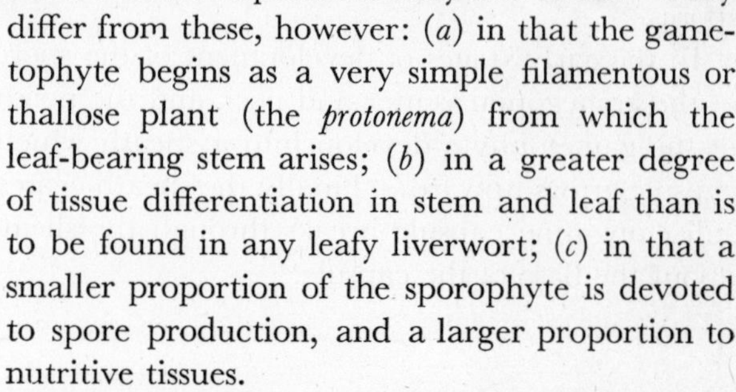

Because they are able to survive under a wide range of conditions that do not favor the growth of the larger and more complex ferns and seed plants, mosses occupy widely varying habitats and often form conspicuous features of the earth's vegetation. They occur in cold regions; in bogs and marshes; in brooks and shallow ponds; on the faces of rocks where food materials are scanty and where they are exposed to drought; on the soil of cool, deeply shaded forests; on decaying logs, and on the trunks of living trees. Not all mosses are adapted to all these conditions, but each habitat has its characteristic species.

The description which follows applies to any one of many common mosses, such as species of Bryum (Fig. 294) or the hair-cap moss (Polytrichum, Fig. 301). A distinct group, the peat mosses (Sphagnum), will be discussed later.

FIG. 294. A common moss (*Bryum bimum*). After Bruch, Schimper, and Gümbel.

A COMMON MOSS

Gametophyte. A moss spore that has fallen upon a moist rock or upon soil germinates (Fig. 295) by breaking the outer layer of its wall and pushing out a slender green projection which grows in length and is soon divided transversely. As growth continues, more divisions occur, so that the plant soon consists of a filament of cells. The filament branches freely and resembles a branching green alga. This alga-like plant is a *protonema*. Each of its cells contains nu-

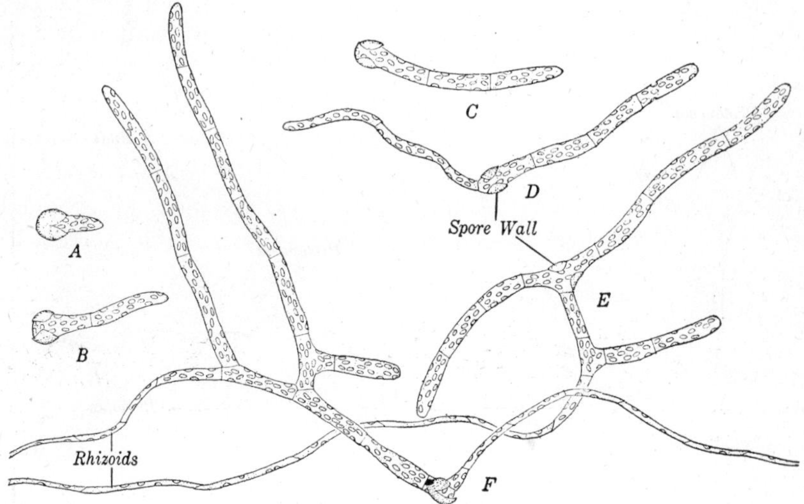

FIG. 295. *A*, germination of a moss spore. *B–F*, successive stages in the development of a protonema.

merous chloroplasts, which enable the protonema to manufacture its own food and to grow indefinitely if conditions are suitable.

Some branches of the protonema grow horizontally, others a very short distance upright in the air, and still others penetrate the substrate upon which the protonema is growing. The last-mentioned branches, which soon lose their chlorophyll and become brown, are *rhizoids;* they are anchoring and absorptive organs. Sooner or later any green cell of the protonema may give rise to a bud, or compact group of cells (Fig. 296), which in time grows into a massive upright or creeping shoot bearing many green leaves and, at least on its basal portion, rhizoids. In many mosses the protonema dies after the production of one or more buds. The leafy shoot then becomes an independent plant (Fig. 297), which is commonly spoken of as a "moss plant." It may branch. In this latter respect, species of mosses differ greatly. Some have both aerial and prostrate, or even underground, branches.

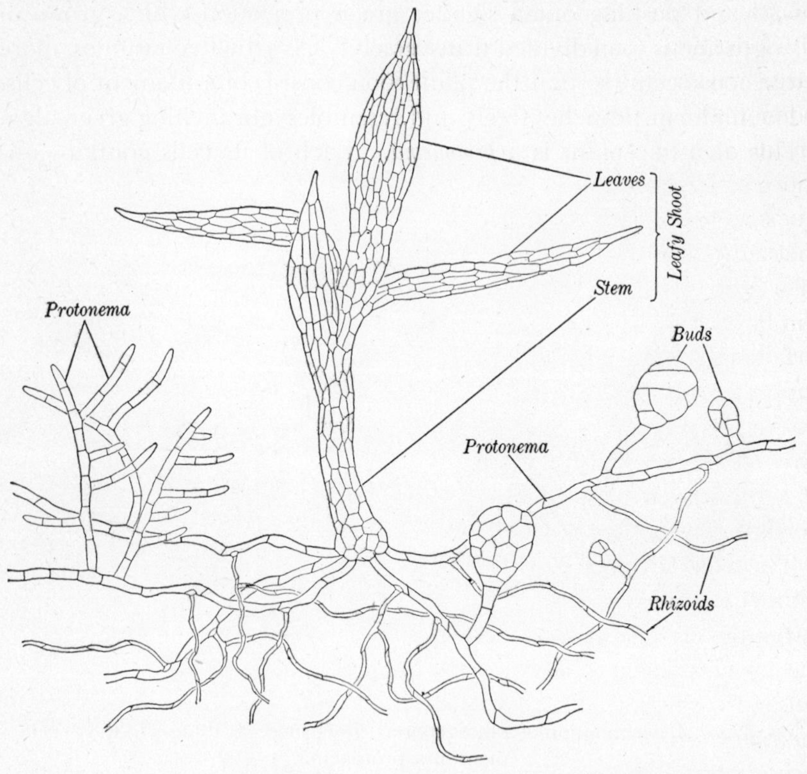

FIG. 296. Formation of buds by a moss protonema, and the development of a bud into a leafy shoot.

The central axis or stem of a leafy shoot is a compact cylindrical structure. At its growing end is a single *apical cell*. This cell has the form of a triangular pyramid with its base (the free face of the cell) turned forward. It divides in a plane parallel to one of its lateral faces. This division forms a flat daughter cell and a larger one which in its turn behaves as an apical cell. This apical cell divides in a plane parallel to a second lateral face; the next division parallels the third lateral face. By a regular succession of such divisions alternately in three planes, three series of flat daughter cells are formed. Each series gives rise, by further cell divisions and growth, to a portion of the stem and to one of the three rows of leaves. The leaves, however, do not long retain their original three-ranked arrangement.

The outer cells of the stem are relatively large and contain chloroplasts. Some of the inner cells are long and slender and often thick-walled. In certain large mosses the interior portion of the stem is differentiated into tissues which more or less closely resemble in structure and arrangement the tissues of the stem of a seed plant. There are similarities in function also, so far as concerns mechanical support and food storage; but it is doubtful whether any of the internal tissues of a moss stem have an important conductive function.

Fig. 297. Leafy shoot of a moss after the disappearance of the protonema and the production of many rhizoids. The shoot has branched.

The rhizoids which grow from the surface cells of the lower part of the stem or of the lower side of a creeping stem are filaments of cells; they extend into the soil or other substrate, often branching, anchoring the plant and absorbing water and dissolved substances. In most mosses the leaves are flat, green, and one cell thick except for the midrib. The midrib (not present in some species) consists of long, slender, colorless cells. A few mosses have thicker leaves; in some of these (for example, Polytrichum) longitudinal plates of cells project from the upper side of each leaf, increasing the surface available for photosynthesis.

Sex Organs. The gametes of a moss are borne in many-celled organs. These organs are produced in groups, each group borne at the end of the stem or of a branch. In some mosses the male organs (*antheridia*) and the female organs (*archegonia*) occur in the same group; in other mosses, in separate groups but on different branches of the same plant; in still other species, archegonia and antheridia are borne on different plants (Figs. 298, 299). Among the sex organs are interspersed upright, hairlike, sterile structures, each composed of a row of cells.

The leaves about a terminal cluster of antheridia are often modified in shape and color, forming a sheath or cup; the leaves about a group of archegonia are ordinarily not modified in this manner, so

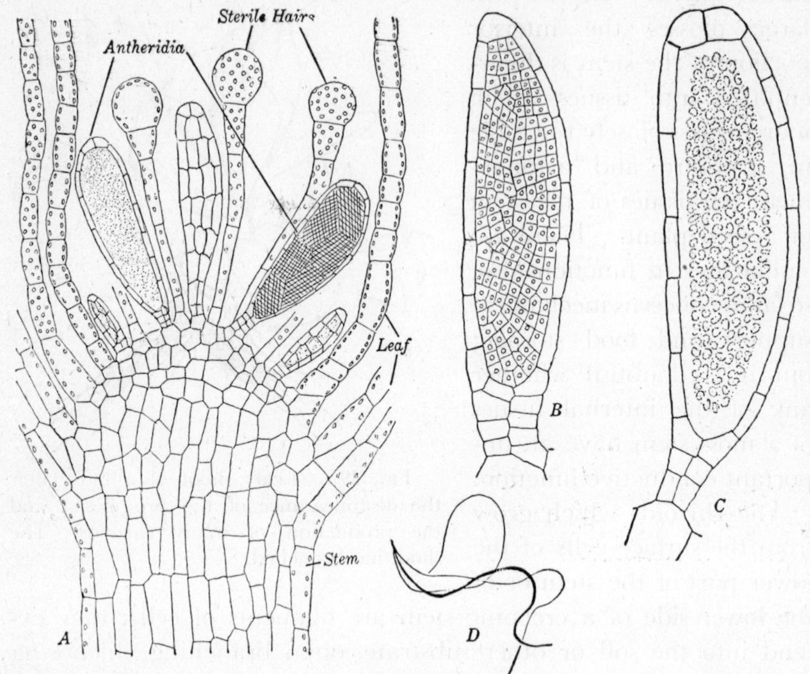

FIG. 298. *A*, vertical section of the apical portion of a stem of *Funaria hygrometrica* bearing antheridia. *B*, developing antheridium. *C*, mature antheridium containing antherozoids. *D*, antherozoid of *Bryum roseum*. *A–C*, after G. M. Smith, *Cryptogamic Botany*, published by the McGraw-Hill Book Company.

that it is often difficult to distinguish plants producing archegonia from those which are sterile. An antheridium (Fig. 298, *B*, *C*) is a rather slender saclike structure, varying in size and shape in different species. It consists of a short stalk and a body. The body has an outer layer or jacket of cells, green while young and often becoming reddish at maturity. Within the jacket are many closely packed small cells. After a series of divisions, each internal cell becomes transformed into a male gamete (an *antherozoid;* Fig. 298, *D*). The slender body of an antherozoid, consisting chiefly of the nucleus, is somewhat spirally coiled and is provided with two long flagella, by means of which it swims freely. When the antheridium is mature, the jacket cells at its apex disintegrate or are separated; and a viscous fluid containing the antherozoids oozes out.

An archegonium (Fig. 299) has a massive stalk, an enlarged basal portion (*venter*), and a long *neck*. The neck and venter of a nearly

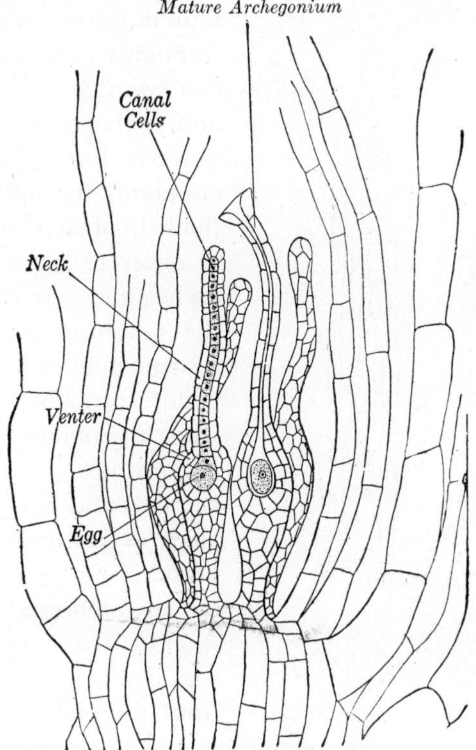

Fig. 299. Lengthwise section of the apical portion of a moss stem bearing archegonia. Modified from Sachs.

mature archegonium consist of a jacket of cells surrounding a single central row of *canal cells*, the basal and usually the largest cell of this central row being the female gamete or *egg*. When the archegonium is mature, the cells of the canal row, except the egg, have disintegrated, and the terminal cells of the neck have broken apart, leaving a passageway filled with a mucilaginous substance leading to the egg. Since the egg is within the venter of the archegonium and has no power of movement, it is evident that a meeting of gametes can be brought about only through the activity of the antherozoids. The presence of water about the archegonium is essential if an antherozoid is to swim to the archegonium and to enter its neck. When both sex organs are produced in the same terminal group, a connecting film of water may be present through which the antherozoids can swim; but when antheridia and archegonia are borne on different branches or on different plants, the antherozoids need the help of some outside agency in order to reach the group of archegonia. It is possible that the splashing of rain drops is instrumental in bringing this about; probably also at times when the plants are submerged, as during heavy rains, water currents may carry the antherozoids to the archegonia. After antherozoids reach the vicinity of an archegonium, they respond to a chemical stimulus supplied by a substance exuding from the opening of the canal at the tip of the archegonium. Many antherozoids may enter and swim down the canal, but as a rule only one unites with the egg. In this way a zygote is formed, about which a cell wall is soon secreted. The other antherozoids die.

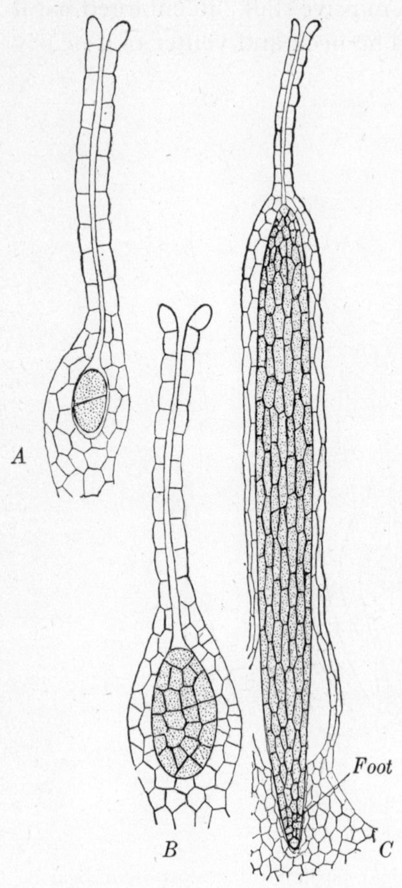

FIG. 300. *A*, very young (two-celled) moss sporophyte within an archegonium. *B*, somewhat later stage. *C*, still older, much elongated sporophyte; the foot is imbedded in gametophytic tissue below the archegonium. All diagrammatic.

Sporophyte. If conditions are favorable, the zygote almost immediately enlarges and by nuclear and cell division followed by further growth develops into a long, slender *embryo* (Fig. 300), the lower end of which digests its way through the stalk of the archegonium into the tissues of the stem beneath. The growth of the embryo into a new plant (the *sporophyte*) is accompanied by a growth of the enclosing venter, and for a time embryo and venter grow at about equal rates. Later the embryo develops so rapidly that the archegonium is broken and the greater part of it is carried up as a *calyptra* on the tip of the elongating embryonic plant, where it may remain for some time. The embryo becomes differentiated into three regions: a *foot*, which is the portion imbedded in the stem or branch of the parent plant and which absorbs water and food materials from the parent; a stalk, or *seta*, which in many mosses is long and slender; and a *capsule*, which is borne at the upper end of the stalk.

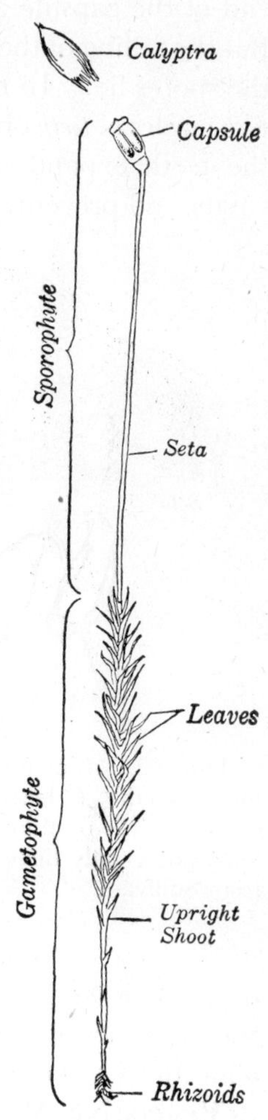

FIG. 301. Leafy shoot of a moss (Polytrichum) bearing a mature sporophyte.

The seta contains a central strand of elongated cells and in many mosses well-developed mechanical tissue. The capsule in most mosses (Fig. 302, *A–C*) is rather complex in structure, but its distinctive function is the production of spores. The central part of a relatively young capsule consists of sterile cells. Surrounding these is a cylinder of *spore mother cells*. Outside this cylinder are nutritive and protective tissues. In many mosses there are no spore mother cells in the lower part of the capsule; but the cells in this particular region contain chloroplasts, and there are even a few stomata in the epidermis. Many of the cells in other parts of the sporophyte, including the spore mother cells, also possess chloroplasts. The sporophyte is thus able to manufacture at least a considerable portion of its own carbohydrate food. It is, however, dependent upon the gametophyte for water and for other substances that must come from the soil and is therefore to this extent parasitic upon the gametophyte.

As the capsule approaches maturity, each spore mother cell divides, and its daughter cells divide (Fig. 302, *D–F*). The four cells so formed from each spore mother cell are *spores*. At the upper end of the capsule a *lid* has been formed, which in time drops off. But the falling of the lid may not leave uncovered the cavity in which the spores lie. In many mosses, plates or, more commonly, one or two circles of *teeth* obstruct the mouth of this cavity. In wet weather the teeth expand or bend inward, covering the entrance to the cavity and preventing the escape of the spores. In dry weather the

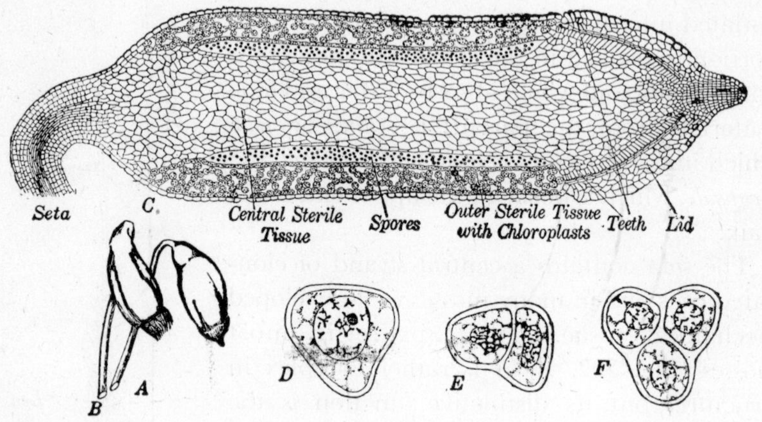

FIG. 302. *A*, mature moss capsule. *B*, capsule whose lid has fallen off, exposing the teeth. *C*, lengthwise section of a capsule. *D*, spore mother cell. *E*, two daughter cells resulting from the division of a spore mother cell. *F*, a group of four spores (only three visible) formed from a spore mother cell. *A*, *B* redrawn from Sullivant.

teeth curve outward or shrivel, or both, and allow the spores to sift out. This behavior favors the liberation of spores at times when they are most likely to be widely distributed. Under appropriate conditions a spore may develop into a protonema.

Vegetative Multiplication. Mosses are characterized by remarkable powers of vegetative multiplication. Indeed, a few species are not known to form gametes at all, seeming to depend entirely upon vegetative means of increasing their numbers. A single protonema may produce several or many leafy shoots, which ultimately become so many separate plants. Leafy shoots, especially if wounded, often produce secondary protonemata which give rise to new, eventually independent, leafy shoots. Even a wounded sporophyte, in some species, may produce a protonema—that is, a new gametophyte. Some mosses bear special buds (*gemmae*) on leaves, branches, or protonemata, which if separated from the parent plant develop into new plants.

Alternation of Generations. There are two distinct phases in the life cycle of a moss (Fig. 303). The germination of a spore

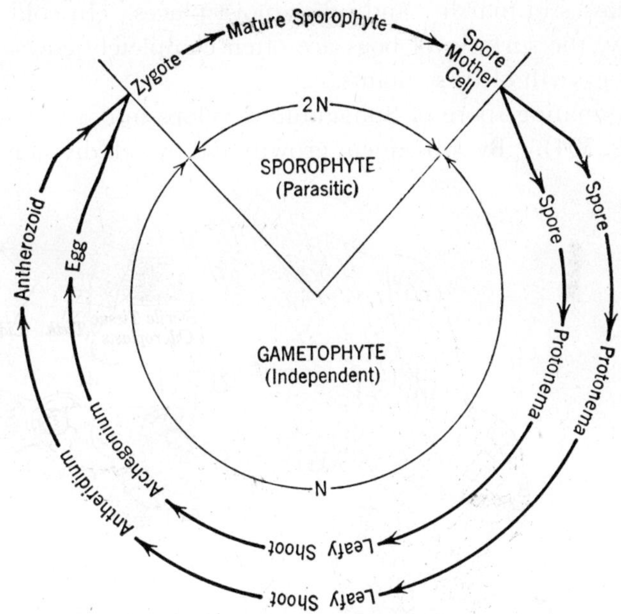

FIG. 303. Life cycle of a moss.

produces a protonema, from which develop one or more green leafy shoots bearing sex organs (antheridia and archegonia) in which gametes (antherozoids and eggs) are formed. The protonema, the leafy branches, and the sex organs together constitute a *generation* which, since it produces gametes, is the gametophyte, or sexual generation. The union of gametes forms a zygote. The zygote develops into a new plant, whose characteristic function is the production of spores and which is therefore the sporophyte, or asexual generation. Each spore may in turn develop into a gametophyte.

This history may be expressed in the following formula: Gametophyte—Gametes—Zygote—Sporophyte—Spores—Gametophyte—

Gametes, etc. Each generation produces by means of its reproductive cells the other generation; hence, there is an *alternation* of the two generations.

SPHAGNUM

Gametophyte. Dense aggregations of plants of the peat mosses (members of the genus *Sphagnum*) form conspicuous tussocks or larger masses in marshes and other moist places. In cold regions especially, the surfaces of bogs are often completely covered bv a compact growth of these plants.

A germinating spore of Sphagnum develops into a row of a few cells (Fig. 304). By subsequent growth and by cell divisions in two

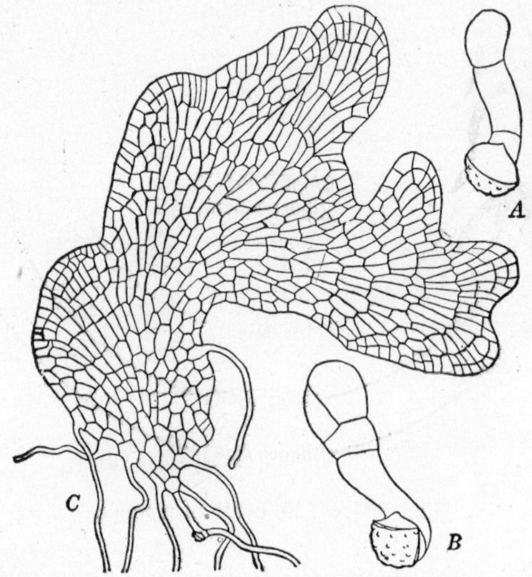

FIG. 304. Sphagnum. *A*, *B*, very young protonemata; redrawn from Müller. *C*, older protonema; redrawn from Ruhland.

planes, this young protonema, except for the few basal cells nearest the spore wall, becomes a flat, green plate one cell thick, very different from the filamentous protonemata of most other mosses. The protonema is heart-shaped or irregularly lobed and is attached to the substrate by rhizoids. On the margin of the protonema a bud arises, which grows into a leafy shoot. The stem of this shoot, while young, bears a few rhizoids. It grows upright, often attaining a length of a foot or more, and branches freely (Fig. 305). Both stem and branches bear leaves. Near the apex of the stem are a number of short branches, each of which forms a cluster of secondary branches. These clusters of branches, crowded together about the apex, form the conspicuous, compact "head" of the plant,

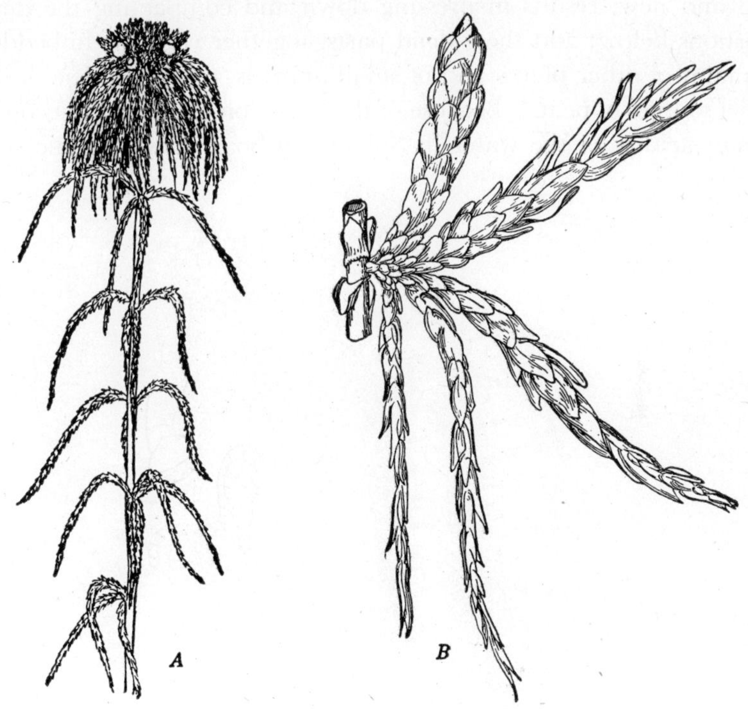

FIG. 305. *A*, leafy shoot of Sphagnum bearing sporophytes (appearing white) at its apex. *B*, small portion of the stem, bearing leaves and a tuft of branches. *B* redrawn from Sullivant.

which is commonly pale green but sometimes yellow, brown, purple, or red. At intervals on the lower parts of the stem occur other branches, usually in tufts of three to eight. In those species of Sphagnum which ordinarily do not grow submerged in water, some of the branches of a tuft are comparatively long and slender; these branches hang downward close to the stem and, with similar branches from other tufts, form a loose covering about the stem. Other branches of each tuft extend outward or upward. Most of these latter branches remain short, but occasionally one of them continues the growth upward and repeats the structure of the stem, like it branching and forming an apical cluster of branches. The progressive death of the basal portion of the stem finally separates each such upright branch as an independent plant and is thus one effective means of vegetative multiplication.

The continued upward growth from year to year of the plants, old and new, results in pressing down and compacting the dead portions below; and these dead parts, together with the imbedded remains of other plants and of small animals, constitute one of the chief sources of peat. Because of the exclusion of air and the consequent acidity of the water in Sphagnum bogs, these organic sub-

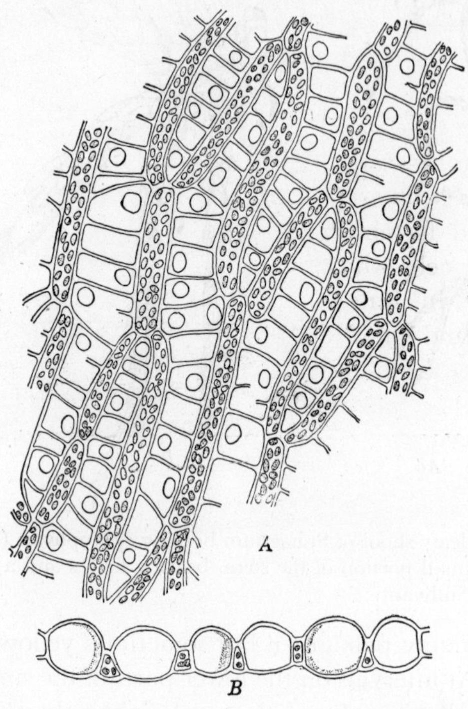

FIG. 306. The structure of a leaf of Sphagnum; small green cells alternate with large dead ones. *A*, portion of a leaf as seen from above. *B*, part of a cross section.

stances are not completely decomposed by those bacteria and other fungi that cause decay. Chemical changes due largely to anaerobic bacteria result in the formation of the spongy, dark-colored substance known as peat. Further changes in the peat may in the course of long periods of time lead to the production of certain types of coal.

At the growing end of the stem and of each branch is an apical cell, resembling in shape and function the apical cells of the mosses already described. As in other mosses, leaves are formed in three rows; but as the stem and leaves grow, the latter become displaced and lose their three-ranked arrangement. A mature leaf (Fig. 306) is composed of cells of two types. Alternate cells have grown both in length and in breadth and have ultimately died, leaving only their walls. The inner surfaces of these walls are frequently characterized by spiral and ring-shaped thickenings; and often the walls are perforated, the openings (pores) being variable in size and shape. Between these large cells and forming a network are other cells which have grown chiefly in length, remained alive, and retained chlorophyll. Large dead cells like those in the leaves occur in the cortices of the stems and branches of some species. Cells of this character in leaf and stem play an important part in the absorption and retention of water. Both stem and branches, except in species that grow submerged in water, possess mechanical tissues also.

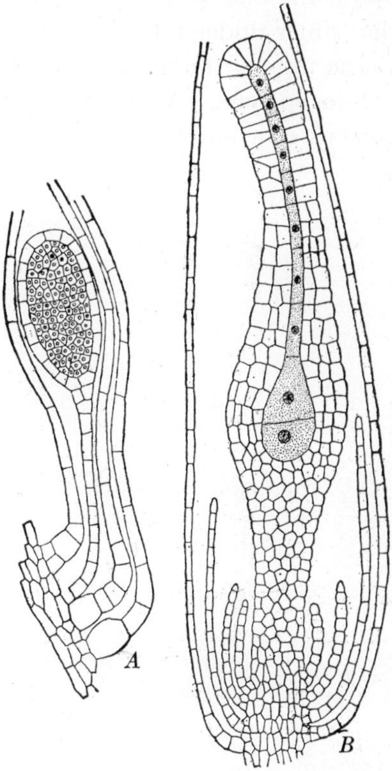

FIG. 307. Sex organs of Sphagnum. *A*, portion of an antheridial branch with an antheridium. *B*, apex of an archegonial branch, the archegonium enclosed by leaves.

Sex Organs. Antheridia and archegonia (Fig. 307) are produced usually in late summer and early autumn on short branches borne near the apex of the stem. Antheridial and archegonial branches may, according to the species, be borne on the same plant or on separate plants; but antheridia and archegonia never occur on the same branch. The leaves on an antheridial branch are often brown, purple, or red, even in those species in which the leaves on other branches are green. An antheridium resembles one of Porella (Fig. 288, *A*), and as in Porella each antheridium is borne in the axil of a leaf.

The very short archegonial branches are closely crowded at the apex of the stem. One archegonium is developed from the apical cell of each branch, and several other archegonia may be formed about the base of the first. In cold countries the sex organs pass the winter under the snow, and gametic union occurs in the spring at the time of the melting of the snow and ice.

Sporophyte. A mature sporophyte of Sphagnum (Fig. 308) consists of a bulblike foot which is imbedded in the tissues of the

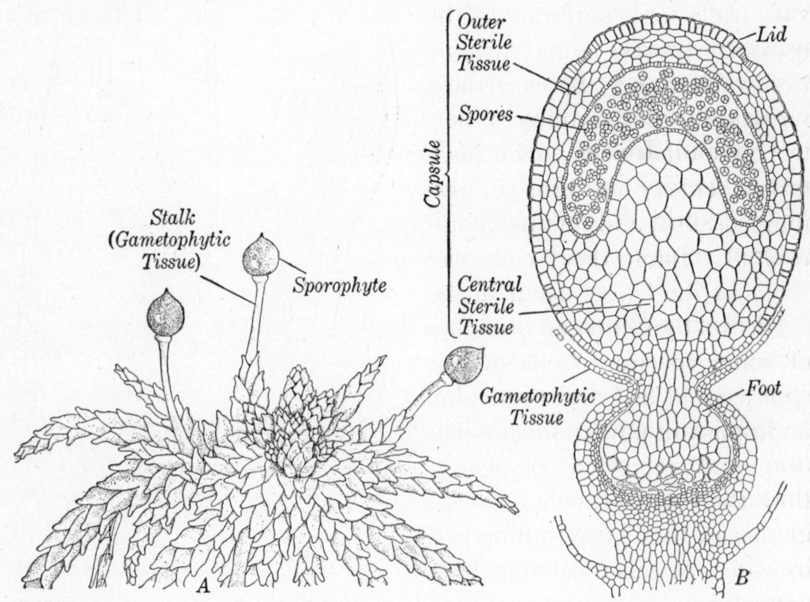

Fig. 308. *A*, apical portion of a leafy shoot of Sphagnum bearing sporophytes. *B*, lengthwise section of a nearly mature sporophyte. The spores are in groups of four, each group derived from one spore mother cell.

branch beneath the archegonium, and a terminal capsule, almost spherical in shape, separated from the foot by a constriction. Spores are formed in a relatively thin, dome-shaped zone in the upper part of the capsule. When the spores are nearly mature, a portion of the branch beneath the foot of the sporophyte elongates and carries the sporophyte beyond the enveloping leaves. A dome-shaped lid is formed at the apex of the capsule. The lid is thrown off by an explosive action of the capsule, which also ejects the spores.

Uses of Sphagnum. The part played by Sphagnum in the formation of peat and of some kinds of coal has been mentioned. Dried peat has been employed as a fuel for centuries in some countries, particularly in Ireland. While it has never been so used to any extent in this country, vast deposits of peat are available.

Sphagnum is much used as a packing material for live plants which are to be shipped, as well as a substrate in which seeds are germinated and in which some types of plants are grown. Its value for these purposes results from its ability to absorb moisture and to retain it for a considerable time. Masses of Sphagnum of certain varieties have been found to take up from 15 to 20 times their own weight of water.

The absorptive power of Sphagnum has led also to its use in surgical dressings. It has long been used in the dressing of wounds in Scotland, Ireland, and the Scandinavian countries. It was extensively employed for this purpose in the Russo-Japanese war and in the World War of 1914–18. Now, however, other and better absorptive materials have been developed.

Distinctive Features of Bryophytes. Liverworts and mosses together constitute the division known as Bryophyta. About 8500 species of liverworts and 14,000 species of mosses are now recognized.

Although conspicuous differences distinguish various liverworts and mosses, their relationship is clearly shown by a close similarity throughout the division in the form and structure of sex organs and gametes. Both antheridium and archegonium are characterized by the presence of an outer layer of sterile cells. In this respect the gamete-producing organs of a bryophyte differ from the corresponding organs of any thallophyte.

Liverworts and mosses are alike also in having an alternation of generations; the gametophyte is, in every case, the larger, longer-lived, independent generation; the sporophyte is smaller, shorter-lived, and parasitic upon the gametophyte. While an alternation of generations occurs in many thallophytes (algae and fungi), in no alga or fungus are the relations between gametophyte and sporophyte closely comparable to those existing between the two generations of a bryophyte.

The bryophytes display a high degree of sexual differentiation, marking a great advance over the primitive form of gametic union that occurs in Chlamydomonas, in which the two uniting gametes are to all appearances alike. In various lines of evolution among plants, a differentiation has appeared between the gametes. Some of the steps in this type of evolutionary development are illustrated by algae and fungi described in previous chapters. One type of gamete performs especially the function of storing food to be used by the zygote and, in many-celled forms, by the young plant (embryo) which will develop from the zygote; in adaptation to its function, this female gamete has become larger and has lost the power of movement. The male gamete, on the other hand, retains the power of movement, which is essential to its union with the female gamete; and, relieved of the necessity of food storage, it has become smaller and better adapted to rapid movement. The female gamete (egg) and the male gamete (antherozoid) of a bryophyte have thus come to be very different in size and structure, the antherozoid being reduced to little more than a nucleus and a pair of flagella.

This differentiation of gametes into two sorts, each adapted to a particular function, is the basis of what is commonly known as *sex* in both plants and animals. Sexual differentiation extends in the bryophytes also to the production of distinct organs (archegonium and antheridium) in which the respective gametes are formed; and in a number of liverworts and mosses it has extended to a differentiation in size or in external form between the female gametophyte, which produces only eggs, and the male gametophyte, which produces only antherozoids. In some species the male gametophyte is much smaller than the female gametophyte.

CHAPTER XXV

REDUCTION OF THE NUMBER OF CHROMOSOMES

Chromosome Numbers and the Alternation of Generations. The number of chromosomes in each cell of the gametophyte of a liverwort or of a moss may be represented as *n*. The numerical value of *n* differs in different species; for example, in some common mosses *n* equals 7, that is, each cell of the gametophyte contains seven chromosomes. When any nucleus of the gametophyte divides, by the process described in Chapter X, each parent chromosome is divided, and its daughter chromosomes pass to the respective daughter nuclei; hence, the chromosome number in each daughter cell is the same as that in the parent cell. Every cell throughout the life of the gametophyte, then, contains *n* chromosomes; and consequently each gamete (egg or antherozoid) which is produced by this plant has *n* chromosomes.

The union of the gametes involves a union of their cytoplasm and of their nuclei but not of their chromosomes. Therefore, the zygote nucleus contains 2 *n* chromosomes; *n* are of maternal origin because they were contributed by the egg; *n* chromosomes, contributed by the antherozoid, are of paternal origin.

The zygote, with 2 *n* chromosomes, is the starting-point of the sporophytic generation. When the zygote nucleus divides, each of its chromosomes divides; each daughter cell, therefore, formed by the division of the zygote receives 2 *n* chromosomes—*n* maternal and *n* paternal. In the nuclear divisions which follow during the development of the sporophyte, each chromosome is divided, and each of its daughter chromosomes passes to one daughter nucleus; hence, each cell of the sporophyte has *n* maternal and *n* paternal chromosomes. One important difference between gametophyte and sporophyte, therefore, is the presence in the two generations of different numbers of chromosomes—respectively, *n* and 2 *n*. If each cell of the gametophyte of a moss contains 7 (*n*) chromosomes, each cell of the sporophyte contains 14 (2 *n*). Among the values of *n* found in various species of mosses are 7, 8, 10, 12, 16, 20, and 32. In *Riccia natans* and in *Marchantia polymorpha*, *n* equals 9.

Reduction of the Chromosome Number. The doubling of the number of chromosomes each time two gametes unite would result, if nothing occurred to prevent, in a continuous increase in chromosome number. It is clear that such an accumulation of chromosomes from generation to generation could not long continue. As a matter of fact there is no such accumulation, because in each life cycle, at some point between one gametic union and the next, the chromosome number is reduced. In liverworts and mosses and in the plants above them in the evolutionary scale, the reduction is brought about in the two successive nuclear divisions that occur when a spore mother cell is divided to form four spores (Fig. 302, *D–F*). The spore mother cell when it was formed, like any other cell of the sporophyte, received 2 *n* chromosomes; but in the divisions of the spore-mother-cell nucleus and of its daughter nuclei, the chromosome number is reduced to *n*. These two nuclear divisions (reduction divisions) are different, therefore, from all other divisions in the history of the plant. Since each spore, possessing *n* chromosomes, is the starting-point of a gametophyte, each cell of the gametophyte has *n* chromosomes.

This history of the chromosomes may be summed up by saying that in the union of gametes—the point of transition from gametophyte to sporophyte—the chromosome number is doubled (from *n* to 2 *n*) and that in spore formation—the point of transition from sporophyte to gametophyte—the chromosome number is reduced (from 2 *n* to *n*).

First Reduction Division (Fig. 309, *A–F*). When the nucleus of a spore mother cell begins to prepare for division, it possesses, as has been seen, 2 *n* chromosomes. Just as at the beginning of an ordinary nuclear division, each chromosome consists essentially of two tightly coiled chromatids. But soon the chromosomes come together in pairs (Fig. 309, *C*), each pair composed of one maternal and one paternal chromosome; and those of each pair, each still composed of two chromatids, coil about each other. This pairing of chromosomes distinguishes the first reduction division from all other nuclear divisions in the history of a plant. The chromosomes of each pair are in general alike in size and form.

As they shorten and thicken, the paired chromosomes become partly untwisted. Now it can sometimes be seen that while they were closely coiled an interchange of parts of chromatids has occurred. At particular points, as at *a* and *b*, Figure 309, *D*, one chromatid of each chromosome has broken; and the broken ends

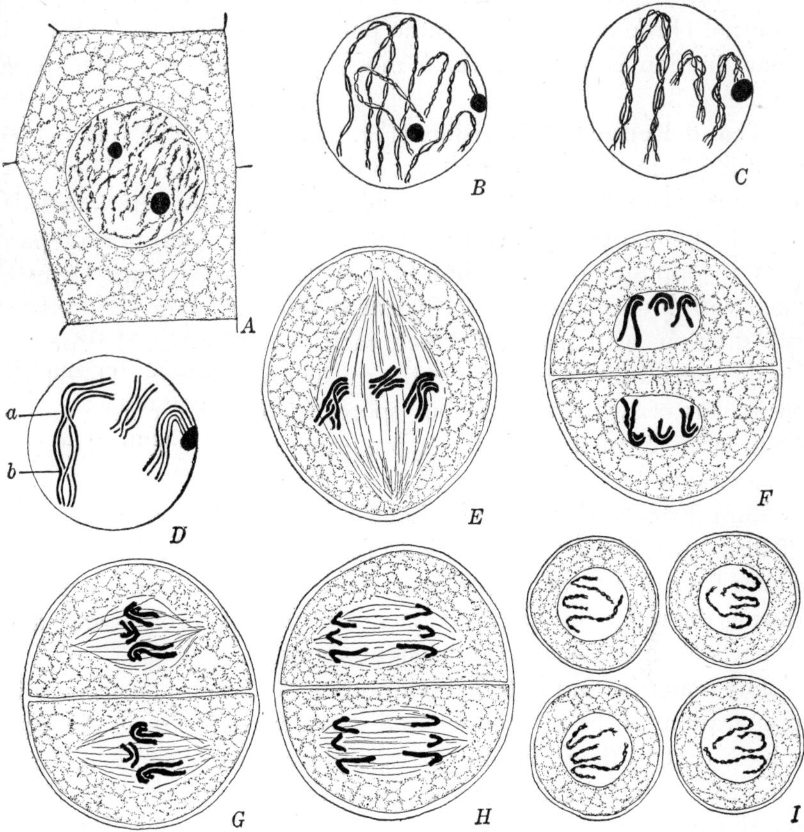

FIG. 309. The reduction divisions, and the formation of four spores each with *n* chromosomes from a spore mother cell with 2 *n*. For description see text. Diagrammatic.

have rejoined in such a way that parts of the two chromatids have been exchanged. Two, three, or more such exchanges may occur between the chromatids of a single pair of chromosomes; the number of exchanges depends in part upon the length of the chromosomes. Only two chromatids, one belonging to each chromosome of the pair, are concerned in the exchange at any one point.

The chromosome pairs become arranged in an equatorial plate (Fig. 309, *E*). Then the maternal chromosome of each pair, still composed of two chromatids, passes to one spindle pole, the paternal chromosome to the opposite pole. But because of the exchanges of parts that may have occurred earlier, one or both of the chromatids of the maternal chromosome may contain parts derived from the paternal chromosome of the same pair, and vice versa. This nuclear division is followed (in a moss) by a division of the spore mother cell.

Second Reduction Division (Fig. 309, *G–I*). The two nuclei resulting from the first division soon themselves divide. The chromosomes of each nucleus become arranged in an equatorial plate, and the two chromatids (now daughter chromosomes) of each pair pass to opposite poles. Thus four daughter nuclei are formed, each with *n* chromosomes. Nuclear division is again followed by cell division, as a result of which each of the four nuclei formed by the second division becomes the nucleus of a spore. Therefore, by means of two divisions, four spores each with *n* chromosomes have been formed from the spore mother cell which had 2 *n* chromosomes.

Some Effects of the Reduction Divisions. One obvious effect of these two nuclear divisions is to reduce the number of chromosomes from 2 *n* to *n*. More important, however, is the fact that during the reduction divisions *new combinations* of chromosomes and of parts of chromosomes are brought about.

The maternal and paternal chromosomes of each pair formed in preparation for the first reduction division are *corresponding* chromosomes; that is, they contain corresponding parts of the hereditary substance. But since the two parents which contributed the chromosomes were in most cases different in respect to many characters, the chromosomes of any pair are practically never exactly alike. When, in the course of the first reduction division, the chromosomes of each pair separate, it is a matter of chance to which spindle pole the maternal, and to which pole the paternal, chromosome will pass. Hence, in general, each daughter nucleus receives some maternal and some paternal chromosomes—but regularly one of each pair. Thus, new chromosome combinations result. It follows that the nuclei formed in the first reduction division and consequently those formed in the second division differ in respect to the inheritance which they will pass on to the next generation. Since in any sporophyte many spore mother cells are produced and since, in consequence of the chance separation of maternal and paternal chromosomes, different combinations are brought about in the division of different mother-cell nuclei, a single sporophyte may produce many hereditarily different types of spores.

The possibilities of different new combinations are greatly increased by the exchanges of parts which may occur between chromosomes in the early stages of the first reduction division. Such exchanges of chromosome parts, together with the random separation of the paired chromosomes, make it not surprising that offspring differ from their parents and that offspring of the same parents differ from one another.

Chromosome Reduction in Thallophytes. In bryophytes (liverworts and mosses) and in the plants that stand above them in the evolutionary scale (pteridophytes and seed plants), the reduction of the chromosome number occurs regularly at the same stage in the life cycle—namely, in the division of the nucleus of a spore mother cell. The plants of these higher groups agree, therefore, in possessing a sporophytic generation characterized by the presence of $2n$ chromosomes and a gametophytic generation each of whose cells has n chromosomes.

Among thallophytes, however, there are great differences with respect to the stage at which the chromosome number is reduced. In many green algae, chromosome reduction occurs in the division of the zygote nucleus and of its daughter nuclei. This is the case in Chlamydomonas, Volvox, Ulothrix, and Oedogonium. In any of these algae the zygote is the only cell possessing $2n$ chromosomes, and there is no generation corresponding to the sporophyte of a moss. In Spirogyra, similarly, chromosome reduction is effected in the two divisions that occur shortly after gametic union. Of the four nuclei, each with n chromosomes, formed from the zygote nucleus by these divisions, it has been seen that three nuclei degenerate. Hence, the single nucleus present in the zygote of Spirogyra during its later history has but n chromosomes. The filament resulting from the germination of the zygote consists of cells with n chromosomes each—that is, it is a gametophyte. Spirogyra, therefore, also has no sporophytic generation. In a few green algae, including Ulva and some marine species of Cladophora, there is an alternation of generations; the two generations are exactly alike except for their reproductive structures, whereas in the bryophytes and higher groups the two generations are very unlike.

In one fresh-water species of Cladophora, reduction is reported to occur in the nuclear divisions immediately preceding gamete formation; the gametes then are the only cells with *n* chromosomes, all the rest of the life cycle having 2 *n*. In this respect, this Cladophora resembles the higher animals in which there is no generation corresponding to the gametophyte of a moss. Some, perhaps all, of the diatoms, follow the same rule.

The brown algae possess an alternation of generations comparable in principle with that in bryophytes. In some, including Ectocarpus, the gametophyte and sporophyte are alike. In other brown algae the two generations are very unlike. For example, the sporophyte of Laminaria is a large, complex plant, and the gametophyte is small and simple. In Fucus, chromosome reduction occurs in the first two nuclear divisions in oögonium and antheridium, respectively; the only nuclei with *n* chromosomes are those of the four-nucleate and succeeding stages in these organs.

In Nemalion and in its closest relatives among the red algae, chromosome reduction occurs, as in many of the green algae, when the zygote nucleus and its daughter nuclei divide. But in the majority of red algae, including Polysiphonia, the double chromosome number (2 *n*) present in the zygote persists in the carpospore-bearing branches, in the carpospores, and in the tetraspore-bearing plant. Reduction occurs in the divisions which form the tetraspore nuclei.

Differences appear among fungi as great as those among algae with respect to the time of chromosome reduction.

In Rhizopus, chromosome reduction is probably effected during some of the nuclear divisions that occur at the time of, or shortly after, the germination of the zygote. The particular divisions with which chromosome reduction is connected have not yet, however, been certainly recognized.

In the ascomycetes (with perhaps some exceptions) the chromosome number is reduced by the first two nuclear divisions in the ascus.

Among basidiomycetes, chromosome reduction is brought about in the rusts (again with possible exceptions) by the two nuclear divisions in the germinating teleutospore; in smuts, probably by the two nuclear divisions in the germinating winter spore; and in mushrooms, by the two divisions in the basidium.

Relation of Chromosome Reduction to Gametic Union. A knowledge of the steps in the reduction of the chromosome number throws some additional light upon the real nature and significance of gametic union. The pairing of chromosomes that takes place early in the first reduction division is the final step in a history that began with the union of gametes. Every case of gametic union, then, involves three steps:

(*a*) The union of cells.
(*b*) The union of nuclei.
(*c*) The pairing of chromosomes.

Among the plants thus far described, steps *a*, *b*, and *c* are separated from one another in different degrees. In Spirogyra, the union of cells (step *a*) is followed closely by the union of nuclei (step *b*) and this very soon by the pairing of chromosomes (step *c*). In the wheat rust, there is a long period (represented by the aecidiospores, the mycelium in the wheat, and the uredospores) between steps *a* and *b;* step *b*, however (taken during the maturing of the teleutospore), is followed by step *c* as soon as the teleutospore germinates. In bryophytes and higher plants, steps *a* and *b* are close together in time; and a long gap (represented by the sporophytic generation) occurs between steps *b* and *c*.

Since step *c* (the pairing of chromosomes) results in a redistribution of chromosomes and of their parts, one of the important consequences (if not *the* important consequence) of a gametic union is this ultimate redistribution, with the result that new combinations of inherited qualities may appear. In other words, the union of gametes, because it results ultimately in chromosome pairing, is a means of securing variation, in the sense of a new grouping of inherited possibilities.

CHAPTER XXVI

PTERIDOPHYTA: FILICINEAE (FERNS)

Pteridophytes. The commonest and best-known classes of living pteridophytes are the Filicineae (ferns), the Equisetineae (horsetails), and the Lycopodineae (club mosses). Another class, the Psilophytineae, with but few present-day representatives, will be discussed in Chapter XXXII. All these plants stand at approximately a similar evolutionary level in that their sporophytes possess roots, stems, and green leaves and are consequently independent; but none of them have attained to the production of seeds, which characterizes the highest level of the plant kingdom. The gametophytes of pteridophytes, on the other hand, are always very small and inconspicuous; but they still bear their characteristic sex organs (antheridia and archegonia) and hence still depend upon an external supply of water for the process of fertilization.

Nature and Distribution of Ferns. The sporophytes of ferns possess certain characteristics that distinguish them from the sporophytes of other pteridophytes. For example, fern leaves are relatively very large and are spirally arranged on the stems. In their growth and development most fern leaves have the habit of unrolling from base to apex. Sporangia are borne in clusters (*sori*), commonly on the under sides of the leaves, more rarely on the margins. No other pteridophytes have these characteristics.

As a class ferns have been in existence for a very long time. The age of several fossil genera related to certain present-day families has been estimated at 200,000,000 years; that of other more primitive fossil ferns at 350,000,000 years. There are about 9000 species of living ferns. Like the mosses, ferns are widely distributed in nature. Some grow in the crevices of rocks and on the faces of cliffs where they find a scanty foothold; others in fields and open woods; but most ferns thrive best in cool, damp, shady places. In certain areas of the tropics ferns are very abundant both in number of individuals and in number of species. This is particularly true of the tropical rain forests, where certain kinds of ferns grow profusely even to the extent of covering the trunks and branches of trees. It is commonly in the tropics also that the largest ferns are found. These are the tree ferns (Fig. 310) with erect cylindrical

FIG. 310. Tree ferns (*Dicksonia fibrosa*) in a clearing in a New Zealand rain forest. The ferns (in the foreground) survived a fire that killed many of the other trees. Photograph courtesy of T. L. Lancaster.

stems, each bearing at its apex a crown of huge, wide-spreading, compound leaves. In temperate regions most ferns have stems which grow at or just beneath the surface of the soil. From such a stem grow numerous hairlike adventitious roots and relatively large leaves with conspicuous petioles; the leaves are then the only prominent aerial parts of the plant.

THE BRACKEN

Sporophyte. Among the common ferns living in temperate regions is a group of very similar species all generally known as the *brake fern* or *bracken.* The bracken of eastern North America is *Pteridium latiusculum* (Fig. 311). It grows in woods or clearings and is often abundant in sandy regions. In some parts of the world the leaves of brackens growing from the underground stem form dense undergrowths. In most parts of the United States these leaves are relatively short, ordinarily not attaining the height of a man; but those of the bracken living in the rich soils of the forests of western Washington and Oregon may grow to as much as twice that height.

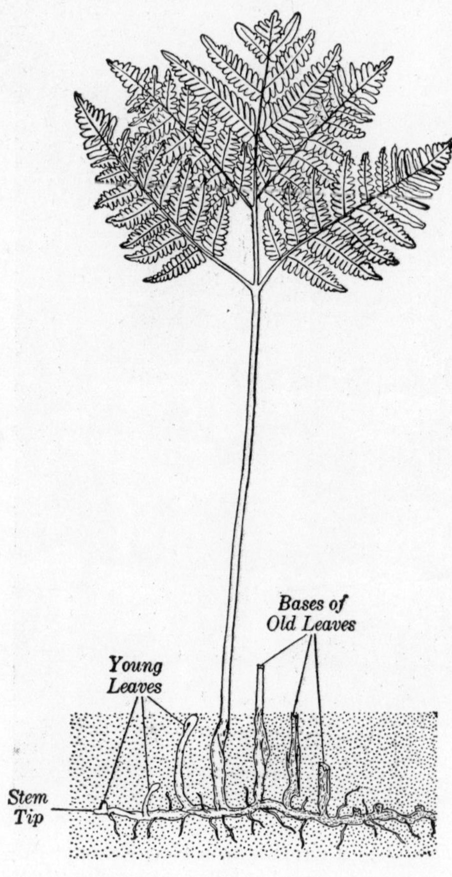

FIG. 311. The bracken. Diagrammatic.

Stem. The stem of Pteridium, growing a few inches beneath the surface of the ground, is long and slender and sparingly branched. At the anterior end is the growing region, new cells being formed by the division of an apical cell; in time the older tissues at the posterior end gradually die. When the progressive death and decay of the older parts of the stem extend to a point at which branching has occurred, the branch becomes separated from the main stem. Then, if conditions are favorable, it continues its development as an independent plant. By this means the number of plants may be greatly increased.

The epidermis of a stem (Fig. 312) is composed of thick-walled cells; next within is a sheath of mechanical cells several cells in thickness. The greater part of the interior of the stem consists of parenchymatous cells which often contain an abundance of starch grains. Near the center of a section cut through an internode are two well-defined strands of mechanical tissue. Between these strands, in the central part of the stem, are usually two vascular bundles; and in a zone outside the strands of mechanical tissue are

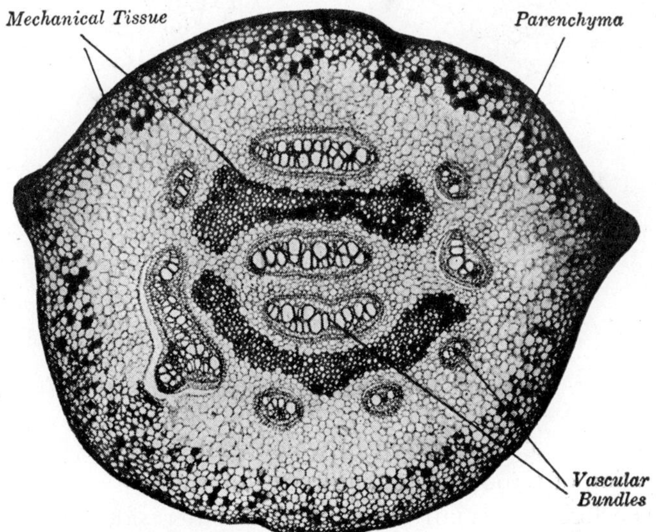

FIG. 312. Cross section of the underground stem of the bracken.

a variable number of vascular bundles some of which are relatively small. Each bundle (Fig. 313) is surrounded by a single layer of endodermal cells, just within which are one or two layers of cells constituting a pericycle. The phloem lies next within the pericycle and almost surrounds the central xylem. There is no cambium between xylem and phloem, and consequently no secondary thickening occurs. The vascular bundles extend approximately parallel through the internodes; but at each node some of them unite, and new branch bundles are formed.

Roots. As the stem of the bracken elongates, it gives rise to many adventitious roots, which are long, slender, and occasionally branched. Each spring and summer, as the stem resumes its growth, a new group of adventitious roots may be formed on the younger part of the stem. The growing end of a root is covered by a root cap and, as in the case of the stem, new cells arise at the growing end by the division of an apical cell. A short distance back

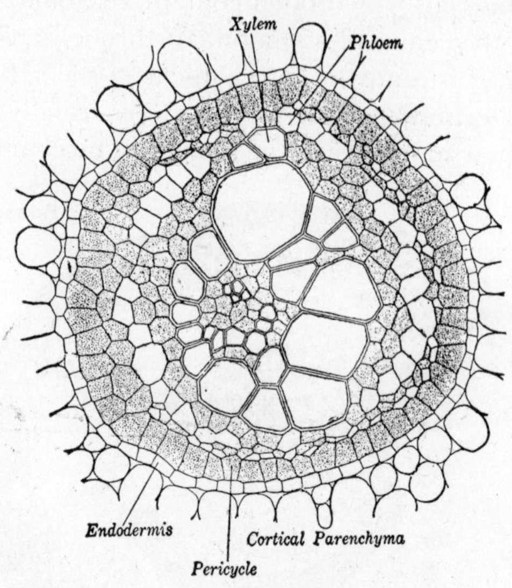

FIG. 313. Cross section of a vascular bundle of the bracken stem.

from the root cap is a region in which root hairs are formed. A cross section of a root in the mature region shows a relatively thick cortex enclosing a small stele. On its outer side the cortex is bounded by an epidermis one cell in thickness. The cells of the endodermis are distinguished by thickenings on their radial walls. Just within the endodermis is the pericycle, consisting of one or two layers of thin-walled cells. Next within the pericycle are two or three strands of xylem and a similar number of small phloem strands. The xylem and phloem strands alternate with one another. The xylem strands extend to and occupy the center of the stele. Since no cambium is formed between xylem and phloem, the roots, like the stem, are incapable of secondary thickening.

Leaves. Each leaf of a mature plant begins its development as a small hump of meristematic cells at the growing tip of the stem. The early development of a young leaf therefore occurs underground. In time the elongation of the lower part of the petiole pushes the tightly coiled upper portion of the leaf through the soil into the air. Here the leaf continues its development by unrolling from base to apex—a feature characteristic of nearly all ferns. A mature leaf consists of a slender petiole and a much-divided blade. Borne upon the central axis of the blade are two rows of primary leaflets, the basal pair being much the larger. Several pairs of the lower primary leaflets may themselves be divided, but the smaller upper primary leaflets are usually undivided.

The internal structure of a leaflet (Fig. 314) is in general similar to that of the leaves of many seed plants. The leaflet has an

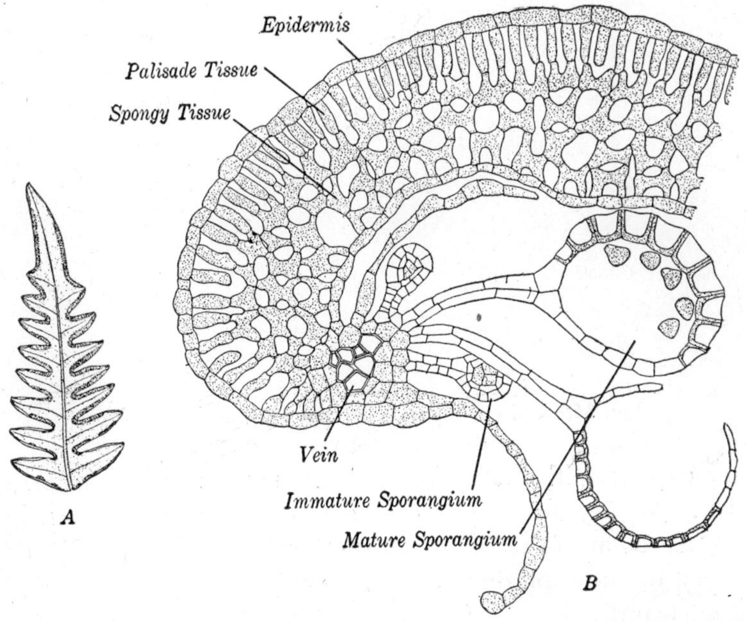

FIG. 314. *A*, a fertile leaflet of the bracken. *B*, cross section through a portion of a fertile leaflet; sporangia are partly enclosed by the curved margin. *B*, semi-diagrammatic. After G. M. Smith, *Cryptogamic Botany*, published by the McGraw-Hill Book Company.

upper and a lower epidermis, a palisade-like layer, spongy tissue, and veins. Stomata are abundant in the lower epidermis.

Sporangia. In spite of the fact that all the leaves of a bracken are green and superficially alike, a careful examination discloses that some of them bear sporangia and some do not. In the bracken, as in all other ferns, a leaf which bears sporangia is a *sporophyll.* The sporophylls of the bracken manufacture foods and also produce sporangia. The sterile leaves of the bracken, on the other hand, are food-making organs only. On the under side of each leaflet of a sporophyll and along each edge, a narrow ridge of tissue develops from whose surface grow many sporangia (Fig. 314, *B*). This ridge and the sporangia borne on it are covered by the curved margin of the leaflet. Each sporangium (Fig. 315) consists of a slender stalk

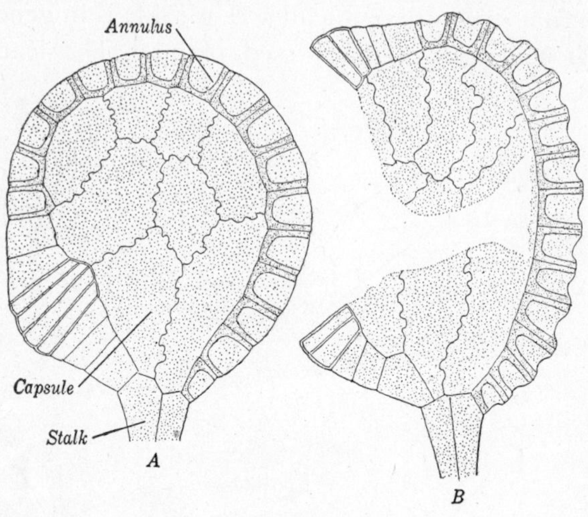

Fig. 315. Mature sporangia, closed (*A*) and open (*B*).

and a capsule. The outer layer of cells of the capsule constitutes a jacket. Within the jacket, as a result of a series of divisions, spore mother cells are formed. Each spore mother cell by two nuclear and cell divisions produces, just as in a moss, four spores. In the two nuclear divisions, as in the corresponding divisions in a moss, the chromosome number is reduced from 2 n to n. All the cells of the jacket are thin-walled except those of one row. Each cell of this row has thick walls on all sides except the outer one. This row of cells, extending from the base of the capsule up one side, over the end, and partly down the opposite side, is the *annulus*. When the spores are mature, all the cells of the jacket are dead and dry. The cell walls of the annulus are sensitive to changes in moisture. As a result of such changes the annulus straightens, breaking open the capsule, and then snaps forward. In this latter movement most of the spores are thrown out.

Gametophyte. The spores of the bracken mature and are shed in late summer. The wall of each spore has two layers: the inner one thin; the outer hard, brown, and irregularly thickened. When a spore germinates, the thick outer layer of the wall breaks; and the protoplast surrounded by the inner layer of the wall forms a short green outgrowth, from which a colorless projection, the first rhizoid, grows. As a result of growth and of cell divisions, the green outgrowth develops into a flat green plate one cell in thickness (Fig. 316). If this small *prothallium* is not crowded and is exposed to

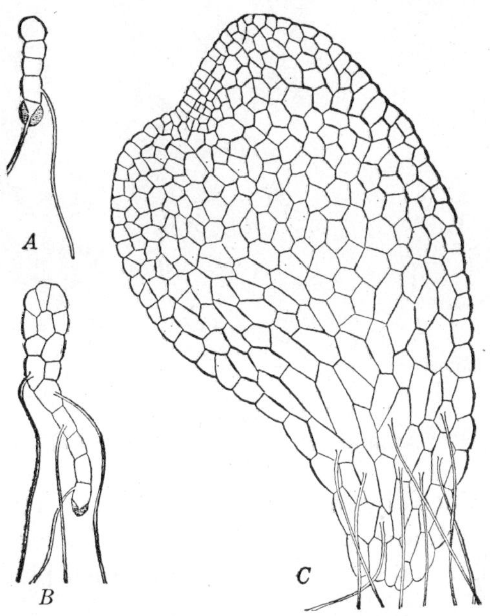

FIG. 316. *A, B,* early stages in the development of a prothallium from a fern spore. *C,* half-grown prothallium.

favorable conditions of light and moisture, it develops typically into a heart-shaped plant with a shallow notch at its anterior end. A mature prothallium (Figs. 317, 318) is one cell in thickness except just back of the apical notch, where a cushion several cells thick is formed. Slender, colorless rhizoids which anchor the plant and absorb water and nutrient substances from the soil grow out from various cells of the under surface of the plant and particularly from those in the posterior (older) portion. Prothallia may reach maturity in a few months, but they remain so small that they are rarely observed in nature unless sought for. Fully grown prothallia are usually not more than a quarter inch in diameter.

The prothallium is the gametophyte of a fern; like the gametophyte of a moss, it produces antheridia and archegonia. Under favorable conditions for growth and development both sorts of sex

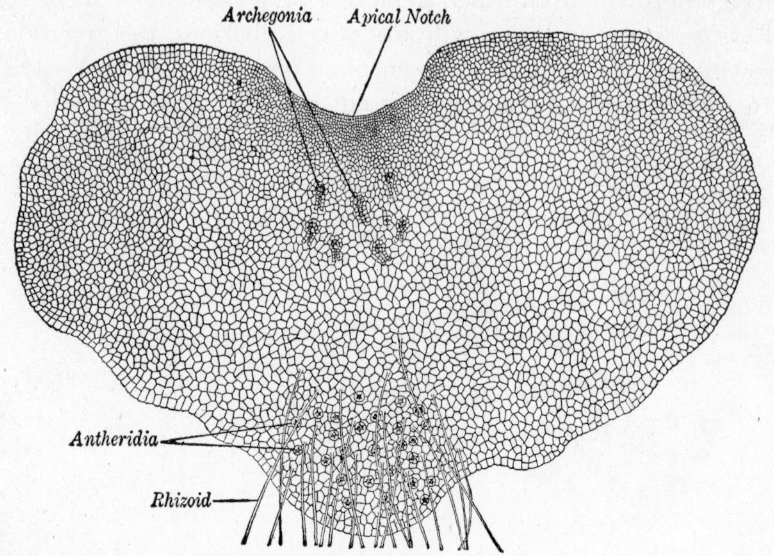

FIG. 317. Mature fern prothallium viewed from below.

organs are produced by the same gametophyte. However, if conditions for growth are not altogether favorable, the resulting prothallia are small and irregular in shape. Such plants commonly

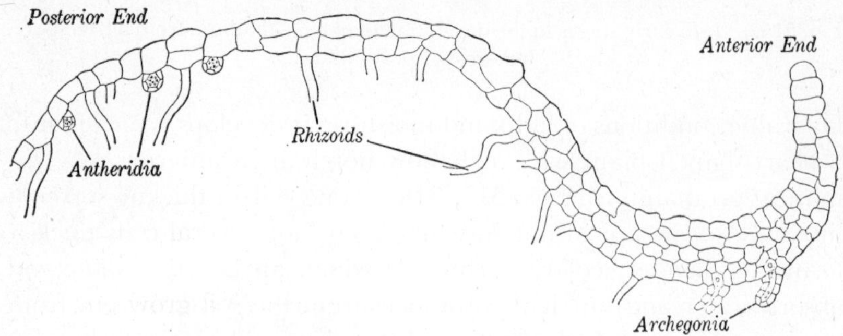

FIG. 318. Vertical lengthwise section of a fern prothallium.

form only antheridia, but if they are placed under better growth conditions they may later develop archegonia. Antheridia may appear on almost any part of the plant but are usually most numerous on the under surface of the older (posterior) portion of the prothallium, where rhizoids also are abundant. Archegonia are usually restricted in their distribution, developing only on the under surface of the cushion of cells just back of the apical notch.

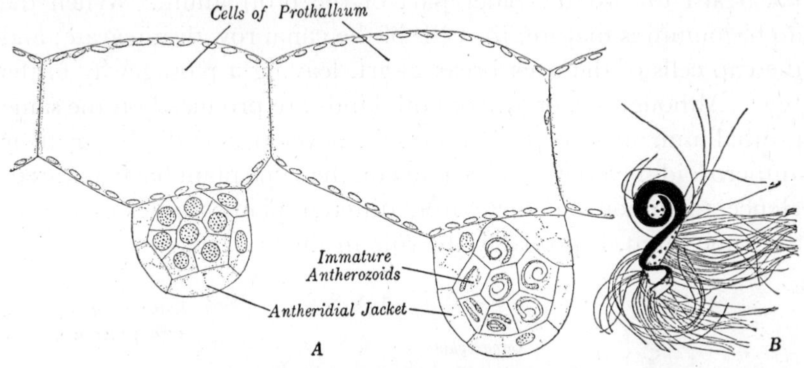

FIG. 319. *A*, antheridia of a fern. *B*, antherozoid of the ostrich fern. *B* after W. N. Steil in the *Botanical Gazette*.

An antheridium (Fig. 319, *A*) is dome-shaped and is much smaller than an antheridium of a moss. An outer layer of a few cells constitutes the jacket. After a series of divisions each interior cell develops into an antherozoid (Fig. 319, *B*), which has the form

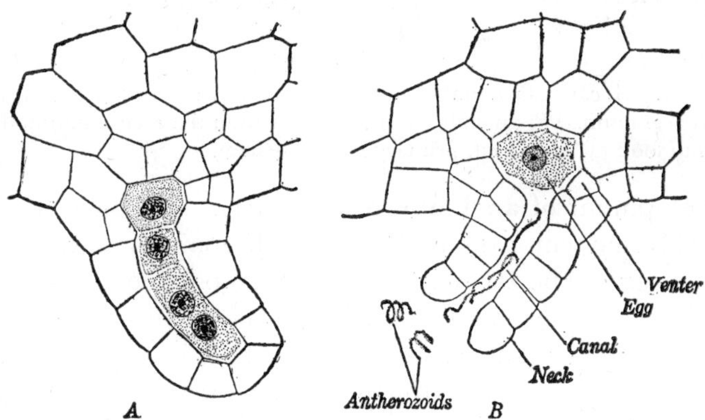

FIG. 320. *A*, nearly mature archegonium of a fern. *B*, archegonium at the time of the entrance of antherozoids.

of a short spiral. Borne on its slender anterior portion are many flagella. This antherozoid differs somewhat in shape and structure from that of a moss, which possesses but two flagella.

An archegonium (Fig. 320) has essentially the same structure as an archegonium of a liverwort or moss, but is smaller and is composed of fewer cells. The venter is imbedded in the cushion of the prothallium, and the short neck of the archegonium usually curves backward toward the older part of the prothallium. When the archegonium is mature, the cells of the canal row disintegrate; and the cap cells of the neck break apart, leaving a passageway to the egg. Although sex organs of both kinds are produced on the same prothallium, most of the antheridia develop and discharge their antherozoids before the archegonia on the same plant have matured. Hence, the union of gametes from different plants, rather than from the same plant, is probably the rule in the bracken.

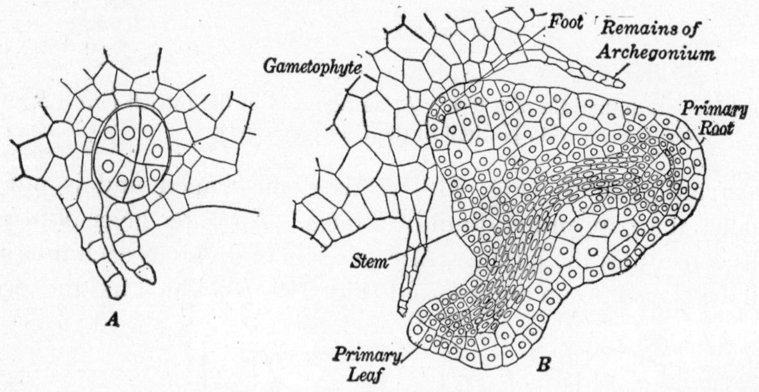

Fig. 321. *A*, early stage in the development of a fern embryo within the venter of an archegonium. *B*, an embryo, still partly within the archegonium, differentiated into foot, primary root, primary leaf, and stem.

Development of an Embryo (Fig. 321). Although many antherozoids may enter the neck of an archegonium, only one unites with the egg. The zygote, like that of a moss, remains within the venter of the archegonium and there develops into a small mass of cells, the *embryo* (young sporophyte). This becomes four-lobed. By further divisions and growth one lobe develops into a *foot*, a small organ imbedded in the prothallial cushion. The foot is a temporary organ, whose function is to absorb from the gametophyte food for the growing embryo. Two other lobes of the embryo enlarge rapidly. One of these becomes a *primary root*, which pushes downward through the surrounding tissues and grows into the soil; the other gives rise to a *primary leaf*, which, growing outward and forward beneath the prothallium, turns upward at the notch and develops a small green blade of simple form. From the fourth lobe the *stem* slowly develops. At first the embryo (young sporophyte) is parasitic upon the gametophyte (Fig. 322). But when the primary leaf and the primary root are fully developed, the young sporophyte is no longer dependent upon the gametophyte, which dies shortly afterward. The stem of the developing sporophyte grows slowly into the soil, producing secondary leaves and secondary (adventitious) roots. After the formation of several secondary leaves and secondary roots, the primary leaf and the primary root die. Thus, the mature sporophyte has been derived from only one lobe of the embryo, namely, that which developed into the stem. The organs derived from the other three lobes functioned only in the early stages of the development of the young sporophyte.

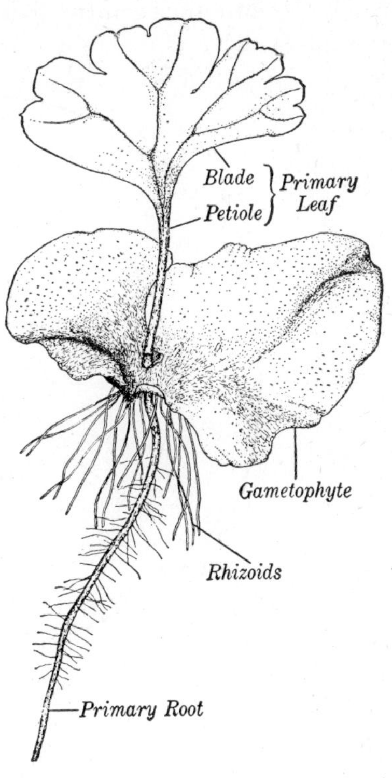

FIG. 322. Young sporophyte still attached to, and parasitic upon, the gametophyte.

Life Cycle (Fig. 323). The life cycle of the bracken, like that of a liverwort or moss, includes two distinct phases or generations. The gametophytic phase begins with a spore possessing *n* chromosomes, which gives rise to a very small green plant, the gametophyte. The gametophyte forms sex organs (antheridia and archegonia), which in turn produce, respectively, antherozoids and eggs. The union of gametes forms a zygote having 2 *n* chromosomes, which begins the sporophytic phase. On germination the zygote forms a parasitic, four-lobed embryo that undergoes differentiation into a foot, a primary root, a primary leaf, and the beginning of a stem. The formation of primary root and primary leaf enables the young sporophyte to become independent. Its independence is perpetuated by the stem segment, which grows out into a large green sporophyte consisting of roots, stem, leaves, and sporophylls. On the sporophylls are borne sporangia which contain spore mother cells. Each spore mother cell by division forms four spores, so completing the life cycle.

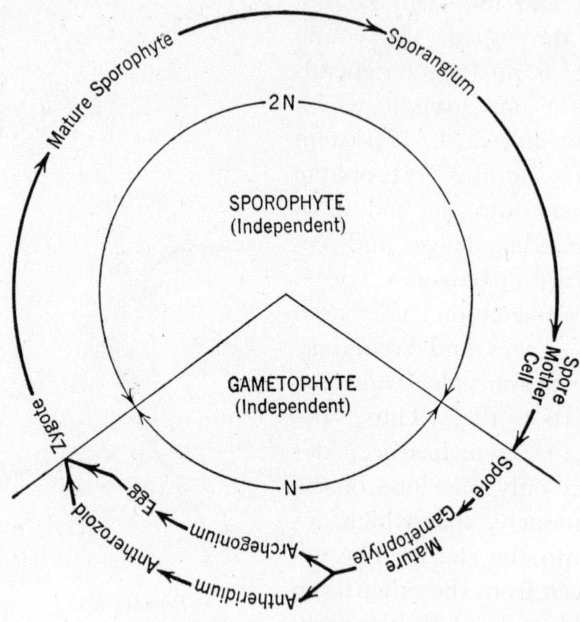

FIG. 323. Life cycle of a fern.

While the life cycles of moss and fern are alike in general outline, there are important differences. The gametophyte of a moss is relatively large and may live for many years, whereas the sporophyte is relatively small and short-lived. In a fern, on the other hand, the gametophyte is very small and comparatively short-lived, but the sporophyte is large and may live for many years. The conspicuous moss plant is the gametophyte; the conspicuous fern plant is the sporophyte.

OTHER FERNS

Leaves. Although the general characteristics of all ferns are sufficiently alike to indicate their relatively close relationship, different species vary in details of form and structure. The variations are evident chiefly in the sporophyte. The gametophytes of most ferns are essentially like that of the bracken.

One conspicuous feature in which ferns differ from one another is in the form of the leaf blade. The walking fern represents a simple

FIG. 324. The polypody (*Polypodium vulgare*). *Left*, a leaf seen from the lower side, showing sori; *right*, a leaf seen from the upper side.

type of fern leaf whose blades are not lobed or divided. A leaf blade of this fern has the shape of a greatly elongated triangle whose slender tip may grow and bend over until it touches the soil. At the point of contact a small bud develops, which may give rise to a new plant. A repetition of this process by successively formed new plants explains the name given this fern. Some ferns, such as the common polypody (Fig. 324), have simple but deeply lobed leaf blades. Others, such as the sensitive fern and the Christmas fern,

FIG. 325. Tree ferns (*Cyathea medullaris*) in a New Zealand rain forest. The lower tree fern *at the extreme left* is *Cyathea dealbata*. Photograph courtesy of T. L. Lancaster.

have leaves once compound. Still others, including the royal fern (Fig. 327) and the lady fern, have leaves twice compound, many of the primary leaflets being divided into secondary leaflets.

The leaves of many tree ferns (Fig. 325) are huge, often 10 to 12 feet in length, and have petioles as large around as a man's arm.

FIG. 326. The interrupted fern (*Osmunda Claytoniana*). The small dark leaflets in the middle portion of the leaf bear sporangia.

A few genera of ferns (occurring mostly in the tropics or subtropics) possess leaves that continue to grow for more than one season. Such leaves may assume a vinelike form, and in one genus (Lygodium) they have been known to reach a length of 100 feet.

Sporangia and Sporophylls. The sporangia of most ferns, unlike those of the bracken, are produced in sharply defined groups (*sori*), which may be rounded or linear, on the under surfaces of the sporophylls. Each sorus is borne upon an elevated cushion of tissue, and in many ferns it is covered by an outgrowth of the leaf (an *indusium*) whose form is characteristic for each genus.

FIG. 327. The royal fern (*Osmunda regalis*). Sporangia are borne on a few leaflets at the upper end of the leaf.

In the bracken it has been seen that all the leaflets of a sporophyll are green, but they also bear sporangia. However, in the sporophylls of the interrupted fern (Fig. 326) the production of sporangia is confined to several pairs of leaflets near the middle of the blade. When these leaflets are mature, they are small and brown and bear on their margins many sporangia. The other leaflets of the sporophyll are large, green, and sterile—that is, they do not bear sporangia. After the spores are shed in the early summer, the spore-bearing leaflets wither and fall off. The sporophylls of the royal

FIG. 328. The grape fern (*Botrychium virginianum*). The leaf is in two distinct parts, one sterile, one fertile.

fern (Fig. 327) also have separate fertile and sterile leaflets, but in this species the fertile leaflets are borne at the apex of the blade. The grape fern (Fig. 328) has a sporophyll consisting of two distinct parts: a flat, several-times-compound blade, which is the chief photosynthetic organ; and a slender, upright portion, which has as its function only the production of spores. In the ferns mentioned thus far, the sporophylls are both photosynthetic and spore-producing. In a few species, however, such as the sensitive fern and the ostrich fern (Fig. 329), these functions have been completely separated. Such ferns bear sterile leaves that are broad,

Fig. 329. The ostrich fern (*Onoclea Struthiopteris*). *Left*, a fertile leaf (sporophyll); *right*, a sterile leaf.

green, and photosynthetic; their sporophylls are leaves of a very different type, brown at maturity, and function only in the production of spores.

Roots. The roots of most ferns, like those of the bracken, are adventitious in origin. Such a continually produced adventitious root system is characteristic also of nearly all other pteridophytes. In many seed plants, on the other hand, the primary root may be persistent and may give rise to all or most of the root system. The roots of ferns are essentially alike in the internal structure and arrangement of their tissues. The number of xylem strands may range from two to ten or more (Fig. 330), but whatever the number

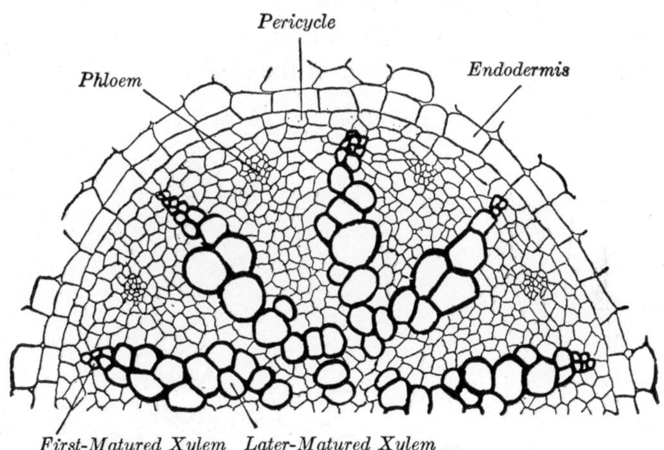

FIG. 330. Cross section of a portion of the stele and cortex in a root of Angiopteris.

there is always an alternation of xylem and phloem strands. This alternate arrangement of xylem and phloem is a character common to the roots of pteridophytes, gymnosperms, and angiosperms. As in seed plants, a pith may be present in the stele of some fern roots; but in most cases the xylem completely occupies the center of the stele.

Stems. The stems of ferns vary greatly in respect to the places in which they grow and in their direction of growth. Some ferns of temperate regions have stems which, like that of the bracken, grow horizontally beneath the soil; in others, such as the royal fern and the ostrich fern, the stem is more or less upright at the surface of the soil. Stems of the latter type are commonly completely covered by the closely overlapping and persistent bases of old leaves together with great numbers of adventitious roots. In the tropics, however, there is much more diversity in habitat and in direction of growth. Here the stems of a few species climb like vines; others grow perched on the limbs and branches of trees; and still others creep on or just beneath the surface of the soil. The tree ferns, found chiefly in the tropics, have erect stems that may reach a height of 40 to 50 feet and commonly appear to be 1 or 2 feet in diameter. Much of this relatively large diameter is due, at least in certain genera, to the presence of tightly interwoven adventitious roots, which give strength and rigidity to the stem.

Unlike their roots, the stems of ferns vary greatly in internal structure. In a few ferns, as in certain species of Gleichenia (Fig. 331, *A*), the xylem fills the center of the stele and is surrounded by

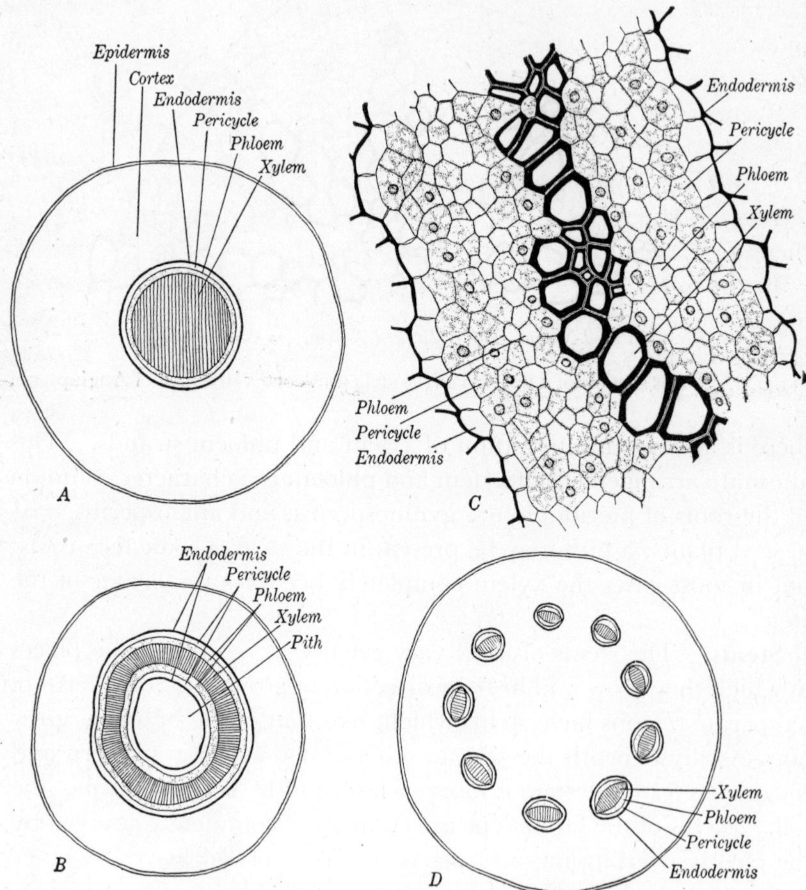

FIG. 331. *A*, diagram of a cross section of the stem of Gleichenia. *B*, diagram of a cross section of the stem of Adiantum. *C*, cellular detail of a portion of the stele of the Adiantum stem. *D*, diagram of a cross section of the stem of Polypodium.

a thin cylinder of phloem, outside which are, successively, pericycle, endodermis, cortex, and epidermis.

In another type, represented by the maidenhair fern (*Adiantum pedatum;* Fig. 331, *B*, *C*), the stele includes a central pith. In the stele is a continuous cylinder of xylem, having on both its inner and outer faces, successively, phloem, pericycle, and endodermis.

In a third type, illustrated by Polypodium (Fig. 331, *D*), small vascular bundles are arranged in a circle about a large central pith. Each bundle is composed of a solid core of xylem, about which are, successively, phloem, pericycle, and endodermis. The arrangement of bundles in the stem of the bracken represents a modification of this type.

A cambium is found in only two genera of ferns. Members of these two genera commonly possess very small upright stems. Since the cambium is relatively inactive, producing only small amounts of secondary xylem and secondary phloem each year, the stems of these ferns remain small and inconspicuous.

Bryophytes and Ferns. Ferns as a class stand conspicuously higher than the bryophytes in the sense that they have advanced further from the primitive condition. Like the bryophytes, the ferns have a distinct alternation of generations. The sporophyte of a bryophyte is small, relatively simple, and is always attached to and partly dependent upon the gametophyte. The sporophyte of a fern, on the other hand, is a relatively large, complex plant, differentiated into stem, leaves, and roots, and has become independent of the gametophyte. The fern gametophyte, however, does not show a corresponding complexity. Although an independent green plant, it is always very small and simple in structure. In spite of the radical change in relative size and complexity whereby the sporophyte has become the large, conspicuous generation, the gametophyte of a fern still retains the function of producing gametes; and the sporophyte continues to produce spores.

CHAPTER XXVII

SOME OTHER PTERIDOPHYTA

EQUISETINEAE (HORSETAILS)

Nature and Distribution. The sporophytes of horsetails differ from those of other pteridophytes in a number of respects. The stems appear jointed, having well-defined nodes and internodes. At each node the leaves, which are usually small and scalelike, are borne in whorls. The surface of the stem in each internode is longitudinally ribbed, the parallel ribs extending through the length of the internode. The sporangium-bearing structures are compactly grouped, forming a cone at the end of a branch. On each sporangium-bearing structure are several saclike sporangia.

The class Equisetineae includes but one living genus, *Equisetum*, whose members are found on all the continents except Australia. Only about 30 species of this genus have been described, as compared with about 9000 ferns. These few living horsetails are related to a group of plants which during at least one period of the earth's history seem to have formed a conspicuous feature of its vegetation. Some of these ancient plants were treelike, but the present-day species are mostly small. In tropical South America the stems of one species grow to a height of about 30 feet. Its stems, however, are very slender and lean upon the shrubs and trees among which they grow.

Equisetum thrives in a wide variety of habitats. Certain species grow in shallow ponds and swamps; others in meadows and damp, shaded places; and still others in relatively dry and exposed situations such as sandy embankments.

Sporophyte. *Equisetum arvense* (Fig. 332) grows in a variety of places but is frequently found in dry locations. The sporophyte consists of a horizontal, branching underground stem bearing aerial branches, some sterile, some fertile, which grow upward from nodes of the stem. The stem bears at each of its nodes a whorl of brown, slender, scalelike leaves which are more or less united; and from the nodes grow also slender, branching roots. A sterile aerial branch is green and produces a whorl of slender green branches at each node. These latter secondary branches may in turn bear at some

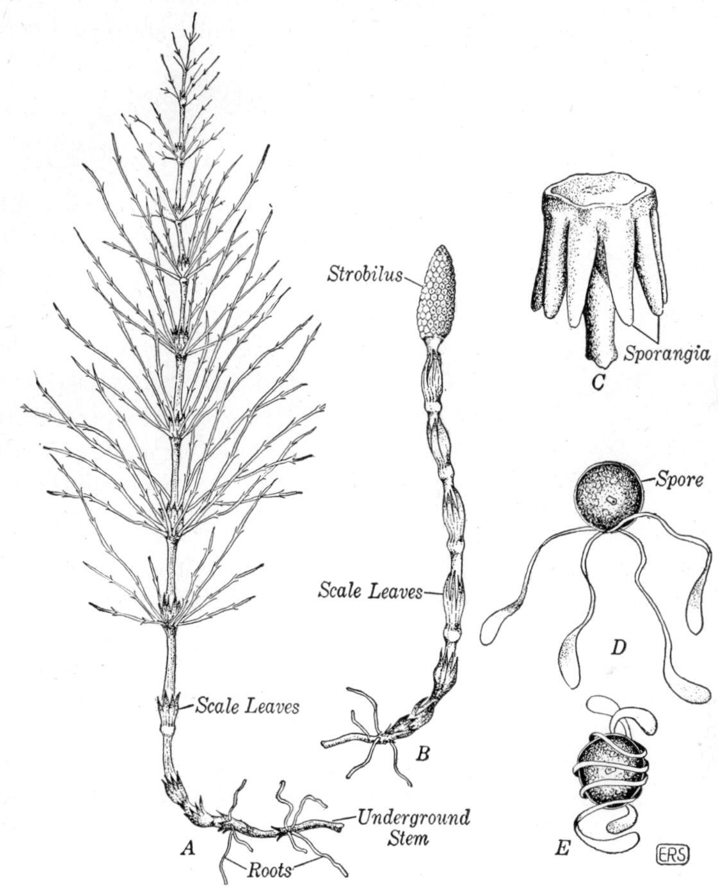

FIG. 332. Sporophyte of *Equisetum arvense*. *A*, sterile aerial branch. *B*, fertile aerial branch bearing a strobilus. *C*, sporangiophore and sporangia. *D*, *E*, mature spores with spiral bands uncoiled (*D*) and coiled (*E*).

of their nodes smaller whorls of branches. The bushy appearance resulting from this arrangement of branches suggested the name "Equisetum" or "horsetail." Each node of an aerial branch bears a sheath of small, scalelike leaves somewhat similar to those on the underground stem. The scalelike aerial leaves play little part in food-making; but the green aerial branches are well adapted to carry on photosynthesis. The internodes of these aerial branches are longitudinally ridged.

A cross section through an internode of an aerial branch (Fig. 333) shows a well-defined epidermis, cortex, and stele. The thick outer walls of the epidermal cells are made hard and rough by an

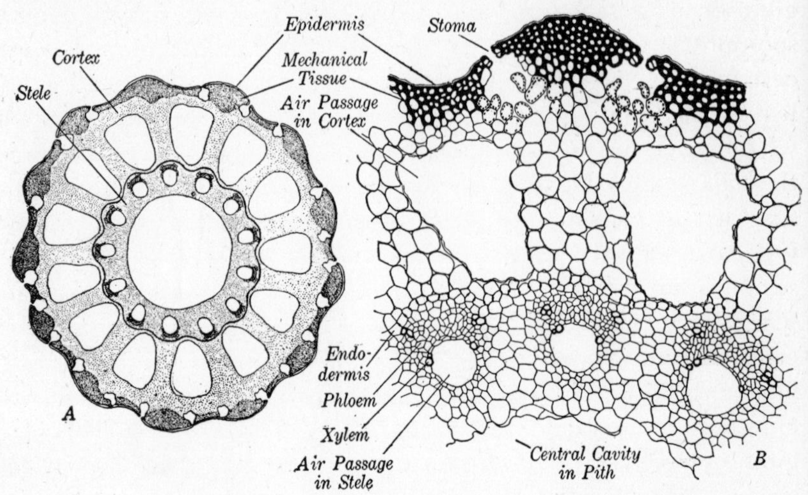

FIG. 333. *A*, cross section through an internode of an aerial branch of Equisetum. Diagrammatic. *B*, portion of a section more highly magnified.

abundant deposit of silica. It is the presence of silica that led to the use in earlier days of some of the larger species of Equisetum as "scouring rushes." The cortex contains a vertical strand of mechanical cells beneath each external ridge and a vertical air passage beneath each furrow between two ridges. Stomata are confined to those portions of the epidermis between the ridges. Each stoma opens into an intercellular space bordered by thin-walled, chlorophyll-containing cells of the cortex. It is in these cells that much of the photosynthetic activity of the plant occurs. An endodermis marks the inner boundary of the cortex. The pericycle, like the endodermis, consists of a single layer of cells. Within the pericycle the vascular bundles are arranged in an interrupted cylinder, each bundle lying opposite an external ridge of the stem. A bundle consists of xylem toward the inside and phloem toward the outside. On the inner side of each bundle is an air passage. The central portion of the branch is hollow, in consequence of the breaking down of most of the cells of the pith.

Spore Formation. The fertile branches are usually first to appear above the ground in the spring. They are yellowish, unbranched, and bear a conspicuous sheath of scale leaves at each node. At the apex of each branch are a number of compact whorls of sporangium-bearing structures forming a *strobilus*. Each sporangium-bearing structure is called a *sporangiophore* rather than a sporophyll (the term used in the case of a fern) because it is not certain that these sporangium-bearing organs of Equisetum are leaves. A sporangiophore (Fig. 332, *C*) has a slender stalk, at whose outer end is a shieldlike portion flattened at right angles to the stalk. This flat outer portion of the sporangiophore is regularly six-sided in consequence of the lateral pressure of its neighbors. On its inner side, and therefore toward the central axis of the strobilus, are borne a variable number of slender saclike sporangia which have no stalks. A sporangium on approaching maturity contains many spore mother cells, each of which divides to form four spores. In the two nuclear divisions which occur here, the chromosome number is reduced. When fully mature the sporangium opens by a longitudinal slit, which permits the escape of the spores. Shortly after the spores have been liberated, the entire fertile branch withers and dies.

The outer layer of the spore wall becomes divided (Fig. 332, *D*, *E*) into four spiral bands before a spore is shed from the sporangium. The bands, which remain attached to the spore at a common point, are extremely sensitive to changes in moisture, straightening when dry and curling about the spore when moist. The spores, because of the entangling of their bands, are frequently shed in small clusters and may germinate to form groups of gametophytes.

Gametophyte and Embryo. A spore is relatively large and contains many chloroplasts. Its germination results in the formation of a small green prothallium (Fig. 334, *A*). This prothallium differs from that of a fern both in its form and in the location of the sex organs. When mature it is usually a disk-shaped cushion several cells in thickness, from whose upper surface arise irregularly lobed, flattened branches, each one cell in thickness. Rhizoids grow from the lower surface of the cushion. Antheridia are borne usually near the upper ends of the vertical branches; archegonia, on the upper surface of the cushion at the bases of the branches. An antherozoid resembles one of a fern in having many flagella.

An embryo sporophyte (Fig. 334, *B*) in its early stages of development is in some respects similar to that of a fern. Lobes of a young embryo develop, respectively, into a foot, an erect primary stem bearing at each node a whorl usually of three leaves, and a primary root. The primary stem is green and remains very small and

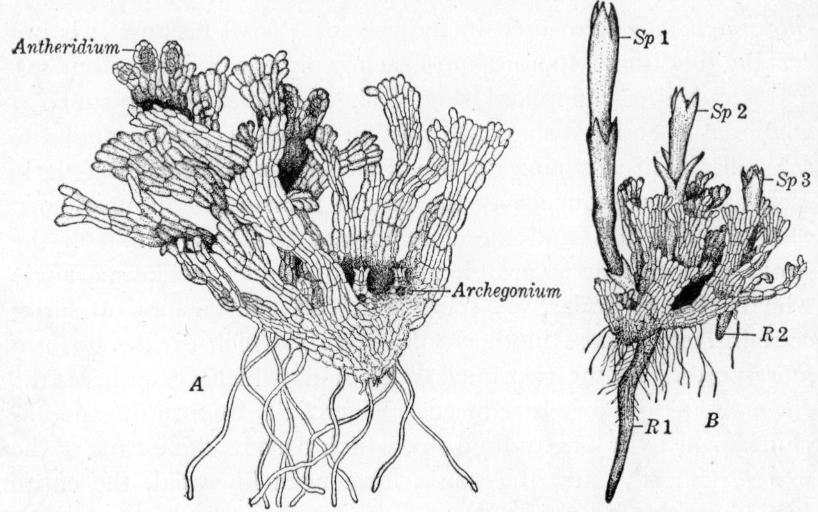

Fig. 334. *A*, mature gametophyte of Equisetum. *B*, a gametophyte bearing two young sporophytes. *Sp* 1 and *Sp* 2 are branches of one sporophyte; *Sp* 3 is separate. *R* 1 and *R* 2 are the respective primary roots of the two sporophytes.

slender. At its base a bud arises that grows into a larger, erect green branch. In like manner, at the base of this first branch a second erect branch arises, and the process is repeated. Eventually one of the later-formed branches grows horizontally through the soil and develops into the characteristic underground stem from which sterile and fertile aerial branches subsequently arise.

LYCOPODINEAE (CLUB MOSSES)

Nature. The main genera of club mosses are Lycopodium and Selaginella. The sporophytes in both genera are evergreen and are always small and inconspicuous. The leaves of living species are small but photosynthetic; and each possesses but one vascular bundle, which extends the length of the blade. The sporophylls are usually grouped in cones at the ends of branches. A sporophyll bears a single sporangium on its upper face near its base. Like the horsetails, the club mosses are related to an ancient group of plants once very abundant. Some of these ancient club mosses developed into large trees.

LYCOPODIUM

Distribution. Sporophytes of species of Lycopodium (Figs. 335, 336) are sometimes collected and sold under the names of club moss or ground pine for Christmas decorations. The genus is of world-wide distribution in both temperate and tropical regions. About 175 species of Lycopodium have been described. Many tropical species grow on the trunks and branches of trees. A majority of those of temperate regions have prostrate stems growing on or beneath the surface of the soil and bearing adventitious roots and erect branches. The stems and branches that grow above ground are covered with small, sessile green leaves, which are relatively simple in structure. A stem or branch has an epidermis, a thick cortex, and a stele. The structure of the stele varies with the species as well as with the direction of growth of the stem.

Sporophylls and Spores. Lycopodium forms *sporophylls.* Each is a small leaf

FIG. 335. A club moss, the "ground pine" (*Lycopodium obscurum*); strobili are borne at the ends of upright leafy branches.

which bears on its upper side and near the base a single sporangium. In some species of Lycopodium, the sporophylls are not readily distinguishable, either by appearance or by position,

Fig. 336. A club moss (*Lycopodium clavatum*); strobili at the ends of stalks which bear minute leaves.

from the sterile (foliage) leaves. In other species the sporophylls are borne, more or less compactly grouped, on the terminal portions of some of the upright branches, which thus constitute *strobili* (Figs. 335, 336). In such a case the sporophylls are smaller and contain a lesser proportion of chlorophyll than the foliage leaves. Each sporangium has a short stalk (Fig. 337, *B*, *C*) and a jacket several cells in thickness. Within the sporangium are developed many spore mother cells, each of which finally divides to form four spores.

Gametophyte and Embryo. The gametophytes of Lycopodium can not readily be grown in culture and consequently are not so easily obtained as are those of ferns and Equisetum. The spores of many species lie dormant for several years after being shed. The gametophytes developing from spores grow slowly to become small, subterranean, saprophytic structures. In some species the gametophyte has the form of a top or of a turnip (Fig. 338); in others it resembles a convoluted disk. Whatever the form, a fungus invades

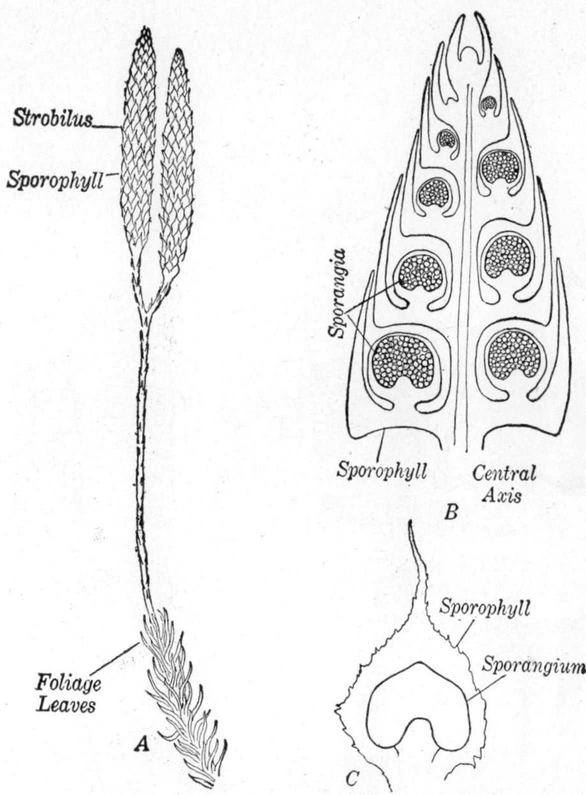

FIG. 337. Lycopodium. *A*, branch bearing two strobili (compare Fig. 336). *B*, lengthwise section of the tip of a strobilus. Diagrammatic. *C*, sporophyll bearing a sporangium.

the tissues of the gametophyte and probably plays some part in its nutrition. Antheridia and archegonia are borne on the upper surface of the gametophyte. In general plan these sex organs resemble somewhat those of the bracken except for the fact that the antheridia are imbedded in the gametophyte. An antherozoid, unlike one of a fern or of Equisetum, has two flagella, resembling in this respect the antherozoids of liverworts and mosses.

The zygote divides by a transverse wall into an outer and an inner cell. The outer cell ordinarily elongates, becoming a *sus-*

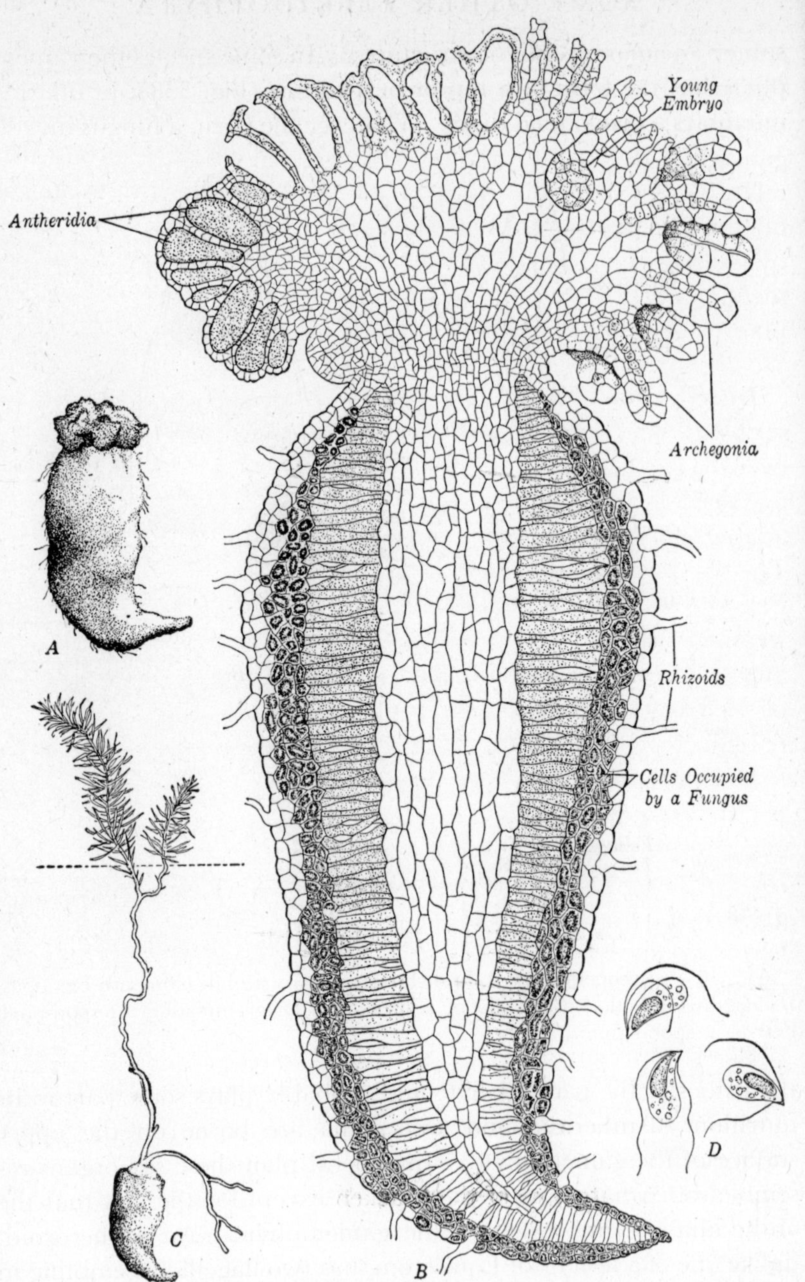

FIG. 338. *A*, an underground gametophyte of *Lycopodium clavatum*. *B*, a median lengthwise section of the same, highly magnified. *C*, a gametophyte with young sporophyte attached. *D*, antherozoids. All after Bruchmann.

pensor. The inner cell, which has been pushed by the elongation of the suspensor deeper into the tissue of the gametophyte, develops into an embryo. The suspensor is therefore only a temporary organ, which functions in bringing the embryo into a better nutritive relation with the gametophyte. The embryo is at first dependent upon the gametophyte, securing its food by means of a foot. Later, by the growth of stem and leaves above the soil and by the development of a first root in the soil, the embryo becomes an independent plant.

THE SMALLER CLUB MOSS, SELAGINELLA

Distribution. About 700 species of Selaginella have been described. The members of this genus, although widely distributed over the earth, are most abundant in the tropics. Of the relatively few species growing in temperate regions, some are particularly adapted to dry environments, living on rocks or on dry sandy soil. The so-called "resurrection plant" of the southwest United States is a species of Selaginella living in such a habitat. When the weather is dry, the plant rolls up into a more or less compact ball and may survive a considerable period of drought. Other species of temperate regions thrive best in relatively moist and shaded habitats.

Sporophyte. The conspicuous plant, as in the case of a fern, is the sporophyte (Fig. 339). In some species the branching stem grows along the ground and bears two rows of small leaves and two rows of larger leaves. In other species the branches of the stem grow more or less upright, and the leaves are uniform in size. The leaves are always narrowly triangular and pointed. Roots develop directly from the stem in certain species; in others, they arise at the ends of short, leafless branches.

The stem in some species contains a small, centrally placed stele; in other species there are several independent steles. The xylem of a stele is surrounded successively by phloem, pericycle, and endodermis, the latter in some species being peculiar in that it is interrupted by large intercellular spaces. The inner part of the cortex is commonly composed of thin-walled cells, but the cells of the outer portion are usually thick-walled. An epidermis encloses the cortex.

Sporophylls and Sporangia. Selaginella shares with some species of Lycopodium the characteristic of producing more or less compact strobili on the terminal portions of many of the branches. A strobilus possesses many sporophylls, each bearing on its upper side and near its base a small, short-stalked sporangium. However,

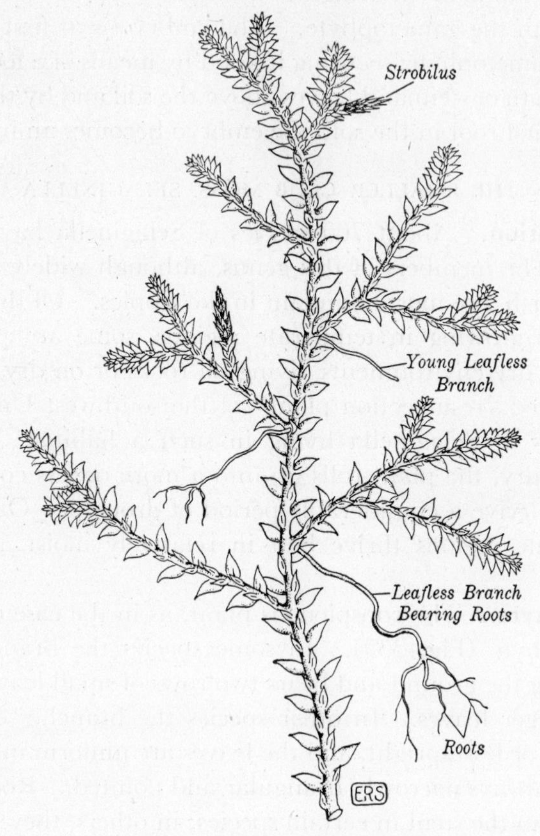

FIG. 339. Portion of a mature sporophyte of Selaginella.

the sporangia, instead of being all alike as in Lycopodium, are of two distinct kinds (Fig. 340, *A*). A sporangium of one kind contains commonly four large spores; one of the other kind contains many very small spores. The large spores are *megaspores*, the sporangium which contains them is a *megasporangium*, and the leaf on which this sporangium is borne is a *megasporophyll*. Similarly, the small spores are *microspores*, the sporangium which contains them is a *microsporangium*, and the leaf on which this sporangium is borne is a *microsporophyll*. The distribution of micro- and megasporophylls upon the axis of the strobilus differs. In some species the lower sporophylls are megasporophylls, the upper are microsporophylls; in others (Fig. 340, *A*) one side of the strobilus bears

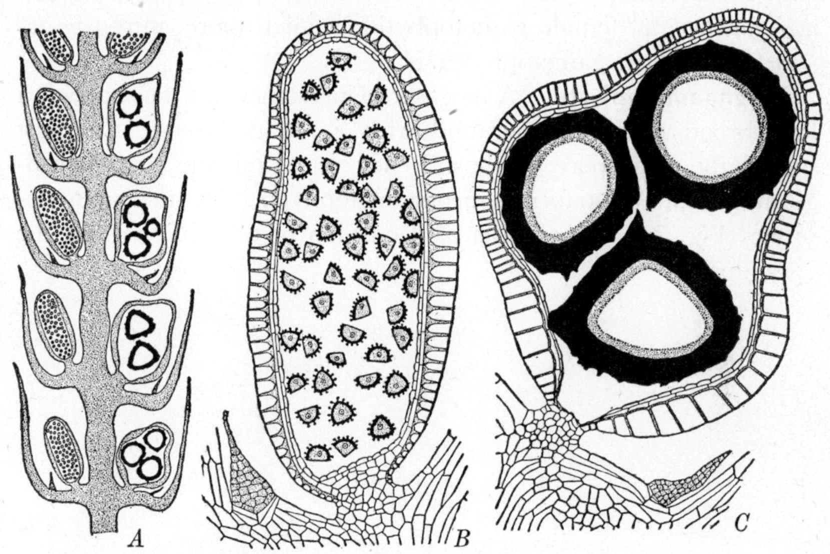

Fig. 340. *A*, portion of a lengthwise section of a strobilus of *Selaginella elegans*. *B*, section of a microsporangium. *C*, section of a megasporangium. All from G. M. Smith, *Cryptogamic Botany*, published by the McGraw-Hill Book Company.

microsporophylls, the other side megasporophylls; in still other species the two types of sporophylls are intermingled. A mature sporangium of either type has a short stalk and a jacket several cells in thickness. In most species megasporangia are larger than microsporangia and are generally lobed, the lobes corresponding to the positions of the megaspores within.

All sporangia develop alike to the stage at which they contain numerous spore mother cells. In the microsporangia most of the spore mother cells divide to form four spores each. The result is the production of a large number of spores (microspores) within the sporangium. In megasporangia all the spore mother cells but one usually disintegrate. The persisting spore mother cell divides to form four spores (megaspores), some or all of which increase greatly in size and develop thick corrugated walls. In a few species of Selaginella more than one megaspore mother cell may persist and function; consequently, in such a case, more than four megaspores may be found in a megasporangium.

The difference in size between the two kinds of spores is associated with a difference in their function. A megaspore develops into a *megagametophyte* (female gametophyte); a microspore, into a *microgametophyte* (male gametophyte).

Megagametophyte. A megaspore has somewhat the shape of a low, broad triangular pyramid with a rounded base. In most species the megaspore, while still enclosed within the megasporangium, germinates to form a megagametophyte. The megagametophyte (Fig. 341, *A*) consists of a cushion of cells just within the

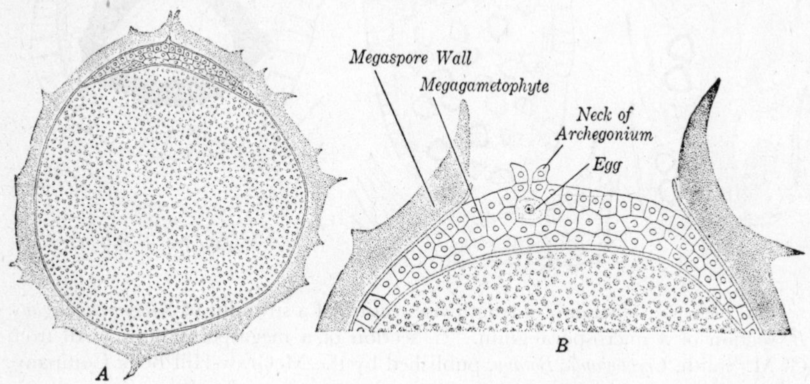

Fig. 341. *A*, section through a developing megagametophyte of Selaginella. *B*, portion of a mature megagametophyte.

pointed end of the spore wall, and below the cushion a large multinucleate cell occupying most of the space within the spore wall. On the cellular cushion archegonia are formed. At about this stage of development the pointed end of the megaspore wall cracks open, exposing the archegonia and some of the neighboring tissue (Fig. 341, *B*). Although the exposed portion may protrude and develop a small amount of chlorophyll, the megagametophyte is dependent chiefly upon the food manufactured by the sporophyte and stored in the spore. In nearly all species of Selaginella the megasporangia break open; and the megagametophytes, having reached some stage of the development described above, fall to the ground. If the megagametophytes are still immature, further development occurs on the soil, provided conditions are favorable.

Microgametophyte. A microspore (Fig. 342, *A*, *B*), except for its much smaller size, closely resembles a megaspore. It germinates while still within the microsporangium. The first division results in the formation of a large and a small cell, both of which lie wholly within the microspore wall (Fig. 342, *C*). The smaller is the *prothallial cell*, so called because this single cell is thought to correspond to the vegetative tissue of a fern prothallium. From the larger cell, by further divisions, is developed a central group of cells surrounded by a single layer of jacket cells (Fig. 342, *D*). Each cell of the central group is finally transformed into a spirally coiled antherozoid (Fig. 342, *F*) with two flagella, the jacket cells meanwhile having disintegrated.

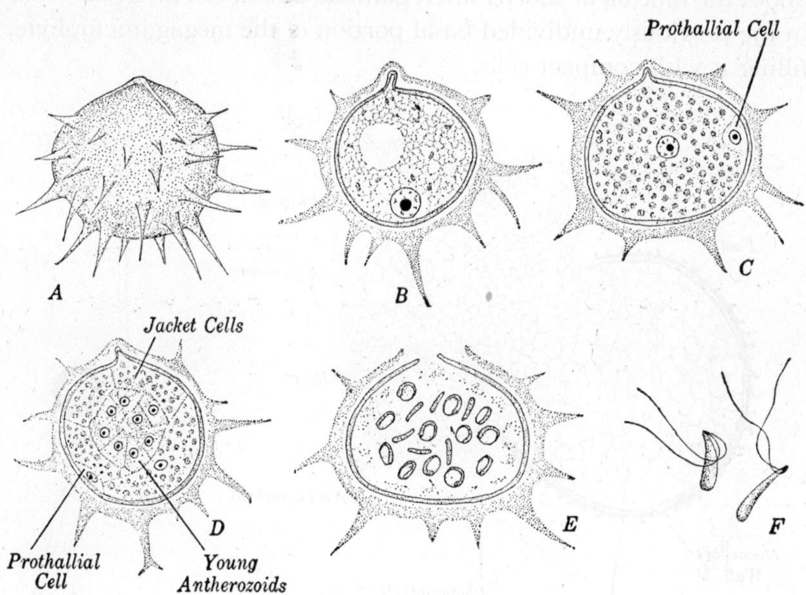

FIG. 342. *A*, microspore of Selaginella. *B*, same in section. *C*, two-celled microgametophyte. *D*, nearly mature microgametophyte. *E*, mature microgametophyte. *F*, antherozoids.

Gametic Union. The microsporangia of Selaginella become mature and break open before the microgametophytes that they enclose have reached maturity. In many species these developing microgametophytes are shed from the sporangium and fall to the ground, where they complete their development. After antherozoids have been formed, the layers of the spore wall break open, and the antherozoids are liberated. If the micro- and megagametophytes lie near together on the ground, a film of water connecting them will enable the antherozoids to swim to the archegonia. As in mosses and ferns, one antherozoid unites with each egg. At about the time of, or shortly after, gametic union, cell divisions occur in the previously undivided basal portion of the megagametophyte, filling it with compact cells.

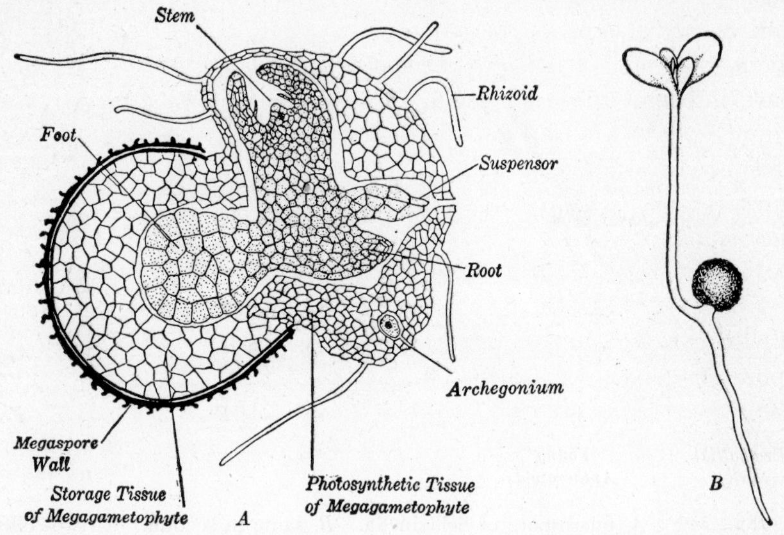

FIG. 343. Megagametophyte of Selaginella with a young sporophyte; redrawn from Bergen and Davis. *B*, older sporophyte still attached to the megagametophyte.

Embryo. The zygote divides into two cells. The daughter cell nearer the neck of the archegonium elongates, forming a *suspensor* which pushes the other daughter cell farther into the tissue of the megagametophyte. The latter daughter cell develops into an embryo, consisting of a foot, a stem bearing two primary leaves, and a primary root (Fig. 343, *A*). The primary root and the stem bearing the primary leaves grow outward from the tissue of the megagametophyte, and the young sporophyte becomes independent (Fig. 343, *B*). As the stem continues its growth, there develop from it secondary leaves and adventitious roots; the primary leaves eventually disappear.

An Approach to the Seed Habit. Although the history of the gametophytes recited above is characteristic of many species of Selaginella, a modification of the story is found in certain species. These latter forms are of interest because they closely approach the seed habit characteristic of spermatophytes. In these species, megagametophytes begin to develop in the manner already described. When a megasporangium is mature, it cracks open but not sufficiently to permit the escape of the developing megagametophytes. The microsporangia, however, when mature burst open, and the developing microgametophytes are thrown out. Some of them, sifting down between the sporophylls, fall by chance into the partly opened megasporangia. Lying now in the same sporangium, the two kinds of gametophytes complete their development. If sufficient water is present, gametic union occurs. At some time later, the opening of the megasporangium becomes larger, and the megagametophytes with the developing embryos may fall to the ground.

Life Cycle (Fig. 344). A strobilus produces two kinds of sporophylls, two kinds of sporangia, and two kinds of spores. A megaspore develops into a megagametophyte, which forms archegonia, each containing an egg. A microspore develops into a microgametophyte, which produces antherozoids. The union of antherozoid and egg forms a zygote. The zygote grows into an embryo parasitic on the megagametophyte. By further growth and development the embryo becomes a mature sporophyte—an independent plant composed of stem, roots, and leaves and bearing strobili.

As in a moss or fern, the chromosome number is doubled in gametic union; it is reduced in the two successive nuclear divisions which occur when four megaspores are formed from a megaspore mother cell and likewise in the nuclear divisions involved when four microspores are formed from each microspore mother cell. In Selaginella, therefore, as in mosses and ferns, the gametophytic generation (here including megagametophyte and microgametophyte) is marked by the presence in each of its cells of n chromosomes; and the sporophytic generation, by the presence in each of its cells of $2n$ chromosomes.

New Features in Selaginella. From an evolutionary standpoint, Selaginella shows certain marked advances over the pteridophytes previously described. One notable advance is in the production of two kinds of spores, each of which develops into a specific kind of gametophyte. A microgametophyte is a greatly reduced

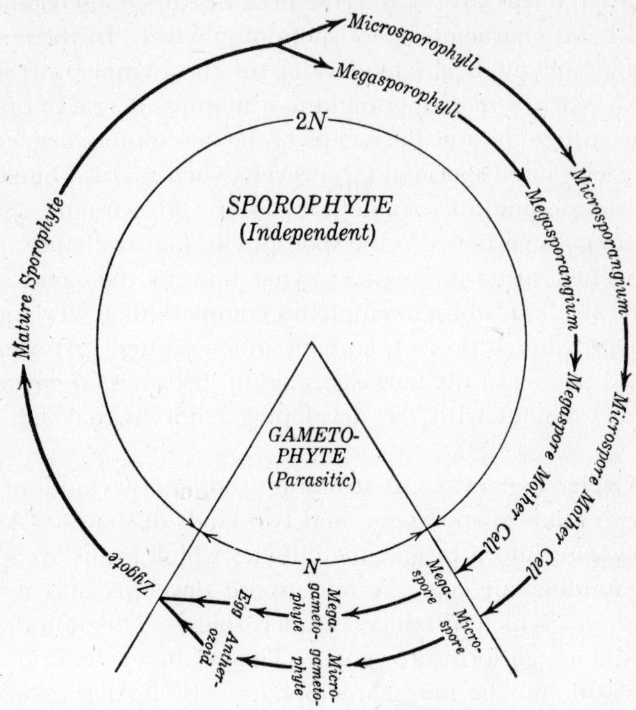

FIG. 344. Life cycle of Selaginella.

plant in that it develops to maturity within the wall of the microspore and consists of relatively few cells. In the same sense, a megagametophyte also is greatly reduced as compared with the gametophyte (prothallium) of a fern. A megagametophyte develops chiefly within the wall of the megaspore and barely protrudes from this wall when mature. The male (micro-) and female (mega-) gametophytes are markedly different in size and structure. But in Selaginella sexual differentiation is not limited to the gametophyte, as it is in bryophytes and ferns. Instead, this differentiation has been pushed back, as it were, to the sporangia, which are structures belonging to the sporophyte. Hence, the difference between the sporangia, although these are strictly asexual reproductive structures, is nevertheless actually a sexual difference.

Another important difference concerns the nutrition of the gametophytes. A microgametophyte, having no chlorophyll, is entirely dependent upon foods received from the sporophyte; that is, it has become indirectly parasitic upon the sporophyte. A megagametophyte also is chiefly dependent upon food derived from the sporophyte, although in its later development that part of a megagametophyte which is exposed to the light by the cracking of the megaspore wall may develop chlorophyll and carry on a limited amount of photosynthesis. Thus, the nutritive relationships which existed between gametophyte and sporophyte in the mosses and liverworts have been virtually reversed in Selaginella. In a moss or liverwort, the sporophyte is in part parasitic upon the gametophyte. In Selaginella, the gametophytes have become in effect parasitic upon the sporophyte.

A third important characteristic of certain species of Selaginella is that a young microgametophyte, on being discharged from its sporangium, may sift into a partly open megasporangium and there, in close proximity to a developing megagametophyte, continue its development.

A fourth new feature in the species just referred to is that the megagametophyte, surrounded largely by the megaspore wall, may remain within the partly open megasporangium during gametic union and the early stages of embryo development. Hence, these species of Selaginella approach closely the formation of a seed, whose production is one of the outstanding features of seed plants.

SUMMARY

The ferns, horsetails, and club mosses are representatives of the division Pteridophyta, whose members stand at a higher evolutionary level than do bryophytes. Some pteridophytes approach but do not attain the seed habit characteristic of seed plants.

The sporophyte of a pteridophyte is in general a relatively large, independent plant differentiated into stem, leaves, and roots. Sporangia are usually borne on leaves. Sporophylls are therefore an important feature of this division of the plant kingdom. In some pteridophytes the sporophylls bear sporangia in which the spores are all alike; in others there are two sorts of sporophylls, of sporangia, and of spores. In certain pteridophytes sporophylls are grouped together, forming cones (strobili).

The gametophytes of pteridophytes, always small, are variable from genus to genus, both in structure and in method of nutrition. Some gametophytes, such as those of most ferns and of Equisetum, are green, independent prothallia; others, including those of Lycopodium, grow underground and are saprophytic.

Those pteridophytes with two sorts of spores have extremely small, simple gametophytes which, developing almost entirely within the old spore wall, are indirectly parasitic upon the old sporophytes. The antherozoids, however, are motile; and the presence of external water is still essential to gametic union. A sporophyte begins its existence as a parasite but eventually, through the production of stem, roots, and leaves, becomes an independent plant.

CHAPTER XXVIII

GYMNOSPERMAE (GYMNOSPERMS)

Seed Plants. The Spermatophyta, or seed plants, are the most advanced division of the plant kingdom. It is in this division that the sporophytic plant body reaches its greatest size and complexity. On the other hand, the gametophytes are always of microscopic size and directly parasitic upon the sporophyte. Spermatophytes make up the dominant vegetation on much of the earth's surface, and representatives of the division are to be found in the widest possible variety of habitats. From the economic standpoint they are of prime importance to mankind. They supply most of our food, clothing, shelter, and medical supplies.

Spermatophytes are divided into *gymnosperms*, whose seeds are borne exposed on sporophylls, and *angiosperms*, whose seeds are enclosed by one or more sporophylls. Of nearly 200,000 known living species of spermatophytes, less than 700 are gymnosperms.

Gymnosperms. The geological record indicates that during certain periods of the earth's history gymnosperms were relatively abundant. Indeed, some genera and even orders, now extinct, are known only from their fossil remains; and one order is represented by but a single surviving species. The largest orders of living gymnosperms are the *Cycadales* and the *Coniferales*. The Cycadales are relatively rare plants of tropical or subtropical regions; the Coniferales, which include the pines, spruces, and related trees and shrubs, are mainly inhabitants of the temperate regions, where some of them form extensive forests.

ZAMIA

Sporophyte. The Cycadales, of which the genus *Zamia* may be taken as an example, are the most primitive of living seed plants and in certain respects show marked similarities to the ferns. Species of Zamia (Fig. 345) occur in portions of Florida, Mexico, and tropical South America. The plant (sporophyte), which commonly grows in open woodlands, rarely attains a height of more than four feet. Its stem is short, thick, erect, and sometimes branched, its greatest portion frequently being underground. At the center of a young stem (Fig. 346) is a large pith, surrounded by a cylinder of small vascular bundles. Each bundle consists, like a bundle of a dicotyledonous stem, of xylem, cambium, and phloem. As the stem grows older, only small amounts of secondary xylem and secondary phloem are added by the activity of the cambium. The new xylem so formed is not differentiated into annual rings and is interrupted by relatively wide rays. In the thick cortex starch is stored, the amount of starch being so great that the plant was used as a source of food by the Seminole Indians under the name of "conti."

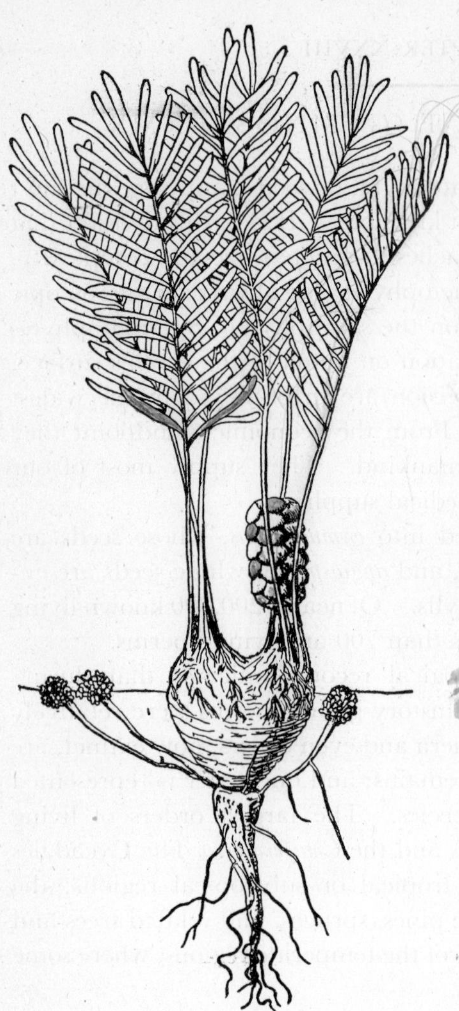

FIG. 345. Mature sporophyte of Zamia bearing a carpellate strobilus.

The foliage leaves arise at the apex of the stem, some new leaves usually being produced each year. The leaves are leathery in texture and resemble those of many ferns in being pinnately divided. The tip of each young leaf unrolls slightly, in this respect also somewhat resembling a fern leaf. The individual leaflets, however, do not unroll, as is the case in a pinnately divided fern leaf. A leaf of Zamia may live for several years. As the older leaves die and wither, their bases remain for a short time attached to the stem.

The relatively large tap root gives rise to a few slender branch roots. A blue-green alga gains entrance into the cortices of some of the smaller roots; the stimulus resulting from its presence causes

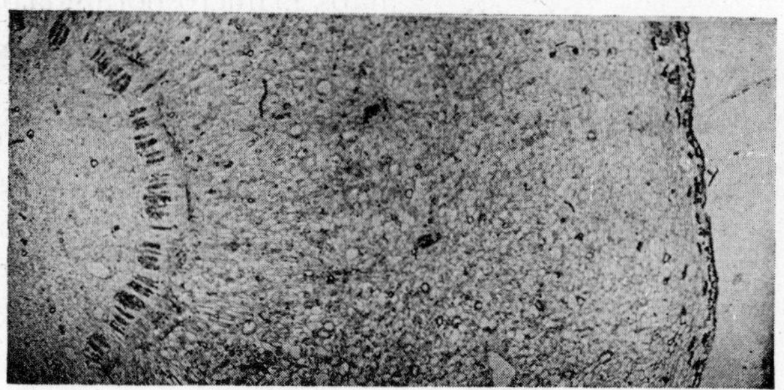

FIG. 346. Cross section of a portion of the stem of Zamia.

each invaded root to change its direction of growth and to produce a compact cluster of small, tubercular branch roots at or near the surface of the soil.

In a root, primary xylem and primary phloem alternate in the radial arrangement characteristic of roots. Secondary xylem and secondary phloem are formed by cambial activity. In the younger portions of a tap root the cortex is relatively thick and stores abundant food. In older portions a cork cambium is formed in the pericycle. After this cork cambium has produced cork cells on its outer side, the cortex and epidermis are sloughed off.

Strobili and Sporophylls. Zamia, like Selaginella, produces two sorts of sporophylls, microsporophylls and megasporophylls. But, unlike Selaginella, the sporophylls differ greatly in structure and appearance from foliage leaves, and the two sorts of sporophylls are borne on separate plants. On a *staminate* plant microsporophylls are compactly grouped on the terminal portions of upright branches, which constitute *staminate strobili* (cones; Fig. 347). In like manner, on a *carpellate* plant megasporophylls are borne, compactly grouped, in *carpellate strobili* (Fig. 349). Any one plant produces only carpellate or only staminate strobili.

Each microsporophyll in a staminate strobilus consists of a short stalk and a flattened, expanded portion (probably representing a reduced blade) on the under surface of which are from 30 to 40 small microsporangia. Within each microsporangium (Fig. 348), as within a microsporangium of Selaginella, many microspore mother cells are produced; and each microspore mother cell gives rise by division to four microspores. Since a microsporangium produces about 500 microspores and since there are on an average perhaps 35 microsporangia on each of the 200 or more microsporophylls, a single strobilus may produce 3,000,000 or more microspores.

FIG. 347. *A*, staminate strobilus of Zamia. *B*, microsporophylls bearing on their lower surfaces many microsporangia.

A megasporophyll (Fig. 349, *B*, *C*, *D*) is larger and fleshier than a microsporophyll. When mature, it consists of a stalk and an expanded outer portion; to the inner side of the latter—that is, to the side toward the central axis of the strobilus—are attached two *ovules*.

An ovule (Fig. 350) begins its development as a bluntly conical protuberance, the *nucellus* (megasporangium), on the inner surface of the expanded portion of the young megasporophyll. From its base an enclosing *integument* grows about the nucellus but leaves a small tubular opening, the *micropyle*, leading to the outer end of the nucellus. The integument is a structure not found in pteridophytes, the sporangium proper being the nucellus. But since nucellus and integument are closely combined, the two together are commonly treated as a single organ, the ovule. As development continues, a small depression (*pollen chamber*) is developed at the end of the nucellus next the micropyle. Only one megaspore mother cell becomes differentiated within the nucellus, and so but four megaspores are formed. These megaspores lie in an axial row in the central part of the nucellus.

Megagametophyte (Fig. 350, *B*, *C*). One fundamentally important feature of seed plants is the firm and permanent enclosure of the megagametophyte not only within the wall of the megaspore but, still more important, within the nucellus (megasporangium), which in turn is enclosed by the integument. The megagameto-

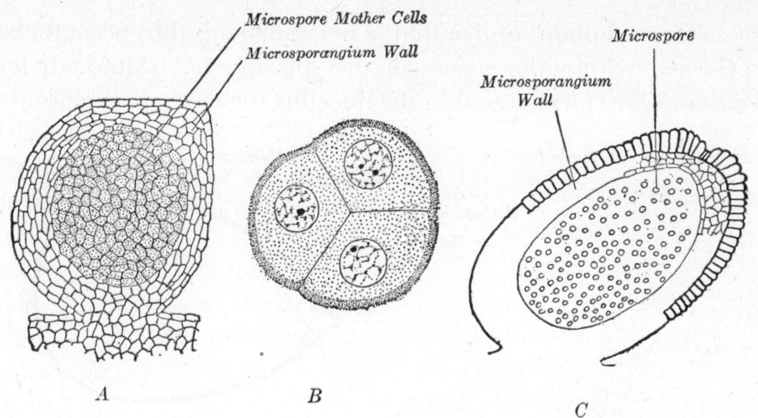

FIG. 348. *A*, lengthwise section of a young microsporangium of Zamia containing microspore mother cells. *B*, spores resulting from the division of a microspore mother cell. *C*, mature microsporangium.

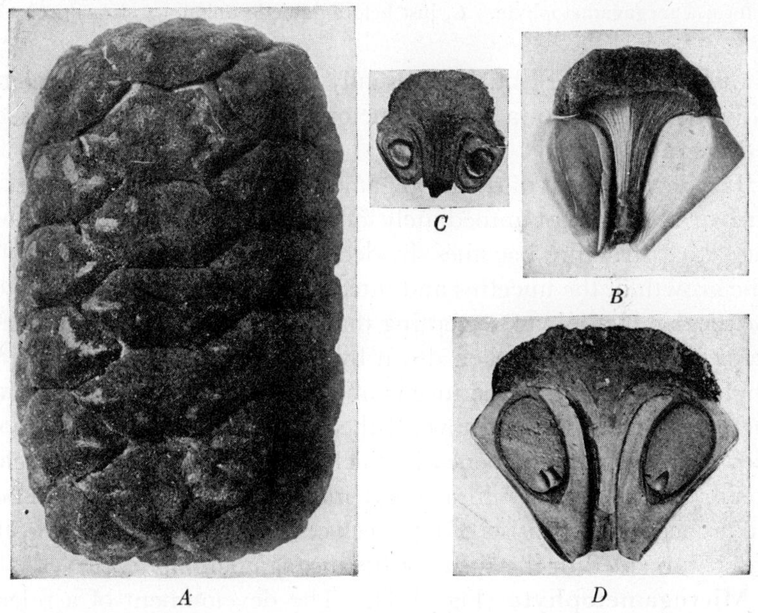

FIG. 349. *A*, carpellate strobilus of Zamia. *B*, megasporophyll bearing two ovules. *C*, lengthwise section of a young megasporophyll, showing an early stage in the development of megagametophytes. *D*, similar section at a later stage; megagametophytes fully developed.

phyte of a seed plant, unlike that of Selaginella, is thus permanently imprisoned within the tissues of the sporophyte. Although four megaspores are formed within the nucellus (or megasporangium) of

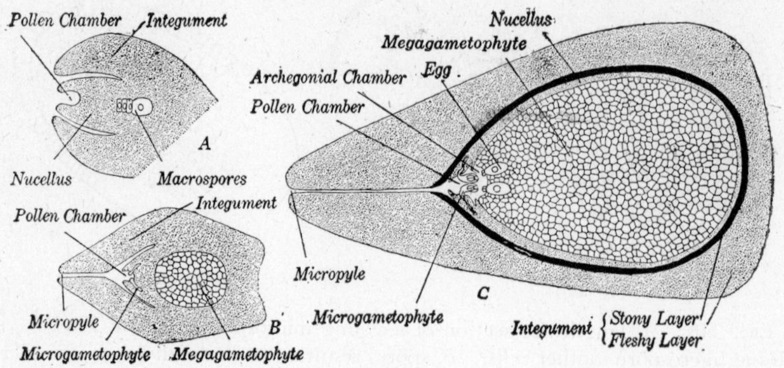

FIG. 350. Zamia; stages in the development of an ovule and of its included structures. *A*, four megaspores are formed. *B*, one megaspore has germinated to form a megagametophyte. *C*, just before gametic union.

Zamia (Fig. 350, *A*), but one, usually that farthest from the micropyle, develops into a megagametophyte; the other three soon disintegrate.

The development of the megagametophyte begins with a series of nuclear divisions not immediately followed by cell divisions. Later, the whole structure becomes divided into many one-nucleate cells. The growth of the nucellus and integument keeps pace with that of the megagametophyte, excepting that some of the nucellar tissue is being digested and broken down by the developing megagametophyte. Still later, as the megagametophyte approaches maturity, there appears in the end toward the micropyle a small depression, the *archegonial chamber*, beneath which are formed two to six archegonia. Each archegonium opens into the archegonial chamber. An archegonium consists of two neck cells and a very large egg, the latter imbedded in the tissue of the megagametophyte.

Microgametophyte (Fig. 351). The development of a microgametophyte from a microspore begins while the latter is still within the microsporangium. The microspore divides to form two daughter cells of unequal size. The smaller is the *prothallial cell*, so called because this single cell is thought to correspond to the vegetative tissue of a fern prothallium; the other and larger cell soon divides into a small *generative cell* and a large *tube cell.* Both these divisions occur within the microspore wall. The development of the microgametophyte then ceases for a time. This three-celled immature microgametophyte is a *pollen grain.*

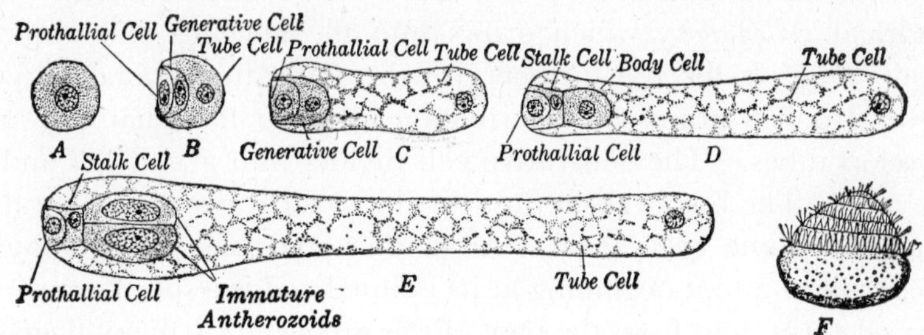

FIG. 351. Zamia; stages in the development of a microgametophyte. *A*, *B*, stages passed through in the microsporangium; *C–E*, while the pollen tube is growing through the nucellus. *A*, microspore. *B*, three-celled microgametophyte (pollen grain) at the time of its liberation from the microsporangium. *C*, early stage in the "germination" of a pollen grain. *D*, the generative cell has divided into stalk and body cells. *E*, the body cell has divided to form two antherozoids. *F*, mature antherozoid.

The microsporangium now breaks open, and the pollen grains are distributed by winds. Some of the dustlike grains may be blown to a carpellate strobilus. At this time, in consequence of an elongation of the central axis of the carpellate strobilus, the megasporophylls are not closely pressed together. Some pollen grains, therefore, may sift between the megasporophylls and lodge in the vicinity of the ovules. At the end of the micropyle of each ovule is a drop of a sticky liquid in which some pollen grains become caught. Later this liquid, with the imprisoned pollen grains, is withdrawn through the micropyle to the pollen chamber (Fig. 350, *C*).

The transportation of young microgametophytes (pollen grains) from the microsporangium to a specific place in the vicinity of the megagametophyte (a process known as *pollination*) is one of the features especially characteristic of seed plants. Zamia, like other gymnosperms, is dependent upon wind for the transfer of its pollen grains. The great number of pollen grains produced even by a single staminate strobilus makes pollination reasonably certain when staminate and carpellate plants grow near together. But when the two sorts of plants are widely separated, the chances of pollination are greatly reduced, since the vast majority of grains will not be carried to a place where they can function.

A pollen grain resumes development after it reaches the pollen chamber. This further development (the "germination" of the pollen grain) begins with an elongation of the tube cell into a cylindrical *pollen tube*, which grows into the nucellus and absorbs food materials for the further growth of the microgametophyte. Several pollen grains may germinate in the pollen chamber and develop tubes. The generative cell divides into a *stalk cell* and a *body cell*. The body cell in turn divides to form two cells that ultimately become *antherozoids*. An antherozoid has approximately the shape of a top; beginning at its pointed end is a spiral groove of several turns, and from the base of this groove grow many flagella.

Gametic Union. At the time of pollination the megagametophyte is still in an early stage. The completion of its development

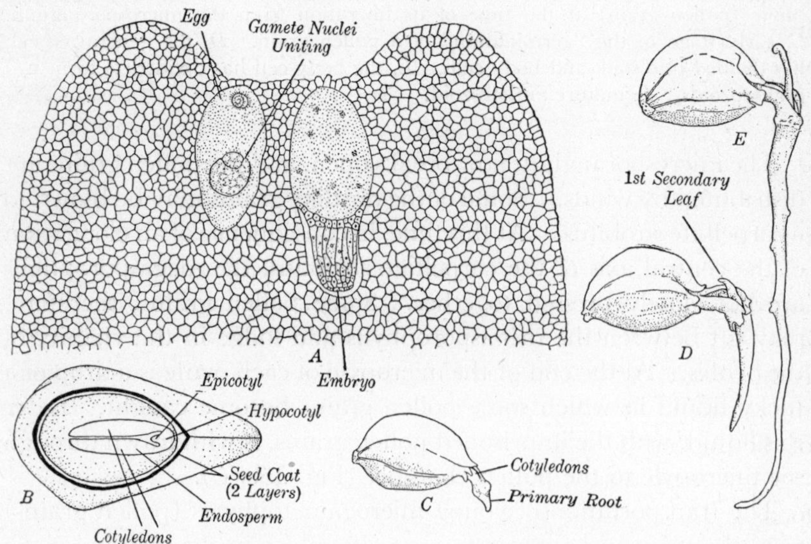

FIG. 352. Zamia. *A*, apical portion of a megagametophyte; gamete nuclei uniting *at the left; at the right*, a young embryo. *B*, lengthwise section of a mature seed. Semidiagrammatic. *C*, *D*, *E*, stages in the germination of a seed and the development of a young sporophyte.

requires several months, during which time the pollen tube is growing in the nucellus. Finally, when the megagametophyte and eggs are mature, the basal end of the tube—that is, the end still in the pollen chamber—grows through the nucellus directly to the archegonial chamber, and the end of the tube bursts. Since several tubes usually reach the archegonial chamber, a number of antherozoids may be discharged into, and swim about in, the liquid of the chamber. These antherozoids, or some of them, make their way through the necks of the archegonia and within the archegonia unite with the eggs (Fig. 352, *A*)—only one antherozoid uniting with any one egg.

Development of a Seed. The nucleus of the zygote divides, and the daughter nuclei by repeated divisions give rise to a many-nucleate *proembryo*. Still later, cell divisions occur, chiefly between those nuclei of the proembryo which lie in the basal part of the old archegonium. Some of the uppermost of the cells so formed elongate and push the basal portion of the proembryo deep into the tissue of the megagametophyte. The elongating cells form a long, slender, much-coiled *suspensor*. The cellular mass which is thrust, by the growth of the suspensor, deep into the megagametophyte and which feeds upon the cells of the megagametophyte is the *embryo*. The proembryo has, in this manner, become differentiated into embryo and suspensor. The embryo continues to grow and develop slowly.

The whole structure ultimately developed from the ovule and its inclusions is a *seed* (Fig. 352, *B*). It consists of:

(*a*) The embryo (the new sporophyte), which becomes differentiated into two large primary leaves (*cotyledons*) and a central axis. The part of this axis below the level of attachment of the cotyledons is the *hypocotyl;* the part above, a small mass of embryonic tissue, is the *epicotyl*. The suspensor is still discernible, attached to the end of the hypocotyl.

(*b*) A large mass of nutritive tissue (*endosperm*) filled with reserve foods. The endosperm is the persisting tissue of the megagametophyte.

(*c*) A *seed coat*, composed of an outer fleshy layer and an inner stony layer, both developed from the integument. A thin, papery layer immediately about the endosperm is derived chiefly from the nucellus. The integument and the nucellus are parts of the old sporophyte. The seed, therefore, consists of structures belonging to three distinct generations—the new sporophyte, the megagametophyte, and the old sporophyte.

Germination of a Seed (Fig. 352, *C*). When the seeds are mature, the megasporophylls shrivel, and the seeds drop from the strobilus to the ground. Under suitable conditions they may later germinate. In germination the cotyledons, although remaining largely within the seed, elongate sufficiently to thrust their basal portions, together with the epicotyl and the hypocotyl, out of the seed coat. The hypocotyl bends toward the earth; its terminal portion forms the primary root, which quickly penetrates the soil. Stem and leaves develop slowly from the epicotyl.

Until this time the young sporophyte has been unable to manufacture its own carbohydrates and has been dependent upon reserve foods stored in the endosperm (megagametophyte). These foods

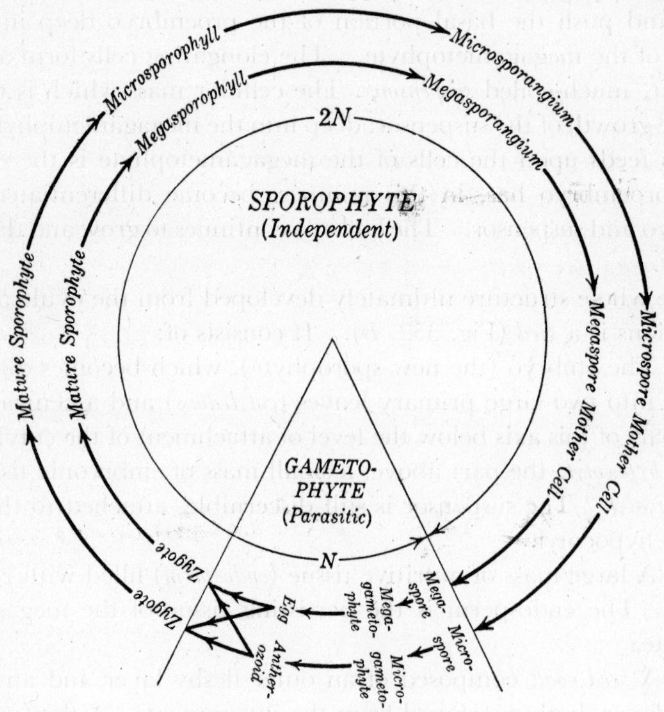

FIG. 353. Life cycle of Zamia.

were derived by the megagametophyte from the cells of the parental sporophyte. As soon as the epicotyl has developed chlorophyll-containing leaves, the young sporophyte is independent.

Life Cycle (Fig. 353). Two sporophytic plants are necessary in the life cycle of Zamia. One sporophyte bears staminate strobili with microsporophylls, microsporangia, and microspores. Another sporophyte bears carpellate strobili with megasporophylls, ovules (megasporangia with integuments), and megaspores. A microspore develops into a microgametophyte which produces antherozoids; a megaspore into a megagametophyte which produces archegonia and eggs. The union of an antherozoid with an egg forms a zygote. After gametic union a proembryo is formed, whose apical portion develops into an embryo. The embryo and the surrounding structures of the ovule mature into a seed. On germination the embryo within the seed develops into either a staminate or a carpellate sporophyte.

THE PINE

Coniferales. The Coniferales are far more abundant than the Cycadales, both in number of species and in number of individuals. Most of the conifers grow in temperate regions and include such familiar plants as pines, spruces, firs, hemlocks, and junipers. In most species the leaves, small and evergreen, persist for several years before they are shed. This is one of the reasons conifers are so frequently used in ornamental planting.

There is wide variation in the form of the plant (sporophyte). In several species it is prostrate, but in the great majority it is either an erect shrub or a tree. Among the largest and the oldest living objects on the earth are the famous "big trees" of California (Fig. 47). Certain individual trees have a reported height of about 350 feet, a diameter of 30 to 35 feet at some distance above the flaring base, and an age estimated at about 3000 years.

Economic Uses of Conifers. From an economic standpoint conifers are of great importance. They once formed forests of vast extent in various parts of North America. In the lumbering operations of earlier days, since these forests seemed inexhaustible, only the largest trees were selected and only the better portions of the felled trees were used. The remainder, being left on the ground, became dry; and in the "slashings" serious forest fires often started, which destroyed great acreages of uncut timber. Sawmills, too, made use only of the better parts of a log; and it has been estimated that not more than one quarter of a selected tree was made into lumber. As a result of these wasteful methods and because the demand for lumber outstripped the supply, only small portions of the once extensive forests of white and Norway pine remain in the north Atlantic and north central states. Much southern yellow pine also has been destroyed.

FIG. 354. Cut- and burned-over forest lands in Minnesota. Photograph by the U. S. Forest Service.

At present lumbermen are using larger portions of the trees that are cut; the fire risk is minimized by the careful handling of slashings; and much of the former waste material is being converted into a variety of by-products. In addition, an active forest-conservation policy supported by the national government, states, and individual timber owners is doing much to check timber waste. The replanting of cut-over areas is adding each year many thousands of acres to the available timber supply.

A number of conifers, such as the western firs, the redwoods, and various species of pine, are widely used as sources of lumber in building, providing such items as beams, flooring, and window sashes. Tables, chairs, and inexpensive grades of furniture also are sometimes made from such lumber. Spruce has been very extensively used in the manufacture of wood pulp. Recently a method has been devised for making wood pulp from certain of the southern pines. Spruces and firs together constitute the great bulk of the evergreens sold annually as Christmas trees.

FIG. 355. Chipping a southern pine in the process of turpentining. Photograph by the Forest Products Laboratory, Madison, Wis.

Telegraph and telephone poles, railroad ties, and lumber for crates, baskets, and boxes are made in part from various conifers.

Shingles of the best quality are derived from the western cedar and the redwood and from the bald cypress of the South. In the manufacture of pencils and penholders the wood almost exclusively employed is that of certain cedars. Fragrant cedar wood is a moth repellent, and for this reason cedar chests are favorite containers for clothing.

The balsam fir yields a resin from which Canada balsam is derived. This is employed in mounting specimens for microscopic study. The resin is used also in varnishes and in a few medicinal preparations.

FIG. 356. Pine; a mature sporophyte. Photograph by L. S. Cheney.

Southern pines (particularly the longleaf pine) are rich in resin from which turpentine, rosin, and pitch, commonly known as "naval stores," are obtained. By distillation, the wood of these pines, including the waste materials of sawmill operations, yields turpentine, rosin, lampblack, charcoal, tar, and other products.

Sporophyte of the Pine. The pine tree (Fig. 356) is the sporophyte. At its apex is a relatively large terminal bud. Since this bud grows more rapidly than the terminal buds of the branches, a conspicuous central trunk is formed. The lateral buds which are to develop into *long branches* are generally borne in whorls. The gradual transition in length of these branches from the lowermost and longest to the uppermost and shortest gives the tree as a whole, when it stands in the open, a conical form. If it grows in a dense stand, however, the tree bears branches in its upper portion only, the lower branches having died and fallen early. In addition to the long branches, the pine has branches of another sort (*spur branches*, Fig. 357) which, although they may live for a num-

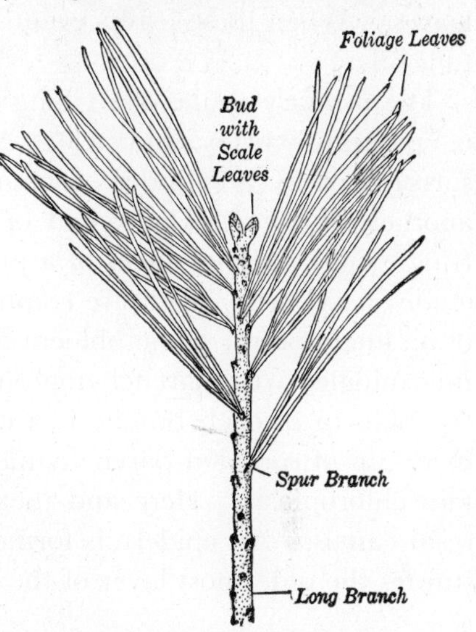

FIG. 357. Apical portion of a stem or branch of the white pine.

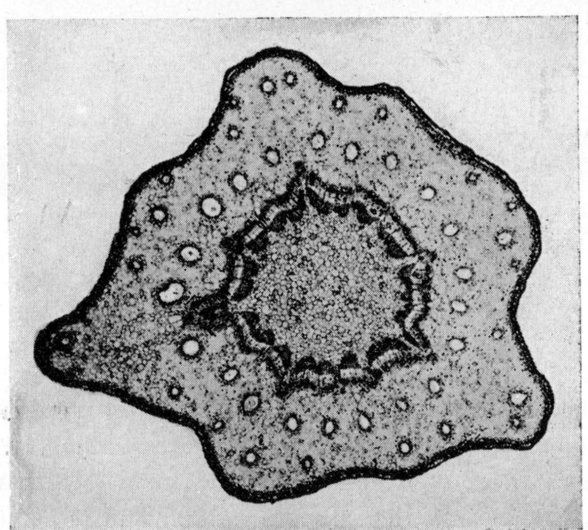

FIG. 358. Cross section of a young pine stem. The primary bundles are evident, although cambial activity has begun.

ber of years, remain very short and slender. At the end of each of these branches is a single cluster of needle-shaped foliage leaves. When these leaves eventually die, the branch too dies and falls off.

The primary tissues of a young pine stem (Figs. 358, 359) consist of epidermis, cortex, and stele. At the center of the stele is a pith, surrounded by a cylinder of vascular bundles separated from one another by rays. The xylem of each bundle contains tracheids (single cells). The xylem of a pine, as of most gymnosperms, includes no vessels, which are commonly characteristic of the xylem of an angiosperm. The phloem consists of thin-walled sieve tubes intermingled with parenchymatous cells. Between the xylem and the phloem of each bundle is a cambium. The cortex is largely made up of rounded parenchymatous cells, which frequently contain chloroplasts. Here and there in the cortex are longitudinal resin canals. An epidermis formed of heavily cutinized cells constitutes the outermost layer of the stem.

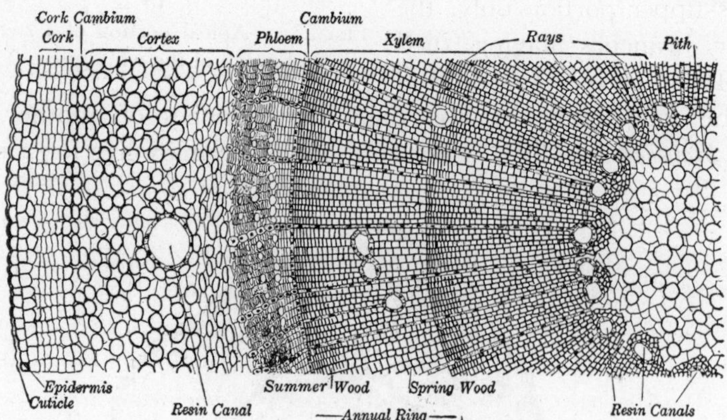

FIG. 359. Cross section of a portion of an older pine stem, showing its component tissues.

Growth in thickness of the stem is due mainly to the formation of secondary xylem and secondary phloem by cambial activity. The tracheids produced by the cambium are of much the same size as those in the primary xylem. Since the tracheids produced at the beginning of each growing season are somewhat larger than those developed later in the year, there are well-defined annual rings in the secondary xylem (Fig. 29). It is chiefly because of the approximate uniformity in size of the tracheids and because of the hardness of their walls that the pine is so valuable as a source of lumber. The original rays are continuous through the secondary xylem. The cambium gives rise to new rays from time to time, so that the later-formed rings of xylem contain many more rays than do those parts of the xylem formed earlier. Resin canals occur here and there in the secondary xylem and extend for considerable distances up and down the stem. These canals appear in cross section as large pores bordered by small thin-walled cells, and some of them are connected to other resin canals that run horizontally in certain of the rays. The cells of the secondary phloem ordinarily remain functional for only one year, the phloem of previous years persisting as a crushed mass of dead cells on the outer side of the new living phloem.

At about the time that cambial activity begins in the stele, a continuous cylinder of cork cambium is formed from the cortical cells just beneath the epidermis. Later, additional layers of cork cambium are developed successively, deeper and deeper in the cortex, and eventually in the outer part of the secondary phloem. Each of the later-formed layers of cork cambium, instead of being a continuous cylinder, is composed of overlapping segments of cylinders (see Fig. 34). As is the case among angiosperms, the cork cambium forms cork on its outer side and parenchyma on its inner side. In this manner a pine tree builds up a thick, protective hard bark.

Roots. The root system of the pine is extensively branched, and the roots may live and grow for many years. In some species the primary root usually grows into a large and deeply penetrating tap root. In other species the primary root often dies when the plant is young, and the root system consists entirely of branch roots. The root of a pine, like that of an angiosperm, consists of epidermis, cortex, and stele. Near the center of the stele are two, three, or four groups of primary xylem, alternating with a corresponding number of groups of primary phloem cells. The primary xylem may occupy all the region at the center of the stele; or the cells at the center may remain thin-walled and so form a small pith. The outer portion of the stele is a pericycle several cells in thickness. Often a resin canal is formed just outward from each group of primary xylem cells. The innermost layer of the cortex constitutes the characteristic endodermis. The remaining cells of the cortex and epidermis resemble those of a dicotyledonous root.

As the root grows older, certain strips of thin-walled cells between primary xylem and primary phloem begin to function as a cambium; still later, cambial activity extends to the cells of the

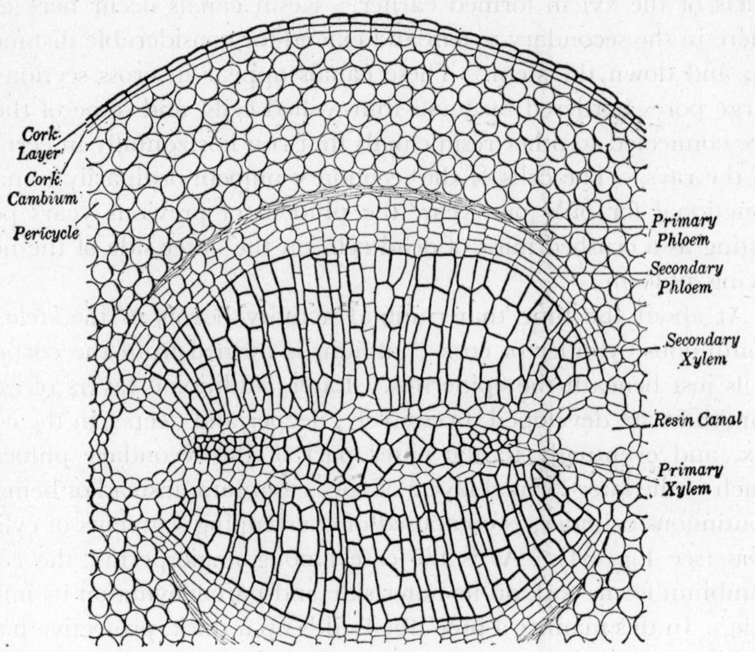

FIG. 360. Cross section of a portion of the stele of a root of the larch. Cortex and epidermis are not shown.

pericycle just outside each group of xylem cells. The primary xylem is now completely surrounded by a cylinder of cambium. This cambial cylinder, like the cambium of a stem, develops secondary xylem on its inner, and secondary phloem on its outer side (Fig. 360); an old root, therefore, has much the same appearance in cross section as an old stem. A cork cambium is formed from the outermost cells of the pericycle; after this cork cambium has begun to develop cork cells on its outer side, the cortex and epidermis of the root die and disappear. Hence, the older portions of a root are derived entirely from the stele.

Leaves. The pine has leaves of two distinct types: green "needles" (foliage leaves) and small, brownish scale leaves. The most conspicuous scale leaves are those which during the winter enclose the bud at the end of the stem or of a branch. These scale leaves spread outward when the bud opens in the spring and later drop off. The needles are borne at the ends of spur branches (Fig. 357). Except in one species, each spur branch bears a cluster of two, three, or five leaves, the number varying with the species. The Austrian pine and the Scotch pine have two, the white pine has five needles in a cluster. A needle shows no division into parts such as petiole and blade. Nor are veins externally visible, although there are in different species either one or two veins which run lengthwise, deeply imbedded, in the leaf. A pine needle is a foliage leaf of a highly specialized type, peculiarly adapted by its structure to withstand adverse conditions, such as low temperatures or a deficient water supply.

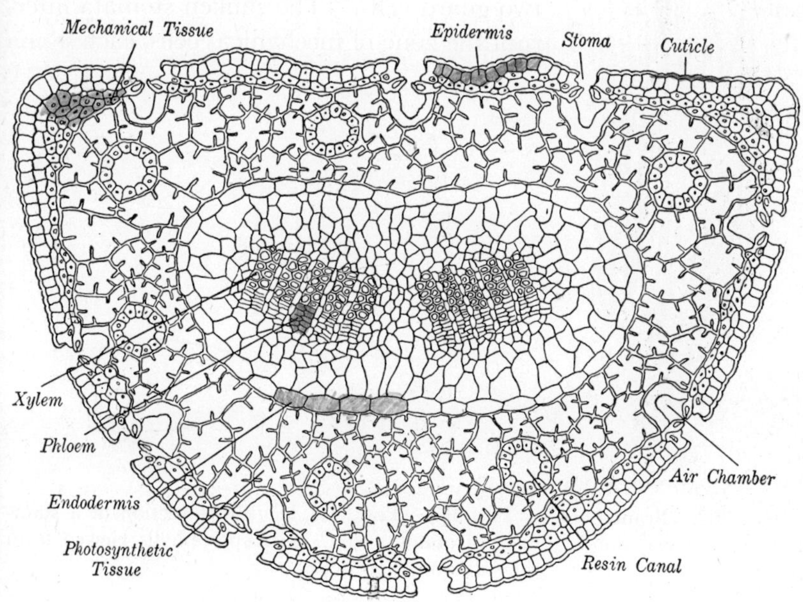

FIG. 361. Cross section of a leaf of the Austrian pine.

A cross section of a leaf of a "two-needle" pine (Fig. 361) is almost semicircular and shows three distinct regions. The central region is surrounded by an endodermis. Outside this is a zone of chlorophyll-containing cells whose walls have peculiar platelike infoldings. This zone in turn is bounded on its outer side by mechanical cells, outside which is the epidermis. The central region contains two parallel vascular bundles, the xylem of each bundle lying toward the flat upper surface of the leaf and the phloem toward the convex lower surface. Between the bundles and the endodermis are thin-walled cells. Longitudinal resin canals are present in the chlorophyll-containing region. The mechanical cells outside this region are small in cross section, very thick-walled, and are elongated in a direction parallel to the long axis of the leaf. The epidermal cells have very thick and heavily cutinized walls. Some of the cutin forms a thin, separable layer (cuticle) on the outer surface of the leaf. At many points the epidermis is depressed, and at the bottom of each minute depression is a stoma between two guard cells. The sunken stomata interrupt the zone of mechanical cells, each stoma

FIG. 362. Branch of a pine bearing staminate strobili.

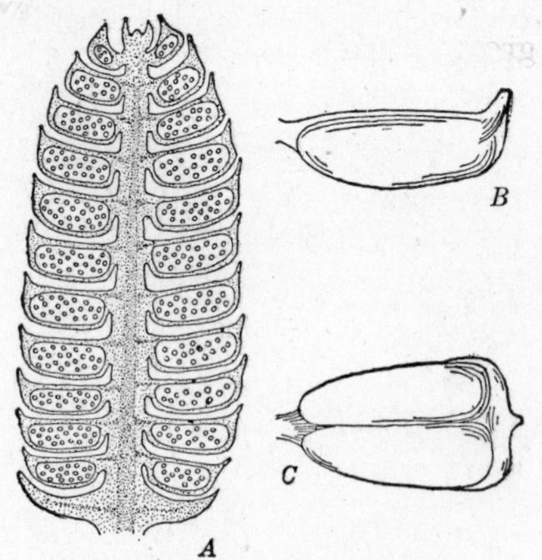

FIG. 363. Pine. *A*, lengthwise section of a staminate strobilus. *B*, *C*, microsporophylls viewed from the side and from below.

opening into a small cavity in the region of chlorophyll-containing cells.

Strobili and Sporophylls. Like Zamia, the pine produces *microsporophylls* in *staminate strobili* and *megasporophylls* in *carpellate strobili;* but both kinds of strobili occur on the same plant. As in Zamia, but differently from the condition in Selaginella, the sporophylls differ greatly in structure and appearance from foliage leaves.

Staminate strobili (Fig. 362) are produced in clusters near the ends of long branches. Each strobilus is comparatively small, rarely more than a half inch in length. It consists of a central axis bearing many compactly arranged, scalelike microsporophylls (Fig. 363). On the under side of each sporophyll are two ovoid *microsporangia*, whose long axes are parallel to the long axis of the sporophyll. Within each microsporangium are produced many *microspore mother cells*, each of which by division gives rise to four *microspores.*

FIG. 364. Branch of a pine bearing carpellate strobili.

Carpellate strobili (Fig. 364) eventually grow much larger than staminate strobili. A young carpellate strobilus has a central axis bearing numerous bracts. As the strobilus grows older (Fig. 365), a scalelike structure, several times the size of a bract, develops in the axil between each bract and the central axis. This scale bears two *ovules* on its upper surface. Opinions differ as to whether the scale is a megasporophyll or whether it represents a reduced branch.

An ovule (Fig. 366) begins its development as a mass of embryonic tissue—the *nucellus* or megasporangium—on the surface of a scale. From the base of the nucellus an enclosing *integument* grows up and about it, leaving an opening, the *micropyle*, leading to the outer end of the nucellus. The integument seems to be a structure distinct from the sporangium (nucellus). The two together constitute an ovule. A very small depression (*pollen chamber*) is formed at the end of the nucellus next the micropyle. A single megaspore mother cell becomes differentiated near the center of the nucellus. From this cell, by division, is later formed an axial row of four megaspores.

Megagametophyte. Only one megaspore in a nucellus, usually that one farthest from the micropyle, develops into a megagameto-

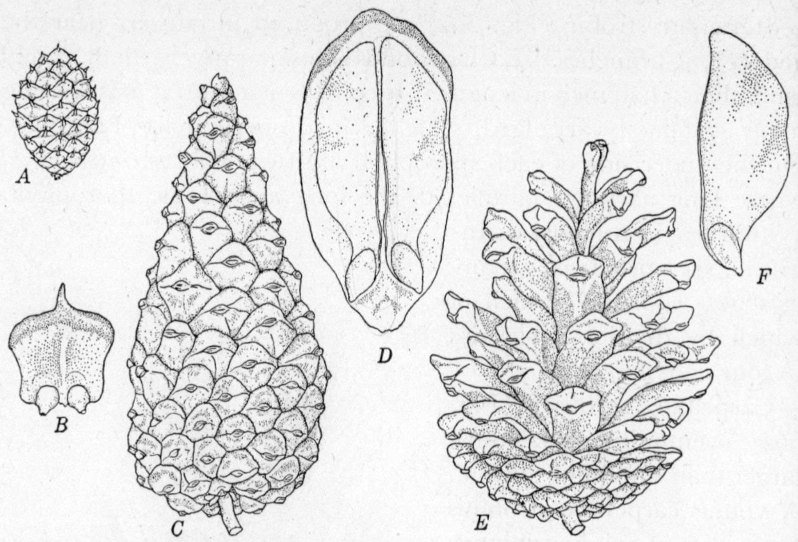

Fig. 365. Austrian pine. *A*, young carpellate cone a few weeks after pollination (early July). *B*, a scale from *A* bearing two young ovules. *C*, similar cone a year later. *D*, scale from *C* with ovules, at the time of fertilization. *E*, several months later; scales are spread apart and seeds are shed. *F*, winged seed.

phyte; the other three spores soon disintegrate. The development of the functional megaspore into a megagametophyte begins with a series of nuclear divisions (Fig. 367, *A*). Later, by cell division, a many-celled megagametophyte is formed which, by the repeated growth and division of its cells, increases in size (Fig. 367, *B*, *C*). As a rule, two or three archegonia are formed at the micropylar end of the megagametophyte. Each archegonium consists usually of four or eight neck cells and a very large egg, the latter being imbedded in the megagametophyte.

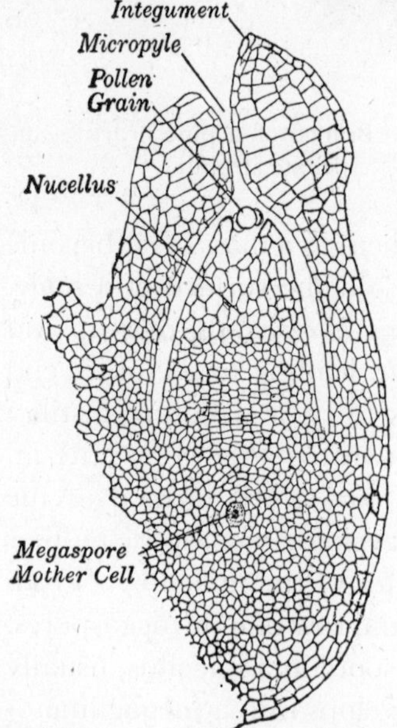

Fig. 366. Pine. Lengthwise section of an ovule: the megaspore mother cell is differentiated.

Microgametophyte and Gametic Union. The development of a microgametophyte from a microspore (Fig. 368, *A*, *B*) begins while the latter is still within the microsporangium. The microspore divides into a small *prothallial cell* and a much larger *apical cell;*

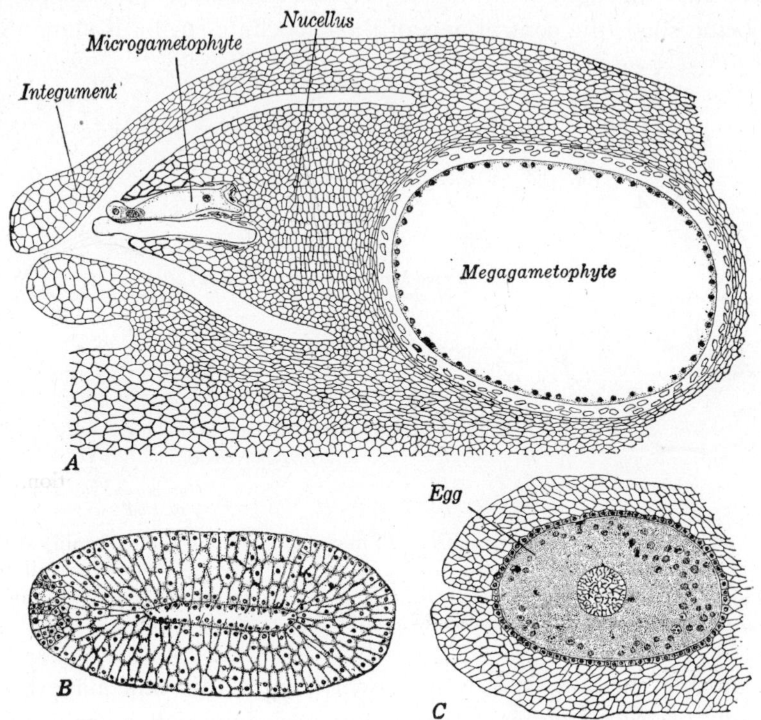

Fig. 367. Pine. *A*, lengthwise section of an ovule, showing an early stage in the development of the megagametophyte; a microgametophyte growing through the nucellus. *B*, a young megagametophyte, shortly after the formation of archegonia. *C*, apical portion of a mature megagametophyte, showing one archegonium.

a similar division of the apical cell forms a second small prothallial cell and a larger cell, the latter still called an apical cell. Both prothallial cells begin to disintegrate soon after they are formed. The apical cell in time divides into a small *generative cell* and a large *tube cell*. It is at this four-celled stage (that of the tube cell, generative cell, and two disintegrating prothallial cells) that the partially developed microgametophyte (now a *pollen grain*) is shed. The pollen grain of the pine has two lateral inflated appendages ("wings") that give it buoyancy. These wings were developed from the wall of the microspore before it germinated to form a microgametophyte.

The transfer of pollen from a microsporangium to a carpellate strobilus is brought about by winds. At about the time that pollen is being shed, the central axis of the carpellate strobilus elongates,

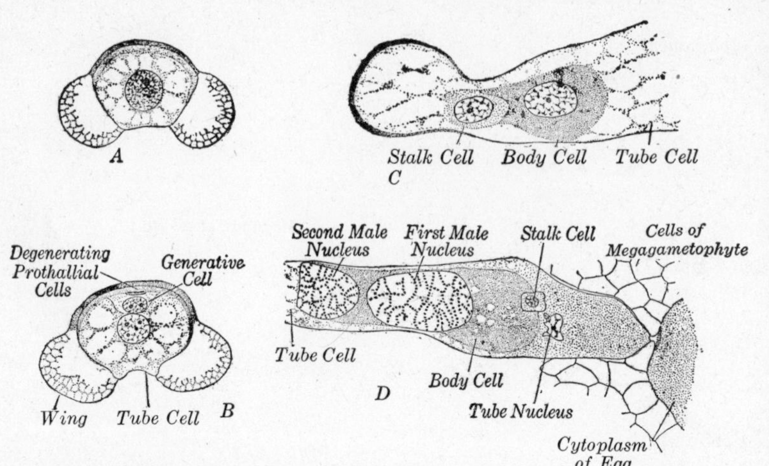

FIG. 368. Pine. *A*, microspore. *B*, microgametophyte (pollen grain) at the time of its liberation from the microsporangium. *C*, the generative cell has divided to form stalk and body cells. *D*, distal end of the pollen tube, shortly before gametic union. *C*, *D* after Margaret Ferguson.

separating the megasporophylls, which until this time have been closely pressed together. In consequence, some pollen grains may sift between the megasporophylls and lodge in the micropyle. A growth in thickness of the apical portion of the integument now closes the micropyle and permanently imprisons these pollen grains in the pollen chamber. The transportation of young microgametophytes (pollen grains) from the microsporangium to a specific place in the vicinity of the megagametophyte (a process known as *pollination*) is one of the features especially characteristic of seed plants.

The development of the microgametophyte is resumed after it reaches the pollen chamber. In this "germination" of the pollen grain the tube cell elongates into a *pollen tube* which, penetrating the nucellus, slowly grows toward the developing megagametophyte. Meanwhile, the generative cell has divided into a *stalk cell* and a *body cell*, and the prothallial cells have completely disintegrated. The stalk cell and the body cell now leave the old wall of the pollen grain and migrate through the tube. During their migration the nucleus of the body cell divides to form two male gamete nuclei. The end of the pollen tube eventually completes its growth through the nucellus and then to and through the neck of the

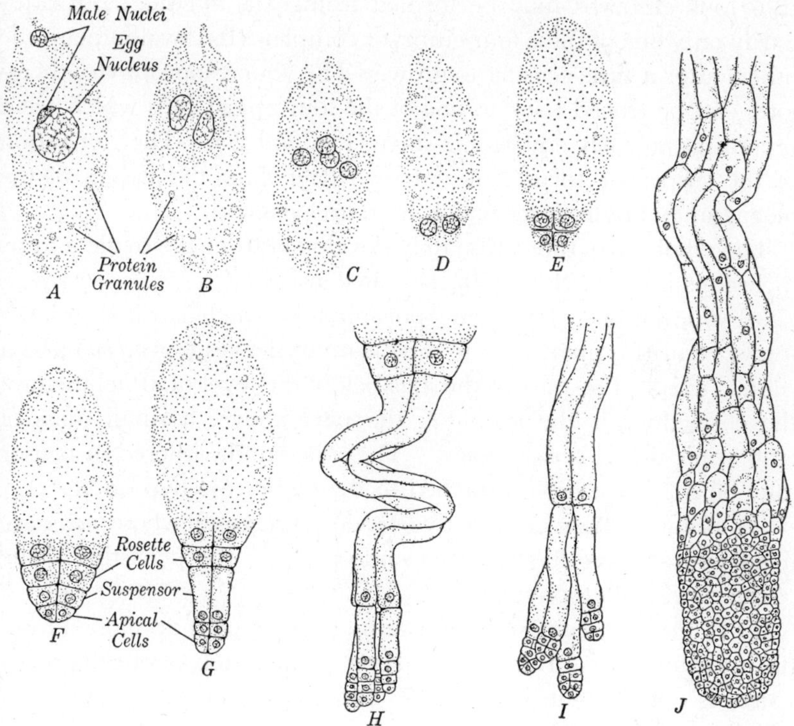

FIG. 369. Pine: gametic union and embryo development. *A*, union of one male gamete nucleus with the egg nucleus. *B*, two nuclei, resulting from the division of the zygote nucleus, are now present. *C*, four nuclei have been formed by the division of the two nuclei in *B*. *D*, the four nuclei (only two shown) sink to the base of the egg. *E*, the four nuclei have divided simultaneously; two rows of four cells each (two cells of each row shown) are now present. *F*, further divisions have formed four rows of four cells each (two of each row shown). *G*, the suspensor cells have elongated, and the apical cells have divided. *H*, initiation of four embryos by the separation of the four rows of apical cells. *I*, later stage in the development of the four embryos. *J*, one embryo persists, the other three disintegrating. *F–J* after J. T. Buchholz in the *Botanical Gazette*.

archegonium. Now the end of the tube bursts, and the two male gamete nuclei are discharged into the apex of the egg. One male gamete nucleus disintegrates; the other migrates to and unites with the egg nucleus (Fig. 369, *A*), forming a zygote nucleus.

Development of a Seed. After gametic union the zygote gives rise to an embryonic structure consisting of four *apical cells* and a *suspensor* (Fig. 369, *F–I*). Very commonly, however, the four apical cells split apart (each remaining attached to its own suspensor), and thus four embryos may be formed from each zygote. But ordinarily only one of these four embryos completes its development, the others after a time ceasing to grow. The young sporophyte, therefore, can be traced back to one of the four apical cells which were present at an early embryonic stage (Fig. 369, *F*). The elongation of the suspensor thrusts the embryo deep into the tissues of the megagametophyte, from which it secures its food.

The whole structure ultimately developed from the ovule and its inclusions is a *seed* (Fig. 370, *A*). It consists of:

(*a*) The embryo (the new sporophyte), which is differentiated into several (frequently six to ten) primary leaves (*cotyledons*) and a central axis. The part of the axis below the level of attachment of the cotyledons is the *hypocotyl;* the part above, a small mass of embryonic tissue, is the *epicotyl*. The coiled and withered suspensor may be still discernible attached to the end of the hypocotyl.

(*b*) A large mass of nutritive tissue (*endosperm*) whose cells are filled with reserve foods. The endosperm is the persisting tissue of the megagametophyte.

(*c*) A *seed coat*, composed of a stony layer of cells developed from the integument. A thin, papery layer immediately about the endosperm is derived chiefly from the nucellus. The integument and nucellus are parts of the old sporophyte. The seed, therefore, consists of structures belonging to three distinct generations—the new sporophyte, the megagametophyte, and the old sporophyte. In many species of pine a portion of the scale remains attached to each seed, forming a wing that assists in the dispersal of the seed by winds (Fig. 365, *F*).

Time Interval in Development. The lapse of time between pollination and fertilization is one of the marked features of the pines. For example, in southern Wisconsin pollination usually occurs about the end of May or early in June. Fertilization, however, ordinarily does not take place until early in July of the following year. While the precise times vary with the species and with the locality, a period of about 13 months commonly elapses between the time of pollination and that of fertilization. After fertilization the development of seeds is relatively rapid. In most species they reach maturity by the close of the year in which fertilization occurred. After pollination and until the maturation of the seeds, the scales of the cone (carpellate strobilus) are firmly and closely appressed. In most species when the seeds are mature, the cone scales again become separated by the elongation of the central axis, permitting the seeds to fall out and to be dispersed. In some

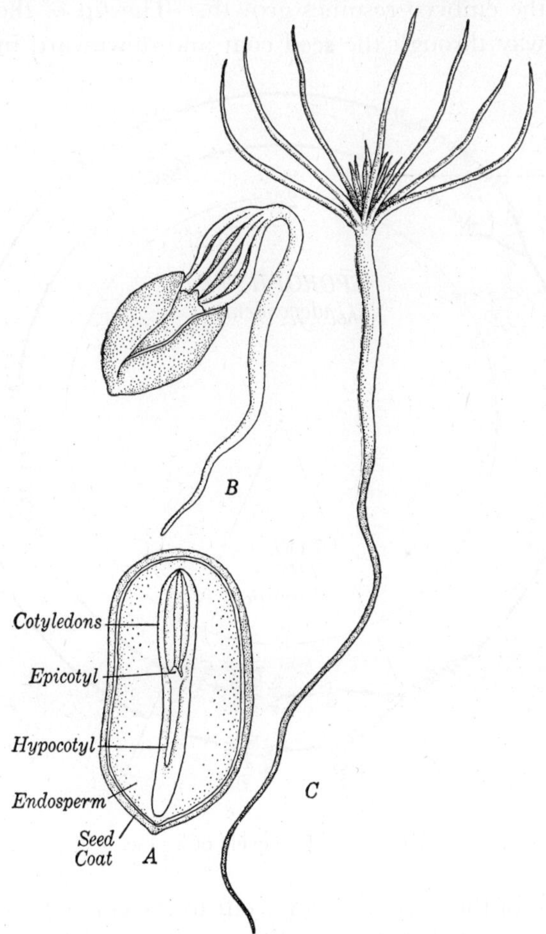

FIG. 370. *A*, lengthwise section of a pine seed. *B*, *C*, germination of a seed.

species of pine the cones remain closed indefinitely. In certain of these species the seeds are liberated only by the eventual decay of the cones or by the activity of squirrels or other animals in search of food; in other species the cones may remain closed on the trees for many years, finally opening in unusually hot weather or when scorched by forest fires.

Germination of a Seed (Fig. 370, *B*, *C*). A pine seed may germinate in the spring following its maturation, or it may remain dormant for several years if conditions are not favorable for germination. When conditions are suitable, the seed absorbs moisture, and the embryo resumes growth. The tip of the hypocotyl pushes its way through the seed coat and downward into the soil.

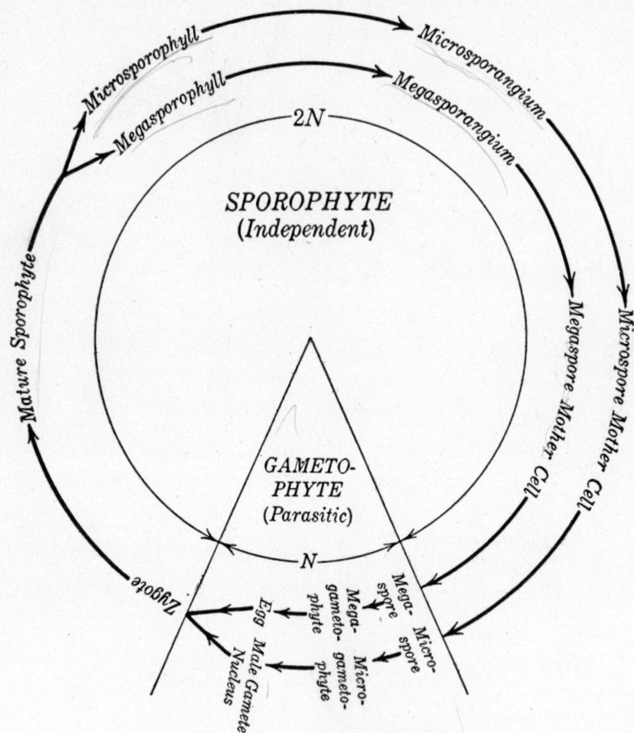

FIG. 371. Life cycle of a pine.

The portion of the hypocotyl adjacent to the cotyledons bends and grows upward. When the cotyledons emerge from the seed coat, they spread apart and become green. Growth to this stage has been accomplished by the absorption of water and the use of foods stored in the endosperm; after the cotyledons develop chlorophyll, the young sporophyte, being able to manufacture foods, becomes independent of the endosperm. Still later, when the portion of the stem derived from the epicotyl has developed secondary leaves, the cotyledons wither and die; and the secondary leaves now perform the photosynthetic work of the plant. The young plant may in time, by the growth and development of its parts and by the formation of new branches, leaves, and roots, become a mature sporophyte or pine tree.

Life Cycle (Fig. 371). The sporophyte (pine tree) produces staminate and carpellate strobili. A staminate strobilus bears many microsporophylls, on each of which are two microsporangia. In a microsporangium are formed many microspore mother cells. Each microspore mother cell divides to form four microspores. A microspore develops within the sporangium into a young male gametophyte (pollen grain).

A carpellate strobilus bears many megasporophylls, each bearing two ovules. An ovule is a megasporangium covered by an integument. Within a megasporangium (nucellus) one megaspore mother cell is differentiated; this divides to form four megaspores. Of these, three degenerate. The persisting megaspore grows into a megagametophyte which bears archegonia.

A pollen grain reaching the nucellus develops a pollen tube, within which two male gamete nuclei are formed. The tube finally penetrates an archegonium and liberates the male gamete nuclei. After gametic union a cellular structure develops from the zygote and becomes differentiated into embryo and suspensor. By further development the embryo forms epicotyl, hypocotyl, and several cotyledons. The ovule has become a seed, in which lies the embryo enclosed by the endosperm (megagametophyte), which in turn is covered by the remains of the nucellus and by a seed coat derived from the integument.

When the seed germinates, the embryo resumes growth, developing into a long-lived pine tree. This produces branches, leaves, roots, and eventually staminate and carpellate strobili.

New Features in Gymnosperms. Gymnosperms stand higher in the evolutionary scale than do pteridophytes. Important new features evolved by such gymnosperms as Zamia and pine are:

(*a*) The production of two kinds of strobili which bear, respectively, microsporophylls and megasporophylls.

(*b*) The retention for a time of the developing microgametophytes (pollen grains) in the microsporangium.

(*c*) The permanent retention of the megaspore and the megagametophyte within the megasporangium (nucellus).

(*d*) The development of a covering (integument) about each megasporangium.

(*e*) A further simplification of the microgametophyte.

(*f*) Pollination and the formation of a pollen tube.

(*g*) Direct parasitism of both gametophytes upon the sporophyte.

(*h*) The establishment of the seed habit.

CHAPTER XXIX

ANGIOSPERMAE (FLOWERING PLANTS)

Nature. Spermatophyta which produce seeds enclosed by one or more sporophylls belong to the subdivision *Angiospermae* (*angiosperms*). Another characteristic feature of angiosperms is the production of flowers; and since they are the only plants producing flowers, the angiosperms are often called *flowering plants*. The xylem of angiosperms also differs from the xylem of pteridophytes and gymnosperms in that true vessels are usually present.

Fossil remains of true angiosperms are found only in the later geological formations; and it seems clear that as a group they are more modern than are bryophytes, pteridophytes, or gymnosperms. However, in spite of their comparatively recent origin angiosperms predominate in the land flora of today. There are approximately 9000 genera and 200,000 species of angiosperms. Included among them are all the "wild flowers" and, with the exception of conifers, almost all trees and shrubs. The great majority of plants cultivated by man are angiosperms. These include many grown for food, for medicinal purposes, for the beauty of their flowers, for the manufacture of textiles, and for a wide variety of materials used in industry.

The angiosperm plant that one sees, whether tree, shrub, or herb, is the sporophyte. The general structure of the vegetative parts of the sporophyte of an angiosperm has been discussed in Chapters IV–VII. There remain for consideration the gametophytes and those portions of the sporophyte (flower, fruit, and seed) which are intimately associated with the gametophytes.

THE FLOWER

Nature of a Flower. A flower, like a strobilus, is a branch (or the terminal portion of a stem or branch) which bears sporophylls. Flowers of all angiosperms are alike in that each possesses one or more sporophylls. Flowers of most angiosperms also have either one or two kinds of lateral appendages (floral leaves) surrounding the sporophyll or sporophylls. In nearly all flowers the sporophylls and lateral appendages are arranged in spirals or in concentric whorls upon a shortened, somewhat flattened axis. Flowers of angiosperms differ markedly from genus to genus both in number, size, and arrangement of sporophylls and in number, size, shape, and color of the floral leaves.

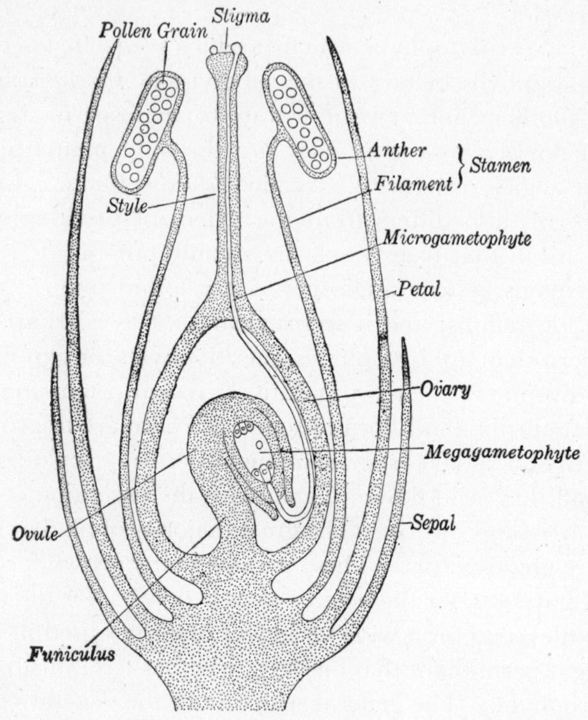

FIG. 372. Diagram of an angiosperm flower in lengthwise section.

Structure of a Flower (Fig. 372). The following structures are present in a flower which has all the characteristic parts:

(*a*) An outer set of green floral leaves (*sepals*) which enclose the other parts of the flower until these are nearly mature. Collectively the sepals comprise the *calyx*.

(*b*) An inner set of colored or white floral leaves (*petals*) constituting the *corolla*. In many flowers the petals are showy and may aid in attracting the attention of insects which assist in pollination.

(*c*) Within the petals, one or more sets of *stamens* (microsporophylls).

(*d*) At the center of the flower, one or more *pistils*. A pistil may consist of a single *carpel* (megasporophyll) or may be formed by a union of two or more carpels.

(*e*) A *receptacle*, the terminal portion of the branch or stem, which bears the calyx, corolla, stamens, and pistil or pistils.

The apple, primrose, strawberry, sweet pea, and violet are examples of angiosperms whose flowers possess all the parts above mentioned. The flowers of many other angiosperms lack one or more of these parts. In the flowers of willows and of cereal grains, both sepals and petals are absent or are reduced to small, inconspicuous bracts. Many flowers regularly have sepals but no petals. In these, as in many members of the nettle family, the sepals may be small and green; or they may be colored and showy, as in clematis.

In the majority of angiosperms both stamens and pistil (or pistils) occur in the same flower. But a considerable number of species have separate staminate and pistillate flowers. The two kinds of flower often appear on the same plant, as in the cucumber and the Indian corn. The tassel of the corn is a branching system bearing staminate flowers, and the ear is a branch bearing pistillate flowers. In some other angiosperms, including willows, the hop, and the date palm, staminate and pistillate flowers are commonly borne on separate plants.

Evolution of Flowers. It is probable that the flowers of primitive angiosperms were somewhat similar to gymnosperm strobili. Such a flower would have had an elongated central axis that bore many spirally arranged sporophylls and nothing closely corresponding to sepals or petals. The evidence now available indicates that in this primitive state each flower possessed both microsporophylls (stamens) and megasporophylls (carpels), although it is possible that in some lines of descent staminate and pistillate (carpellate) flowers were originally separate, as is now commonly the case in willows. Beginning with such a strobilus-like structure, the following general tendencies seem to have marked the evolution of flowers in different families of angiosperms:

(*a*) The differentiation of accessory leaves—sepals, or sepals and petals—borne below the stamens and carpels.

(*b*) A change from a spiral arrangement of each set of floral parts (sepals, petals, stamens, and carpels) to a cyclic or whorled arrangement of one or more sets.

(*c*) A reduction of the primitively large and indefinite numbers of floral parts to smaller and definite numbers.

(*d*) A shortening of the receptacle, which became broadened and flattened or in some cases concave.

(*e*) An advance from a condition of *radial symmetry*, in which all the members of any particular set of floral parts are alike and symmetrically arranged around a central axis, to one of *bilateral symmetry*, in which the members of at least one set differ in size and shape and are so arranged that there is but one plane in which the flower can be divided into two equal parts.

(*f*) An advance from a condition in which all the members of each set of floral parts are distinct and separate to one in which they are united in varying degrees with one another, with members of another set or sets, or in some cases with the receptacle.

The progressive changes just enumerated are the chief criteria for deciding whether the flowers of a particular genus are of a primitive or of an advanced type. In making such a decision one feature must be balanced against another, because a flower is frequently advanced in certain respects and primitive in others. For example, in the flower of a buttercup the sepals and petals are not of a primitive type, since their number is small and definite and they are borne in whorls. On the other hand, the stamens and carpels are distinctly primitive, since both are spirally arranged and both are produced in large and indefinite numbers. Flowers considered of an advanced type are usually advanced in all features. Asters and orchids are examples of these. Such flowers have a whorled arrangement of all floral parts, a small and definite number of parts in each set, bilateral symmetry, and a fusion of floral parts.

SPOROPHYLLS AND GAMETOPHYTES

Stamens. A stamen (microsporophyll) consists usually of a more or less elongated stalklike *filament* and an enlarged lobed *anther*, which is borne at the apex of the filament. Within the anther are a variable number of *pollen sacs* (microsporangia). Very commonly the young anther is two-lobed, each lobe containing two pollen sacs (Fig. 373). Within each young pollen sac of an angiosperm, as within a microsporangium of Selaginella or of a gymnosperm, are produced a number of microspore mother cells. These are surrounded by a conspicuous layer of nutritive cells. Each microspore mother cell, after two successive divisions of its nucleus (reduction divisions), divides to form four microspores. While the microspore mother cells are dividing, the cells of the nutritive layer and

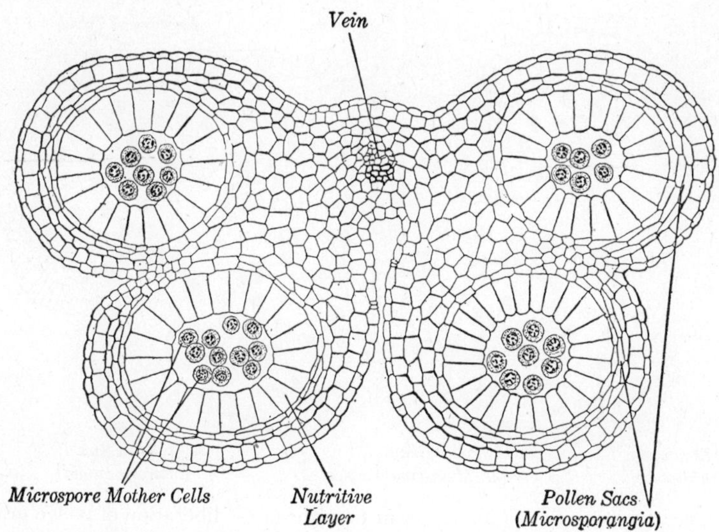

FIG. 373. Cross section of an anther before the division of microspore mother cells. Diagrammatic.

some of the adjoining cells of the anther disintegrate. If there are two pollen sacs in each lobe, the tissue between them also disintegrates.

The microspores begin to develop into microgametophytes while still within the pollen sac (Fig. 378). However, the developing microgametophytes, now *pollen grains*, are soon liberated by a splitting of the anther (Fig. 374). In most angiosperms the splitting is lengthwise. In some instances, as in the potato, the anther opens by a terminal slit or pore.

Pistils. A pistil is usually differentiated into three regions (Fig. 372): a swollen hollow basal portion, the *ovary;* a narrow, more or less elongated portion, the *style;* and at the apex or along the side of the style, the *stigma.* In certain flowers the pistil has no style, and the stigma is attached directly to the upper portion of the ovary.

A pistil consisting of one carpel (megasporophyll) only is a *simple pistil* (Fig. 375, *A*). In such a pistil the margins of the carpel are usually so united—as in the bean or pea—as to enclose a single cavity. A pistil may, however, be formed by the union of two or more carpels (Fig. 375, *B*, *C*). The ovary of such a *compound pistil*

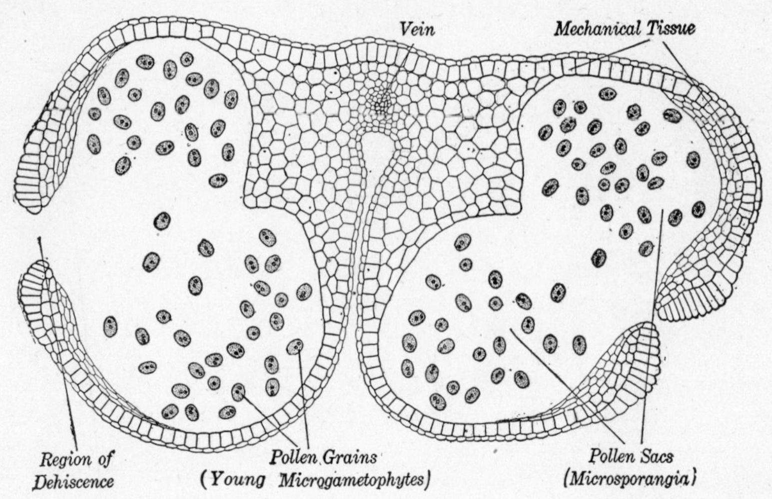

FIG. 374. Cross section of an anther at the time of the liberation of pollen grains. Diagrammatic.

may enclose one or more than one cavity. For instance, the pistil of a lily or of a hyacinth is made up of three carpels united in such

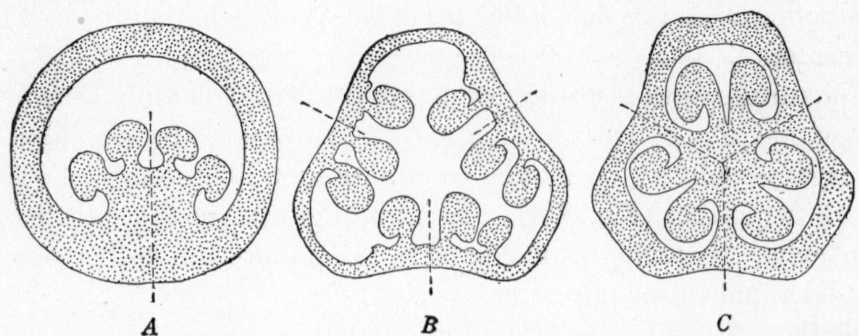

FIG. 375. Cross sections of ovaries; the united margins of the carpel or carpels are indicated by dotted lines. Diagrammatic. *A*, May apple; a simple ovary. *B*, violet; a compound ovary with one cavity. *C*, lily; a compound ovary with as many cavities as carpels.

a way as to form three cavities within the ovary. In the pistil of the violet, three carpels are so united that there is but a single cavity.

Within the cavity or cavities of the ovary are one or more ovules. An ovule (Fig. 376) may arise from the base of the ovary or from the inner surface of a carpel. As in gymnosperms, the megasporangium (nucellus) is the first part of the ovule to develop. From

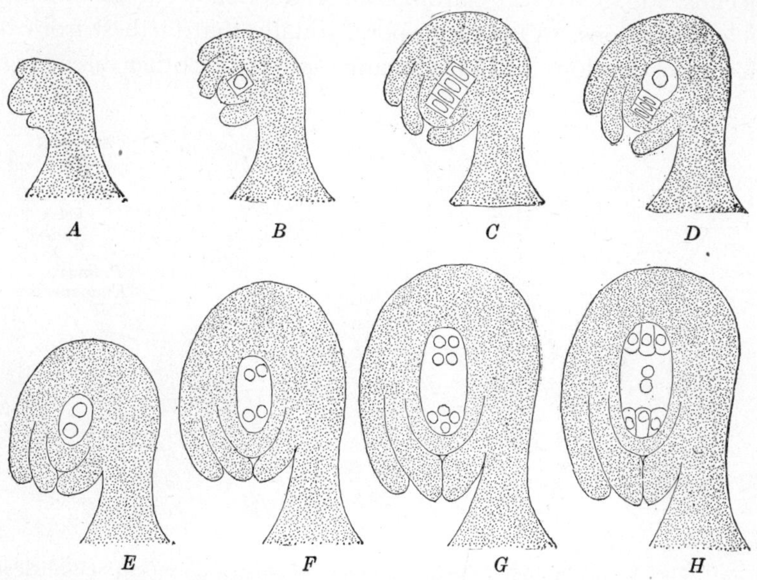

FIG. 376. Diagrams showing, in lengthwise section, the development of an ovule and a megagametophyte. *A*, very young ovule; the inner integument has appeared. *B*, both integuments are present; the megaspore mother cell is differentiated. *C*, the nucellus is nearly enclosed by the integuments; four megaspores have been formed by division from the mother cell. *D–H*, successively later; the stages of megagametophyte development in *D*, *E*, *F*, *G*, and *H* correspond respectively to those shown in *A*, *B*, *C*, *D*, and *E*, Figure 377.

the basal portion of the nucellus one or two integuments grow up and around it, leaving a passageway (the micropyle) at the nucellar apex. Each ovule is borne on a distinct stalk, the *funiculus*.

Pollen grains can not come into direct contact with the ovules because of the enclosing ovary. This condition is very different from that in gymnosperms, whose pollen grains eventually reach the ovules. The difference in this respect is a fundamental one between gymnosperms and angiosperms.

Megagametophyte. The megagametophyte of an angiosperm develops within the nucellus of an ovule. In most angiosperms a single megaspore mother cell is differentiated within the nucellus.

Development from the megaspore mother cell varies from genus to genus; most commonly there is a division of its nucleus followed by cell division, then a second nuclear division and a second cell division, forming four megaspores which lie in an axial row within the nucellus (Fig. 376, *C*). Chromosome reduction occurs in these two nuclear divisions. One megaspore, usually that farthest from the micropyle, develops into a megagametophyte; the other three mega-

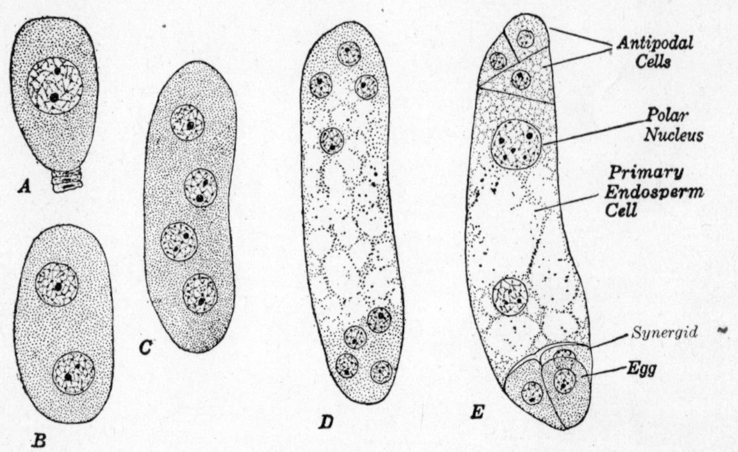

Fig. 377. *A*, beginning of the development of a megaspore (still one-nucleate) into a megagametophyte. *B–D*, two-, four-, and eight-nucleate stages. *E*, mature megagametophyte. All diagrammatic.

spores disintegrate. While there is considerable variation among angiosperms in the development of a megaspore into a megagametophyte, most frequently it is as follows:

The functional megaspore enlarges greatly (Fig. 377), its nucleus divides, and the two daughter nuclei migrate to opposite ends of the cell. Each of these two nuclei divides, and their daughter nuclei in turn divide. The megagametophyte is now a large eight-nucleate cell, four of its nuclei lying in the micropylar end of the cell and four at the opposite end. One nucleus from each group of four moves to the center of the eight-nucleate cell, after which, by cell division, the megagametophyte becomes seven-celled (Fig. 377, *E*). At each end are three small cells, each with a single nucleus; in the central part is a large cell containing two nuclei. The cells at the micropylar end of the megagametophyte are the *egg* and two *synergids;* the three at the opposite end are *antipodal cells;* and the large two-nucleate cell in the central region is the *primary endosperm cell.*

One of the more striking variations from the just-described development of a megagametophyte is that found in the evening primroses. Here cells are formed at the four-nucleate stage of development, and the mature megagametophyte is three- instead of seven-celled. Another variant condition occurs in species of Peperomia, a genus of the pepper family. Its developing megagametophyte has 16 instead of 8 nuclei; the number of cells in the mature megagametophyte varies with the species.

Microgametophyte. The development of a microspore into a microgametophyte begins while the microspore is still within the pollen sac. The microspore divides to form a relatively large *tube cell* and a smaller *generative cell* (Fig. 378, *B*). Since a prothallial cell is usually not produced, the history of development of an angiosperm microgametophyte is somewhat simpler than that of a gymnosperm microgametophyte. In most angiosperms the microgametophyte is liberated from the pollen sac at the two-celled stage of development. The liberated

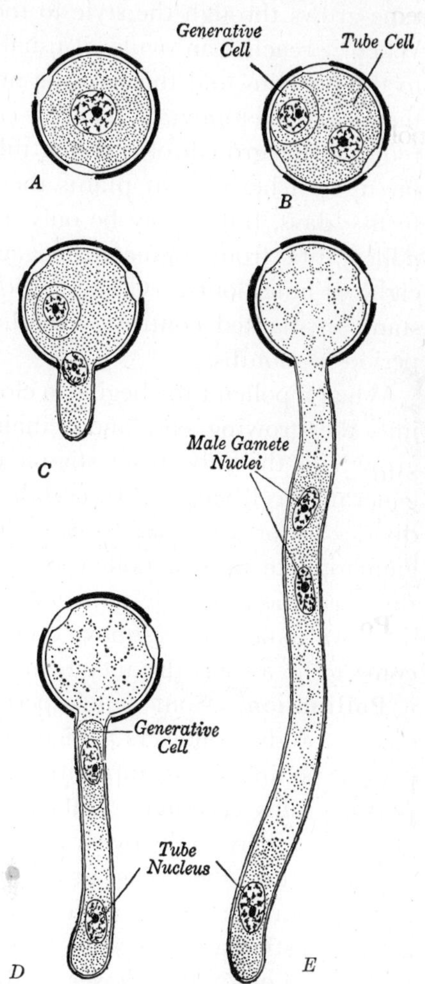

FIG. 378. *A*, microspore. *B*, a pollen grain (young microgametophyte); the microspore has divided into a generative and a tube cell. *C*, "germination" of a pollen grain; formation of a pollen tube. *D*, the generative cell has moved into the pollen tube. *E*, the generative nucleus has divided into two male gamete nuclei. All diagrammatic.

microgametophyte (now a *pollen grain*) may be carried to the stigma of the same or of another flower. Transportation from pollen sac to stigma (*pollination*) is usually effected by winds or by insects, but it may be brought about by various other agencies.

If conditions are favorable, the tube cell grows out as a *pollen tube* (Fig. 378, *C–E*) shortly after a pollen grain lodges on a stigma. The tube grows through the style to the ovary and finally to an ovule. When it reaches an ovule, it usually grows through the micropyle to the nucellus and through the nucellus to the micropylar end of the megagametophyte. There is considerable variation in the time required for growth of a pollen tube from stigma to megagametophyte. In herbaceous plants the time interval is commonly two to five days, but it may be only a matter of hours. Growth of a pollen tube from stigma to megagametophyte of a bean requires eight to nine hours. Certain woody plants, as beeches and oaks, stand in marked contrast. In these the time interval is often a period of months.

When a pollen tube begins to elongate, the tube nucleus migrates into the growing end and remains there throughout the entire growth of the tube from stigma to ovule. The behavior of the generative cell varies. In certain angiosperms the generative cell divides to form two *male gametes* before the liberation of a microgametophyte from a pollen sac. However, in most angiosperms this formation of male gametes is delayed until after pollination. The two male gametes move down the elongating pollen tube and come to lie a short distance behind the tube nucleus.

Pollination. Some angiosperms, including certain species of violet, produce flowers which never open. In these cases, of course, pollination is impossible. In such *cleistogamous* flowers the pollen grains germinate within the anther, and the pollen tubes grow from there to the ovary and ovules. But apart from instances of this nature, the pollen grains of an angiosperm must be transferred from the anther to a stigma. The transfer may be from anther to stigma of the same flower (usually called *self-pollination*), to a stigma of another flower on the same plant, or to a stigma of a flower on a different plant. Both the latter two cases are referred to as *cross-pollination*, but sometimes only the transfer of pollen to a flower of another plant is so designated. Pollination is brought about in different species by a variety of agencies. In the great majority of angiosperms it is effected either by winds or by insects. Not infrequently pollen grains are more or less accidentally distributed by birds and other animals. In some instances the force of gravity effects pollination, pollen grains falling from an anther landing on the stigma of the flower that produced the pollen. The pollen of plants that live submerged in water floats and is carried about by water currents.

Wind-pollinated species are chiefly those living in localities exposed to the wind or those that grow close together in large numbers. The grasses, which form extensive stands of one or a few species, as in meadows where the wind has a free sweep, are largely wind-pollinated. Many trees, whose flowers are high above the ground and are thus exposed to the wind, also are wind-pollinated. Wind-pollinated flowers produce relatively large amounts of pollen. Their stigmas are large and frequently rough or hairy, so that the lodging of pollen grains upon them is favored.

Flowers and Insects. Insect pollination is especially effective in species whose individual plants are scattered or more or less isolated one from another. It has certain advantages also over wind pollination. Insect pollination is more economical, because the pollen-carrying insect commonly travels from flower to flower of the same species. Consequently, pollen grains have a better chance of reaching an appropriate stigma even if they are not produced in enormous numbers. Another advantage in many cases seems to be the greater opportunity offered for cross-pollination involving the flowers of different plants.

Insects visit a flower either to obtain a sweet food substance (*nectar*) that is secreted in special organs (*nectaries*) associated with the flower, or to obtain pollen which they use as food, or to deposit their eggs within the flower. Some insects, including many moths, gather nectar only; others, such as bees, secure both nectar and pollen.

Radially symmetrical flowers with separate wide-spreading petals, as those of apples and buttercups, are open to all comers and may be visited by a wide variety of insects. Nectar and pollen in flowers with partly or completely united petals are usually available only to certain insects. If the corolla is long and tubular, the nectar can be obtained only by moths and other insects with elongated mouth parts. In certain bilaterally symmetrical flowers, as those of the clovers, bees are the only insects that can reach the nectar or pollen. Regardless of the availability of a flower to insects, the arrangement of stamens and pistils is usually such that, when an insect enters, portions of its body become dusted with pollen, which may be rubbed off on the stigma of the next flower visited.

Cross-pollination between flowers on different plants is brought about in various ways. One of the simplest cases is that of the Chinese primrose. Some of the plants have flowers with long styles and short stamens, the latter being borne near the base of the corolla tube. The flowers of other plants possess very short styles, but their stamens are attached near the upper part of the corolla tube. When

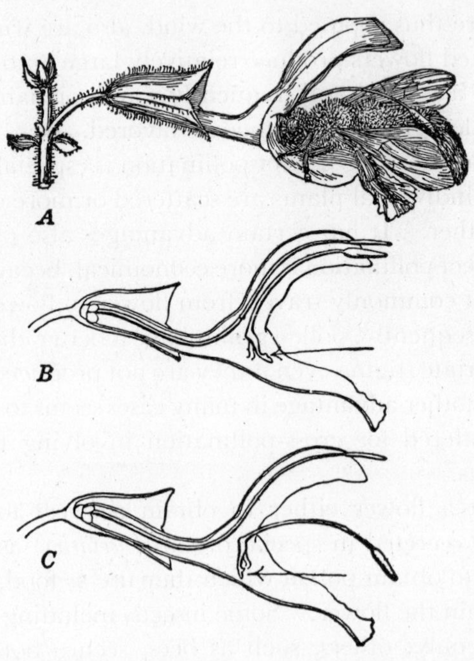

FIG. 379. Pollination of salvia. *A*, a bee has entered the flower. *B*, *C*, lengthwise sections of the flower before and after the bee enters, showing the effect of its entrance upon the position of a stamen; arrows indicate the direction taken by the bee. All after Kerner.

an insect such as a bee visits a long-styled plant, that portion of the insect's body that comes in contact with the low-placed stamens may acquire a load of pollen which is most readily brushed off on the stigma of a short-styled flower. In like manner, the pollen from a short-styled flower whose anthers are near the upper part of the corolla tube may be transferred to the stigma of a long-styled flower.

Salvia (Fig. 379) illustrates structural correlation between flower and insect. The corolla of Salvia is tubular below; its upper portion is divided into two lips. The lower lip of the corolla serves as a landing-stage for insects visiting the flower; the upper lip constitutes a protective shield for the stamens and stigma. There are two stamens. The basal part of each filament is fixed; jointed to the upper end of this short basal part is a curved lever whose two arms are unequal in length. The shorter arm is sterile; the longer arm bears an anther and extends within the curved upper lip of the corolla. When a bee alights upon the lower lip and attempts to thrust its nectar-collecting appendages into the corolla tube, its head presses against the short arm of the lever. When this sterile arm is depressed, the basal part of the filament serving as a fulcrum, the longer arm swings into contact with the hairy surface of the insect's back. If the pollen in the anther is mature, it is dusted upon the bee's body. Smaller insects attempting to secure nectar are not strong enough to depress the short arm of the lever. In a young flower of Salvia, the style lies within the concavity of the upper corolla lip. As the flower matures, the style elongates and curves so that the stigma is midway between the upper and lower lips of the corolla. If a bee sprinkled with pollen visits such a flower, its pollen-dusted back rubs against the stigma and there deposits some of the pollen.

The Smyrna fig supplies another often-cited example of correlation. The flowers of this fig (Fig. 380), borne within the hollow enlarged end of the flower stalk which is to form the fig fruit, are pistillate. Another type of tree (the caprifig), belonging to the same species, itself produces no edible fruit; but it has staminate flowers and *short-styled* pistillate flowers. Pollination is brought about by a particular wasp. The young wasps ordinarily hatch from eggs previously deposited in the short-styled flowers. As an adult wasp emerges from a caprifig it brushes against the staminate flowers, which are near the open end of the fig. If it visits a Smyrna fig to deposit eggs, the pollen brought on its body from the caprifig is deposited on the stigmas of the flowers. The styles of these flowers are so long that the insect eggs do not reach the ovary of the flower and so fail to develop. The result of such pollination is the development of seed and fruit. It has been customary since antiquity to insure the development of Smyrna figs by placing flowering branches of caprifigs in Smyrna fig trees. Other varieties

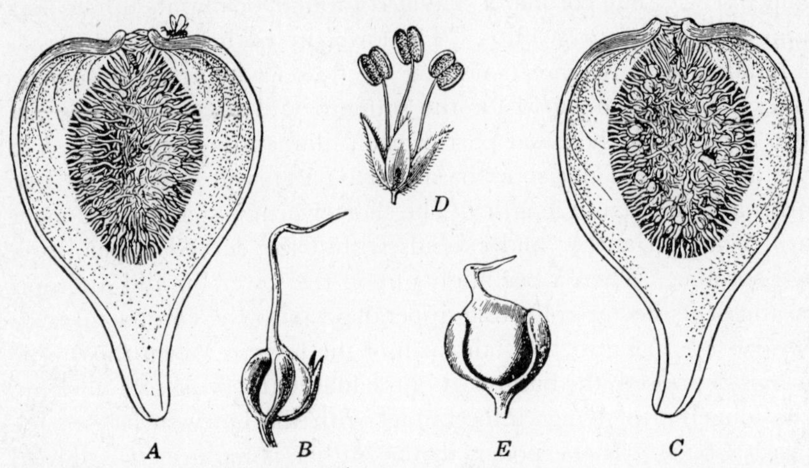

FIG. 380. *A*, end of a flower stalk of the Smyrna fig. *B*, a long-styled pistillate flower; the ovary is developing into a fruit. *C*, end of a flower stalk of the caprifig. *D*, a staminate flower. *E*, a short-styled flower developing into a gall within which is a wasp larva. All after Kerner.

of fig are not dependent upon the wasp for pollination. In most of them, indeed, the development of the fruit occurs even if seeds are not formed.

The relations of their flowers to insects have apparently been an important factor in the evolution of angiosperms; and one reason why angiosperms as a group have been so successful is the fact that many of them have secured the help of insects in pollination. The relations of insects to flowers have been an important factor likewise in the evolution of insects. These statements imply, not that the advantage of a particular structure of a flower or of an insect has been the cause of the appearance of that structure, but rather that, when a particular structure has once appeared and has proved useful, it has persisted. Hence, the present great variety in form and structure among both flowers and insects may be in part accounted for by the interrelationships between insects and angiosperms, especially with respect to pollination.

Gametic Union. After a pollen tube has grown through the micropyle, its tip penetrates the megagametophyte, enlarges some what, the end bursts, and some of its contents, including the male gametes, are discharged into the megagametophyte (Fig. 381). One male gamete nucleus enters the egg and unites with its nucleus, so forming a zygote with 2 *n* chromosomes. The other male gamete nucleus passes to the primary endosperm cell and unites with the

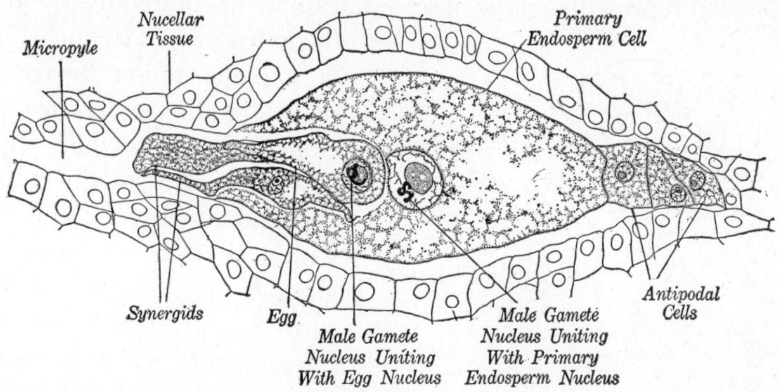

FIG. 381. Mature megagametophyte of prickly lettuce. One male gamete nucleus is uniting with the egg nucleus, one with the primary endosperm nucleus (the latter previously formed by a union of two nuclei). Drawing courtesy of K. L. Mahony.

two nuclei of that cell; sometimes these two nuclei have united before the male nucleus reaches them. The union of three nuclei in the primary endosperm cell is a feature peculiar to angiosperms. Since these nuclei are gametophytic, the nucleus formed by their union contains 3 *n* chromosomes. On the basis of its chromosome number, therefore, the primary endosperm cell, after this union of three nuclei, is neither gametophytic (with *n* chromosomes) nor sporophytic (with 2 *n* chromosomes).

SEED AND FRUIT

The Seed. Just as in a gymnosperm, the structure from which the seed of an angiosperm is matured (the ovule) is well along in its development at the time of gametic union. As in a gymnosperm, also, the zygote of an angiosperm develops into the embryo of the mature seed; and the integument (or integuments) matures into the seed coat (or coats). Differently from the condition in gymnosperms, the megagametophyte does not persist as a tissue in which most of the reserve food is stored. Instead, the primary endosperm cell, containing a nucleus with 3 *n* chromosomes, develops into a temporary or permanent food-storage tissue of the maturing seed. In most angiosperms the synergids and antipodal cells, as well as the nucellus, disappear shortly after the formation of the endosperm begins.

Development of a Dicotyledonous Seed. The shepherd's purse (*Capsella*) represents a type of seed development commonly found in dicotyledons. At the time of gametic union the ovule of Capsella contains an elongated, somewhat crescent-shaped, seven-celled megagametophyte. This lies within a thin megasporangium (nucellus), which in turn is surrounded by two integuments. Shortly after gametic union the ovule grows rapidly, chiefly through a great increase in size of the primary endosperm cell. Enlargement of this cell involves the development of a large central vacuole, the dense cytoplasm thus being limited to a peripheral layer which is thickest in the regions at the ends of the cell. Growth of the primary endosperm cell is accompanied by a division of the primary endosperm nucleus and by the repeated division of the nuclei derived from it. The primary endosperm cell eventually contains many nuclei, each with 3 *n* chromosomes, which are fairly evenly distributed throughout the dense cytoplasm (Fig. 382). Considerably later, by cell division, the many-nucleate primary endosperm cell becomes a many-celled tissue, the endosperm, with one-nucleate cells.

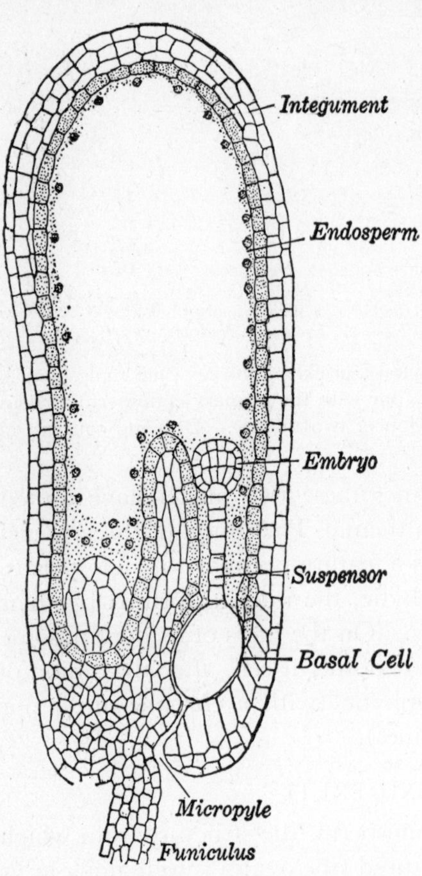

FIG. 382. Capsella; an immature seed containing a young embryo.

The endosperm of an angiosperm should not be confused with that of a gymnosperm. In gymnosperms the endosperm is the old megagametophyte, each of whose cells contain *n* chromosomes. In angiosperms the endosperm is a new structure developed after gametic union and one whose cells each contain 3 *n* chromosomes. Despite these differences, the endosperm has the same function in both gymnosperms and angiosperms—that of providing for the nutrition of the embryo.

The endosperm of Capsella is in time almost entirely digested and absorbed by the developing embryo. In some angiosperms, the endosperm persists to form a relatively large portion of the

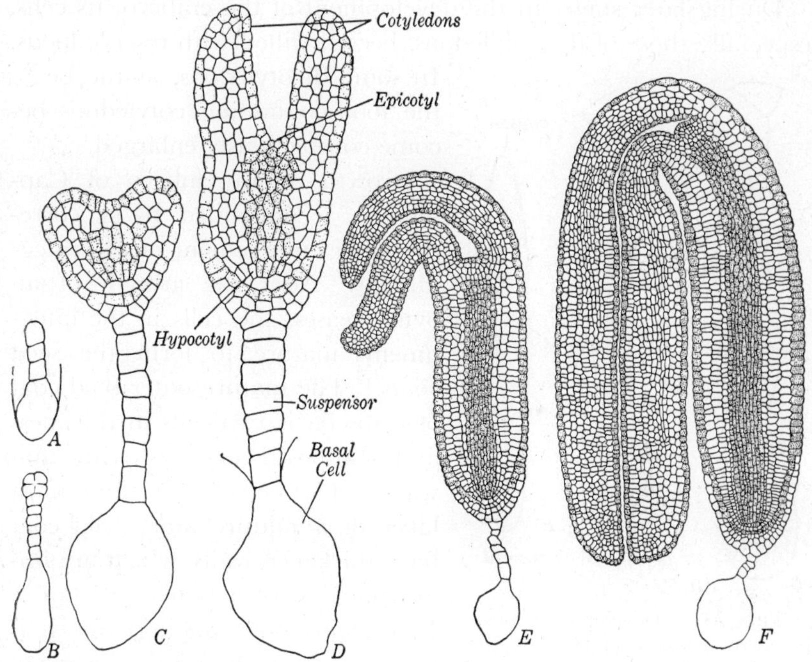

FIG. 383. Development of an embryo of Capsella. *A*, *B*, early stages. *C*, *D*, stages showing the development of cotyledons, epicotyl, and hypocotyl. *E*, *F*, still later stages, less highly magnified; the tissues of the cotyledons and hypocotyl are being differentiated. All after Mabel Schaffner in the *Ohio Naturalist*.

mature seed. Here it constitutes a tissue filled with reserve foods which may be used by the embryo during germination of the seed.

While the endosperm is beginning to develop, there is formed from the zygote a short row of cells (Fig. 383, *A*). Of these cells, the one farthest from the micropyle will develop into most of the embryo; the other cells of the row constitute a suspensor. The embryo formed from the terminal cell becomes a multicellular structure, which eventually differentiates into two cotyledons, an epicotyl, and a hypocotyl. The end of the hypocotyl directed toward the micropyle gives rise to the primary root, the root cap being formed from adjacent suspensor cells. Close to the farther end of the embryo the two lateral cotyledons have grown out (Fig. 383, *D*), and between them lies a small group of embryonic cells, the epicotyl. Later the two cotyledons grow rapidly and, arching over, come to lie parallel to the hypocotyl (Fig. 383, *E*, *F*).

During later stages in the development of the embryo, its cells, especially those of the cotyledons, become filled with reserve foods. In some dicotyledons, as the bean, the food-containing cotyledons become conspicuously enlarged.

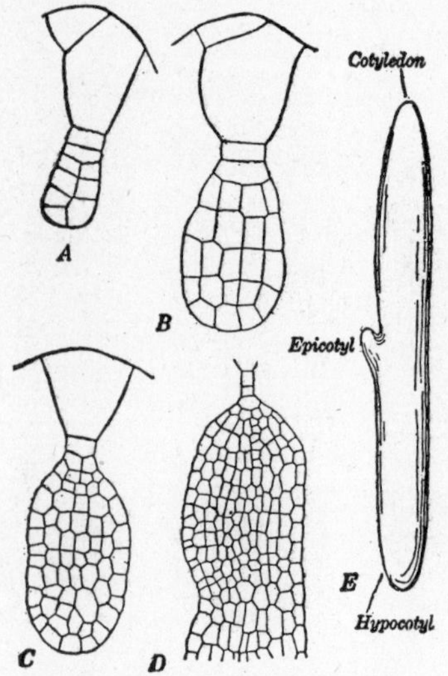

FIG. 384. Development of a monocotyledonous embryo (Sagittaria). *A–D*, early stages; redrawn from J. H. Schaffner in the *Botanical Gazette*. *E*, mature embryo.

Growth of an embryo of Capsella is accompanied by a corresponding enlargement of the integuments. After the growth of an ovule ceases, the cells in the integuments mature to form the seed coats. The mature outer seed coat of Capsella is two cells in thickness and composed of cells with thin walls. The cells of the innermost layer of a mature inner seed coat have thickened walls, which are impregnated with a fatlike substance. In certain other angiosperms it is the cells of the outermost, instead of the innermost layer whose walls are thickened and impregnated. In either case it is the impregnated portion of a seed coat which prevents undue loss of water during the interval between the ripening of a seed and its germination.

Development of a Monocotyledonous Seed. Development of the endosperm and of the seed coat (or coats) is essentially the same in monocotyledons as in dicotyledons. In contrast with dicotyledons, the endosperm in monocotyledons is usually a persistent tissue and the chief region for storage of reserve foods in the seed.

Embryos of monocotyledons and of dicotyledons are strikingly different. An embryo of a monocotyledon has a single large cotyledon, apparently borne terminally, and a laterally borne epicotyl between the cotyledon and the hypocotyl. The method by which the embryo develops in the arrowhead (Sagittaria, Fig. 384) is characteristic of many monocotyledons. Here the zygote develops into a row of three cells. The basal cell is much the largest and does not divide; the median cell by division and growth develops into a suspensor, a hypocotyl, and a lateral epicotyl; the terminal cell develops into a single cotyledon.

Fruits. Angiosperms differ from gymnosperms in the development of a carpel (megasporophyll) or carpels into a pistil whose lower portion, the ovary, completely encloses the ovules. Another feature peculiar to angiosperms is the development of the ovary and its contents into a *fruit.*

Pollination and gametic union influence the subsequent development both of the ovules and of the ovary enclosing the ovules. Maturation of the tissues of an ovary into a fruit may or may not involve a very considerable increase in size. The different parts of the ovary in different genera mature into tissues and structures of varied nature. Different angiosperms, therefore, display great variation in size, form, and structure of their mature fruits. Development of a fruit often involves other parts of a flower than the ovary, such as the sepals and the receptacle. A *true fruit,* however, includes only structures derived from the ovary.

When fruit and seed are mature, the seed is shed, either separately or still enclosed by the fruit. Under appropriate conditions the seed may germinate and the resting embryo resume development and grow into a free-living independent sporophyte.

Life Cycle (Fig. 385). The sporophyte (whether tree, shrub, or herb) produces flowers. All flowers of a species may be alike and contain both stamens and carpels; or a species may have two kinds of flowers, one with stamens, the other with carpels. A stamen (microsporophyll) bears an anther containing a variable number of pollen sacs (microsporangia). In a microsporangium are many microspore mother cells, each of which divides to form four microspores. A microspore develops into a young microgametophyte (pollen grain) while still within the microsporangium; later it may be transported to the stigma of a pistil. There it develops a pollen tube containing two male gametes. The pollen tube grows down

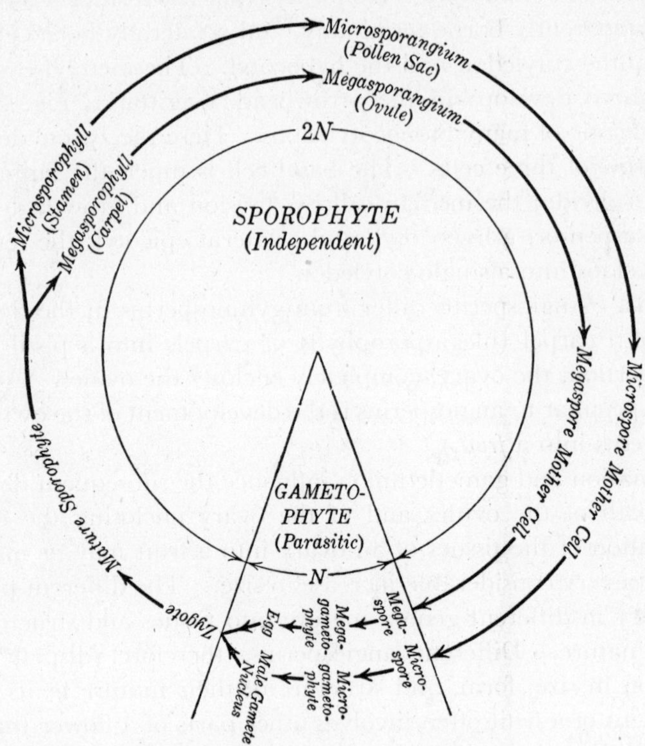

FIG. 385. Life cycle of an angiosperm.

to the megagametophyte, into which it discharges the two male gametes.

A carpel (megasporophyll) or carpels develop into a pistil whose lower portion, the ovary, completely encloses one or more ovules. An ovule is a megasporangium surrounded by either one or two integuments. Within the megasporangium (nucellus) is a single megaspore mother cell; this usually divides to form four megaspores, three of which disintegrate. The persistent megaspore develops most frequently into a seven-celled megagametophyte. Of the two male gametes entering the megagametophyte from the pollen tube, the nucleus of one unites with the egg nucleus, that of the other unites with the two nuclei of the primary endosperm cell. The endosperm tissue developing from the primary endosperm cell has nuclei with 3 *n* chromosomes. The zygote develops into an embryo with hypocotyl, epicotyl, and either one or two cotyledons. The embryo, when the seed is mature, may or may not be surrounded by an endosperm. The embryo lies within a seed developed from the ovule. The ovary with its inclusions becomes a fruit. When a seed germinates, the embryo resumes growth and develops into a free-living sporophyte.

Classes of Angiosperms. Angiosperms are divided into two classes, *Dicotyledoneae* and *Monocotyledoneae*. These classes are named for the number of cotyledons which respectively characterize their embryos. The embryo of a dicotyledon usually has two cotyledons; that of a monocotyledon usually has one. Attention has already been called (Chapters IV–VII) to certain characteristic differences between the two classes in the structure of the plant body (sporophyte). These and other features which chiefly distinguish the two may be summarized as follows:

(*a*) Most dicotyledonous stems are characterized by the presence of a single cylinder of vascular bundles; in most monocotyledonous stems the bundles are scattered throughout the stele.

(*b*) Each vascular bundle in a dicotyledonous stem possesses a cambium; that of a monocotyledonous stem lacks a cambium.

(*c*) A dicotyledonous root has, as a rule, but few ridges radiating from the central mass of primary xylem; a monocotyledonous root usually has numerous xylem ridges.

(*d*) A dicotyledonous root develops a cambium; a monocotyledonous root rarely forms one.

(*e*) The leaves of dicotyledons are netted-veined; those of monocotyledons are usually parallel-veined.

(*f*) The parts of a dicotyledonous flower (sepals, petals, stamens, and carpels) are very commonly in fours or fives or in multiples of four or five; in monocotyledons the floral parts commonly occur in threes or in multiples of three.

(*g*) An embryo of a dicotyledon usually has a terminal epicotyl and two lateral cotyledons; that of a monocotyledon usually has a lateral epicotyl and a single terminal cotyledon.

There are no characteristic differences between dicotyledons and monocotyledons in the structure or development of microgametophyte or megagametophyte.

New Features in Angiosperms. Angiosperms and gymnosperms are alike in the essential points that distinguish the seed plants from plants below them in the evolutionary scale. Angiosperms, however, are more advanced than gymnosperms in the following respects:

(*a*) In the presence of sepals, petals, or both, in addition to sporophylls.

(*b*) In the development of the megasporophyll or megasporophylls into a pistil.

(*c*) In some further reduction of the microgametophyte.

(*d*) In the lodging of a young microgametophyte (pollen grain) on the stigma at some distance from the megasporangium.

(*e*) In the marked reduction of the megagametophyte to a few-celled structure.

(*f*) In the functioning of a male gamete in initiating the development of the endosperm.

(*g*) In the development of a fruit.

(*h*) Typically, in the presence of vessels in the xylem.

Progress from Bryophytes to Angiosperms. In the evolutionary series leading from bryophytes through pteridophytes to seed plants, there has been no modification of the most fundamental features of the life cycle. Throughout the entire series the gametes unite to form a zygote, which develops into a sporophyte, whose distinctive function is the production of spores. A spore, in turn, develops into a gametophyte, whose distinctive function is the production of gametes. Throughout the entire series, also, the chromosome number is doubled when gametes unite; and the number is halved when spores are formed. Each cell of the gametophyte has n chromosomes; each cell of the sporophyte, $2n$.

Despite these basic similarities, however, the series from bryophytes to spermatophytes displays certain evolutionary tendencies that culminate in the angiosperms.

(*a*) The gametophyte of a bryophyte is the larger, independent generation; in a fern it is the smaller generation but still independent. In Selaginella and a few other pteridophytes the gametophyte is much reduced and essentially parasitic upon the sporophyte; in seed plants it is still more reduced and entirely parasitic, reaching the extreme of reduction in angiosperms.

(*b*) The evolution of the sporophyte has followed an opposite course. Sporophytes of bryophytes are small and more or less parasitic throughout their entire development; those of ferns are larger than the gametophyte and parasitic only in an embryonic stage. In Selaginella and in gymnosperms the sporophyte is but briefly parasitic upon the very small megagametophyte. In angiosperms the nutritive function of the megagametophyte has been transferred to a unique tissue, the endosperm, whose cells contain $3\ n$ chromosomes. In addition, in both gymnosperms and angiosperms the old sporophyte has become responsible for the nourishment and protection of the young sporophyte.

(*c*) In bryophytes and pteridophytes gametic union depends upon the presence of water, by means of which the male gametes reach the eggs. In seed plants the male gametophyte possesses a new structure, the pollen tube, which insures the transport of male gametes to the neighborhood of an egg. Male gametes of Zamia and of certain other primitive gymnosperms are motile but depend upon the pollen tube to supply a pathway to the megagametophyte; male gametes of most gymnosperms and of all angiosperms have lost their flagella.

(*d*) In bryophytes and in most pteridophytes all spores are substantially alike in size. In many bryophytes spores are sexually differentiated in the sense that some are destined to give rise to male, and some to female, gametophytes. This is not the case, however, in many other bryophytes or in most ferns. In Selaginella and a few other pteridophytes, spores are of two distinct sorts: large (female) and small (male). Sexual differentiation in Selaginella does not begin with the spores: here it has been pushed back to the sporangia, structures of the sporophyte. Although the sporangia are asexual reproductive structures, they are sexually differentiated. In most gymnosperms sexual differentiation has been pushed farther back; namely, to the sporophylls and strobili. In angiosperms with separate pistillate and staminate plants, the whole sporophyte may be sexually differentiated.

(*e*) In most bryophytes and pteridophytes a spore is shed from the sporangium before it begins development into a gametophyte. In some species of Selaginella the production of two kinds of spores is correlated with the fact that the larger (female) spore develops into a megagametophyte entirely within the megasporangium.

However, in most of these species of Selaginella the megagametophyte is liberated from the megasporangium before gametic union. A megagametophyte of a gymnosperm is not similarly liberated. Consequently, during the early development of a new sporophytic generation it is surrounded both by the megagametophyte and by structures of the old sporophyte.

Permanent retention of the megagametophyte within the sporangium, the beginning of development of the zygote into a new sporophyte while still enclosed within megagametophyte and megasporangium, and the maturation of the integument, or of nucellus and integument, into protective tissues mark the appearance of a wholly new structure—the seed. Another novel feature connected with the evolution of seeds is the temporary cessation of growth of the new sporophyte at a certain stage. The seed of an angiosperm shows a further advance in that the megagametophytic tissue is obliterated after gametic union, reserve foods for the young sporophyte being stored in a newly evolved tissue, the endosperm, or in the young sporophyte itself.

CHAPTER XXX

SEEDS AND FRUITS

Nature of Seeds. A seed develops from an ovule. After the union of the two male gamete nuclei with the egg nucleus and primary endosperm nucleus, respectively, the zygote develops into an embryo, the primary endosperm cell into a nutritive tissue (the endosperm), and the integument or integuments into a seed coat or coats. Development of an integument into a seed coat results from a stimulus arising in the developing embryo, endosperm, or both. The endosperm may persist in the seed, or it may be absorbed by the developing embryo. In the seeds of a few plants a portion of the nucellus persists as a food-storage tissue.

Seeds of angiosperms differ widely in structural details. The two classes of angiosperms, dicotyledons and monocotyledons, are named from a striking difference between their respective embryos. The embryo of a dicotyledon has a hypocotyl, typically two approximately equal lateral cotyledons, and, between the cotyledons, a terminal epicotyl. The embryo of a monocotyledon has a hypocotyl, one large cotyledon apparently borne terminally, and a lateral epicotyl. Many angiosperm seeds, such as those of a lily, contain a considerable amount of endosperm when mature. In the development of the seeds of other angiosperms, such as the shepherd's purse and bean, the endosperm, although formed, is quickly absorbed; and reserve foods are stored in the cotyledons instead of in an endosperm. In general, the mature seed of a moncotyledon contains an endosperm; the mature seeds of some dicotyledons possess endosperm, those of others do not.

A Seed without Endosperm. On the concave edge of a bean seed (Fig. 386) is a fairly large scar, the *hilum*, marking the former point of attachment of the seed to the short stalk (*funiculus*) which connected the ovule with the edge of the carpel. Near one end of the hilum is the micropyle. There are two seed coats, developed respectively from the two integuments, the inner coat being somewhat thicker and heavier than the outer and the two more or less firmly united. The embryo occupies all the space within the seed coats. It has two large, thick, firm cotyledons, closely appressed

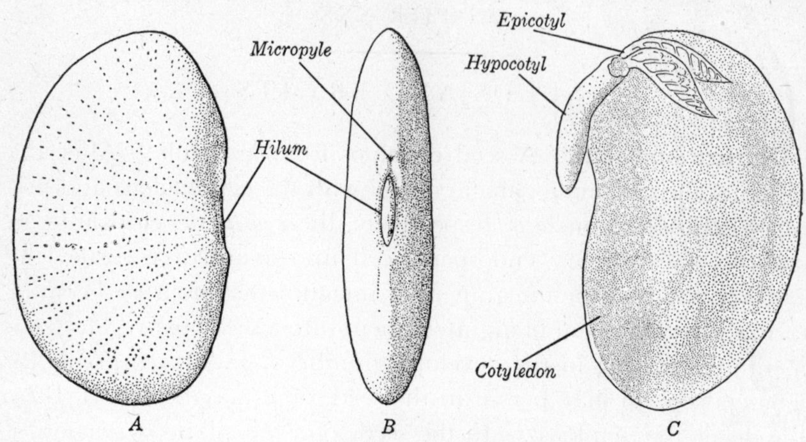

FIG. 386. Seed of bean. *A*, side view. *B*, as seen from the inner (attached) edge. *C*, embryo; seed coats and one cotyledon removed.

and enclosing the epicotyl, which bears two opposite, overlapping, immature foliage leaves. The hypocotyl lies outside the cotyledons and is bent backward along the line of meeting of the cotyledons within the concave edge of the seed. The cotyledons contain large reserves of starch and proteins, as well as some sugars, fats, hormones, and enzymes.

A Seed with Endosperm. A lily seed (Fig. 387, *C*) is broad and flat. Its seed coats are thin and membranous, sometimes forming a narrow, winglike expansion about the entire circumference of the seed. Within the seed coats is a firm, starchy endosperm, imbedded in which is the relatively small embryo. The embryo is long and narrow, nearly cylindrical, and slightly curved. The hypocotyl is near the micropylar end of the seed and frequently projects a short way beyond the surrounding endosperm. The long, massive cotyledon partly surrounds the small epicotyl. The embryo contains some fats and proteins. The endosperm is rich in starch.

Ability of Seeds to Germinate. One great difference between a seed and most other plant organs, such as root, stem, or leaf, is that in the dormant seed the processes characteristic of living matter may go on very slowly. Such a seed respires, but respiration in an air-dry seed is almost infinitesimal in amount as compared with respiration in a stem or leaf. The partial suspension of activity in

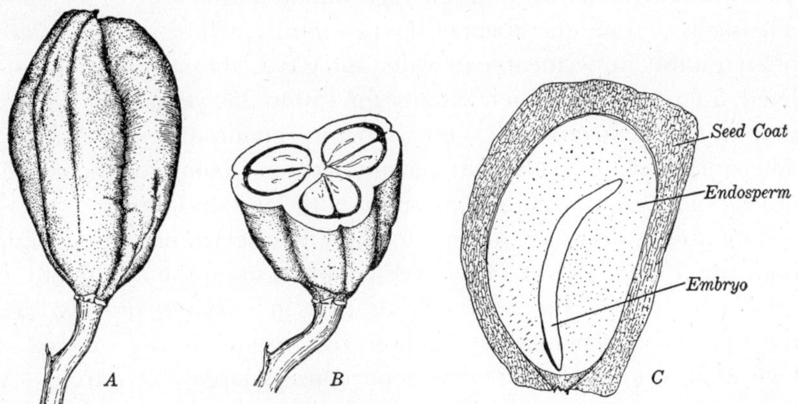

Fig. 387. *A*, *B*, surface view and cross section of a lily fruit. *C*, lengthwise section of a lily seed.

a seed results primarily from its comparative dryness. During the maturing of a seed the greater part of its contained water has been lost. Although the amount of water in seeds is usually small, some water must be present if the embryo is to survive; and this small amount of water is tenaciously held.

It is commonly said that a seed is *ripe* at the time of its separation from the parent plant, but it does not follow that the seed at this time is ready to germinate. Many seeds germinate at maturity or shortly thereafter if conditions are suitable. This is especially true of short-lived plants, including many crop plants, whose seeds usually germinate as soon as they are scattered. Such early germination is sometimes a disadvantage; in warm, moist autumns, for example, corn grains may germinate while still upon the ear. A common present-day agricultural practice is the artificial drying of corn in order to preserve it over winter in better condition for germination.

The length of time during which seeds remain capable of germination varies greatly. At one extreme are those of willows and poplars, which must germinate within a few days or not at all. Some acorns will not germinate after a year; coffee beans, not after six months. Among common crop plants, tobacco has probably the longest-lived seeds; they have been known to germinate after storage for 20 years. Seeds of other, less well-known, plants remain capable of germination even longer. Those of certain species from dated herbarium collections have germinated after 87 to 130 years. The seeds of some members of the pea family, whose seed coats are often notably impermeable to water and gases, are probably longest-lived, a few retaining their vitality for 150 to 250 years. However, despite these extreme cases, no seeds can remain alive indefinitely. The stories told of seeds that germinated after being for thousands of years in Egyptian tombs are quite without foundation.

The ability of a seed to remain capable of germination depends both upon the structure of the seed coat and upon the nature of the substances within the seed. Seeds rich in enzymes quickly lose their power of germination. Those rich in fats do not survive as long as do those whose reserve food consists largely of starch. A low water content, which reduces the rate of respiration and of other processes to a minimum, is primarily responsible for the longevity of many seeds.

Although the presence of water is essential to germination, submergence in water for any great length of time results in the death of many seeds, including those of rye, oats, and corn. Seeds of some plants, however, can withstand submergence for years, probably because of the extreme resistance offered by their seed coats to the penetration of water and oxygen. If deeply buried in soil, some seeds retain the needed water and the power of germination for a long time. Indian lotus seeds buried in the mud of Manchuria for 200 years have germinated after treatment with certain chemical substances which modified their permeability to water and gases. A considerable number of plants become weed pests because of the longevity of their buried seeds.

Many seeds must undergo *after-ripening* before germination can occur. Among other things, after-ripening may involve: changes in the acidity of the seed contents; the formation, or changes in content, of certain enzymes; and the transformation or digestion of stored foods. In some seeds these changes require days; in others, weeks, months, or even years are necessary.

In certain cases the prolonged postponement of germination is due to the hardness and thickness of the seed coat. The impermeability of the seed and fruit coats of certain crop plants and weeds, excluding water or oxygen from the embryo, is responsible for the expression "hard seeds." A large percentage of the seeds of alfalfa and tobacco, for example, exhibit "hardness" because their seed coats contain waxlike products impervious to water. A more uniform and prompter germination of such seeds is made possible by grinding away the hard surfaces with abrasive agents, such as sand or sandpaper, or by employing a scarifying machine when the quantity of seed justifies this mechanical aid. Etching the seed coats with strong sulphuric acid is another procedure. The cocklebur, some other representatives of the composite family, and certain grasses produce a high percentage of fruits impervious to oxygen. Variations in permeability of seed coats may account for the fact that often some seeds germinate long before others of the same species. Such variations, in annuals, insure the persistence of the species even though a particular season proves unfavorable for germination.

Germination (Fig. 388). Germination depends upon certain external factors; of these the most important are the presence of water and of oxygen and a suitable temperature. Water is essential to the expansion of certain parts of a seed, as well as to the initiation of activities within, including the digestion of stored foods and their translocation to the parts of the embryo where they are to be utilized.

Temperature is an important factor, since, up to a certain point, the higher the temperature the more rapid are various processes within cells. Assimilation and respiration are much more active at 20° than at 5° C. Temperatures for the germination of most seeds range from 3° to 49° C., the optimum being about 33° C. The minimum temperature at which seeds will germinate varies greatly with the species.

Oxygen is essential to the respiration of a developing seedling, both before and after it emerges from the seed coat. A germinating seed is the seat of a series of processes, all involving the expenditure of energy. Since the energy to be used in these processes must be released by respiration and since, therefore, respiration is characteristically rapid in germinating seeds and in seedlings, a considerable supply of oxygen is necessary, although at the beginning of germination anaerobic respiration (not requiring a supply of free oxygen) may play an important part.

When germination begins, the embryo and endosperm imbibe water, swell, and their expansion finally ruptures the seed coat. In some cases the breaking of the seed coat is irregular, as in the bean; in others it takes place along definite lines. The seed coat of a germinating squash seed is broken first at its narrow end. At first the growth of the embryo involves chiefly an enlargement of already existing cells as a result of the intake of water, rather than a formation of new cells by division. Growth is at first largely localized in the hypocotyl, which elongates and soon emerges from the seed coat. Seeds of some plants are so constituted that the part of the seed containing the hypocotyl is that which is most likely to be turned toward the soil. For the majority of seeds, however, this is not the case; and it is a matter of chance whether the side of the seed from which the hypocotyl emerges is toward or away from the soil. In any case, the primary root, which develops from the lower end of the hypocotyl, curves under the influence of the stimulus of gravity until it is growing directly downward. This curvature is due to the strongly positive geotropism of the hypocotyl.

At least after the first stages of germination, the growth of the hypocotyl and of other parts of the embryo involves the formation of new cells by division as well as the enlargement of already existing cells. The formation and growth of new cells necessitate the use of foods. Until the seedling has developed chlorophyll, it can not carry on photosynthesis and hence is dependent for the foods needed in its growth, as well as for those to be utilized in respiration, upon the reserves stored in the seed. If, as is frequently the case in dicotyledons, reserve foods are stored in the cotyledons, these foods are digested by enzymes produced in certain parts of the embryo. The digested foods are then translocated to the growing portions of the seedling, where they are chiefly utilized. In seeds containing endosperm, the secretion of enzymes and the absorption of digested foods from the endosperm are brought about largely or entirely by the cotyledon or cotyledons. This is especially true of members of the grass family such as wheat and corn, in which the cotyledon is a digestive and absorptive organ that never emerges from the seed coat.

During its further growth the hypocotyl frequently becomes arched in such a manner as to pull the cotyledons out of the seed coat. This arching is well illustrated in the seedlings of the common bean (Fig. 388, *A*). In the development of the seedlings of the squash and of some of its relatives, the removal of the cotyledons from the seed coat is assisted by a peglike outgrowth from the hypo-

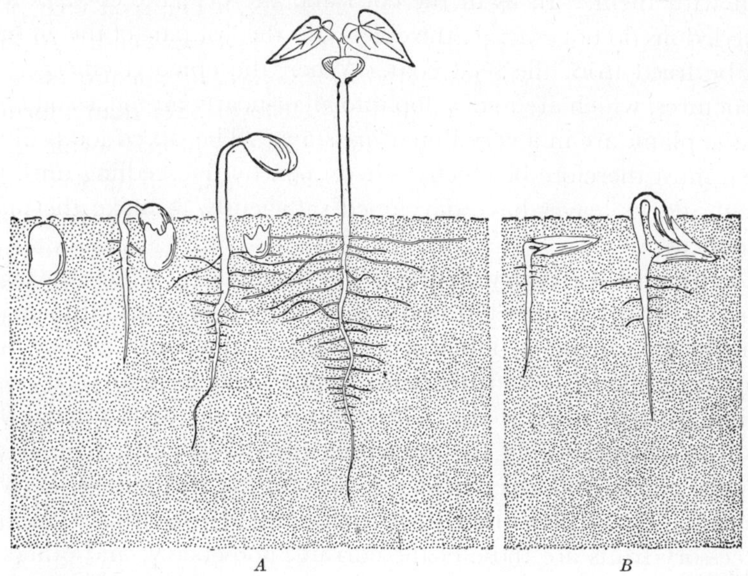

FIG. 388. *A*, stages in the germination of a bean seed. *B*, germinating seed of squash; the emergence of the embryo from the seed coat is assisted by a peglike outgrowth of the hypocotyl.

cotyl (Fig. 388, *B*). The arching of the hypocotyl and its later straightening result from a negative rather than a positive geotropism of the portion of the hypocotyl in the vicinity of the cotyledons. Sometimes, as in the pea and the scarlet runner bean, the hypocotyl remains short and unarched; the cotyledons, like the single cotyledon of the corn, never emerge from the seed coat, and the shoot which issues above ground and produces foliage leaves is developed entirely from the epicotyl.

In those cases in which the cotyledons are withdrawn from the seed coat and pushed above the soil, they form more or less chlorophyll and to some extent function as foliage leaves. Often, however, as in the common bean, the cotyledons are thick and soon shrivel and drop off. Cotyledons of other seedlings, such as those of the castor bean, become flat, expanded leaves, which persist and function for some time in photosynthesis. As a rule, cotyledons are different in form from the leaves developed later, often being smaller and simpler than these leaves.

If the cotyledons emerge from the seed, the epicotyl is brought out with them. If, as in the corn and the pea, the cotyledon or cotyledons do not emerge, the epicotyl is the last part of the embryo to be freed from the seed coat. When the epicotyl emerges, its structures, which are to develop into all or nearly all the aerial parts of the plant, are in a very immature state. The stored foods in the seed must therefore be chiefly relied upon by the seedling until the stem and its leaves have developed sufficiently to make the plant independent.

True and Accessory Fruits. The changes by which an ovule and its inclusions develop into a seed within an ovary are accompanied by a metamorphosis of the ovary into a fruit. A *true fruit*, strictly speaking, is a structure developed solely from an ovary containing one or more seeds. Often, however, the development of a fruit involves not only the ovary but additional parts, such as the sepals, petals, and receptacle. A structure of this nature, derived from the ovary plus other structures, is an *accessory fruit*. Among accessory fruits are those of the currant, gooseberry, and others to be mentioned later.

Simple Fruits. When but a single ovary, with or without surrounding structures, develops into a fruit, the fruit is *simple*. At the

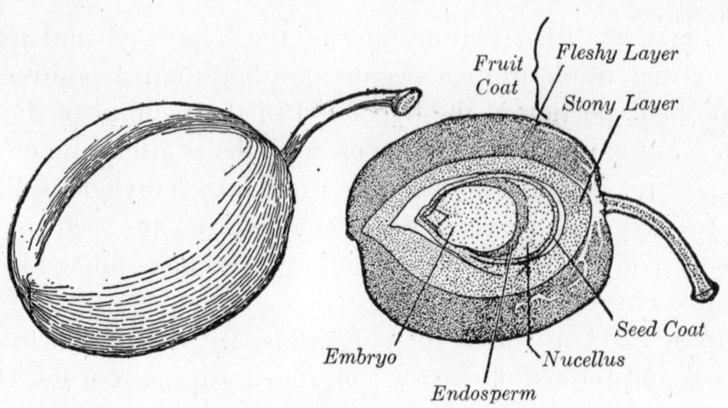

FIG. 389. The plum, a stone fruit (immature).

time of pollination and gametic union the ovary walls of all species are essentially alike in that they consist of tissues which, except for vascular bundles and provascular strands, are homogeneous in structure. The growth and maturation of the ovary wall after pollination result, however, in different species in the development of fruits which differ markedly with respect to the tissues that compose them. Simple fruits are either *fleshy* or *dry*.

Fleshy Simple Fruits. In a stone fruit (*drupe*), such as a plum (Fig. 389), peach, or cherry, the outermost layers of the ovary wall form the skin; the layers next within become fleshy or, as in the almond, fibrous; and the innermost layers, becoming hard and stony, form the "pit," which encloses the comparatively soft, thin-coated seed.

If the fruit is one in which the ovary wall (at least its inner portions) and the interior structures of the ovary have become enlarged and juicy, the fruit is a *berry*. The seeds, each with a hard coat of its own, are imbedded in the juicy flesh of the fruit. A berry may develop from an ovary composed either of a single carpel or of more than one carpel. The tomato, orange, and grape are berries. The tomato (Fig. 390) is a large berry consisting in primitive forms of two carpels, although in many cultivated varieties there are five or more. The fleshy portion of the fruit is developed from the ovary wall, the very greatly enlarged ovule-bearing ridges, and the partitions between the carpels. A citrus fruit, such as an orange, lemon, or grapefruit, is a berry with a tough, leathery rind. Each section of an orange or grapefruit represents a carpel, the carpels being firmly attached to one another at their outer surfaces but readily separable along their

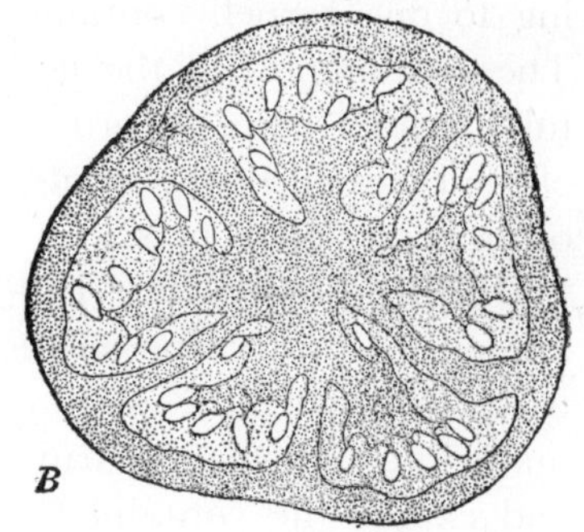

FIG. 390. *A*, the tomato, a berry whose ovary wall has become greatly thickened and juicy. *B*, the same in cross section. The fruit here shown was developed from five carpels.

lateral faces. Except for the space occupied by the seeds, each carpel is filled with many small hairlike outgrowths arising from its inner surface. As the fruit matures, these outgrowths become filled with juice. The date is a berry with a single hard seed, the fleshy part having developed from the ovary wall.

Some berries are accessory fruits. Among these are the currant, gooseberry, blueberry, and cranberry. In the flower of each of these is a floral tube surrounding and fused with the ovary. A considerable part of the juicy portion of the fruit is derived from this tube. Opinions differ as to whether in various instances the floral tube represents the receptacle, the united bases of sepals, petals, and stamens, or both sets of structures. In the blueberry and cranberry, at least, the tube seems to consist chiefly of the bases of the sepals, petals, and stamens. Melons and squashes are essentially berries of a similar sort. The "peel" of a banana is a development from the floral tube.

In the apple type of fruit (*pome*), the carpels are more or less firmly united with one another, at least at their inner edges, and are surrounded by, and united with, the floral tube. The outer portion of the ovary wall constitutes part of the pulp of the apple; the inner part of the wall is leathery, and each division of the core, corresponding to one carpel, contains usually two, sometimes more, seeds. The greater part of the fleshy tissue is developed from the floral tube, which here, according to the latest studies, consists chiefly of the bases of sepals, petals, and stamens. The upper (free) ends of the sepals often persist at the outer end of the fruit.

Dry Simple Fruits. Instead of becoming fleshy, an ovary may mature into a dry, more or less hard fruit. There are two general types of dry fruits: *indehiscent* fruits, which do not split open at maturity; and *dehiscent* fruits, which regularly split when mature and expose the contained seed or seeds. As a general rule, an indehiscent dry fruit contains a single seed, and a dehiscent dry fruit contains more than one seed.

If an indehiscent dry fruit includes but one seed, the seed being attached to the fruit wall at only one point, the fruit is an *achene*. Achenes are produced by the buckwheat, sunflower (Fig. 1, *A*), and buttercup. Since the fruit wall of an achene is merely a thin, dry layer enclosing the seed, the fruit is seedlike in appearance. The achenes of many plants are commonly called "seeds."

If the thin, transparent fruit wall is attached at all points to the seed coat, the dry indehiscent fruit is a *grain*. Fruits of this type are produced by many members of the grass family, including the corn (Fig. 391), wheat, and other cereals. In a corn grain an

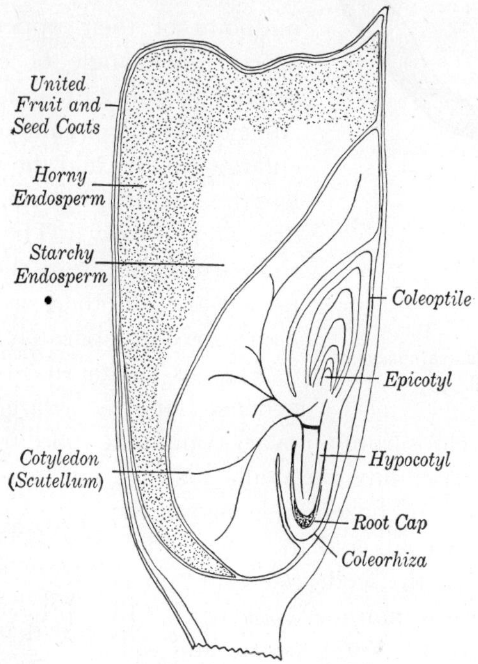

FIG. 391. Lengthwise section of a fruit (grain) of corn.

abundant endosperm completely fills the seed coat except for the space at one side that is occupied by the embryo. The greater part of the embryo consists of a broad cotyledon (*scutellum*) whose infolded edges almost completely enclose the epicotyl. The small epicotyl bears several immature leaves, the oldest one of which constitutes a sheath (*coleoptile*) that encloses the younger leaves and the epicotyl. Extending in a direction opposite to that taken by the epicotyl is a small hypocotyl, surrounded by a special sheath (*coleorhiza*) and partly surrounded by the large cotyledon. The endosperm consists of an opaque starchy and a transparent horny portion, the latter containing the major part of the protein foods. The embryo contains reserves of fats, sugars, some proteins, and small amounts of starch.

In some cases the margin or the apex of an indehiscent dry fruit develops into a winglike structure. A fruit of this type is a *samara* (Fig. 392). The maple, ash, and elm bear samaras. In the flower of a maple two ovaries are side by side, a compound style arising at the midpoint of their upper edge. The outer upper angle of each ovary is extended and flattened into a wing. After the union of gametes, the ovaries enlarge greatly; and the wings grow in length and breadth, finally becoming dry and papery. The two ovaries (now fruits) fall from the tree still attached to each other; or they may split apart and fall separately.

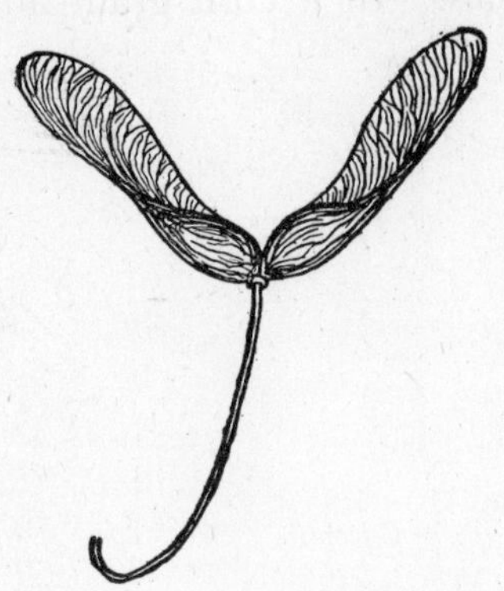

FIG. 392. Fruits (samaras) of maple.

A *nut* is similar in structure to an achene; but it is of larger size, and it frequently develops from an ovary containing more than one ovule. In the latter case, only one ovule matures into a seed. In such nuts as the chestnut, hazelnut, or acorn, the shell is the fruit coat, and the softer edible portion within is the seed. Certain "nuts" are something less than the whole fruit. In the hickory nut (Fig. 393), pecan, and walnut, the hard shell is formed from the inner part of the ovary wall; the outer part becomes the husk. An almond corresponds to the stone of a drupe, the outer fibrous part of the fruit coat having dried and fallen away. In a coconut, likewise, the hard shell is the inner part of the fruit coat. Some true seeds are commonly called "nuts." A Brazil nut is a seed, 18 to 24 such seeds being borne in a single fruit. A horse chestnut likewise is a seed; the fruit, a prickly capsule, contains from one to three seeds.

FIG. 393. Fruits (nuts) of hickory, each containing one seed.

A compound pistil, each carpel enclosing a single ovule, may mature into an indehiscent fruit whose parts (the carpels) separate from one another at maturity. The fruits of mallow and geranium and of members of the parsley family are examples of this type, the *schizocarp*.

Dehiscent dry fruits may be developed from either simple or compound pistils. One type of dehiscent dry fruit is the *legume*, characteristic of the bean, pea (Fig. 394), and other members of

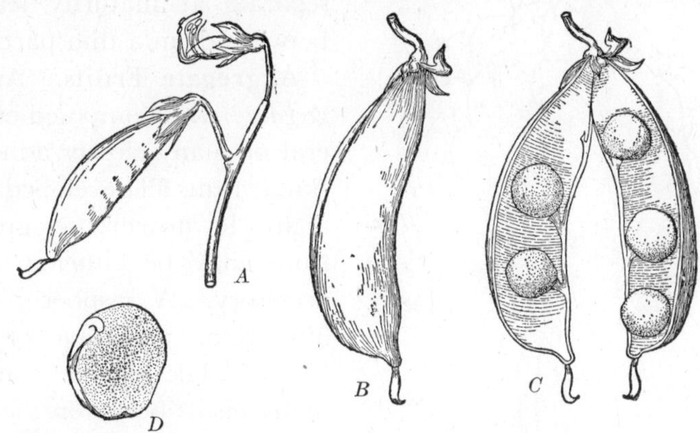

FIG. 394. Fruit (legume) and embryo of pea. *A*, immature fruits. *B*, surface view of a mature fruit. *C*, mature fruit split open. *D*, embryo, with one cotyledon removed.

the pea family. A legume develops from a pistil consisting of a single carpel whose edges are united. Seeds are borne attached alternately to the two edges; but, since the edges are united, the seeds lie in a nearly straight line. When a legume splits open, some of the seeds may remain attached to one edge and some to the other. The fruit of the peanut forms an exception in that it does not open at maturity. It is, however, a legume.

A *follicle* is like a legume except that it splits longitudinally along but one edge, whereas a legume splits along two opposite edges. The fruits of milkweed and columbine are follicles.

A *capsule* also is a dry fruit which cracks or breaks open at maturity; differently from a legume or follicle, it is developed from an ovary composed of more than one carpel. Capsules open in various ways when the seeds are mature; most commonly they split lengthwise into a definite number of segments, the number corresponding to the number of carpels. In the lily the split is along the line corresponding to the midrib of each carpel; in the mountain laurel and rhododendron the split occurs along each line of juncture between adjacent carpels. In a poppy capsule, the opening is by means of a circle of pores in the upper edge.

The fruit characteristic of the mustard family is called, depending upon its form, a *silique* or a *silicle*. In either case it consists of two many-seeded carpels which separate at maturity leaving between them a thin partition.

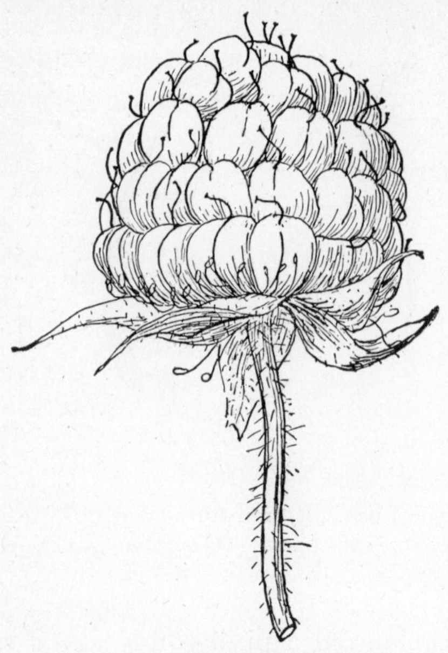

FIG. 395. Aggregate fruit of raspberry.

Aggregate Fruits. An *aggregate fruit* is composed of several or many closely adherent simple fruits all developed from a single flower. Aggregate fruits may be either true or accessory. A raspberry (Fig. 395) is an aggregate of true fruits. The flower contains many pistils borne on the conical terminal portion of the receptacle. The ovary of each pistil develops into a small stone fruit. However, the many stone fruits are densely crowded and become so firmly attached during maturation that they adhere in a single mass when separated from the receptacle. A blackberry also is an aggregate fruit of this type, but the receptacle becomes softened and juicy and breaks off with the "berry."

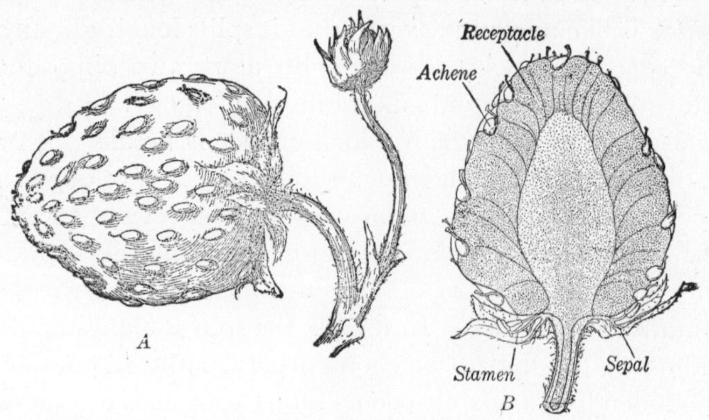

FIG. 396. Aggregate accessory fruit of strawberry, bearing many true fruits (achenes) on its surface. *A*, surface view. *B*, lengthwise section.

A strawberry (Fig. 396) is an aggregate accessory fruit developed from a single flower. The flower, like that of the raspberry, has a conical receptacle bearing many pistils. During maturation, the receptacle becomes greatly enlarged both beneath and between the pistils, the pistils thus being more widely separated. The ovary of each pistil develops into an achene; the numerous achenes, or true fruits, are thus borne on and somewhat imbedded in the colored, juicy structure developed from the receptacle.

Multiple Fruits. A multiple fruit is developed not from a single flower but from a cluster of flowers. The individual fruits in such a case are characteristically accessory fruits. In a mulberry (Fig. 397), the ovary of each flower of a cluster becomes a one-seeded fruit with a hard coat. The calyx lobes persist, become fleshy, and enclose the ovary. The adherence of the simple fruits so formed gives rise to a multiple fruit.

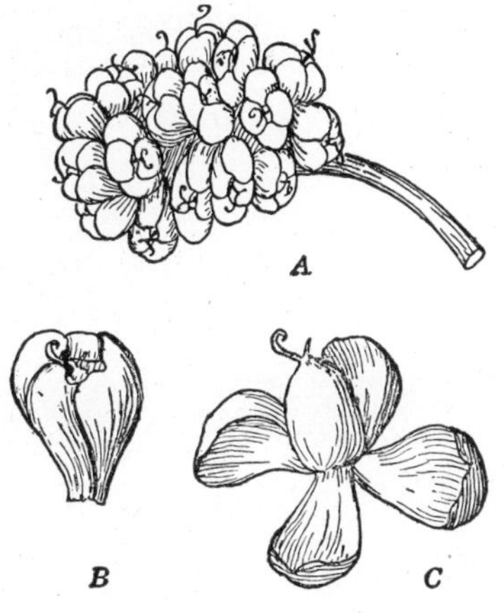

Fig. 397. *A*, multiple accessory fruit of mulberry. *B*, surface view of an individual fruit. *C*, the same, with the fleshy sepals bent back, exposing the true fruit.

Fig. 398. Multiple accessory fruit of pineapple.

In a pineapple (Fig. 398), as in a mulberry, a number of closely united accessory fruits are spirally arranged about a more or less fleshy axis Each flower of the cluster is borne in the axil of a bract.

The fleshy fruit maturing from each flower consists of the united ovary and receptacle, together with the basal parts of the sepals and bract. The exposed hard, scaly portion of each fruit is composed of three more or less overlapping sepals, which in turn are overlapped by the erect tip of the bract. Most commercial varieties of pineapple do not contain seeds. At the apex of the whole multiple fruit are many greenish bracts in whose axils no flowers were borne.

The fig (Fig. 380) resembles a multiple fruit in that it includes many individual fruits, each developed from a single flower. It differs in the fact that the individual fruits are not adherent. The flowers are borne within the enlarged hollow end of a branch. Some flowers are staminate, some pistillate, the distribution of the two kinds varying as between different varieties and species of fig. A pistillate flower may produce a true fruit which is an achene similar to a true fruit of the strawberry but usually smaller and more nearly spherical. The hollow end of the branch bearing the flowers grows still larger and its tissues form the fleshy part of the "fruit."

Classification of Fruits.

1. Simple:
    - (*a*) Fleshy:
        - Drupe or stone fruit (plum).
        - Berry (grape).
        - Pome (apple).
    - (*b*) Dry:
        - Indehiscent:
            - Achene (sunflower).
            - Grain (corn).
            - Samara (maple).
            - Nut (acorn).
            - Schizocarp (geranium).
        - Dehiscent:
            - Legume (pea).
            - Follicle (milkweed).
            - Capsule (lily).
            - Silique (mustard).
            - Silicle (candytuft).
2. Aggregate (raspberry).
3. Multiple (pineapple).

Dispersal of Seeds and Fruits. In a seed plant the seed represents the point in the life cycle at which a wider distribution of the species may chiefly be brought about. It follows that means for the dispersal of seeds to a greater or less distance from the plant that bore them are of importance to the perpetuation and extension of many species. Varied means of dispersal have appeared in the course of the evolution of different families of angiosperms.

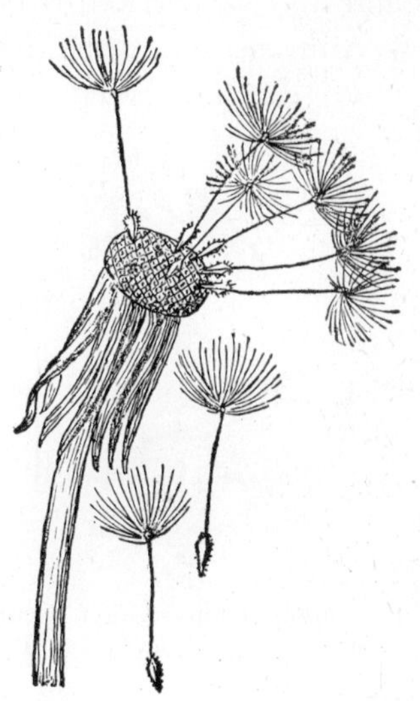

Fig. 399. Achene-like accessory fruits of dandelion; the plumelike structures facilitate dispersal by winds.

Very many seeds, either separately or still enclosed within the fruits, are scattered by winds. Fruits and seeds that are so carried are usually small and light; and in case the whole fruit is blown about, it is usually a single-seeded fruit. Besides being small enough to be easily carried by winds, some seeds and fruits bear outgrowths or appendages which assist in their dispersal. Such outgrowths may be flat wings which, as in the catalpa and the trumpet creeper, are developments of the seed coat or, as in the elm and maple, expansions of the ovary wall. Sometimes there are hairlike or plumelike outgrowths of the seed coat, as in the milkweed, poplar, cotton, and willow, or similar outgrowths of the ovary wall, as in the anemone. In the dandelion (Fig. 399), thistle, and other composites, the plumelike structures attached to the fruit are developments of the calyx. Another method by which the wind aids in seed dispersal is seen in "tumble weeds." These consist of entire plants, as in the case of the Russian thistle, or in some species of flower clusters which become detached and are blown about over the surface of the ground, scattering their seeds as they go.

Water plays an important part in the dispersal of seeds and fruits of some plants, especially of those living in water or along the borders of streams and the shores of oceans. Either the seeds or the fruits of such plants are themselves lighter than water, or they have structures that render them buoyant. Among seeds dispersed by water are those of the white water lily, the iris, and some sedges. It has been thought that the wide distribution of the coconut palm throughout the tropics results from the nature of the outer portions of its fruits, which are spongy and especially resistant to salt water. In consequence, the fruit may float for a long time without injury and may be carried by ocean currents to great distances.

Animals, too, assist in scattering seeds and fruits. The fruits of many common weeds bear hooks or barbs (Fig. 400) by means of

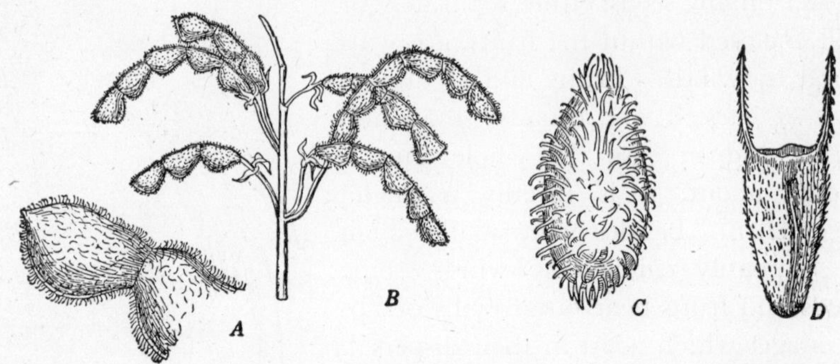

FIG. 400. Fruits which become attached to coats of passing animals. *A*, *B*, sticktight (Hedysarum). *C*, cocklebur. *D*, beggar-ticks. All after Kerner.

which they become attached to the coats of passing animals or to human clothing, being then carried to varying distances. Such outgrowths, in the cases of sticktights, beggar-ticks, cocklebur, and stickseeds, are developments from the fruit coat; those of the burdock are the developed bracts of the floral head. The horny and barbed fruits of some grasses wound the mouths of grazing animals; and burs adhering to the fleece of sheep reduce the value of their wool. The mud collected by the feet and legs of wading birds often contains seeds, which are thus distributed. Some fruits and seeds have sticky coverings by means of which they may adhere to the bodies of animals.

A very common means of dispersal is the production of edible seeds or fruits. Fruits of such trees as the walnut, hickory, and oak are carried away and hidden by squirrels, often in places where, if not eaten, the seeds may germinate. Other animals, especially birds, eat such edible fruits as berries. In such a case the seeds are usually swallowed; but these seeds are commonly protected by their coats from the action of the animal's digestive juices, and hence they pass uninjured through its alimentary tract and are deposited at a distance from the plant that produced them.

Man has played a larger part in the distribution of seeds and fruits than has any of the lower animals. His rôle has consisted both in the intentional extension of the range of cultivated plants and in the accidental dispersal of seeds, particularly those of weeds. A weed is any plant that is growing where it is not desired, especially if its presence is objectionable or injurious. Weeds are spread largely by means of seeds that are sown with those of cultivated plants; the weeds are then harvested and distributed with the crop. In this way chess is spread with wheat, wild oats with cultivated oats, and dodder with clover or alfalfa. Weed seeds are disseminated too by various accidental means: in dust and stable manure, by threshing machines and other farm implements, by automobiles and railway trains. Weeds such as the Russian thistle and the Canada thistle often occur along railways, where their seeds have dropped from passing trains. Many troublesome weeds represent species that are not objectionable in their native lands but that, when carried to other countries, find favorable conditions for rapid multiplication.

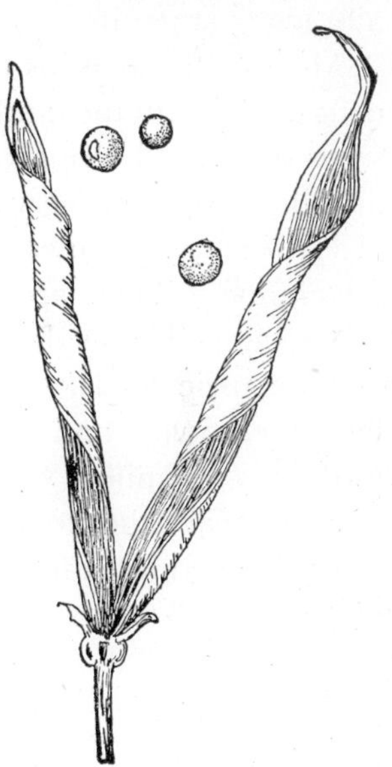

FIG. 401. Legume of a vetch, which opens suddenly and hurls the seeds.

Some plants have means by which their seeds, when mature, are explosively discharged from the fruits. The seeds of a violet are squeezed out by a contraction of the sectors into which the fruit coat splits. The fruits of vetches (Fig. 401) and of the witch hazel open suddenly so as to shoot out the seeds by a method comparable to that found in the violet. In the cranesbill the fruit coat splits suddenly, and its parts curl in such a way that the seeds are discharged. In touch-me-nots the explosion of the fruit is brought about by the pressure of turgid tissues; and the seeds of the "squirting cucumber" are ejected through an opening produced in the base of the mature fruit by its separation from the flower stalk.

Importance of Seeds and Fruits to Man. Aside from their chief functions—the perpetuation and spread of their own species— many seeds and fruits are sources of useful substances. Familiar instances of foods are the fruits of the cereal grains and a great number of other edible fruits and seeds, some of which have been mentioned in the pages preceding. Various beverages are derived from fruits or seeds, including coconut milk, coffee, chocolate, cocoa, extracted fruit juices, and alcoholic drinks. Fats and oils stored in fruits and seeds are of great commercial value. Some of these fats are used in soap-making or as sources of glycerin, the base of various explosives. Olive oil, cottonseed oil, peanut oil, corn oil, soybean oil, and coconut oil are extensively used in human foods. Linseed oil, from flax seed, and tung oil enter into the manufacture of paints, varnishes, linoleum, and printer's ink; soybean oil has an even wider range of commercial uses. Among spices and condiments, nutmeg and white and black mustard are from seeds, pepper and allspice from fruits.

Most of the poisons of plant origin are useful in small doses as drugs. Strychnine and brucine are alkaloids derived from the seeds of a small tree growing in India and the Philippines. They are stimulants and nerve tonics. The seeds of the Calabar bean or ordeal bean contain alkaloids whose action is opposite to that of strychnine. They are used as antidotes in cases of strychnine poisoning. The seeds of the bitter almond, containing hydrocyanic acid (prussic acid), supply a sedative used in medicine. Anise, fennel, caraway, and coriander contain volatile oils which are used as drugs. Vanilla "beans," furnishing a flavoring extract as well as a drug, are the fruits of a Mexican epiphytic orchid. Opium is the thickened latex from the fruit coat of the poppy. It contains a number of alkaloids, including morphine and codeine.

CHAPTER XXXI

FLORAL ARRANGEMENT, AND THE FAMILIES OF ANGIOSPERMS

Arrangement of Flowers. The flowers of some plants are solitary; that is, they are borne singly, as in the trillium and the May apple, each at the end of a stem or of a branch. If the flower terminates a branch, this branch (the flower stalk), like most branches, commonly arises in the axil of a leaf. Sometimes, as in Fuchsia, this is an ordinary foliage leaf; but often the leaf from whose axil the flower stalk grows is small and sessile. Such a leaf is a *bract*.

More often flowers are not solitary but occur in clusters. A flower stalk which bears either a solitary flower or a cluster of flowers is a *peduncle*. The smaller stalks that bear the individual flowers of a cluster are *pedicels*. Pedicels, as well as peduncles, may arise in the axils of bracts.

Two main types of flower cluster are recognized, depending upon the relative times at which different flowers of the cluster mature. If the flowers which open first are those attached nearest the base of the peduncle, the cluster is *indeterminate*. It is so called because the floral axis can continue indefinitely to grow and to produce new flowers.

The form of an indeterminate cluster depends largely upon the relative lengths of pedicels and peduncle. If, as in the lily of the valley, the currant, and the chokecherry, both peduncle and pedicels are fairly long and all pedicels are of about the same length, the cluster is a *raceme* (Fig. 402, *A*). If the flowers are arranged as in a raceme but the pedicels of the lower flowers are longer than those of the upper ones, so that the flowers are borne at nearly or quite the same level and the cluster is approximately flat-topped, it is a *corymb* (Fig. 402, *B*). In an *umbel* (Fig. 402, *C*) the pedicels arise at about the same level on the peduncle. Since the pedicels are all of the same or nearly the same length, an umbel, like a corymb, is flat-topped. If the peduncle is elongated, the intervals between the flowers are short, and the pedicels are short or lacking, the flowers therefore being borne close to the peduncle and to each other, the flower cluster is a *spike* (Fig. 402, *D*). The common

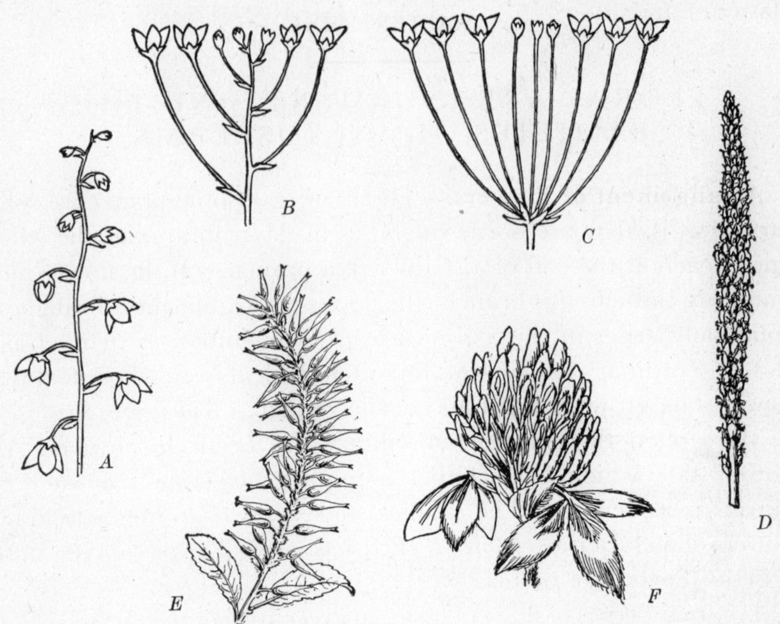

Fig. 402. Types of flower clusters. *A*, raceme; *B*, corymb; *C*, umbel; *D*, spike of plantain, after Bailey; *E*, catkin of willow; *F*, head of clover, after Smalian. *A–C* diagrammatic.

mullein and the dooryard plantain bear spikes. A *catkin* (Fig. 402, *E*), such as is borne by a willow or a poplar, is a spike with scaly bracts. If the peduncle is so shortened and broadened, as in the red clover or sunflower, that the cluster is more or less round- or flat-topped, it is a *head* (Fig. 402, *F*).

In a *determinate* flower cluster the central or terminal flower is the first to open, later flowers arising below the first one. The upward growth of the main floral axis is terminated by the development of the central flower. A cluster of this type is called a *cyme* (Fig. 403, *A*). Cymes may resemble in form either racemes or corymbs.

Apart from the simple forms of cluster already mentioned, there are many types of *compound* flower clusters. In these the peduncles are branched, each branch bearing pedicels. A common compound type is the *panicle* (Fig. 403, *C*), such as is borne by the oat and by many other grasses; other types are compound corymbs, compound umbels, and compound cymes (Fig. 403, *B*).

Classification of Angiosperms. The chief characters of the two classes of angiosperms (dicotyledons and monocotyledons) have already been mentioned. In arranging the members of these classes into orders, families, genera, and species, the structure and arrangement of flowers and fruits are chiefly used as bases of classification. Monocotyledons include 45 families, divided into approximately 1500 genera and 40,000 species. Dicotyledons include 240 families, with about 7300 genera and 155,000 species. On account of the large number of angiosperms, only a few representative families can be described in the following pages. These families are selected either because of their large numbers of species or because they include especially well-known plants.

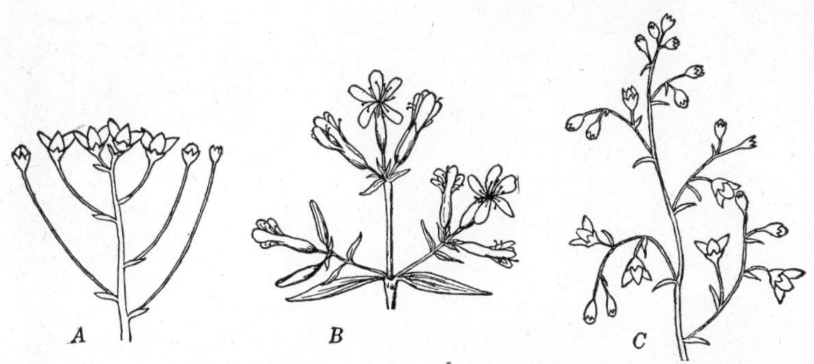

FIG. 403. Types of flower clusters. *A*, cyme; *B*, compound cyme of Saponaria, after Rusby; *C*, panicle. *A*, *C* diagrammatic.

DICOTYLEDONS

Willow Family. A number of common trees and shrubs belong to a group of small families all of which have relatively simple flowers. One of these is the willow family, to which belong the willows (Fig. 404) and poplars. In all members of this family, flowers occur in catkins of two kinds: one kind having pistillate flowers; the other, staminate flowers. Pistillate and staminate catkins are usually borne on separate plants. The flowers are very simple; a pistillate flower of the willow consists of one pistil borne in the axil of a hairy, scalelike bract. The pistil is composed of two united carpels, and the ovary contains a large number of ovules.

A staminate flower, borne likewise in the axil of a hairy bract, consists of two or more stamens, the number varying with the species.

The flowers of poplars are similar in general structure to those of willows. The fruit is a capsule. When the seeds are mature, the

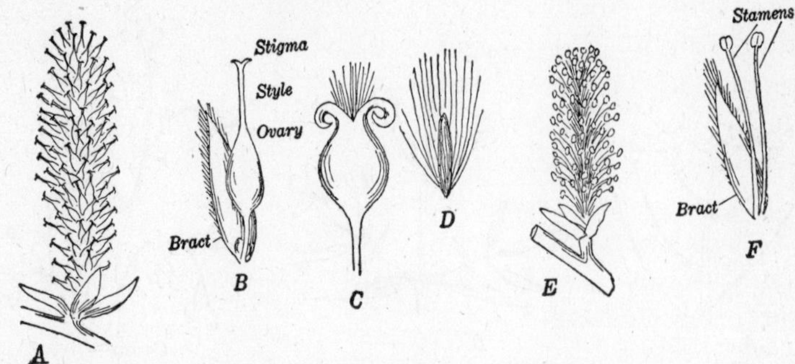

FIG. 404. Flowers, fruit, and seed of willow. *A*, pistillate catkin. *B*, pistillate flower. *C*, fruit. *D*, seed. *E*, staminate catkin. *F*, staminate flower.

capsule opens by a separation of its two constituent carpels. Each of the many seeds bears a circle of hairs at its base, forming a parachute-like structure that facilitates the carrying of the seed by winds. The cottonwood is a species of poplar in which the hairs borne by the seeds are especially long and silky.

Among the relatives of the willow family are the walnut family, which includes the hickory, pecan, and walnuts; the birch family, to which belong hazels, alders, and birches; and the beech family, including chestnuts, beeches, and oaks.

Nettle Family. Among the many members of this family are a number of trees as well as herbaceous plants. The flowers are still simple but somewhat more complicated, especially by the presence of a calyx, than are those of the willows. In most species the flowers containing stamens and those containing pistils are separate, the two kinds of flowers being borne either on the same or on different plants. The stamens are most commonly equal in number to the sepals; there is a one- (rarely two-) chambered ovary which forms a one-seeded fruit. The fruit is a samara, an achene, or a drupe.

The great majority of the family are tropical. The leaves of some members, including the nettles from which the family is named, have hairs that secrete an irritating acid. Among the trees belonging here are elms (Fig. 405), hackberries, and mulberries. The leaves of the white mulberry, which has been cultivated in Mediterranean countries since the twelfth century and in its native country, China, for much longer, are used as food for silkworms. The fruits of this and of other mulberries are edible. Closely related to the mulberries is the Osage orange. Other members of the family are the hop and hemp. Hemp is largely grown for the tough bast fibers in its stem, from which rope, thread, carpet yarns, binder twine, sacking, sailcloth, and oakum are made. The flowering top of the pistillate plant supplies a resin, *cannabin*, used in medicine. The tops, under the name of *ganja* or *gunjah*, are sold in the bazaars of India for smoking. The dried tops or leaves are known in Mexico as *marijuana*. Mixed with aromatic drugs, in the Orient they are called *hashish*. The family includes some other fiber plants in addition to hemp, as well as the breadfruit tree of the tropics.

Fig. 405. Elm twig bearing flowers and fruits. The flowers of the elm, differently from those of most members of the nettle family, are often "perfect"—that is, the same flower contains both pistil and stamens.

Many plants of the nettle family contain a milky juice (*latex*). The latex of the South American cow tree furnishes a nutritive beverage. The latex of several tropical members of the family is a source of rubber. The "India-rubber tree," the best-known rubber-yielding plant native to the eastern hemisphere, is a species of Ficus. Under the name of "rubber plant," small specimens of this tree are grown as house plants in colder climates. (The tree most largely cultivated on plantations for rubber in various parts of the tropics is a member of the spurge family.) To the genus Ficus belong also the cultivated figs and the banyan tree (Fig. 120).

Pink Family. The families thus far mentioned are characterized for the most part by inconspicuous flowers, borne usually in close clusters, which either are naked (that is, without sepals or petals) or have sepals only. Many members of the pink family have large, showy flowers borne singly or in small clusters and provided with both sepals and petals. They are mostly herbs, whereas the more primitive families include a large proportion of trees. The flowers in this family have usually five (sometimes four) sepals, as many petals if petals are present, and not more than twice as

FIG. 406. Flower cluster of sweet william, a member of the pink family.

FIG. 407. A buttercup.

many stamens as sepals. The family includes some plants commonly cultivated for their flowers, the best known of which are the carnations and the related pinks and sweet williams (Fig. 406). The carnations are descendants of a European species that has long been cultivated. Among common wild plants of the family are the chickweeds, catchflies, campions, bouncing Bet, and corn cockle.

Crowfoot Family. This, like the pink family, includes many species with showy, often solitary flowers having either a conspicuous calyx or a green calyx and a showy corolla.

The flower of a buttercup (Fig. 407) is fairly illustrative of the characteristics of the family. The receptacle is dome-shaped. The parts of the flower—sepals, petals, stamens, and pistils—are arranged spirally upon this receptacle, the sepals being lowest and each succeeding set of parts arising from the receptacle above the set just outside it. The sepals are typically five, although there are variations from this number. Next within are five, or occasionally more, almost circular yellow petals, each bearing at the base on its inner side a small scale. Within the petals are an indefinite, rather large number of stamens and within these a likewise indefinite number of pistils. Each pistil consists of a single carpel, and its ovary contains one ovule. A flower, therefore, produces a considerable number of achenes.

The flowers of most other members of the crowfoot family are similar in general plan to that of the buttercup. The numbers of the floral parts vary considerably. In a few species, including the larkspur, the flowers are irregular and bilaterally symmetrical, in consequence of the fact that the sepals of any flower are not all of the same shape, the same being true of the petals. Among the many familiar wild plants belonging to this family, in addition to various species of buttercup, are the anemones, hepaticas, marsh marigold, baneberry, clematis, meadow rues, and columbines. Some of the cultivated members of the family are the peony and species of columbine, clematis, and larkspur. Substances used in medicine, some of them actively poisonous in sufficient quantities, are obtained from hellebore, aconite, black cohosh, and golden seal. The last named supplies also a yellow dye.

Mustard Family. The great majority of plants in this family are herbaceous; their roots, stems, or leaves in many cases contain sharp-tasting substances that make them valuable as condiments.

The flowers of the familiar shepherd's purse (Fig. 408) illustrate a structure characteristic of the family. These flowers are borne in a long raceme. All the parts of each flower arise from a flattened receptacle. There are four green sepals; four small white petals, arranged in the form of a cross; and six stamens, of which two are shorter than the other four. The four long stamens seem really to represent two, each of which is branched close to its base. In the center of the flower is a single pistil composed of two united carpels. The ovary is divided by a partition into two chambers, in each of which are many ovules. The fruit (a silicle) is flattened, approximately triangular in shape, and notched at the apex. Like the ovary from which it developed, the fruit is divided by a partition; at maturity the sides of the fruit separate from the partition, allowing the seeds to be scattered.

The flowers of members of the mustard family are all so similar to that of the shepherd's purse, being marked especially by the cross-shaped corolla, that they are readily distinguished from those of other families. Members cultivated as sources of food are the turnip, rutabaga, radish, horseradish, garden cress, and mustard. A very important species is *Brassica oleracea* (Fig. 449), which by variation seems to have given rise to the cabbage, cauliflower, kohlrabi, Welsh cabbage, and Brussels sprouts. Members grown for their showy flowers are the stocks, or gillyflowers, the sweet alyssum, and the candytuft. The water cress belongs in this family.

Fig. 408. A plant of shepherd's purse, and a raceme bearing flowers in its upper portion and fruits below.

Rose Family. This is one of the best-known families, because it includes a very large proportion of the common cultivated fruits as well as many plants with showy flowers. Among its members are herbs, shrubs, and trees.

In some of the family, as the strawberry and raspberry, the receptacle is cone-shaped. In others, including roses and plums, there is a cup-shaped floral tube composed probably of the united bases of sepals, petals, and stamens—possibly in some cases including part of the receptacle. The sepals, petals, and stamens hence seem to arise from the upper margin of this tube. In still other members, illustrated by the apple, the floral tube is united with the ovary, so that the other floral parts are above the ovary.

The family is divided into seven sections, each characterized by its special type of flower and fruit. One section includes the spireas; another, the apple, hawthorn, and service berry; a third, the strawberry and cinquefoil; to a fourth belong raspberries and blackberries; to a fifth, the agrimony; the sixth section includes roses; and the seventh, the plum, cherry, peach, apricot, and almond.

In the majority of wild species of strawberry, as well as of cultivated varieties, the flowers are of two types: one with functional stamens, the other with functional pistils. In either case, the organs of the other sort are usually present though often not fully developed. The flower cluster of a strawberry is a few-flowered cyme. The flower is of a relatively primitive type. At the outside are five small green bracts which are not strictly parts of the flower. Next within is a whorl of five wedge-shaped green sepals; next, five rounded white petals; then usually three cycles of stamens whose number is variable—typically there are ten stamens in the outer whorl and five in each of the inner two whorls. On the conically elongate central portion of the receptacle are many pistils, each consisting of one carpel, which are spirally arranged and closely packed together. The ovary of each pistil contains a single functional ovule; the style projects upward from the side of the ovary. After pollination and the union of gametes, the petals fall away and the stamens wither. The development of the fruit was described in the preceding chapter.

The flower of a wild rose (Fig. 409, *A*) is especially distinguished from that of a strawberry by the fact that there is an urn-shaped floral tube with a comparatively narrow mouth. Within this are numerous pistils. The tube becomes fleshy after gametic union, forming a rounded structure enclosing many dry fruits, each containing one seed. The flower has usually five petals and a large and indefinite number of stamens. Sometimes there are additional petals, making the number more than five; usually the additional petals replace stamens. By the selection of occasional plants with larger numbers of petals and by a repetition of the selection when another similar variation occurred, cultivated varieties of roses have been developed with many petals and with few or no stamens.

A plum (Fig. 409, *B*, *C*) bears its flowers either singly or in small clusters. The floral tube only partly encloses the single pistil. There are five green sepals, five white petals, and numerous (usually

15 to 20) stamens. The ovary contains two ovules, only one of which develops into a seed. After the gametes have united, the outer parts of the flower fall away; and the ovary develops into a

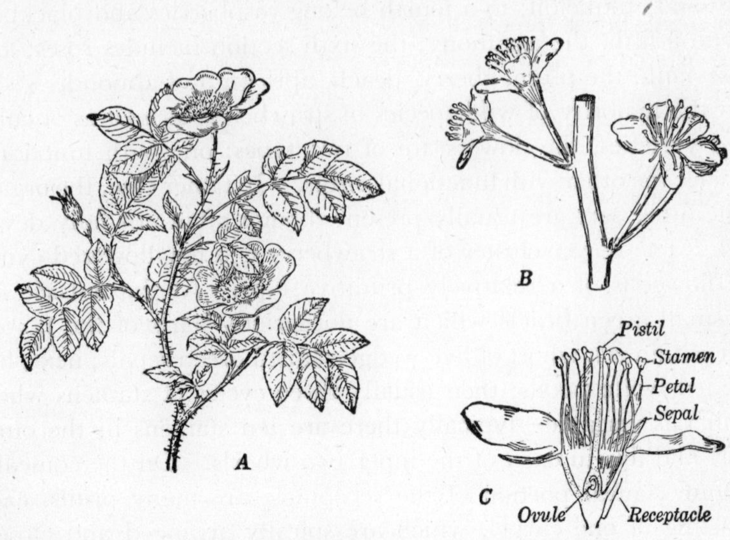

FIG. 409. Members of the rose family. *A*, a wild rose. *B*, flower cluster of the plum. *C*, lengthwise section of a plum flower.

drupe. The outer portion of the ovary wall becomes the skin and the fleshy part of the fruit; the inner portion of the ovary wall forms the hard stone. The soft structure within the stone is the seed. The closely related cherry, apricot, and peach have flowers and fruits of the same type as the plum. The same is true of the almond, but the outer layer of its fruit, which corresponds to the skin and flesh of the plum, dries and is split off; it is the inner part of the fruit, corresponding to the stone of the plum, which is the almond of commerce.

Pea or Pulse Family. This, comprising more than 12,000 species, is, with one exception, the largest family of seed plants. Its members, distributed throughout the world, include herbs, shrubs, and trees. A great majority of the species have bilaterally symmetrical (irregular) flowers of the type illustrated by the bean and pea, although some have regular or nearly regular flowers. All of them bear fruits of the kind known as a legume, developed from the ovary of a simple pistil.

The flowers of the sweet pea (Fig. 410) are borne in loose, open racemes. The peduncle arises from the axil of a leaf, and each pedicel from the axil of a minute bract. The five pointed sepals of a flower are united by their basal parts to form a cup, the three lower sepals being longer than the two upper ones. There are five white or colored petals, although there appear to be but four because two are intimately united. The upper petal (*standard*) is broad and upright; the two lateral petals (*wings*) are borne one at either side of the standard; the two lower petals are united, and their free margins are rolled inward to form a troughlike *keel*. The keel almost completely encloses the ten stamens; nine stamens are united by the expanded bases of their filaments into a sheath surrounding the ovary; the tenth (upper) stamen is separate. The pistil consists of one carpel, whose structure suggests that of a leaf folded on its midrib so that its edges are brought together and united. The ovary contains several ovules, borne in two rows (apparently one) along the infolded and united edges of the carpel. The style curves upward nearly at right angles to the ovary. The stigmatic surface is along one face or edge of the style. This type of flower shows advances over the primitive condition in the union of sepals, the union of two petals, the union of the filaments of nine stamens, and in its bilateral symmetry.

FIG. 410. Sweet pea. The small bracts in whose axils the pedicels arose have disappeared.

After gametic union the pistils and stamens fall off, and the ovary enlarges greatly as the seeds develop. When mature, the fruit formed by the growth of the ovary becomes dry and opens along two lines, one corresponding to the midrib of the carpel, the other to the line of junction of its two united edges.

As described in Chapter XVI, many members of the pulse family are characterized by a peculiar relation to certain bacteria which enables them indirectly to use the nitrogen of the air. In consequence of this relation, several of them are widely used forage plants; and their cultivation plays an important part in conserving and adding to the supply of nitrogenous food materials in the soil. Plants extensively grown for this purpose are the clovers, alfalfa, vetches, cowpea, and soybean. Another important characteristic of members of the family is the habit of storing reserve proteins in their seeds. It is because these contain a much larger proportion of proteins than most other seeds—as well as large carbohydrate or fat reserves—that the seeds of the pea, bean, soybean, and lentil are important as human foods. A peculiar feature of the peanut is that after pollination its pedicels turn and grow downward, pushing the fruits into the soil, where they ripen. Other well-known members of the family are the honey locust, black locust, wisteria, and mimosa. Among the woody tropical and subtropical species are many that supply lumber, resins, gums (including gum arabic), dyes (especially indigo), and drugs. Medicinal products obtained from members are cassia, senna, and licorice.

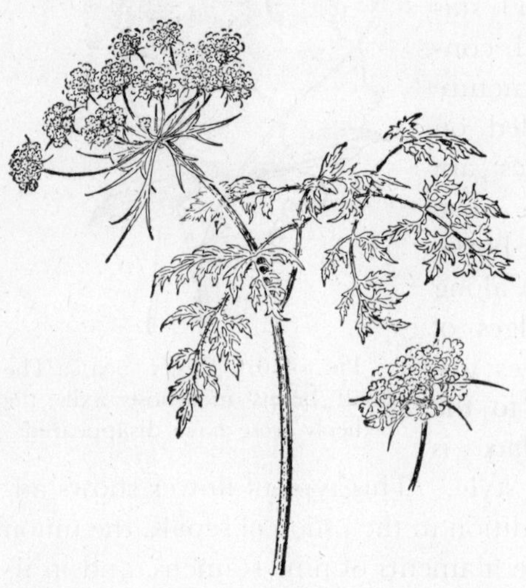

FIG. 411. Wild carrot; a compound umbel, and (*below*) one of the simple umbels of which the compound umbel is composed.

Parsley Family. One general characteristic of this family is the arrangement of the flowers in umbels (Fig. 411). The individual flowers are small and usually white or yellow. Each has five sepals, five petals, and five stamens, all of which parts seem to be borne above the ovary. This appearance is due, as in some of the rose family, to the union of a floral tube with the ovary. The single pistil is composed of two carpels united to form a two-chambered ovary, the two styles, however, being separate. The ovary develops into a hard, dry, two-parted fruit (schizocarp), each part containing one seed. When ripe, the two parts of the fruit separate. The family is characterized also by hollow internodes, by variously lobed or divided leaves with sheathing petioles, and by the secretion of volatile oils and resins which impart characteristic odors and flavors.

The leaves, fruits, and other organs of such species as parsley, celery, anise, dill, fennel, and coriander are used as foods or condiments because of their aromatic flavor. The carrot and parsnip are members of this family; so are several poisonous plants, including the water hemlock and poison hemlock, and some weeds such as the wild carrot. Volatile oils obtained from the fruits of several members, including anise, fennel, caraway, and coriander, are used in medicine.

Mint Family. This family, with over 3000 species, includes plants (mostly herbs) with usually four-sided stems and opposite leaves. In most species, each flower has five sepals which are united except at their tips; five petals united to form a more or less two-lipped corolla, the upper lip composed of two petals, the lower of three; four stamens, of which two are longer than the other two; and a pistil consisting of two two-lobed carpels surrounding a central style. At maturity four nutlets are formed, one from each carpel lobe.

FIG. 412. Spearmint.

The leaves of most species bear small glands containing a volatile oil which makes many of them useful as sources of flavors, perfumes, and drugs. Among cultivated members of the family are horehound, rosemary, lavender, sage, peppermint, and spearmint (Fig. 412). Coleus is cultivated because of its ornamental variegated leaves, and some species of Salvia are grown for their flowers Horsemint and catnip are familiar weeds.

Nightshade Family. To the nightshade family belong many cultivated plants, of which the best known are the potato, tomato, and tobacco. The members are nearly all herbaceous with regular (radially symmetrical) flowers. A flower (Fig. 413) has five sepals united for a varying distance from their bases into a tube, five petals similarly united, five stamens which are united with the bases of the petals, and a pistil composed of two carpels. The fruit is a two-chambered capsule or berry, each chamber containing many seeds. The fruits of many species contain poisonous substances which are used in such drugs as belladonna, hyoscyamus, and stramonium, or narcotics such as characterize the tobacco. Even the tuber of the potato contains a small amount of a slightly poisonous substance. The large genus Solanum to which the potato belongs includes also the black nightshade, eggplant, horse nettle, and buffalo bur. Red peppers, ground cherry, and petunia are other members of the family.

FIG. 413. Apical portion of a plant of tomato, a member of the nightshade family.

Gourd Family. The plants of the gourd family are mostly herbs with thick, juicy stems that bear tendrils. The flowers (Fig. 414) are of two sorts: one with a pistil and rudimentary stamens, the other with stamens and a rudimentary pistil. In some members of the family both kinds of flowers are borne on the same plant; in others, some plants bear usually only staminate, others usually only pistillate flowers. The flowers of both types are marked by a considerable degree of union of their parts. The sepals are united into a tube, and the petals are likewise united. A floral tube is completely

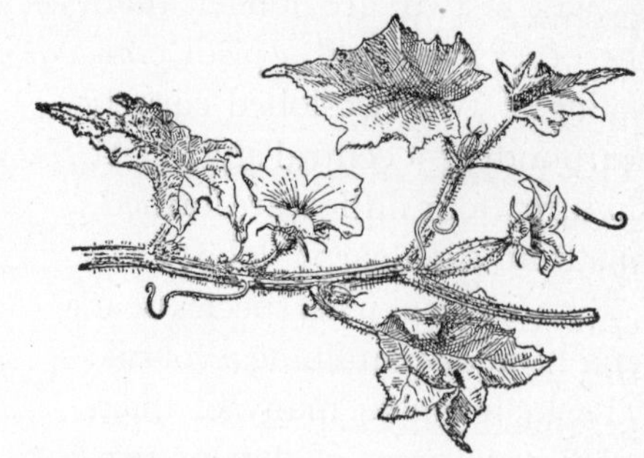

FIG. 414. Portion of a plant of cucumber, a member of the gourd family, with flowers and a young fruit.

united with the large ovary, which therefore seems to be distinctly below the levels of insertion of the other floral parts. The stamens also are often united by their anthers or by both anthers and filaments. The fruit is developed from the ovary together with the surrounding tissues of the receptacle, some of whose outer layers form a hard rind; many seeds are imbedded in the pulpy interior tissues. Most species are tropical or subtropical, and those cultivated in temperate regions have been introduced from warmer climates. Familiar members are the cucumber, pumpkin, squashes, watermelon, muskmelons, and gourds.

FIG. 415. The composite flower cluster (head) of a sunflower.

Composite Family. Not only is this family the most highly developed, it is also the largest family of angiosperms, containing perhaps 20,000 species. Some composites, including the thistles, dandelion, and other very common weeds, have such efficient methods of distribution of their fruits and produce fruits in so great numbers that it is almost impossible to exterminate them. The name "composite" is given because the individual flowers are grouped closely together in a head which has the general appearance of a single flower, the more so because just below the head are green bracts that look like sepals. The tip of the peduncle is thickened and flattened into a broad, disklike or cone-shaped flower-bearing surface.

The sunflower (Fig. 415) illustrates the floral organization typical of the family. At the edge of the flower-bearing disk are two or more cycles or very close spirals of overlapping green bracts. Just within these, and on the face of the disk, the flowers are borne closely packed together, each in the axil of a small bract. The bracts are arranged in incomplete open spirals. There are two types of flowers in the head: the *ray flowers* are borne in a single or double row near the edge of the disk; the *disk flowers* cover the rest of the disk's surface. The receptacle of each disk flower is a hollow, wedge-shaped structure standing almost perpendicularly to the surface of the disk. It partly encloses, and is united with, the ovary. The pistil probably consists of two carpels, although the ovary contains but one functional ovule. Just within the sepals is a long, flaring tube having a conspicuous inflation about one fourth of the way up from its base. The portion of the tube below this inflation is formed by the united bases of the petals and stamens; the part above consists only of the united petals, which are separated at their tips into five blunt teeth. Above the level of their separation from the petals, the filaments of the stamens are separate from one another; but the anthers are united by their edges into a long tube. The top of the ovary extends slightly above the top of the receptacle and completely fills the space at the center of the flower. The style, extending up through the corolla tube and the anther tube, terminates in two relatively large stigmas. A ray flower differs from a disk flower in having one side of its corolla greatly extended into a broad, flat structure. Frequently, also, in a ray flower the inflation near the base of the corolla tube is lacking; the stamens and style may be abortive, and there may be three sepals instead of two.

After the union of gametes, the style, stamens, corolla, and calyx are shed; and the united receptacle and ovary enlarge greatly and become dry and somewhat hard. The single seed fills the space within but is united to the ovary wall only over a very small area.

The composite type of flower and flower cluster represents the climax of floral development among dicotyledons. The union of the receptacle with the ovary, causing the outer parts of the flower to be borne above the ovary, is an advanced feature; other advanced characters are the union of the petals into a corolla tube, that of the anthers into an anther tube, and the occurrence of flowers of two distinct types in the same head. In the last-mentioned respect, however, the sunflower is not typical of all composites. In the dandelion, as in a number of related genera, the head contains flowers of only one type, which are similar in corolla form to the ray flowers of the sunflower.

Among the comparatively few members of the family that supply food for man are the lettuce, endive, chicory, salsify, artichoke, and

Jerusalem artichoke. The sunflower is used as food for livestock. Drugs are obtained from some composites, including camomile, calendula, arnica, tansy, wormwood, dandelion, and burdock. Among ornamental plants of the family are the daisies, sunflower, dahlia, asters, and chrysanthemums. Some of the commonest wild plants and weeds, among them conspicuous members of the autumnal flora, are asters, goldenrods, ragweeds, thistles, the sage-brush, dandelion, beggar-ticks, yarrow, cocklebur, and burdock.

MONOCOTYLEDONS

Cattail Family. The monocotyledons seem to have arisen from some very primitive dicotyledon or dicotyledons. Within the class of monocotyledons, the course of evolution has substantially paralleled that which has marked the history of dicotyledons. In consequence, while preserving the characteristics that distinguish them from dicotyledons (Chapter XXIX), monocotyledons show very much the same steps in the evolution of floral structures that have been described for dicotyledons. The cattail family, with a single genus, is one of the simplest among living monocotyledons and may be thought of as occupying much the same position in this class as that of the willow family among dicotyledons.

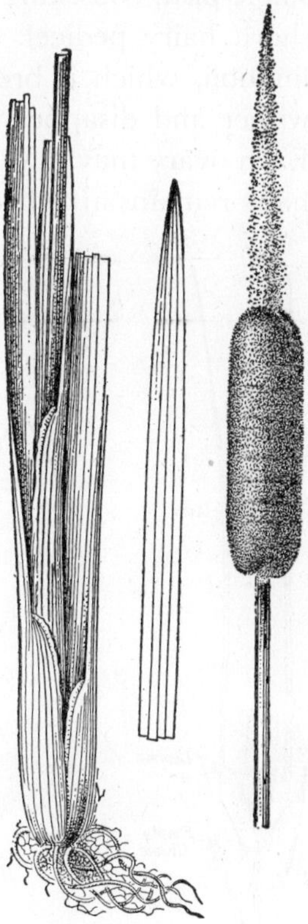

FIG. 416. Cattail. An aerial branch, a single leaf, and a flower cluster (spike).

The characteristics of the family are essentially those of the common cattail (Fig. 416), growing abundantly in wet, marshy places. This plant has a branching horizontal stem that lives in the mud from year to year and each spring sends up aerial branches. Each such branch bears at its base long, sheathing leaves. At the upper end of an aerial branch is a long cylindrical spike of flowers. The central axis of a close cylindrical spike of this nature is a *spadix*. The flowers on the spadix are partly covered while young by long, thin, sheathing bracts (*spathes*); one spathe arises from the base of the spike, and others may appear higher up, interrupting the cylindrical mass of flowers.

The flowers in the upper part of the spike are staminate, those in the lower part pistillate. Each staminate flower consists of two or three stamens borne on a short pedicel, from whose lower part arise a number of hairlike outgrowths. A pistillate flower has a single pistil consisting of one carpel borne, like the stamens, upon a short, hairy pedicel. The ovary contains one ovule. After pollination, which is brought about by winds, the staminate flowers wither and disappear, leaving the upper part of the spadix bare. Each ovary may develop into an achene; the pedicel with its many hairs remains attached to the fruit when the latter is shed, and the hairs assist in the distribution of the fruit by winds.

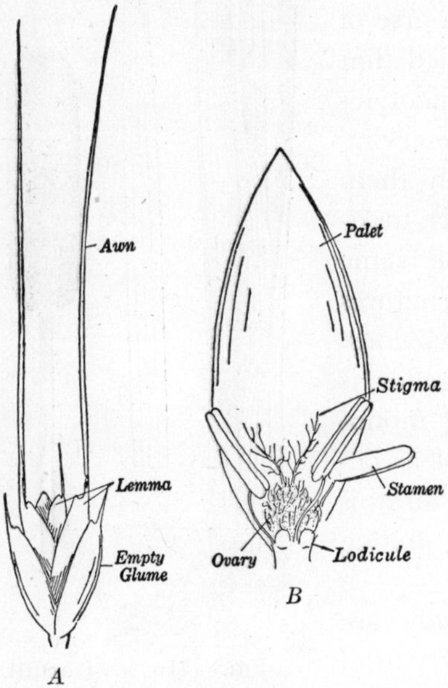

FIG. 417. Wheat. *A*, spikelet. *B*, single flower.

Grass Family. Here belong about 4500 species which, like the cattails, have small, simple flowers and one-seeded fruits. In various respects, however, grasses show a considerably greater degree of specialization than do cattails; and they are very much more widely spread, different species being adapted to very different habitats. Like most monocotyledons they are herbaceous, although the tall, almost treelike bamboos have more or less woody stems. The stems of grasses are jointed, the internodes being commonly hollow; and the leaves are alternately arranged in two vertical rows. Economically the most important grasses are the cereal grains, which include wheat, oats, barley, rye, corn, rice, and millet.

The flower of wheat (Fig. 417) may be taken as typical. The compound flower cluster, commonly called a head or spike, is made up of many small *spikelets*. Beginning at the base of a spikelet, and alternating on opposite sides of its central axis, are two rather large bracts (*empty glumes*), and successively above these a few progressively smaller glumes (*lemmas*), each with a flower in its axil. A lemma has its concave face toward the axis of the spikelet, and the lower lemmas may bear long, stiff bristles (*awns*). Partly enclosed by each lemma is a thin bract (*palet*) which envelops the flower proper. The flower includes a pistil with a short ovary, and two short styles each terminating in a long, feathery stigma; three stamens with long anthers and threadlike filaments; and two small scales (*lodicules*) which may correspond to sepals. The ovary with its single ovule develops into a grain.

In the corn and a few related grasses, stamens and pistils are borne in separate flowers; the staminate flower cluster of the corn is the tassel; the pistillate flower cluster is the ear.

Fig. 418. A sedge.

In addition to cereals, other grasses of economic importance are the sugar cane, sorghum, and broomcorn; the bamboos, which in their native countries are used for a great variety of purposes; and many species which, like redtop, bluegrass, and timothy, are used for forage. The value of wild grasses for pasturage results in large part from their habit of growing together in great numbers, so that a considerable area may be covered by one or a few species. Their power of rapid multiplication by means of seeds as well as by the growth and branching of their underground stems makes some of the grasses, like so many of the composites, troublesome weeds. Some familiar weeds of this family are the wild oat, quack grass, chess, and (in southern states) Johnson grass.

Sedge Family. Very similar to grasses in general appearance and in many characteristics are the sedges (Fig. 418). Most of them have three-sided solid stems, bearing leaves in three rows. The fruits are nutlike and one-seeded; the embryo, instead of being at one side of the seed as in a grass, is near the base and is entirely surrounded by endosperm. Some "rushes" and so-called "marsh grasses" belong to this family; so do the umbrella plant, and the papyrus which was used in ancient times in the manufacture of paper and from whose name the word *paper* is derived.

Palm Family. This is distinguished from other families of monocotyledons by the fact that most of its members have woody stems. Many of them are trees, each bearing at its tip a crown of large leaves. Some palms, such as the rattan palm, are climbing plants. Practically all palms are tropical or subtropical.

In many species the flowers are borne on a spadix that is enclosed in a spathe. Some have branching flower clusters (Fig. 419). A single flower ordinarily has six perianth leaves in two whorls of three each, the outer whorl often being distinguished as a calyx, the inner as a corolla; there are usually six stamens in two whorls of three each, although in some species the stamens are fewer or more numerous than six; there are three carpels, forming either three separate pistils or one compound pistil. In many species staminate and pistillate flowers are separate and borne either on the same or on distinct plants. The fruit, usually one-seeded, is either a stone fruit, as in the coconut, or a berry, as in the date. The embryo is at one side of the seed; the seed contains also an abundant endosperm, which is often hard. The hard part of the fruit of the date palm is the endosperm;

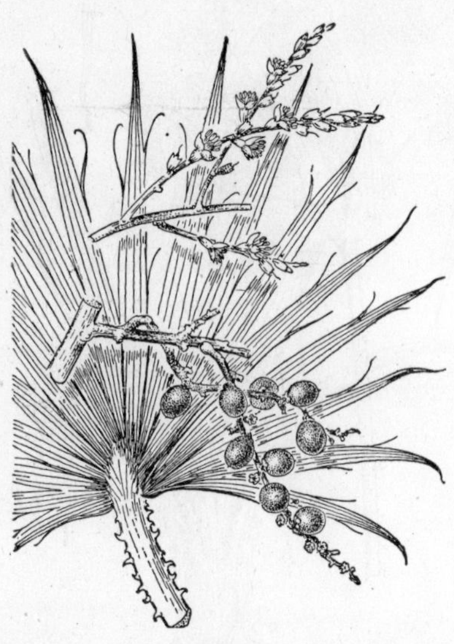

Fig. 419. Flower cluster and fruits of a fan palm (Washingtonia) of southern California.

the endosperm of another palm furnishes "vegetable ivory," used in making buttons. The endosperm of the coconut, instead of being hard, constitutes most of the "meat" of the nut.

Coconut oil is made from copra, which is the dried meat of the coconut. Palm oil is derived from the fruits of certain species of western Africa and eastern South America. The betel nut, extensively chewed by natives of the East Indies, is the fruit of a palm. Sago is made by washing out the starch which is present in great quantities in the piths of some palms. Among the many other products of palms are fibers of various sorts, such as those from the petioles of the raffia palm, building materials, soap, wax (from the surfaces of stems), and alcoholic drinks including arrack.

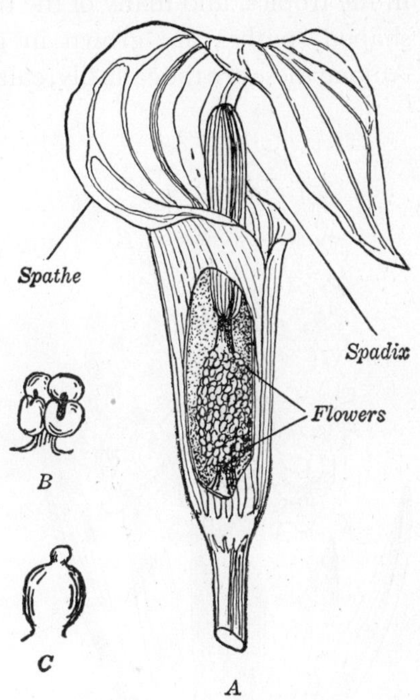

FIG. 420. *A*, flower cluster of jack-in-the-pulpit. *B*, staminate flower. *C*, pistil (constituting a pistillate flower).

Arum Family. Members of this family are characterized by having their flowers crowded on a spadix which is subtended or enveloped by a relatively large, persistent spathe; the spathe is often white or conspicuously colored.

A well-known native member of the family is the jack-in-the-pulpit, or Indian turnip (Fig. 420). The flowers of this plant are of two sorts, the staminate flowers being borne on the upper part of the spadix, the pistillate flowers on the lower part. Not infrequently the flowers of one type abort, so that the functional flowers borne by a particular plant are all staminate or all pistillate. Each staminate flower consists of a varied number of short stamens; a pistillate flower is but a single simple pistil whose one-chambered ovary contains five or six ovules. The fruit is a scarlet berry with one or two seeds. The aerial shoot which terminates in the spathe and spadix and which usually bears also two three-parted leaves is a branch growing from an underground stem. This stem is thick and approximately spherical; like various vegetative parts of many other members of the family, it has an intensely acrid taste.

Other familiar plants of the family are the skunk cabbage, sweet flag, and water arum. The arum family is most largely represented in the tropics, and many of the tropical species with showy or oddly shaped spathes are grown in greenhouses and as house plants. Among these are the calla lily, caladium, dracontium, and anthurium.

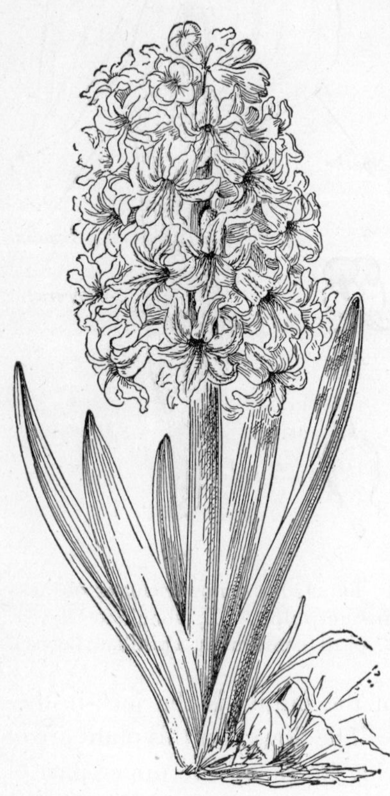

Fig. 421. Aerial portion of a hyacinth plant.

Lily Family. The flower of the hyacinth (Fig. 421) is fairly representative of the flowers of this large family. The hyacinth has a raceme with a thick peduncle, each of the spirally arranged flowers being borne in the axil of a small bract. The perianth consists of two whorls of three leaves each, alike in color and shape and united at their bases to form a tube. The outer whorl of perianth leaves may be considered a calyx, the inner whorl a corolla. Near its middle the perianth tube is considerably constricted. Below the constriction the bases of the filaments of the six stamens are united with the perianth tube, but above the constriction each stamen is separate and distinct. Within the perianth tube but entirely separate from it is the pistil. This consists of three carpels and has a three-chambered ovary, a single style, and a three-lobed stigma. Along each line of junction of adjacent carpels their edges are much swollen, and each swollen edge bears a vertical row of ovules. Hence, there are six rows of ovules extending through most of the length of the ovary; and the ovules, together with the edges of the carpels on which they are borne, nearly fill the cavities of the ovary.

FIG. 422. The coral root (*Corallorhiza maculata*), a saprophytic orchid. Photograph courtesy of John T. Curtis.

The hyacinth flower represents a considerably advanced type in the partial union of the staminal filaments with the perianth tube and in the complete union of carpels. After gametic union, the perianth and stamens are shed; the ovary enlarges greatly and becomes soft and pulpy throughout, except for the many seeds that it contains. Thus, the fruit of the hyacinth is a capsule.

The flowers of other members of the family are in general similar to that of the hyacinth; the fruits of some are capsules, of others berries. Of the true lilies (members of the genus Lilium), some, such as the Easter lily, tiger lily, and Turk's-cap lily, have long been cultivated for their flowers. The same is true of many other plants of the family belonging to other genera, including the lily of the valley, tulip, orange day lily, and yellow day lily. The greenhouse "smilax" and other species of Asparagus are grown for ornamental purposes. Familiar wild plants are the trilliums, Solomon's seal, false Solomon's seal, dogtooth violet, and bellwort. Plants cultivated for food purposes are the asparagus and various members of the genus Allium, which includes onions, garlic, chives, and leeks. A few members of the family, including species of Yucca and the dragon tree (Dracaena), have a special method of secondary thickening, referred to in Chapter IV. The family includes also several drug plants, among the best known being several species of Aloe, whose leaves supply a mucilaginous juice, and some plants which yield fibers.

Orchid Family. In number of species this family, with over 9000 members, is the largest among monocotyledons; few of its species, however, are abundant, and some are very rare. Orchids are characterized by their remarkable bilaterally symmetrical flowers, which show the greatest degree of union of floral parts found among monocotyledons. They occupy, therefore, a position among monocotyledons somewhat similar to that of the composites among dicotyledons.

The great variety of floral forms in the family seems to represent so many adaptations to insect pollination—often to pollination by insects of a certain size and even perhaps of a particular species. The flower of a lady's-slipper (Fig. 423) well illustrates the possibilities of development of an insect-pollinated flower. It has three sepals, of which the two lowermost are united, and three petals, one of which, much larger than the other two, has the form of a slipper-like sac open at the top. The opening is partly closed by a flap. The edges of the opening in front of the flap are curved inward. At the bottom of the sac on the inside are juicy hairs that are eaten by insects which make their way into the sac. On the lower side of the flap is the stigma; at either side of the stigma is an anther, whose pollen remains together as a sticky mass. A third stamen has no anther. Insects, if not too large, can make their way into the sac in front of the flap; but because of the curved edges of the opening they can not readily escape at the same place. If, however, like some bees, they are sufficiently strong, they can push out through the opening at either side of the flap. In such a case the insect brushes against the anther on that side and carries away its pollen mass. The same insect, entering another flower, brushes against the stigma, where the pollen mass may lodge.

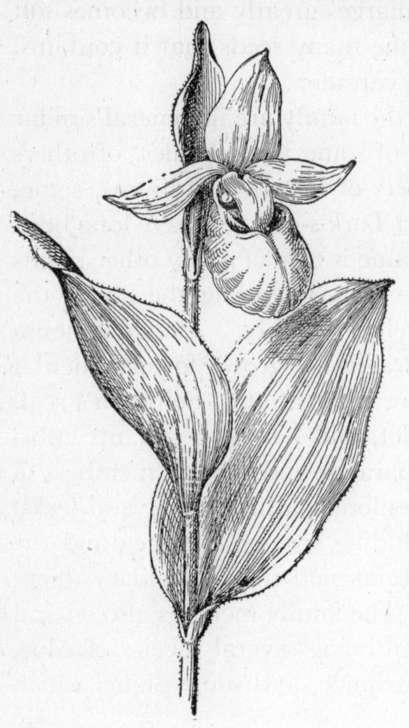

FIG. 423. Lady's-slipper, a member of the orchid family.

Many orchids are grown because of their rarity or for the beauty of their flowers. Not many are otherwise useful, although the fruit of the vanilla, a tropical American orchid, supplies a well-known flavoring extract, and the dried tubers of some old-world orchids are used, under the name of *salep*, both as a food and as a drug.

Some tropical orchids are epiphytes, living high up on the trunks of trees. A few, including the coral root (Fig. 422), possess no chlorophyll; with the aid of fungi in their underground parts they lead a saprophytic life.

CHAPTER XXXII

FOSSIL PLANTS

Fossils. The various sorts of plants that make up the present-day population of the earth have been described in earlier chapters. In the present chapter, a brief account is given of some of those that have lived on the earth in previous ages. The important fact to be emphasized is that plants living today are the surviving members of a population extending back through hundreds of millions of years. In the course of its history the earth has many times changed the composition of its green mantle, and fragments of some of the ancient plants are scattered here and there in certain layers of the earth's crust. These fragmentary remains are *fossils;* and through a study of those that have been found, it has been possible to describe the appearance and even the structure of some of the plants that once inhabited the earth.

During the course of geological time the solid crust of the earth's surface has been in continuous process of weathering—that is, being broken up into small resistant particles of mineral matter. Such particles, commonly in the form of sand or clay, when borne by water were deposited as sediments. The bodies of plants and animals or fragments of those bodies also might be deposited and buried in the sediments. With the passing of time the sediments, buried to greater depth, were converted to rock; and the plant and animal remains, also having undergone certain changes to be described, became fossils imbedded in the layers of the rock. Sedimentary rocks are the chief source of fossils. Occasionally the remains of plants and animals are found buried in volcanic ash or encrusted in mineral deposits such as those of lime or silica.

The term "plant fossils" covers a variety of types of remains, such as *impressions*, *casts*, *compressions*, and *petrifactions*. An impression is a print made by a plant or a portion of a plant coming in contact with a plastic surface such as that of soft clay. The material of the plant decays and disappears, but the impression may remain.

If the clay later is converted into rock, a record of the superficial appearance of the plant is thus preserved. A *cast* is formed when a plant submerged in water is covered by a crust of mineral matter. This may happen if the surrounding water contains a mineral substance, such as lime, in solution. The decay of the incrusted plant leaves a mold which may become filled with clay or sand. The hardened clay or sand filling the mold forms a cast that displays the superficial structure of the plant or part incrusted.

Masses of plants or plant fragments may accumulate under conditions in which decay is greatly retarded. Such remains if deeply covered by sedimentation or by other means are vertically compressed and undergo chemical changes resulting in *compressions*, which are coal. Such compressions may give valuable information as to the outlines or silhouettes of ancient plants. By means of a recently devised technique, leaf remains in coal can be so treated as to show the outlines of epidermal cells and stomata, the course of veins, and other structural features.

Sometimes it happens that plant fragments become saturated with water containing mineral substances in solution. These mineral substances may wholly or in part replace the organic material of the cells and tissues. Such remains are *petrifactions*. If these are cut into very thin translucent slices, cellular arrangement and structure may be studied in favorable specimens almost as well as in the tissues of living plants. For this reason petrifactions are of great value in the study of fossil plants.

It is a basic principle of modern geology that the various forces which now shape the face of the earth are those which have acted upon it in the past. The multitudinous earth changes that have resulted are in large measure correlated with changes in plant and animal life. Long-continued study has established that the simplest types of fossil organisms are found in the older strata of rocks and that strata of more recent origin contain fossils increasingly like the plants and animals now living. This orderly succession of fossils and of the strata that contain them makes possible the construction of a chart in which the geological distribution of ancient plants may be shown in so far as the available evidence permits. The periods of time indicated in the chart (Fig. 424) are estimates based upon several means of attempting to determine the ages of the various rock formations that make up the surface of the earth.

Early Plants. As indicated on the chart, the earliest forms of plants preserved as fossils are certain alga-like remains belonging to the Cambrian, Ordovician, and Silurian periods. The evidence,

TIME CHART

<table>
<tr><th>PERIOD</th><th>YEARS BACK FROM PRESENT</th><th>DOMINANT PLANT TYPES</th></tr>
<tr><td>LATE CENOZOIC</td><td>25,000,000</td><td>Rise of Modern Herbs. Great Climatic Changes.</td></tr>
<tr><td>EARLY CENOZOIC</td><td>60,000,000</td><td>Modernization of Flowering Plants. Gymnosperms and Cycads Dwindle.</td></tr>
<tr><td>UPPER CRETACEOUS</td><td>110,000,000</td><td rowspan="2">Rapid Rise and Distribution of Angiosperms. Conifers and Cycads Still Abundant.</td></tr>
<tr><td>LOWER CRETACEOUS</td><td>140,000,000</td></tr>
<tr><td>JURASSIC</td><td>175,000,000</td><td>Conifers Very Abundant; Cycad-Like Plants; First Known Angiosperms.</td></tr>
<tr><td>TRIASSIC</td><td>200,000,000</td><td>Seed Ferns Disappear; Great Increase in Gymnosperms.</td></tr>
<tr><td>PERMIAN</td><td>240,000,000</td><td>Extensive Climatic Changes. Some Plant Groups Become Extinct.</td></tr>
<tr><td>UPPER CARBONIFEROUS</td><td>280,000,000</td><td rowspan="2">Seed-Bearing Ferns; Primitive Gymnosperms; Ancient Lycopods and Horsetails Very Abundant. Great Coal Beds Formed.</td></tr>
<tr><td>LOWER CARBONIFEROUS</td><td>310,000,000</td></tr>
<tr><td>DEVONIAN</td><td>350,000,000</td><td>Early Land Plants. Possible Ancestors of Lycopods, Horsetails and Ferns.</td></tr>
<tr><td>SILURIAN</td><td>380,000,000</td><td>First Known Land Plants. Algae Dominant.</td></tr>
<tr><td>ORDOVICIAN</td><td>440,000,000</td><td rowspan="2">Abundant Marine Algae.</td></tr>
<tr><td>CAMBRIAN</td><td>550,000,000</td></tr>
</table>

FIG. 424. Chart showing the sequence of geological formations in which plant fossils are found.

both direct and indirect, shows that a wide variety of algae lived in the waters of those ancient times and that some of them played a part in the deposition of lime (just as do certain living algae). The presence of abundant remains of such ancient algae is not surprising, because their bodies encrusted with lime were well adapted to preservation, whereas the delicate cells of algae of other types were much less likely to leave traces of their existence. However, the relations of these fossil algae to algae of living groups are very uncertain because of the meager facts of structure available.

Early Land Plants. From a knowledge of living plants it seems reasonable to conclude that the presence of stomata and cutin, or of xylem, indicates that an organism possessing such characters lived on land. By the use of such criteria fossilized fragments of undoubted land plants have been recognized as far back as the close of the Silurian period. The remains appear to be those of plants which were relatively simple in structure and which possibly had been derived at some earlier time from an alga-like ancestry. It is generally agreed that land plants were developed from plants that lived in water. Bryophytes and pteridophytes still give evidence of an aquatic ancestry in the necessity of external water for the process of fertilization. Just when and by what steps plants, emerging from the water, became adapted to life on land is not known; but it must have been long before any of the fossils now available were deposited. There is evidence that some Silurian plants were similar to certain early and mid-Devonian plants, knowledge of which has been greatly extended within the past 25 years. These Devonian plants are briefly discussed in the next section.

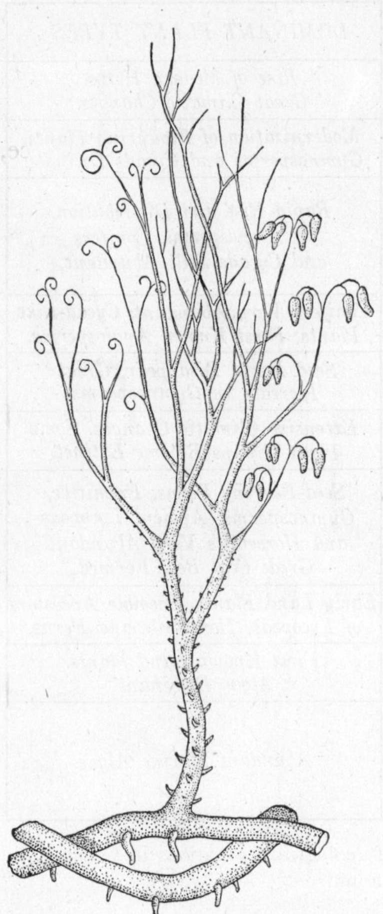

Fig. 425. Portion of a plant of Psilophyton. After W. C. Darrah, *Textbook of Paleobotany*, published by D. Appleton-Century Company.

Psilophytineae: Psilophytales. This order included a group of simple plants which showed relatively little differentiation of the sporophytic body. Their remains have been found widely distributed over the earth in Devonian strata. One of the first of these plants discovered and described was *Psilophyton* (Fig. 425). This plant, which attained the height of about two feet, had a creeping horizontal stem from which grew forking aerial branches. The younger branches were coiled at their tips and probably unrolled as they grew, a character found in living fern leaves. The horizontal stem and the lower portions of the aerial branches bore short spinelike emergences. Stomata were abundant in the epidermis of aerial branches, which were therefore photosynthetic organs. The sporangia, often occurring in pairs, were borne at the tips of slender branches.

More recently other plants, undoubtedly related to Psilophyton, have been found in such an excellent state of preservation that details of internal structure are known. Two of these plants, Rhynia and Asteroxylon, are described below. They were both relatively small, and together with Psilophyton aid in visualizing the flora of a marsh in mid-Devonian times.

Rhynia major (Fig. 426, *A*) possessed a horizontal underground stem, from certain basal surfaces of which grew clusters of rhizoids. As in Psilophyton, roots were entirely lacking. The stem gave rise to upright aerial branches which were slender, cylindrical, and tended to fork equally. No spines were present. The sporangia were slender sacs, each terminating a branch. Many spores, all of approximately the same size, occurred in a sporangium; and in some cases tetrads of spores have been found, indicating the occurrence of reduction divisions and of an alternation of generations. The internal structure of a stem included a central core of xylem, surrounding which was a relatively thin layer of phloem. The cortex was bounded on its outer side by an epidermis in which were many stomata.

Asteroxylon (Fig. 426, *B*) was a larger plant than Psilophyton or Rhynia and was somewhat more complex in structure. The smooth underground stem lacked the rhizoids found in Rhynia but bore slender underground branches which may have served as absorbing organs. The aerial branches, which in turn branched freely, were densely clothed with spirally arranged, scalelike leaves resembling those of club mosses. The sporangia, small and pear-shaped, were borne at the tips of naked branches which arose from the leafy shoots.

From the descriptions given above, it is evident that there lived in early and middle Devonian times a group of land plants with relatively very simple sporophytes. They had no differentiated roots

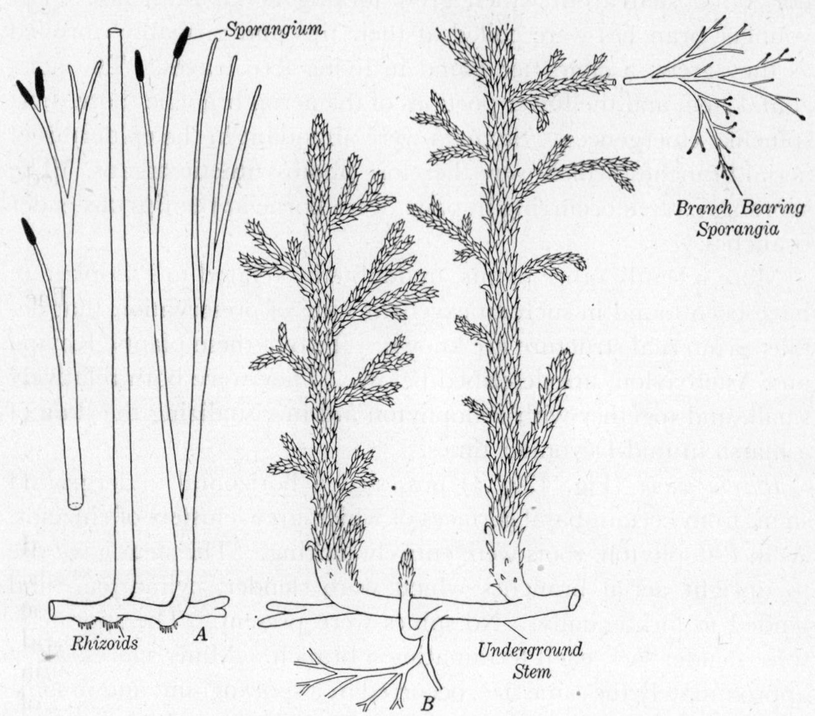

FIG. 426. *A*, plant of *Rhynia major*. *B*, plant of Asteroxylon. Both redrawn from Kidston and Lang.

and were either leafless or possessed small scalelike leaves. Their sporangia were merely the differentiated ends of branches. These plants are the simplest known fossil land plants.

Psilotales. It is clear that some groups of plants which were prominent in past geological periods are represented by survivors in the present-day flora. The question then naturally arises: what living plants, if any, are survivors of the Psilophytales? The answer seems to be found in a small order of inconspicuous tropical and subtropical plants, the Psilotales, represented by the genus Psilotum (Fig. 427). Psilotum has an underground stem but lacks roots. From the stem grow green aerial branches which fork equally and bear minute projections that probably represent leaves. The sporangia appear to be borne at the ends of very short branches. Because the living Psilotales have certain characters in common with the fossil Psilophytales, the two have been grouped in a class—the Psilophytineae. The Psilotales may consequently be regarded as

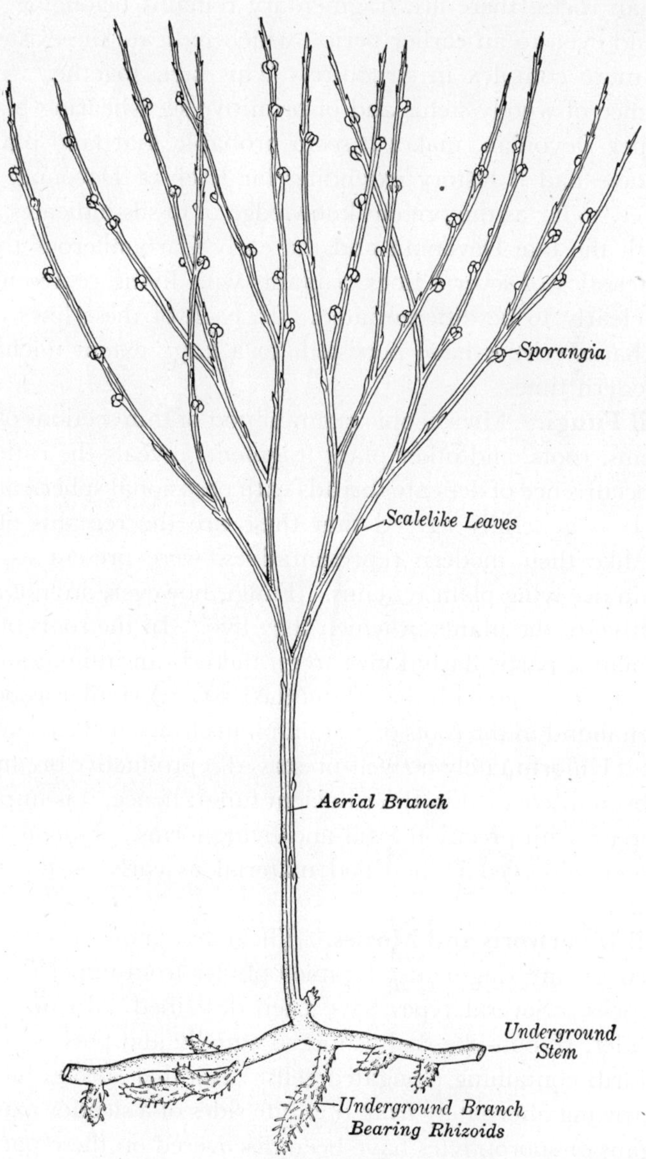

FIG. 427. The plant (sporophyte) of Psilotum.

the living remnants of a flora which was abundant in early and middle Devonian times, before the more highly specialized groups of pteridophytes recognized today had been clearly differentiated.

Although the Psilophytales were abundant in the lower and mid-Devonian rocks, there are fragmentary remains belonging to this same and even to an earlier period which indicate the existence of plants more complex in structure. This fact, together with the occurrence of woody stems and of primitive seed-bearing plants in the upper Devonian, makes it seem probable that land plants, as such, have had a history extending far back of Devonian times. However, so far as the present knowledge of fossils indicates, it was not until the late Devonian and the early Carboniferous that the characteristics of several lines of plants with living representatives began clearly to be differentiated. In each of these lines certain basic characteristics have persisted, to a large extent unchanged, into modern times.

Fossil Fungi. Microscopic examination of thin sections of petrified stems, roots, and other plant fragments reveals the rather frequent occurrence of delicate threads with occasional spherical swellings. It is generally agreed that these are the remains of fungi which, like their modern representatives, were present as saprophytes in decaying plant remains. Fungi, however, are not always destructive to the plants in which they live. In the roots of many living plants, particularly forest trees, there is an intimate association of various fungi with the cells of the host. A similar association has been found in the roots of certain plants from the Carboniferous period. Unfortunately no well-preserved reproductive organs have as yet been discovered in these ancient fungi; hence, it is impossible to compare with precision fossil and living forms. Fungal hyphae have been observed in petrified material as early as the middle Devonian.

Fossil Liverworts and Mosses. The oldest known fossil remains of liverworts are fragments of gametophytes from upper Carboniferous rocks. Several types have been described. In one species the slender, ribbon-like thallus forked equally and possessed a central midrib containing elongated cells. Another species had leafy lobes growing alternately from opposite sides of a slender axis. No sex organs or sporophytes have been discovered on these particular plants. Very recently an account has been given of the structure of a liverwort found in upper Triassic rocks. It possessed a leafy axis bearing rhizoids. At the ends of some branches were capsules containing multicellular gemmae. Archegonia were in evidence along the axis. The sporophyte was small and had a short stalk. The rounded capsule bore spores in tetrads; no elaters were present. Although the remains of these ancient Hepaticae are relatively rare and fragmentary, they afford impressive evidence of the persistence of bryophytic characteristics through a vast period of time.

Knowledge of the existence of mosses in comparable periods is less satisfactory.

Lycopodineae. A wealth of fossil plants bearing certain resemblances to present-day club mosses has been found widely distributed over the earth in Carboniferous rocks and, to a lesser extent, in earlier and later formations. This class of plants, including both treelike and herbaceous forms, reached its climax in size and complexity in the Carboniferous. Among the finest specimens preserved are those of the genus *Lepidodendron* (Fig. 428). These were trees growing to a height of about 100 feet and forming forests. A remarkable example of the remains of such a forest has been found in Nova Scotia, where 96 vertical trunks of Lepidodendron were discovered in an area 120 by 15 feet. Trees closely resembling Lepidodendron are known to have existed as early as the Devonian.

The stem of Lepidodendron was a tall, slightly tapering shaft, which in some species was sparingly branched, in others formed a profusion of equally forking branches near the top. The younger branches bore narrow, pointed leaves arranged in close spirals. The leaves were, relative to the size of the plant, very small but remained on the branches for a considerable time. The ultimate shedding of a leaf was accomplished by an abscission above the large thickened leaf base, which remained on the stem. Impressions or casts of these characteristic leaf bases are among the commonest fossil remains of Lepidodendron. The base of the trunk always forked equally into thick, wide-spreading underground branches, which in turn rebranched. On the younger portions of these underground branches were borne many slender roots. The stele, even in large stems, was very small in spite of cambial activity. The support of such a tall trunk was maintained chiefly through the development of a broad zone of mechanical cells in the outer cortex, which zone increased in thickness as the tree grew older.

Strobili were borne at the ends of the smaller branches and, though very much larger, resembled in shape those of certain living club mosses. In most species of Lepidodendron the cones bore

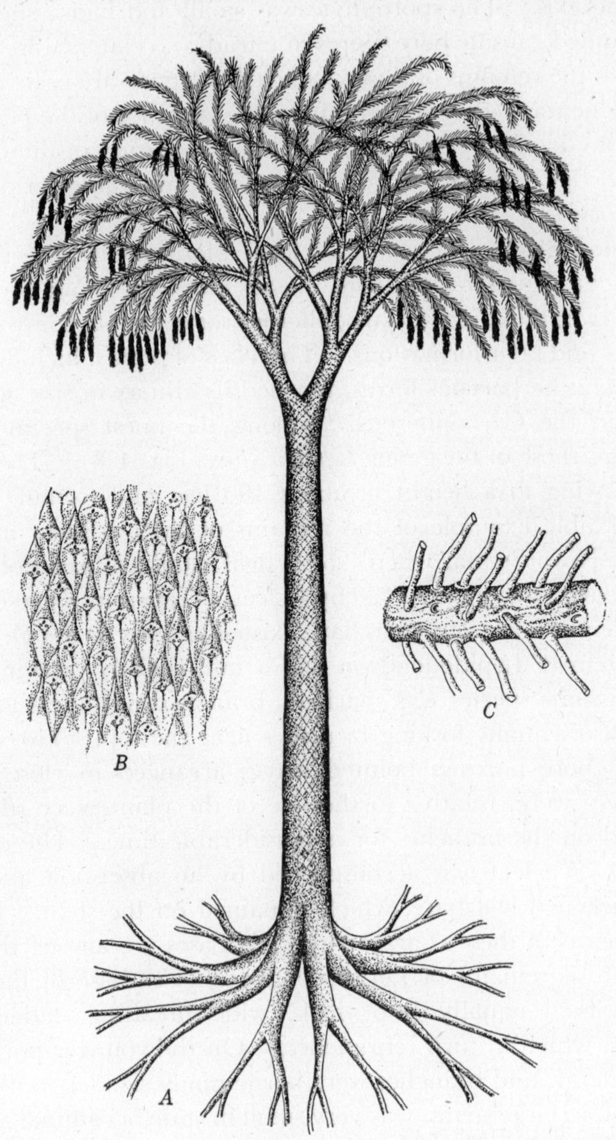

FIG. 428. *A*, the treelike Lepidodendron. After Hirmer. *B*, portion of the surface of the stem, enlarged to show the leaf bases. *C*, the younger portion of an underground branch bearing many roots.

sporophylls, sporangia, and spores of two kinds, the microsporophylls being commonly in the upper part of the strobilus. Each sporophyll bore on its upper surface a relatively large sporangium; and the terminal portion of the sporophyll turned upward into a blade which, with the bladelike parts of other sporophylls, formed the protective outer covering of the strobilus. The microspores were very small and were produced in enormous numbers in each microsporangium. The number of megaspores in a sporangium ranged from 1 to 16. Well-developed megagametophytes have been found within the old megaspore walls. A megagametophyte, projecting somewhat beyond the spore wall, resembled one of Selaginella. Archegonia have been recognized in a few specimens. Certain species of Lepidodendron or of forms closely related are of great interest because they developed along their own line of evolution a kind of seed. In one such species a single megaspore in each megasporangium came to maturity and developed a megagametophyte while permanently enclosed by the sporangium wall. Meanwhile, a covering grew up about the sporangium, entirely enclosing it except for a narrow slit along the top. Such a structure closely paralleled the development of a seed.

In addition to the giant Lepidodendrons, a number of smaller herbaceous lycopods are imperfectly known from the Carboniferous and from later periods. Some of them bear a resemblance to Lycopodium, others to Selaginella. It seems probable that the living club mosses have been derived from the simpler herbaceous forms rather than by reduction from the highly specialized, treelike Lepidodendrons. These latter forms became extinct in Permian and Triassic times.

Equisetineae. In this class are included the members of the living genus Equisetum and a considerable number of extinct plants all of which reveal in their structure certain well-defined characters which have persisted with little change from ancient days. The Equisetineae probably originated in the Devonian, but their greatest development in size and complexity occurred during the Carboniferous, when some of them formed conspicuous elements of the flora. These Carboniferous representatives (Fig. 429), sometimes referred to under the general name *Calamites*, embraced a large and somewhat diverse group. Some were probably herbaceous, but the best known are the giant horsetails, which attained treelike proportions. They had underground, or at least prostrate, stems from which grew tall, upright, treelike branches, both stems and branches possessing sharply differentiated nodes and internodes.

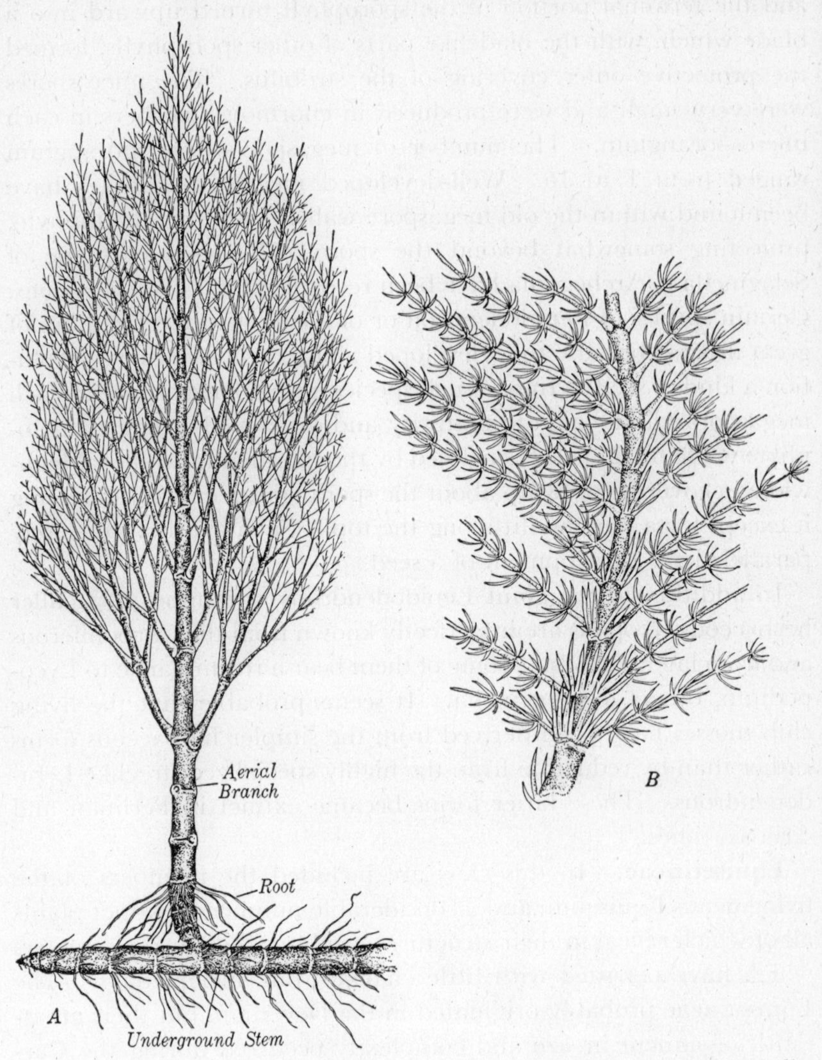

Fig. 429. *A*, a plant of Calamites. After Hirmer. *B*, one of the smaller branches showing the arrangement of leaves. Redrawn from Schimper.

In some species the aerial branches bore whorls of smaller branches at the nodes; in others they were unbranched or branched only at a few nodes. Many slender roots grew from the nodes of the stems and from the basal nodes of the aerial branches. Whorls of leaves were borne at the nodes of the aerial branches. These relatively small, slender leaves undoubtedly served as photosynthetic organs. In some species the bases of the leaves were united, forming a sheath at the node; in others they were free. In regard to the form and arrangement of internal tissues, the structure of the internode of a young Calamite branch is remarkably like that of Equisetum; but the older branches of the Calamite apparently always formed secondary xylem.

The cones of the Calamites were slender and varied in length from a few inches to almost a foot. Attached to the central axis of the cone were whorls of sporangiophores; but, differently from the condition in the cone (strobilus) of Equisetum, whorls of sterile bracts were associated in various ways with the sporangiophores. Commonly, four sporangia were borne on each sporangiophore, and the spores were all alike. However, species producing both microspores and megaspores also are known, in one instance three of the sporangia on a sporangiophore bearing megaspores, the fourth bearing microspores. None of the Calamites are known to have produced seedlike structures.

The giant horsetails probably died out by the close of the Permian; but representatives of the class persisted, and in later periods, particularly in the Triassic and Jurassic, there are abundant fossil remains, world-wide in distribution, of plants strikingly similar to living horsetails. These Mesozoic plants were intermediate in size, being smaller than the giant horsetails of the Carboniferous but more robust than the species living today. It seems clear, therefore, that the living genus Equisetum, with its few species of relatively inconspicuous plants, is the surviving remnant of an ancient race some of whose members attained a conspicuous place in the floras of their times.

Filicineae. Until about forty years ago the abundant fernlike leaves particularly characteristic of the Carboniferous period were generally thought to be those of true ferns. Indeed, some of the older writers on fossil plants described the Carboniferous as an "age of ferns." In recent years an increasingly large number of these fernlike leaves have been found to bear seeds, and therefore such plants can not be classed as true ferns. Nevertheless, there is convincing evidence of the existence of true ferns beginning in the upper

Devonian. Details of structure of the various members of this rather diverse group are not completely known, consequently the brief description of these early ferns (Primofilices) must be in general terms. So far as is known, most of them were comparatively small plants. Some had creeping stems; others had upright stems with crowded leaf-bases. The anatomy of the stems was relatively simple. The leaves were a remarkable feature. They were large branches of the axis, which in some species branched and rebranched in different planes, forming a bushlike structure. The sporangia were relatively large, spherical or pear-shaped, and were commonly borne at the ends of the finer branches of the leaves. None of these early ferns is known to have produced two kinds of spores. It has been suggested that from ancestors like these have come the families to which the grape fern and possibly the royal fern belong.

There lived also in the Carboniferous and in the Permian another group of ferns, which were treelike in appearance (Fig. 430). Their tall, slender trunks bore a crown of large compound leaves, resembling those of living ferns. The stem proper was enveloped in a thick covering of roots growing downward from the stem and felted together by masses of hairs borne partly on the stem and partly on the roots themselves. The sporangia were for the most part united into clusters or groups of definite form. Relatives of these ancient tree ferns appear to have survived as a tropical and subtropical family, the Marattiaceae.

In early Mesozoic times ferns apparently continued their evolution with the appearance of new families. There is evidence that several of these attained their widest distribution and diversity in Jurassic and Cretaceous periods and later declined, being represented today by a few genera with limited distribution. The most recent family to evolve is thought to have been the Polypodiaceae. With nearly a hundred genera and several thousand species, it is the dominant fern family of modern times.

The outstanding characteristic of the Filicineae when compared with the other classes of land plants so far discussed is the possession of large leaves. It appears probable that leaves have arisen in at least two ways. The large and characteristically compound leaf of the Filicineae seems to have arisen through the modification of a lateral branch system of the axis. Such a development might be attained through the expansion and flattening of the tips of minor branches. On the other hand, the small leaves of the club mosses and of some of the Psilophytineae may have originated as simple outgrowths or emergences from the stem or possibly through the

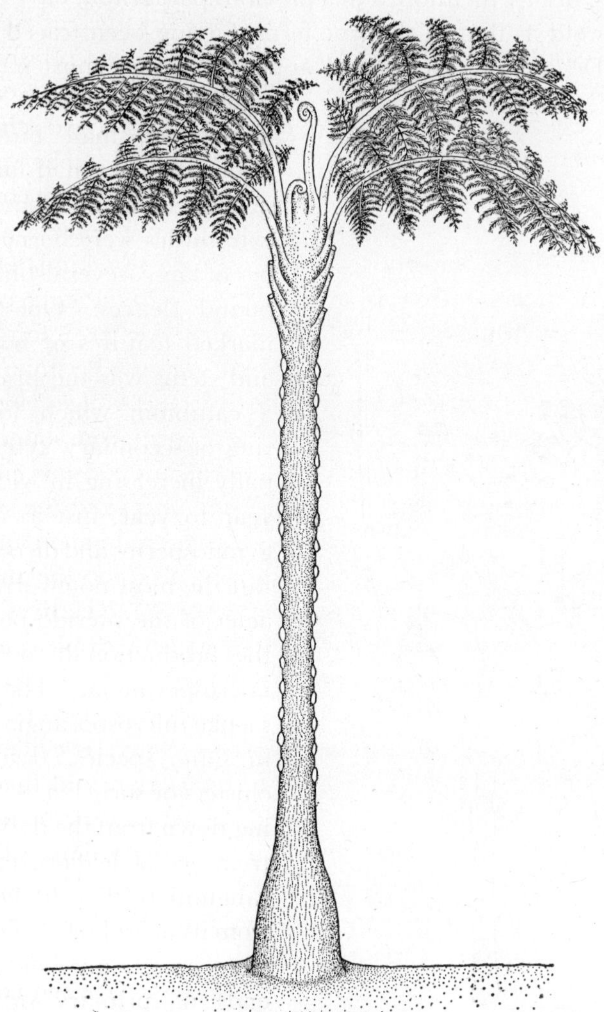

Fig. 430. A tree fern from the Carboniferous. After Hirmer.

modification of a small, simple branch. The origin of roots and of root systems is as yet unsolved. Attention was called to the slender underground leafless branches of Asteroxylon, which possibly functioned as roots. There still, however, remain unexplained the origin of roots arising internally in other roots or in stems and the origin of highly specialized root caps.

Early Seed Plants: Pteridosperms. These fernlike seed-bearing plants, briefly mentioned in a previous paragraph, have a known history as old as that of the true ferns, having been traced back to the late Devonian. In general appearance they must have been completely fernlike. Some of them were small, but for the most part they had fairly tall, slender stems at whose upper extremities were borne a number of large, several-times-compound leaves. One of the marked features of both roots and stems was the presence of a cambium which formed a ring of secondary xylem gradually increasing in width from year to year, just as in living gymnosperms and dicotyledons. But the most noteworthy character of the pteridosperms was the production of ovules and microsporangia. The slender, saclike microsporangia, at least in some species, occurred in clusters or sori (Fig. 431) hanging down from the flattened extremities of leaflets, each sporangium of a sorus being free from its neighbors. The ovules were commonly borne at the ends of primary or secondary leaflets. In some species they were comparable in size to a grain of wheat, in other species much larger. In the smaller kinds the base of each ovule was enveloped by a husk or covering (Fig. 432, *A*) whose upper portion was divided into segments. The structure of the ovule was

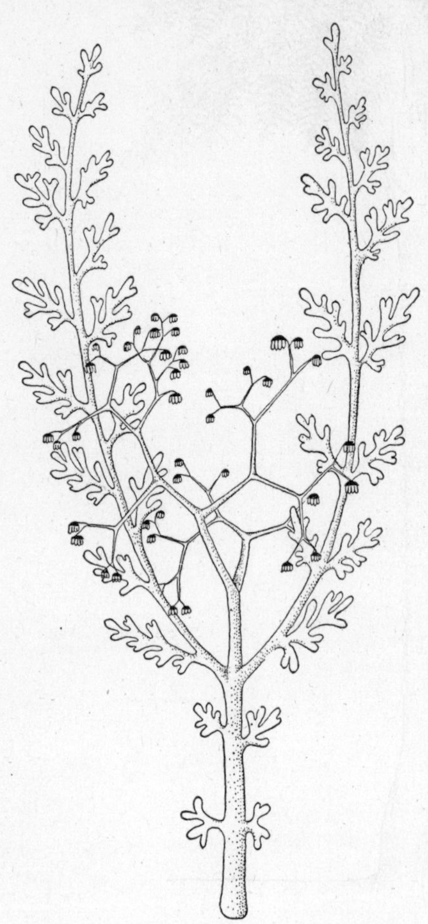

Fig. 431. Sporophyll of a pteridosperm bearing clusters of microsporangia. After Walton.

as complex as is that of any living gymnosperm and will be best understood by reference to Figure 432, *B*. The integument and nucellus were free only at the top of the ovule. A cone of tissue

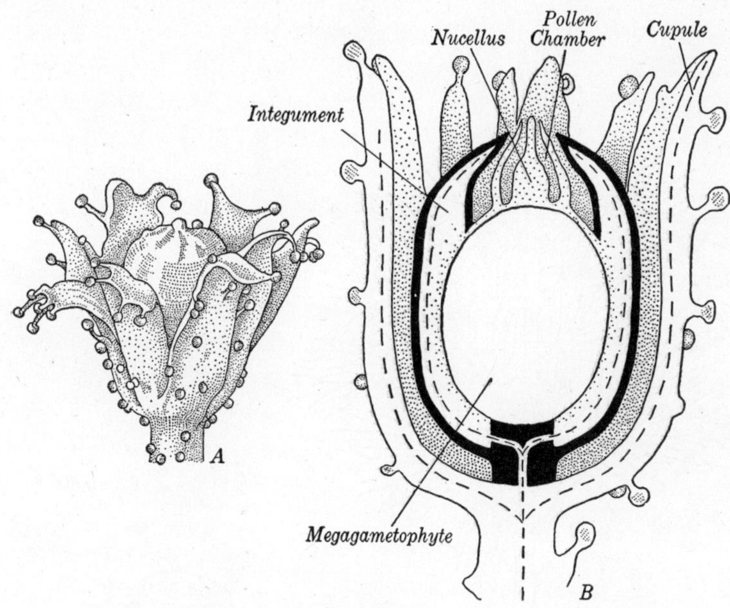

FIG. 432. *A*, seed of a pteridosperm partly enclosed by a husk or cupule. After Arber. *B*, median lengthwise section of a seed and cupule. After Walton.

formed the apex of the nucellus and contained a very deep, circular pollen chamber in which pollen grains have been found. A ring of archegonia was probably developed on the megagametophyte just beneath the cylindrical pollen chamber. The proximity of the base of the pollen chamber to such archegonia makes it improbable that there were pollen tubes. No seeds containing embryos have been found.

Pteridosperms were fairly abundant in Carboniferous and Permian times and may have existed as late as the Jurassic. Their origin is at present obscure. One view, emphasizing their points of resemblance to true ferns, regards them as highly developed offshoots from the same ancestry as that of the true ferns. Another view, emphasizing the differences, holds that they have evolved on parallel lines but independently of ferns. Obviously the seed ferns are transitional between true ferns and cycad-like gymnosperms, to be discussed presently, and are probably related to both. Their relation to other seed plants is debatable.

Cordaitales. These ancient seed plants had their maximum development during the Carboniferous and persisted into the Triassic.

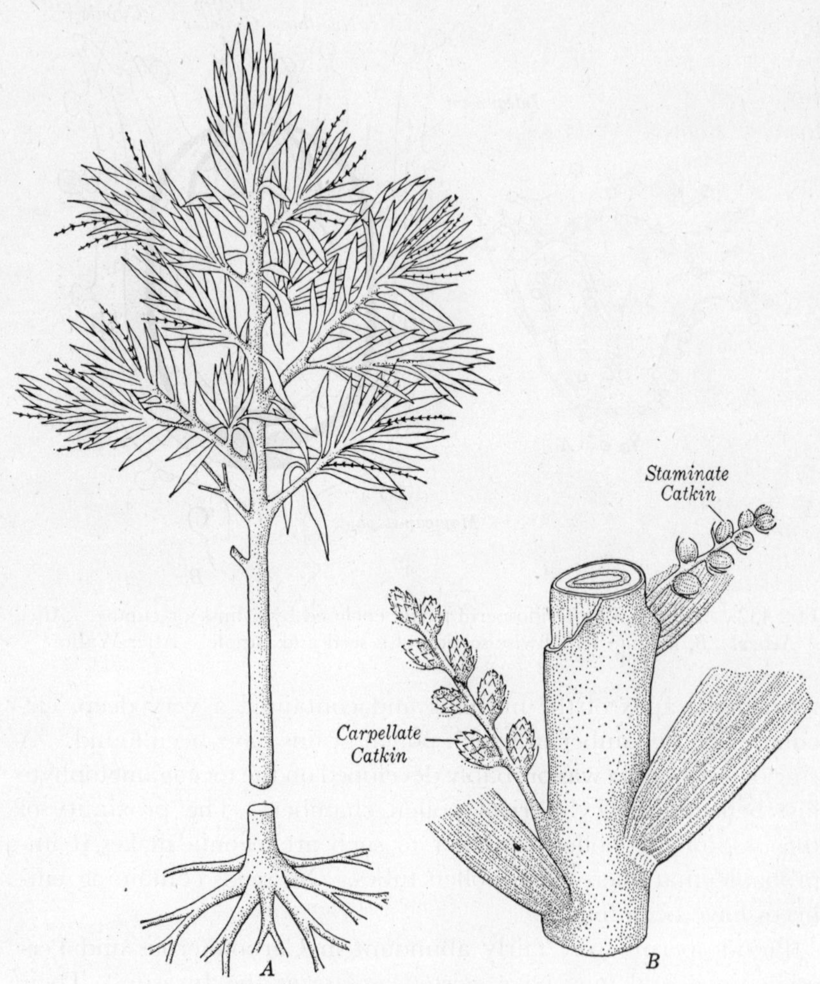

FIG. 433. *A*, a plant of Cordaites. *B*, portion of a branch with leaf bases and two lateral branches bearing, respectively, carpellate and staminate catkins. Both after Grand 'Eury.

They were characteristically tall, slender trees (Fig. 433, *A*), in some instances reaching a height of about 100 feet. Branches were produced near the top of the stem and were clothed with leaves, in some species slender and strap-shaped; in others, long, flat, and pointed, like grass blades. The leaves were highly organized and remarkably adapted by their structure to withstand bending. Strands of thick-walled mechanical cells were concentrated on both upper and lower surfaces of the leaf and in some species were connected between the parallel veins by plates of similar cells. Internally the stem had a relatively large pith surrounded by a zone of wood formed chiefly by cambial activity.

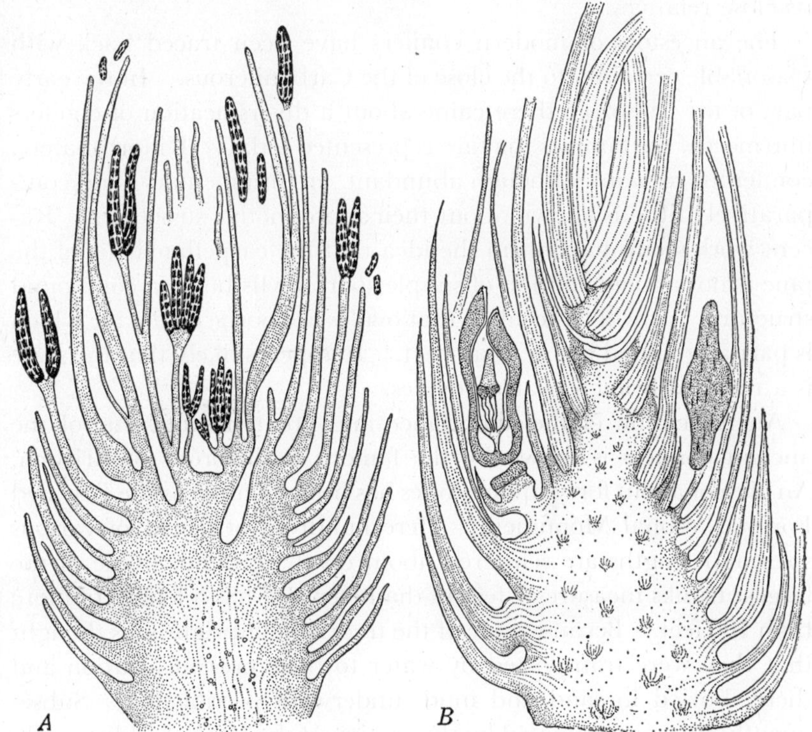

FIG. 434. Cordaites. Lengthwise sections: *A*, of a staminate catkin; *B*, of a carpellate catkin. Both after Renault.

Reproductive structures were present in small catkins (Fig. 433, *B*) which were borne on special branches. A staminate catkin (Fig. 434, *A*) consisted of an axis to which were attached sterile overlapping bracts and, near the top of the axis, several microsporophylls. A microsporophyll was itself bractlike and bore terminally a few slender microsporangia. Catkins of another type (Fig. 434, *B*), very similar to the staminate catkins in general appearance, also possessed sterile bracts; but in the axils of some of the bracts were ovules on short stalks. The ovules were somewhat flattened, and at maturity the integument became differentiated into an outer fleshy and an inner stony covering.

Mesozoic Seed Plants: Coniferales. The Mesozoic has properly been called an "age of gymnosperms." Great numbers of conifers and cycad-like plants overspread the world, and mingled with them were representatives of the maidenhair tree (Ginkgo) or its close relatives.

The ancestors of modern conifers have been traced back with reasonable certainty to the close of the Carboniferous. In the early part of the Mesozoic there came about a diversification of conifers into most of the families that are represented today. Unfortunately, coniferous remains, although abundant, are fragmentary; and comparatively little is known about their reproductive structures. Recent work seems to confirm the idea that the carpellate cone of the pine is not an aggregation of simple sporophylls but is a compound structure. It will be recalled that ovules are borne on a scale which is partially united below to a bract. It appears likely that the scale is a reduced branch bearing ovules.

An indication of the abundance and great size of some of the ancient conifers is shown by the famous fossil forests of Arizona. An area of about forty square miles has been set aside as the Petrified Forest National Monument. Here hundreds of trunks of various sizes and lengths are scattered about on the ground. One of the largest trunks measures 7 feet in diameter and has a length of more than 100 feet. Because none of the trees stand upright, it is thought that they were transported by water to their present location and there, buried in sand and mud, underwent petrifaction. Subsequently they were exposed by the erosion of the soft imbedding rock.

Mesozoic Cycad-like Plants. In a previous paragraph it was noted that the pteridosperms reached their maximum development in the Carboniferous. From this pteridosperm complex there probably evolved two separate groups of cycad-like plants: the Cycadales, having a scanty fossil record but living representatives; and the Bennettitales, having abundant fossil remains but no direct living descendants. The Bennettitales were abundant in Jurassic and Cretaceous times but became extinct at the close of the Cretaceous. Most of the Bennettitales resembled the Cycadales in bearing a crown of large compound leaves and in the general appearance and structure of their stems. But the outstanding feature of the Bennettitales was in the arrangement and structure of the microsporophylls and ovules. In some species these reproductive organs were borne together at the ends of short lateral branches wedged in between and scarcely projecting beyond the armor of leaf bases on the stems. Several hundred such short reproductive branches have been found on one stem, and all bore organs at about the same stage of development. It appears likely that the plants did not reproduce until they had reached a certain stage and then, having suddenly produced seeds, died. Such a story of development finds its counterpart in some living angiosperms, such as the bamboos and the century plant. The axis of a short reproductive branch ended in an elongated receptacle on which were many ovules packed in between slender scales (Fig. 435). Each ovule was borne

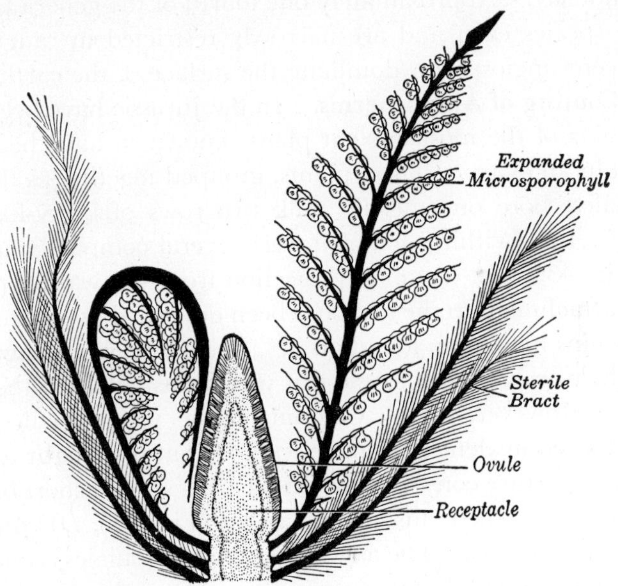

FIG. 435. Lengthwise section of a reproductive branch of one of the Bennettitales. After Wieland in *American Fossil Cycads*, published by the Carnegie Institution of Washington.

at the end of a short stalk. While the ovules were young, a whorl of from 10 to 20 microsporophylls grew from the base and enveloped the receptacle. Outside the microsporophylls was a whorl of slender bracts. Such a reproductive branch of the Bennettitales ha been called a flower, but it should be remembered that it is analo- gous rather than homologous with the flower of an angiosperm Ripe seeds have been discovered. They contained no endosperm, an embryo with two cotyledons filling the seed.

There are living today about 700 species of gymnosperms; by way of contrast, living angiosperms number nearly 200,000. The fossil record makes the reasons for such figures understandable. Gymnosperms are clearly decadent. Extinction or reduction is evident in all of them. The pteridosperms and the Cordaitales were the first to disappear, and later the Bennettitales. The Gink-goales, once abundant, now have a single species lingering on the edge of extinction. Of the nine genera of cycads, several have a very restricted range, and one genus barely survives. The Coni-ferales, with about 40 genera and about 500 species, show the same tendency. Approximately one fourth of the genera have but a single species each and are narrowly restricted in range. The more recent angiosperms dominate the surface of the earth.

The Coming of Angiosperms. In the Jurassic have been found the remains of the most ancient plants known to have had ovules enclosed in an ovary. These plants, grouped together as the order Caytoniales, bore on a fertile stalk two rows of berry-like fruits (Fig. 436, *A*). Within each fruit were several compactly arranged seeds (Fig. 436, *C*). A small projection from the wall of the fruit near its attachment to the stalk has been described as a stigma, and pollen grains have been found on it. The carpel of an angiosperm is thought to represent a single leaf which has enfolded the ovules it bears. However, in the Caytoniales the whole fertile stalk is regarded as equivalent to a single leaf. What is thought to be the staminate structure consists of an axis bearing several short branches to which are attached clusters of stamens (Fig. 436, *D*) containing winged pollen grains. The ancestry of the Caytoniales is uncertain. It has been suggested that they were derived from the pteridosperms. By definition they are angiosperms. But it is considered improb-able that they themselves gave rise to modern angiosperms.

The most puzzling feature of the fossil record is the sudden appearance in the lower Cretaceous of certain undoubted angio-sperms resembling in leaves and fruits those of modern times. Such representatives were apparently highly developed woody types, which have been placed with considerable confidence in families living today, such as the plane-tree family, including the sycamore of North America; the magnolia family; the laurel family; and the

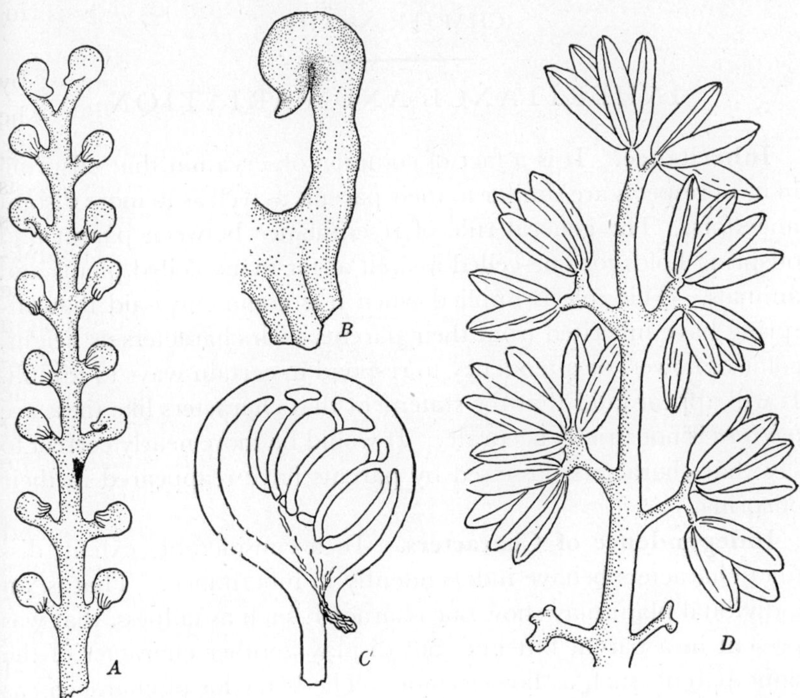

FIG. 436. Reproductive structures of the Caytoniales. *A*, megasporophyll bearing many seed-producing cupules (fruits). *B*, a single fruit, enlarged. *C*, lengthwise section of fruit and seeds. *D*, portion of a microsporophyll. All after Thomas.

breadfruit family. By the close of the Cretaceous the vegetation of the northern hemisphere had become very modern in its aspects, except that herbaceous forms were relatively few. The rarity of herbaceous plants at that time compared with the relative abundance of woody types adds strength to the theory now widely accepted that, speaking broadly, the latest products of evolution among angiosperms are the herbs.

CHAPTER XXXIII

INHERITANCE AND VARIATION

Inheritance. It is a fact of common observation that offspring in most respects are similar to their parents as well as to more distant ancestors. The general rule of resemblance between parent and offspring holds for one-celled as well as for many-celled plants and animals. This rule is implied when it is commonly said that offspring have inherited from their parents such characters as height, color of flower, or a tendency to respond in certain ways to stimuli. It will appear later that the statement that characters like these are *inherited* is not strictly accurate. It would be more nearly correct to say that characters possessed by parents have reappeared in their offspring.

Independence of Characters. To a considerable extent, distinct characters behave independently in inheritance. That is, an individual plant may show one character, such as tallness, that was present in a parent but may not display another character of the same parent, such as flower color. The behavior of characters as something like separate units was demonstrated by the classical experiments of Gregor Mendel (1822–1884). While Mendel was not the first to observe such behavior, he devised a most important method of investigation in his studies on the common garden pea, the results of which were published in 1866.

Mendel first tested varieties of pea to determine whether they were pure-bred—that is, whether they regularly produced offspring like themselves. From among the varieties which proved pure in this sense, he selected some which differed in one or more sharply marked characters. These varieties were then crossed; that is, pollen from flowers of one variety was transferred to the stigmas of another variety.

Varieties Differing in One Character. Some varieties of pea produced plump, round seeds; others, wrinkled seeds. The form of the seed is determined by that of the embryo; the characters in question, therefore, are characters of the embryo (young sporophyte) within the seed. When Mendel crossed two such differing varieties, all the seeds produced were round (Fig. 437). The em-

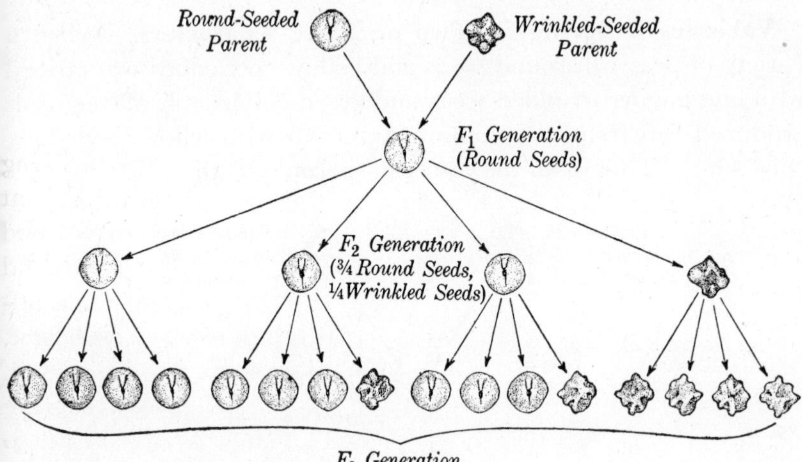

FIG. 437. Diagram illustrating the behavior of the round-seed and wrinkled-seed characters in Mendel's experiments with peas.

bryonic sporophytes in these seeds belonged to the *first filial* (F_1) *generation*. Mendel spoke of the round-seed character as *dominant* and of the alternative wrinkled-seed character, displayed by one parent but not by any of the F_1 generation, as *recessive*.

When the sporophytes of the F_1 generation, grown to maturity, were self-pollinated, three fourths of their seeds, the embryos in which represented the *second filial* (F_2) *generation*, were round; one fourth were wrinkled. The recessive (wrinkled-seed) character, which was absent in the F_1 generation, had now reappeared.

When the F_2 sporophytes from wrinkled seeds were self-pollinated, they produced only wrinkled seeds. The embryos in these seeds were of the F_3 generation. When F_2 sporophytes from round seeds were self-pollinated, two thirds of them produced round and wrinkled seeds in the proportion of three to one; the other third produced only round seeds.

In another experiment Mendel crossed a variety with yellow and one with green cotyledons (also characters of the embryonic sporophyte). The yellow-cotyledon character proved dominant, the green-cotyledon character recessive. In the F_1, F_2, and F_3 generations this pair of characters behaved just as did the round- and wrinkled-seed characters in the previous experiments. In all, seven pairs of characters found in different varieties of pea were similarly tested.

Varieties Differing in Two or More Characters. When a variety of pea with round seeds and yellow cotyledons was crossed with one having wrinkled seeds and green cotyledons, all the seeds produced were round and contained embryos with yellow cotyledons (Fig. 438). That is, all the young F_1 sporophytes displayed the two

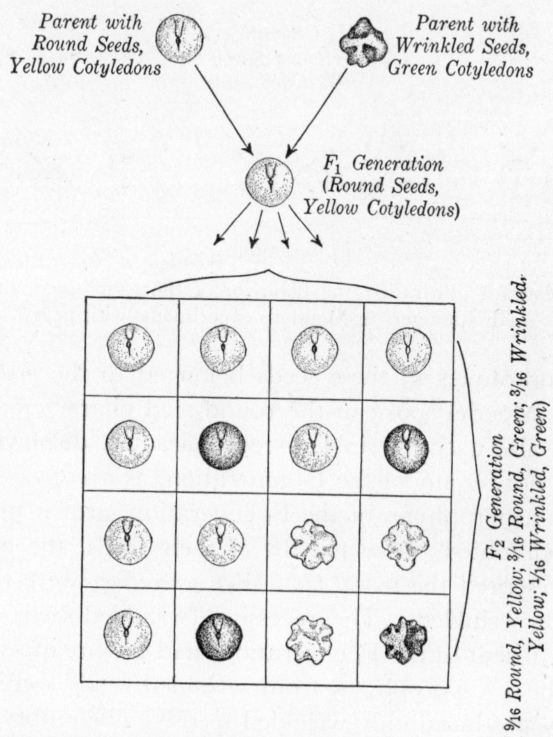

Fig. 438. Diagram illustrating the behavior of the round-seed and wrinkled-seed, yellow-cotyledon and green-cotyledon characters in Mendel's experiments.

dominant characters. When these sporophytes, grown to maturity, were self-pollinated, the resultant seeds presented all possible combinations of the two pairs of characters, these combinations appearing in the proportions that would be expected if the characters of one pair (round and wrinkled) were transmitted independently of those of the other pair (yellow and green). The seeds containing the F_2 sporophytes consisted, therefore, of four classes in the proportions: nine round, yellow; three round, green; three wrinkled, yellow; one wrinkled, green.

Crosses between varieties differing in three pairs of characters—for example, round and wrinkled seeds, yellow and green cotyledons, purple and white flowers—gave corresponding but, of course, more complicated results. As in the preceding experiments, the distribution of the characters of any pair among plants of the F_2 generation bore no relation to the way in which the characters of any other pair were distributed; consequently there appeared in this generation different classes of individuals, in proportions that could be calculated in advance, possessing every possible combination of the characters of the grandparents.

Mendel's description of his experiments was almost completely overlooked until about 1900. Since its rediscovery, studies similar to his have been made upon very many plants and animals. These studies have shown that in large measure characters behave in inheritance as though they were transmitted separately—being, as it were, reshuffled and arranged into varying combinations in each succeeding generation. Often, as in the peas studied by Mendel, a particular character of one parent is dominant in the F_1 generation over a contrasting character of the other parent. For example, red, blue, or yellow flower colors are in most cases dominant over white. Hairiness of stems is dominant over smoothness. Brown eye color in man is dominant over blue or gray.

In other instances, however, there is no dominance; instead, the character that appears in the F_1 generation is in some degree intermediate between the characters of the parents. A case of this nature is that of a cross between a red and a white four-o'clock (Fig. 439), which yielded offspring with *pink* flowers. When these F_1 pink-flowered plants were self-pollinated, their offspring in the F_2 generation were: one fourth red-flowered, one fourth white-flowered, and one half pink-flowered. The latter pink-flowered plants, like their parents, displayed the hybrid character. But whether the F_1 generation shows complete dominance of one parental character, partial dominance, or intermediacy, it is still true that both parental characters are in effect separately transmitted. In the case in question, the pink-flowered plants transmitted to some among their offspring the capacity to produce flowers like those of one or the other of the original parents—namely, red or white.

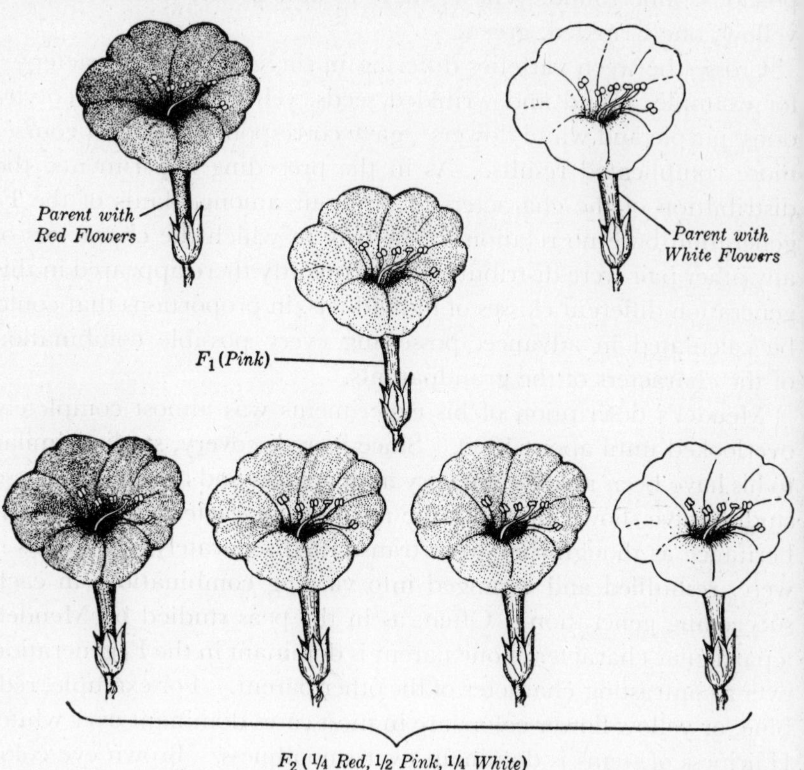

FIG. 439. Results of crossing a red- and a white-flowered four o'clock (Mirabilis). All F_1 plants bear pink flowers. Of the F_2 generation, one fourth bear red, one half pink, one fourth white flowers.

Inheritance and Chromosomes. It was pointed out in Chapter X that all inheritance must be by means of structures or substances that are transmitted from parent cell to daughter cell in the course of nuclear and cell division. It follows that offspring do not literally inherit *characters* from their parents—except, of course, the structural and functional characters of the spore or gametes which gave rise to the offspring. Apart from characters belonging to the cell or cells received from the parent or parents, all that the new generation inherits is certain *substances*, the presence of which in the cells of the offspring makes possible the development of characters like those of the parent. A pine tree does not literally inherit tallness; it inherits certain substances which give it the ability to grow tall.

It has appeared also that in the main the substances concerned in inheritance are carried in the chromosomes—that is, the chromosomes are the essential *mechanism of inheritance.* There is evidence that substances or bodies (such as plastids) present in the cytoplasm play a part also in the transmission of hereditary possibilities. But the rôle of cytoplasmic structures in this respect is clearly subordinate to that of the chromosomes.

However, chromosomal and cytoplasmic substances together do not finally determine the characters of a plant or animal. These substances endow the organism with certain possibilities of development; whether, or to what extent, those possibilities are to be realized depends upon the environment that surrounds the organism while it is developing. The actual characters that the mature plant or animal displays are therefore the result of an interplay of inherited tendencies and environmental influences. A pine tree can by appropriate treatment—such as keeping it in a pot too small to permit the free development of its root system—be induced to grow very slowly and to remain a dwarf throughout a long life; but the inherited capacity for tall growth remains and may be passed on to its descendants.

Characters and Genes. The fact that in large measure characters appear and reappear independently of one another has led to the assumption that characters are in some way represented by small portions or units (*genes*) of the hereditary substance. These, if they exist, are too small to be visible under any power of the microscope. Genes are thought of as borne in or upon the chromosomes —probably not constituting the whole chromosome substance. It is considered that the presence of particular genes in certain chromosomes of the pea makes possible the production of round or of wrinkled seeds, of yellow or of green cotyledons, of purple or of white flowers.

Any pea plant, according to this conception, may possess in each of its nuclei two genes for roundness of seed, having received one such gene from each parent; or two genes for wrinkling; or a gene for roundness derived from one parent and one for wrinkling derived from the other parent. If two genes for roundness are present in the embryo of a particular seed, the seed is round; if two genes for wrinkling, the seed is wrinkled; if one gene for roundness and one for wrinkling are present, the dominant gene prevails and the seed is round. Other genes which affect various characters of the pea seem likewise to belong to contrasting pairs, as the genes for yellow and for green cotyledons or those for purple and for white flowers. A similar statement can be made as to the genes that influence the characters of other species of plants and animals. In the pea more than 50 pairs of genes are recognized; in corn about 400, the largest number yet known for any species of plant. In a small fruit fly (*Drosophila melanogaster*) the number is approximately 1000—the largest known for any animal.

What has been said may seem to imply that each character is influenced by but one pair of genes and that each pair of genes is concerned in the production of a single character. The facts, however, are not so simple. In general, any gene affects not one character alone, but several or many characters. For example, one gene which in the pea influences flower color affects also the color of the seed coats, leaf axils, and pods, as well as the form of seeds. Conversely, each character is the result of the activity of several or many genes. Three pairs of genes are recognized which affect flower color in the pea; Mendel's work dealt with one of these pairs. Similarly, three pairs of genes, of which one pair was involved in Mendel's experiments, influence the color of cotyledons. Eye color in Drosophila is found to be affected by at least 50 genes. The total constitution of a plant or animal depends upon the complicated interaction of all the genes, whose effect in turn is conditioned by the environment.

Even though a character is influenced by many genes, it may in a particular experiment be inherited as though it were represented by but one pair. This is explained by the fact that two races or varieties of a species may be alike with reference to all save one pair of the genes that noticeably affect the character in question. For example, if, as in Mendel's work, plants are crossed that differ with respect to only one pair of genes that may influence the color of cotyledons, then yellow and green cotyledons will appear in the F_2 and later generations in the same proportions as though only that one pair of genes affected cotyledon color. For the purposes of the experiment these may be referred to as a gene for yellowness and a gene for greenness.

Genes and Chromosomes. It has been seen (Chapter XXV) that each cell of a sporophyte contains 2 n chromosomes, of which n are of maternal and n of paternal origin. Each maternal chromosome corresponds to a particular paternal chromosome in the sense that the two bear the same or corresponding genes.

Suppose that two pure-bred plants differ, like those Mendel worked with, in one pair of genes. The chromosomes of one pair in each cell of one plant carry each a gene for roundness of seed. Each chromosome of the corresponding pair in the cells of the other plant carries a gene for wrinkling. When the reduction divisions occur in the first plant, each megaspore and each microspore receives one chromosome bearing a gene for roundness. Since the spores give rise to corresponding gametophytes, each cell of a megagametophyte (including the egg) and each cell of a microgametophyte (including the male gametes) contains in its single set of chromosomes one which carries a gene for roundness. Similarly, each spore, gametophyte, and egg or male gamete produced by the second plant has a chromosome bearing a gene for wrinkling.

Suppose now that the two plants are crossed. An egg from the first plant, one of whose chromosomes carries a gene for roundness (R), unites with a male gamete from the second plant, one of whose chromosomes bears a gene for wrinkling (r). The zygote so formed (Fig. 440) has among its 2 n chromosomes one pair bearing, respectively, a gene for roundness and a gene for wrinkling. A similar pair of chromosomes is present in each cell of the F_1 sporophyte that develops from this zygote. Since the gene for roundness is dominant, the seed containing the embryo sporophyte is round.

When the reduction divisions occur in this sporophyte, the chromosomes of the pair in question (like those of other pairs) conjugate and separate. Hence, half the megaspores, and the megagametophytes and eggs to which they give rise, receive each a chromosome bearing a gene for roundness; and half receive each a chromosome carrying a gene for wrinkling. Similarly with the microspores, microgametophytes, and male gametes: half receive a chromosome bearing a gene for roundness; half receive a chromosome bearing a gene for wrinkling. If eggs of the two classes unite indiscriminately with male gametes of the two classes, the result will be (Fig. 440) that one fourth of the zygotes so formed, and of the F_2 sporophytes developing from them, receive each two genes for roundness; the seeds containing the young sporophytes will be round. One half of the F_2 sporophytes receive each one gene for roundness and one for wrinkling; the seeds containing them also will be round (because

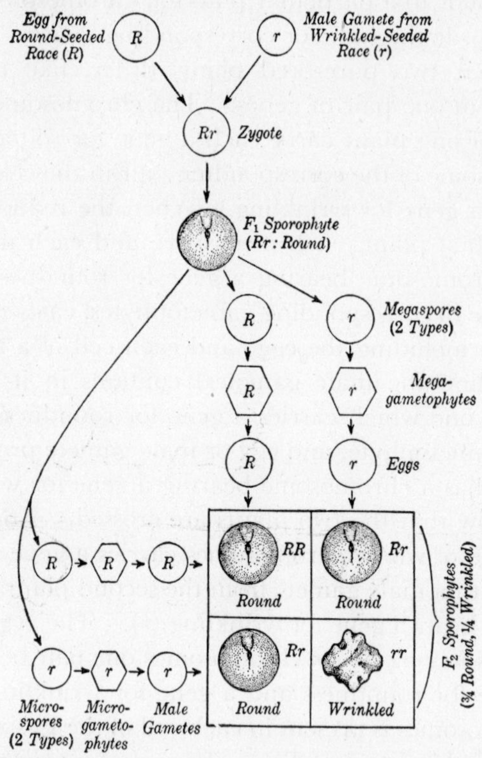

FIG. 440. Diagram illustrating the transmission of genes for roundness and wrinkling of seeds, borne on the chromosomes of one pair. Explanation in text.

roundness is dominant). The remaining fourth of the F_2 sporophytes receive each two genes for wrinkling; the seeds containing them will be wrinkled.

A comparison of Figure 440 with Figure 437 shows how the behavior of the chromosomes and of the genes they carry explains Mendel's results in this and similar experiments.

If the parents of the cross differ in two genes instead of one—for example, in genes for roundness (*R*) and wrinkling (*r*), for yellow (*Y*) and green (*y*) cotyledons, these genes being borne on chromosomes of different pairs—the story will be as shown in Figure 441. In this case the F_1 sporophytes will give rise to four kinds of

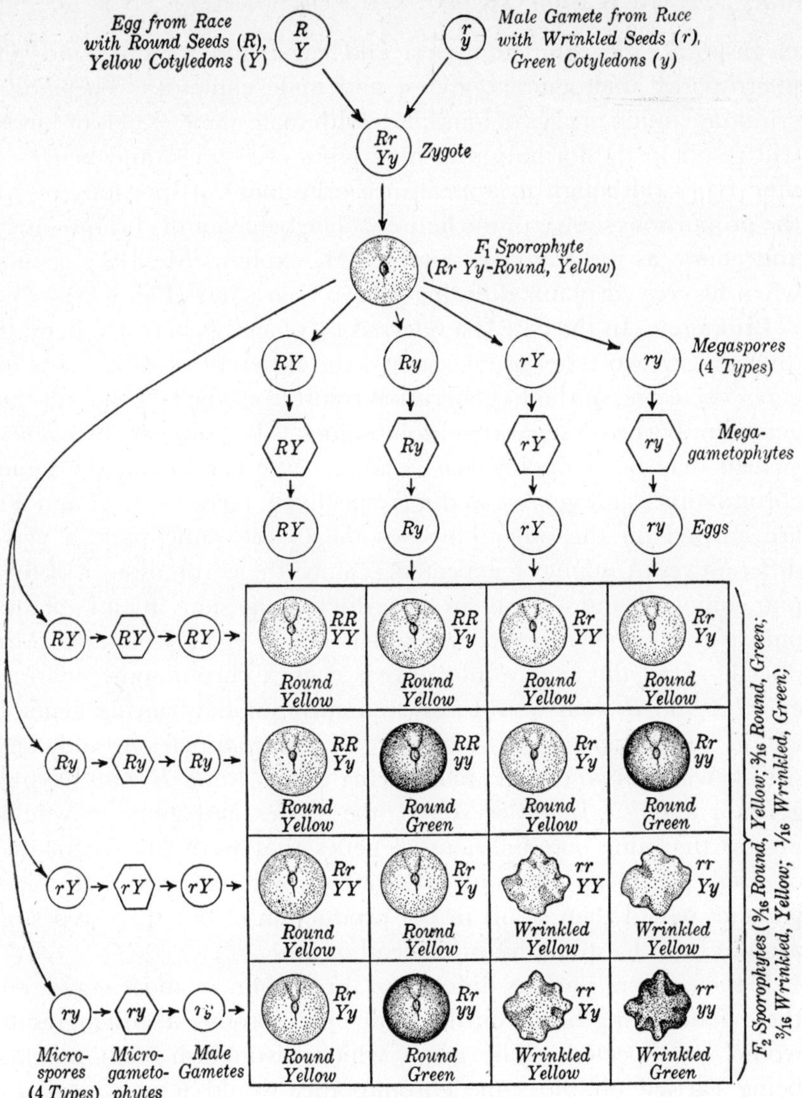

FIG. 441. Diagram illustrating the transmission of two pairs of genes, borne on different chromosomes. Each original parent contributed, through its gamete, one chromosome of each pair. Chromosomes of one pair bear, respectively, genes for the round-seeded (*R*) and the wrinkled-seeded (*r*) character; those of the other pair, genes for yellow (*Y*) and green (*y*) cotyledons. Since *R* is dominant over *r* and *Y* over *y*, the combinations, in F_2 sporophytes, *RRYY*, *RRYy*, *RrYY*, and *RrYy* result in the appearance of round seeds and yellow cotyledons; *RRyy* and *Rryy*, of round seeds and green cotyledons; *rrYY* and *rrYy*, of wrinkled seeds and yellow cotyledons; and *rryy*, of wrinkled seeds and green cotyledons.

megaspores, megagametophytes, and eggs; and to four kinds of microspores, microgametophytes, and male gametes. The indiscriminate union of eggs of four kinds with male gametes of four kinds will result in the formation of nine types of zygotes, and hence of nine types (although in appearance only four) of sporophytes, in the proportions shown in the figure. The behavior of chromosomes and genes, as illustrated in Figure 441, explains Mendel's results when he crossed plants differing in two characters (Fig. 438).

Linkage. In the case last referred to, of a cross between parents differing in two pairs of characters, the different combinations of genes occurring in the F_2 generation result from the fact that all the genes are borne on separate chromosomes. If, however, two genes (which may be symbolized as *A* and *B*) are carried on the same chromosome, and genes *a* and *b* (respectively recessive to *A* and *B*) are carried on the other chromosome of the same pair, a very different result might be expected. Since the chromosomes of this pair conjugate and separate in the reduction divisions in an F_1 plant, only two types of megaspores, and hence of eggs, would be produced. Half the eggs would possess each a chromosome bearing genes *A* and *B;* half would possess a chromosome bearing genes *a* and *b*. The microspores, and hence the male gametes, would consist likewise of two classes: half having genes *A* and *B*, half having genes *a* and *b*. In other words, the spores and gametes would possess the same combinations of genes that were present in the original parents. The indiscriminate union of eggs and male gametes would then result in the production of but three types of zygotes (and F_2 sporophytes) instead of nine.

If the original parents differed in three, four, or more genes, all these genes being borne on the same chromosome, a similar result would be expected. The genes which distinguish each parent, being carried on the same chromosome, would tend to remain together from generation to generation; they would be linked, or would constitute a *linkage group*.

If the original parents differed in many genes, some borne on the chromosomes of each pair, those carried on any particular chromosome would tend to pass together from generation to generation. There would be as many linkage groups as chromosome pairs. It has in fact been found that genes of the pea tend to pass from generation to generation in groups. The question has not yet been tested for all the recognized genes, because to determine with what other genes a given gene is linked requires experiments carried on for a long time and on a large scale. The pea has seven pairs of chromosomes and seven linkage groups. The corn has ten pairs of chromosomes and ten linkage groups. The species of Drosophila already mentioned has four pairs of chromosomes. Of the great number of genes known for this fly, the linkage relations of a large proportion have been determined. All fall into four linkage groups. In no species of plant or animal have the genes been found to constitute a number of linkage groups greater than the number of chromosome pairs.

Crossing Over. Each of the linkage groups just referred to consists of genes which *tend* to remain together. As a rule, however, any two linked genes now and then become separated. For example, a gene for round seeds in the pea (dominant over wrinkled seeds) is linked with one for the presence of leaf tendrils (dominant over the absence of tendrils). If a plant with round seeds and tendrils is crossed with one having wrinkled seeds and no tendrils and if the genes concerned were completely linked, the plants in the F_2 generation would be of two classes: some with round seeds and tendrils, some with wrinkled seeds and no tendrils. As a matter of fact, the F_2 generation produced in one such experiment consisted of 319 plants with round seeds and tendrils, 4 with round seeds and no tendrils, 3 with wrinkled seeds and tendrils, 123 with wrinkled seeds and no tendrils. The occurrence of small numbers of plants of the second and third classes indicates that, in about one of every 64 spore mother cells in the F_1 plants, genes which were linked, and therefore borne on the same chromosome, became separated.

Such a separation of two linked genes seems to result from the occasional interchange of parts of chromatids already described. *A* and *B*, Figure 442, represent pairs of chromosomes at the stage shown diagrammatically in Figure 309, *C*. *Crossing over* (exchange of parts) between the chromatids of the paired chromosomes has occurred at several points. Figure 442, *C*, shows how, in the simplest possible case, crossing over may bring about new combinations of genes. The dominant genes *A* and *B* are borne on one chromosome (and hence on each of its chromatids), and the recessive genes *a* and *b* are borne on the other chromosome of the same pair. A crossing over occurs between two chromatids (one belonging to each chromosome) at a point between *A* and *B* (and between *a* and *b*). When the separation of the four chromatids is finally effected by the first and second reduction divisions, one of the four nuclei formed

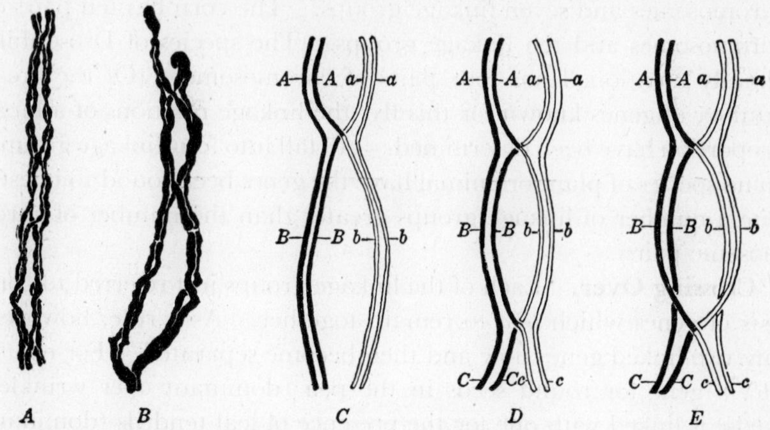

FIG. 442. Crossing-over. *A* and *B*, chromosome pairs at an early stage of the first reduction division in a megaspore mother cell of lily; interconnections between chromatids. Drawings courtesy of D. C. Cooper. *C*, diagram illustrating a single crossing-over. *D*, double crossing-over. *E*, crossing-over (*above*) between two chromatids, and (*below*) between the other two chromatids of the same chromosomes.

by these divisions will contain a chromosome bearing genes *A* and *B;* one nucleus, a chromosome bearing *A* and *b;* one a chromosome bearing *a* and *B;* and one a chromosome bearing *a* and *b*. With respect to the genes on this pair of chromosomes, the megaspore or microspore nuclei formed would be of four different kinds.

Figure 442, *D* and *E*, show more complicated cases of crossing over.

In the study of linked genes in the pea and other organisms, various proportions of crossing over are found. It is considered that the proportion of crossing over occurring between any two linked genes is some measure of the distance between them on the chromosome—those genes showing the larger proportion of crossing over being farther apart than those between which crossing over is relatively rare.

The frequency with which crossing over occurs is affected by temperature, as well as by X rays and radium emanations.

Variation. While resemblance between ancestors and offspring is general, it is not universal. Offspring, though like their parents in most respects, always differ, usually in minor ways, from the parents as well as from other members of the same family. The appearance of such differences is *variation.* The characters of an individual *vary* from the characters of the parent or parents.

In most cases a character in respect to which an individual differs from its parent is not transmitted to future generations; the change that has appeared is not permanent. Variation of this nonheritable type seems in general to result from the development of the new individual under an environment different from that which surrounded its ancestors. Since under natural conditions no two environments are exactly alike, it is not surprising that no two wheat plants, however similar in inheritance, are precise duplicates. The effect of environment in causing variations may, therefore, be observed in any field of wheat or corn or in any community of human

FIG. 443. Nonheritable variation due to the environment. *A*, dandelion plant grown at a low altitude. *B*, plant of the same species grown at a high altitude. Both to the same scale. Redrawn from Bonnier.

beings; in each of these cases many differences between individuals result from differences in inheritance, but many more result from differences in environment. (For an extreme example of variation due to environment, see Fig. 443.)

But sometimes a new character, once it has appeared, is passed on to later generations in the same way as are older characters. While variation producing such heritable changes is less frequent than variation of the nonheritable sort, it occurs often enough to play an important part in giving rise to new kinds of plants and animals. Examples of heritable variation are the appearance of a tree bearing smooth peaches (nectarines) though the tree's ancestors bore peaches of the downy type; the occurrence of a white-flowered plant whose ancestors were red- or blue-flowered; and the occurrence of a beardless wheat plant in a regularly bearded variety. Such an individual may become the starting-point of a new race; if the new race differs sufficiently from the older race from which it arose, it may be considered a new variety or even a new species. Innumerable varieties of cultivated plants and of domestic animals have originated with individuals in which, in consequence of variation of this nature, a new heritable character appeared. Doubtless many wild varieties and species have had a similar origin, although the fact can be known only when, as in cultivated plants and domestic animals, the first appearance of a new character is actually observed.

As has been seen, variation of the nonheritable type is largely if not entirely due to the environment. It is not so clearly true that heritable variation is similarly caused; because the environment seems not, as a rule, to affect the hereditary substances in the chromosomes. It is true, as will appear hereafter, that under experimental conditions certain environmental factors may cause changes in the number and constitution of chromosomes and in the constitution of genes. But to what extent, if at all, such factors produce similar effects in nature is still unknown.

While the underlying causes of chromosomal and genic changes which result in heritable variation are yet obscure, much has been learned regarding the nature of these changes. A few types of change now fairly well known will be mentioned.

Changes in Number of Chromosome Sets. It sometimes happens that a nuclear division once begun is not completed; instead, the chromosomes, partly or entirely separated, are all brought together in a newly organized nucleus. This nucleus then possesses a doubled complement of chromosomes, as do the nuclei derived from it by division. Agencies which are known to be capable of stopping division, and so of doubling the chromosome number, include a lowering or raising of the temperature at the time of division, and treatment with various anesthetics, narcotics, and dilute poisons. Of the latter, colchicine is particularly effective. Its use may induce a doubling of chromosome numbers in a large proportion of the cells of a plant; and a branch arising from a region containing such cells may be separated and give rise to a plant with the new number of chromosomes. In this way new races larger in some or all parts, including flowers and fruits, have been obtained. In some plants, including corn and other cereals and sweet clover, the application of high temperatures at the time of the division of the zygote nucleus has resulted in the production of plants with doubled chromosome numbers.

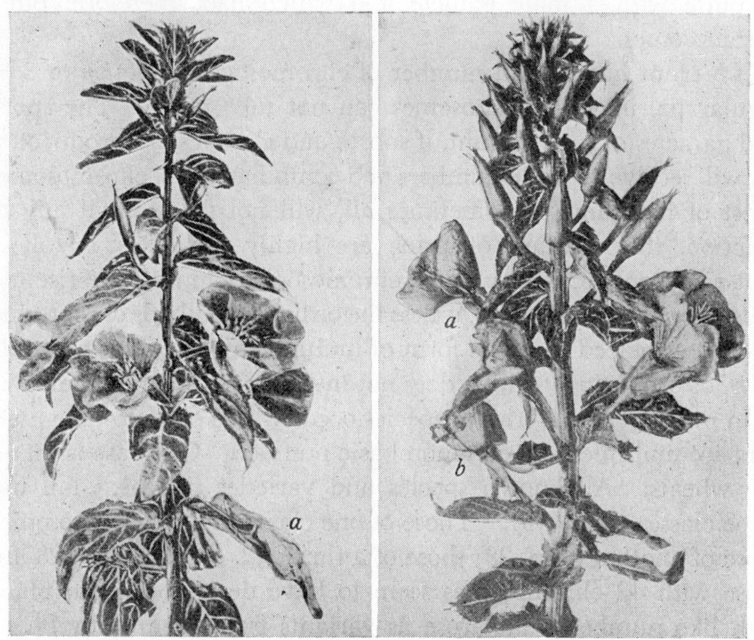

FIG. 444. *Oenothera Lamarckiana* (*A*), with fourteen chromosomes; and a variant form, *Oenothera gigas* (*B*), with twenty-eight chromosomes. After De Vries.

A sudden doubling occurs now and then from unknown causes in wild and cultivated plants. It has happened, for example, in three species of evening primrose (Fig. 444), in the tomato, and in tobacco. The new giant form, with four instead of two like sets of chromosomes, may give rise to a new race with the new chromosome number, although often it is only partially fertile. It is not unlikely that in at least some of these instances the change in chromosome number was due to a marked rise or fall in temperature, which checked a nuclear division, either vegetative or reductional.

The union of a gamete with *n* chromosomes (from a 2 *n* plant) and one with 2 *n* (from a 4 *n* plant) sometimes produces offspring with 3 *n* chromosomes. From similar unions of unlike gametes, combined with chromosome doubling, plants with still higher multiples of *n* chromosomes may result. It has happened too in a number of genera, including evening primroses, tomato, and tobacco, that a plant (sporophyte) appeared with only *n* chromosomes. Such a plant seems to have developed from an egg which had failed to unite with a male gamete and which had, therefore, but *n* chromosomes.

If a plant has an odd number of chromosome sets (as *n* or 3 *n*), regular pairing of chromosomes can not take place. The spores and gametes of such a plant, if spores and gametes are produced at all, will receive variable numbers and combinations of chromosomes. Most of the gametes, sometimes all, will not function; if any do function, the resultant offspring are highly variable. It follows that a sporophyte with *n* or 3 *n* chromosomes can not give rise to a constant variety or species, unless the ordinary methods of reproduction are replaced by some form of multiplication (as, for example, by buds or cuttings) which does not involve the union of gametes.

In many genera, series of species occur whose chromosome numbers are multiples of a common basic number. One case is that of the wheats. All known species and varieties of wheat fall into three classes (Fig. 445). Those of one class have 14 chromosomes; those of another class, 28; those of a third, 42. Those with 28 and those with 42 chromosomes seem to have descended from plants with like numbers that arose as variants from races with 14, although hybridization with plants of a related genus having likewise 14 chromosomes seems to have been concerned in the production of the species with higher numbers. The roses provide a similar but more extensive series. Some species and varieties have 14 chromosomes; others have, respectively, 21, 28, 35, 42, and 56.

Other Changes in Chromosome Number. Another mode of departure from the ordinary course of nuclear division consists in the failure of sister chromosomes (or, in the first reduction division, of the chromosomes of a pair) to separate and to pass to opposite poles. If both pass to the same pole, one daughter nucleus re-

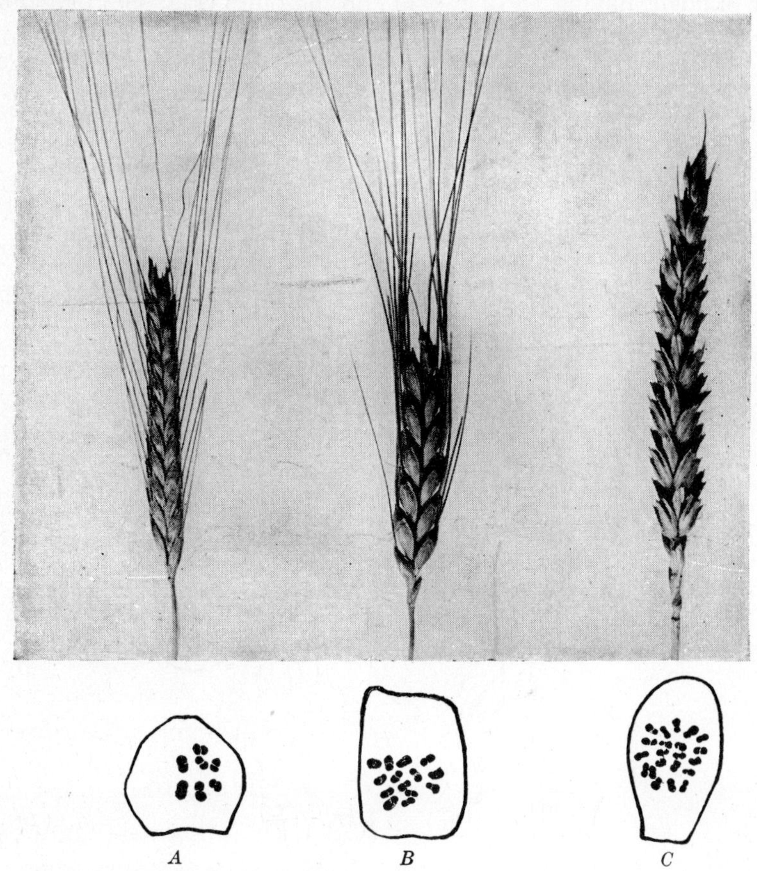

FIG. 445. Species of wheat; *below*. a microspore mother cell from each species. *A*, a wheat with fourteen chromosomes (seven pairs). *B*, one with twenty-eight chromosomes (fourteen pairs). *C*, one with forty-two chromosomes (twenty-one pairs). Figures of microspore mother cells after Sax.

ceives one more, the other daughter nucleus one less, than the usual number. If this occurs in the direct ancestry of spores or gametes, some of these reproductive cells will possess $n + 1$, others $n - 1$, chromosomes. If, then, a plant produces some gametes with each of these numbers, together with other gametes having n chromosomes, haphazard union of such diverse gametes might result in the appearance of offspring some of which would have $2n - 1$, some (the majority) $2n$, and some $2n + 1$ chromosomes.

A much-studied species of evening primrose has produced a number of forms having 15 $(2n + 1)$ chromosomes (Fig. 446, *C*). Fif-

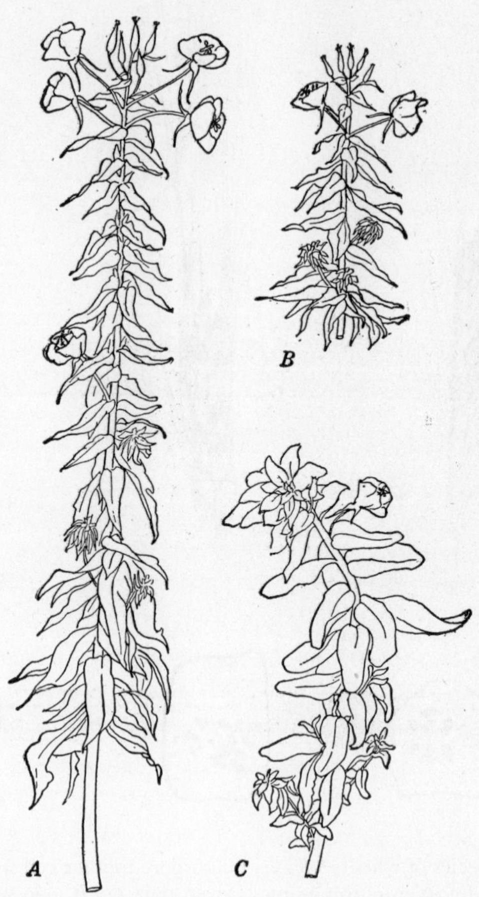

FIG. 446. Shoots of *Oenothera Lamarckiana* (*A*) and of two variant forms derived from it: (*B*) *Oenothera nanella*, a dwarf form having fourteen chromosomes $(2n)$ like the parent species, and (*C*) *Oenothera lata*, with fifteen chromosomes $(2n + 1)$. Redrawn from De Vries.

teen-chromosome plants differ markedly from the parent form in such characters as form of leaf and habit of growth. Each such variant plant seems to have been produced by the union of a gamete with 7 (n) and one with 8 $(n + 1)$ chromosomes. The Jimson weed

(*Datura Stramonium*) also has given rise to a series of forms with $2n + 1$ (in this case 25) chromosomes (Fig. 447). In both of these, as well as in other genera, the theoretically possible forms with $2n - 1$ chromosomes do not occur. Apparently gametes with $n - 1$

FIG. 447. *Above*, a fruit of the Jimson weed (*Datura Stramonium*), which has twenty-four chromosomes ($2n$). *Below*, the fruits of twelve variants, each with twenty-five ($2n + 1$) chromosomes, that have arisen from this species. Photograph by A. F. Blakeslee, in the *Journal of Heredity*.

chromosomes do not function; or, if they do, the resultant zygotes with $2n - 1$ chromosomes do not develop into new plants.

As a result of other irregularities in nuclear division more or less similar to that just described, many different chromosome groupings may arise. Evening-primrose plants have appeared with chromosome numbers ranging from 7 (n) to 30 ($4n + 2$). A corresponding series in the Jimson weed runs from 12 (n) to 51 ($4n + 3$). Evidently many plants with variant chromosome numbers can not, for reasons already stated, perpetuate themselves. Others may do so. For example, if a plant has $2n + 2$ chromosomes, the two extra chromosomes representing the same pair, a regular pairing may conceivably occur; and functional spores and gametes may be produced. There are genera whose species growing in the wild show series of chromosome numbers which may have arisen in consequence of irregular behavior on the part of individual chromosomes. An example is Carex (the sedges), the values of n in whose many species include 6, 8, 9, all the numbers from 12 to 43, 45, 54, 55, and 56.

As to the causes which in nature modify the course of division, affecting either single chromosomes or chromosome sets, nothing is certainly known. There is evidence that high or low temperatures may play a part. Experimentally, the proportional occurrence of such irregularities has been increased by treatment with X rays or with radium.

Changes Affecting Parts of Chromosomes. Apart from cases of unusual behavior of whole chromosomes, irregularities or accidents sometimes cause transverse breaks in chromosomes (or in chromatids which by separation later become chromosomes). Such breaks may take place during nuclear division and also, apparently, at other times as well. They occur under natural as well as under cultural conditions. The proportion of their occurrence, like that of the deviations previously discussed, is increased by treatment with X rays, radium, or ultraviolet light, by bombardment with neutrons, or by subjection to high temperatures.

When a chromosome has once been broken, various fates may overtake its fragments. They may remain separate: in such a case one part is usually lost; but it is possible that both parts sometimes persist, so increasing by one the chromosome number of the nucleus containing it and of the descendants of that nucleus. One fragment may be inverted and reattached to the other part of the same chromosome, or it may become attached to a different chromosome. If two breaks occur in one chromosome, the middle fragment may be inverted and reattached; or it may become separated and the end portions reunited. If breaks occur in two chromosomes, sometimes there is an exchange of segments and a reattachment in new combinations.

Varied effects upon inheritance result from changes such as these. The permanent loss of a part of a chromosome seems not necessarily to be fatal to the cells of the individual in which that loss occurs; but it may result in a failure to produce either functional gametes or functional zygotes. If, on the other hand, both or all fragments of a chromosome are retained, the consequence will be the appearance of a race with an increased chromosome number. Such a series of chromosome numbers as characterizes the sedges may conceivably have resulted in part from chromosome fragmentation. An interchange of segments between two different chromosomes leads to changes in linkage groups and usually to some degree of cross-sterility between the new form and the old. Such segmental interchanges have occurred in the establishment in culture of races of certain plants, including corn and pea.

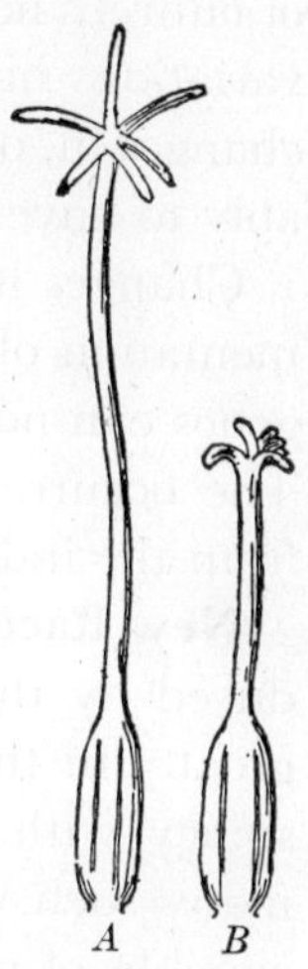

FIG. 448. Pistils of *Oenothera Lamarckiana* (*A*) and *Oenothera brevistylis* (*B*), the latter a variant form with short styles. Redrawn from De Vries.

Changes in Nature of Genes. These, according to current views, explain a large proportion of cases of heritable variation. In many instances a red- or blue-flowered species has been observed to give rise to a white-flowered race. In Drosophila a red-eyed species occasionally produces individuals whose eyes are vermilion or white. The evening primrose has now and then produced a dwarf plant (Fig. 446, *B*) and at other times a plant with especially short styles (Fig. 448). In such cases as these, if the new form is crossed with the parent form, the offspring show a distribution of the pair of characters concerned similar to that which appeared in Mendel's experiments. That is, the offspring behave as though the new race differed from the old in a single gene. It is assumed in such a case that a gene of the parent has become changed and that the change in the gene caused the appearance of the new character. It is assumed also that, when two races occurring in nature are crossed, if the character or characters that distinguish them are distributed among the offspring in a Mendelian fashion, then one of those races was derived from the other (or both from a common ancestor) in consequence of changes in one or more genes. Nothing is known about the influences which in nature cause such changes. It is shown, however, that the proportion in which they occur can be increased by irradiation (with X rays or radium) and by high temperatures.

Changes involving genes may conceivably consist in changes in the nature of old genes, in their complete loss, or in the appearance of entirely new genes. In experimental studies a great number of variations have been observed which can be explained as due to changes in, or loss of, genes, whereas comparatively few seem probably to have resulted from the appearance of new genes.

Changes in number of chromosomes and those due to the fragmentation of chromosomes can be directly observed. Changes in genes can not, since the genes themselves are too small to be seen. The occurrence of such changes, therefore, can only be inferred from the indirect evidence supplied by breeding experiments.

New Races Resulting from Variation. While individuals produced by the methods of heritable variation just discussed differ greatly in their ability to survive and reproduce, and in the constancy with which their characters are transmitted to offspring, many such variant plants and animals have proved vigorous and capable of giving rise to offspring like themselves. Hence, these methods of variation are likewise methods by which new, stable races arise. It is worth noting, however, that races coming into being in consequence of changes in the distribution of chromosomes or of parts of chromosomes possess characters which, however new in appearance, are the expression of previously existing genes now present in changed numbers, changed proportions, or changed combinations. Progress in an evolutionary sense can apparently come about only through the development of new genes; and this, so far as can be seen at present, is a rare occurrence.

New Races Produced from Crosses. When a stable new race has appeared, differing from its parent race in one or more genes, it will usually interbreed with the old race as well as with other new races derived from the same parent race. That is, crosses will occur, or can be brought about, between individuals which differ with respect to one, two, or several pairs of genes. If two individuals differing in two or more pairs of genes are mated, their descendants in the F_2 generation, in consequence of recombinations of chromosomes and of crossing over between chromosomes, will possess varied combinations of grandparental genes. Among these combinations will be some that differ from the combination possessed by either grandparent. Individuals with these new combinations of genes will usually present new combinations of visible characters; and if they are able to live and to reproduce, they may give rise to new races.

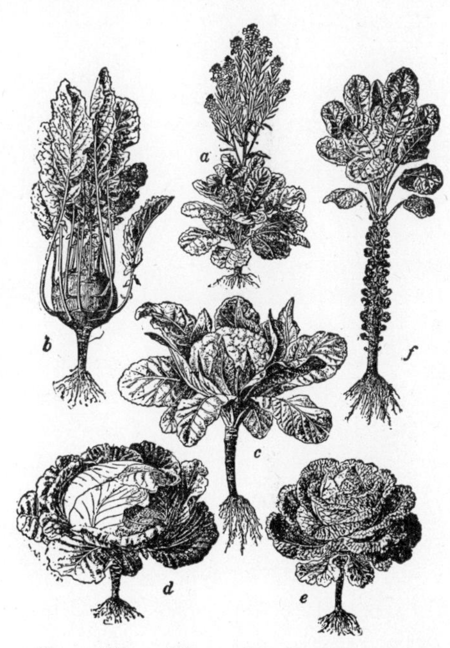

Fig. 449. The wild *Brassica oleracea* (*a*), from which the following cultivated plants seem to have been derived: (*b*) kohlrabi; (*c*) cauliflower; (*d*) cabbage; (*e*) Welsh, or savoy, cabbage; (*f*) Brussels sprouts. After Smalian.

Such production of new races by the crossing of related forms, making possible varieties with new combinations of desirable qualities, is largely used by plant- and animal-breeders. Many varieties of useful plants and animals have resulted from crosses between different varieties or different species —for example, numerous cultivated apples, potatoes, roses, and orchids. New races, varieties, and species are likewise constantly arising in nature from accidental crosses between related but distinct forms. In each case, whether in cultivation or in nature, the varieties or species to be crossed must previously have originated by variation from a common source. This method of producing new races (by crossing) likewise gives rise to no new genes; some of the old genes are combined in new ways.

In the practical development of new useful races, the preservation of forms resulting from crosses and the selection of desirable variations go hand in hand. The series of very different types of plants shown in Figure 449 illustrates the results of selection carried on over a period of many centuries. In this case the differing forms that have been preserved because of their utility probably arose through repeated heritable variations within a single original species. It is possible, in addition, that accidental crosses played some part in the origin of one or more of the varieties here represented.

CHAPTER XXXIV

EVOLUTION

The Facts of Evolution. In the preceding chapter was given a brief outline of what is known regarding the ways in which new races and species of plants and animals come into existence. Observation shows that new races and species do thus appear from time to time, and that some of them increase in numbers and in the extent of territory occupied and become established among older species. It is observed too that some older species are growing fewer in number of individuals and are occupying gradually smaller areas, and that from time to time a species disappears altogether. The plant and animal population of the earth is therefore constantly changing in consequence of the appearance of new species derived from older ones, of changes in the proportional numbers of different species and in the area they occupy, and of the disappearance of some of the older forms. This continuous process of change in the make-up of the earth's population is referred to as *evolution*, or *organic evolution.*

The Evolutionary Generalizations. The constant and gradual change in the population of the earth, now seen to be in progress, has been going on from as early a time as history and archeology record. The process is a slow one, and individual species may continue in existence for thousands or even millions of years. Nevertheless, the present condition of the earth's surface, as concerns the species of plants and animals inhabiting it and their distribution, is, taken as a whole, different from the condition that existed when the Egyptian pyramids were built and still more widely different from that which prevailed in the Stone Age. Upon this well-established *fact* of constant change is based a *generalization* which says that a similar process of gradual change has been continuously in operation since living organisms first appeared upon the earth.

While the constancy of change in population over a very long period of time is established by direct evidence, it can not be directly demonstrated that new species which have appeared from time to time have invariably descended from older species. Such an origin is absolutely shown for a new species only when the origin of that species is actually observed. However, the fact that new species are seen to arise from older ones and the further fact that variation is universally characteristic of living organisms have led to a second generalization; namely, that all species now living arose by descent from older species, those from still older ones, and so on back to the organisms that were first to inhabit the earth.

These two generalizations, supported as will be seen by an immense mass of evidence derived from many independent sources, constitute foundation stones of present-day thought. It was Darwin who first brought together much of the evidence in their favor. No one who, since the publication of his "Origin of Species" in 1859, has impartially investigated this evidence has questioned the validity or the usefulness of the idea of continuous evolution. But it must be remembered that the second generalization in particular is not itself, and probably never can become, an established fact. While all the available evidence tends to confirm the conception, it can not be absolutely proved that all species have arisen, as species are now seen to arise, by descent from older species.

The evidence upon which these important generalizations are based is of six general sorts: the observed origin of new races; the facts of classification; the facts of underlying similarity in structure; the facts of similarity in function and development; the facts of geographic distribution; and the fossil record of extinct species. Of these six classes of evidence, the first-mentioned has been sufficiently discussed.

Evidence from Classification. When a considerable bulk of information accumulates upon any subject, it becomes necessary to classify that information in order that it may readily be utilized. The Greek and Roman observers who, so far as is known, were the first to preserve in writing extended observations upon plants, saw that many individuals possess much the same characteristics; they grouped together under one name all the plants that seemed to them substantially alike. So arose the conception of species, each species including many individuals. As the number of known species increased, those which seemed more or less alike were grouped together in such larger units as are nowadays called genera and families. The first classifications of this nature were *artificial.* The classification of Linnaeus, published in 1753, which was by far the most important up to its time, was strictly artificial; it was based, so far as seed plants were concerned, primarily upon the number of stamens in the flower of each species.

As knowledge of plants increased, it was seen more and more clearly that species fall naturally into larger groups, the similarity between the species within any group being indicated, not by one character alone, such as number of stamens, but by many characters of flowers, fruits, and vegetative parts. Most classifications since Linnaeus' time have attempted to take into consideration these numerous similarities between species; present-day classifications are, therefore, as far as available information permits, *natural* instead of artificial. A natural classification expresses the fact that some species are so closely similar that they belong together in a group called a genus; that several genera, while showing somewhat wider differences than those between closely related species, are sufficiently alike to be grouped in a family; and, likewise, that related families belong together in an order, related orders in a class, and related classes in a division. A natural classification is an expression of varying degrees of likeness that actually exist among plants. Among species of animals, also, varying degrees of similarity appear; and the classification of animals, like that of plants, has progressed from the stage of an artificial to that of a natural system.

It seems impossible to explain the occurrence of such a scale of similarities between species except by supposing that each degree of similarity represents a comparable degree of relationship. Relationship implies that all the species of a genus are descended from a single species, that all the genera of a family are descended from a single but more remote source, and so on for the origin each from a single source of the families of an order, the orders of a class, and the classes of a division.

Evidence from Structure. The classification of plants and of animals is based in the main upon details of structure but ordinarily only upon those details which are found especially useful in making the classification. When, however, a study is made of all the structural characters of particular species, further evidence appears as to the relationships between species and, more especially, between larger groups. For instance, the presence of leaves borne on a stem of the sporophytic generation is a character practically universal throughout pteridophytes and seed plants. Although leaves show the greatest diversity in form and function—for example, foliage and scale leaves, spines and tendrils—their manner of origin and their development show them to be all of fundamentally the same nature. A like statement may be made of the various forms presented by stems and by roots. That is, the same general plan of structure characterizes the sporophytes of all the species that are grouped together as pteridophytes and seed plants. The universality of a general plan of structure throughout these two divisions is most readily explained by supposing that pteridophytes and seed plants are descended from a common ancestry.

Confirmatory evidence is afforded by the occurrence of strobili of similar general plan in various orders of gymnosperms; by the occurrence of flowers, likewise of similar general plan, throughout the angiosperms; and, among internal structures, by general likenesses in the vascular systems of pteridophytes and seed plants. The presence of archegonia, again of the same general plan, in all bryophytes and pteridophytes points, with other similarities in the gametophytic generation, to a relationship between the members of these two divisions. Perhaps the most far-reaching evidence of relationship is offered by the regular recurrence of flagellate cells, in the form of swarm-spores in algae and fungi, and in that of gametes, especially male gametes, in algae, fungi, bryophytes, pteridophytes, and the more primitive seed plants (including Zamia). The widespread power of forming flagellate cells seems to point to the descent of the plants of all these groups from one-celled flagellated organisms.

Evidence from Similarity in Function and Development. The study of the functions of plants, like the study of their structure, shows likenesses in important respects between the members of each major group, as well as similarities of less fundamental character within the limits of smaller groups. Indeed, certain characteristics are common to all living organisms, such as the essential structure of living matter itself and its organization into cells, the power of responding in varied ways to stimuli of many sorts, and the ability to carry on both constructive and destructive metabolism. The universal possession by all plants and animals of these powers and characteristics unavoidably suggests their descent from a common ancestry. On the other hand, many functions are peculiar to, or especially characteristic of, certain groups and, taken together with other similarities, indicate a relationship between the members of each such group. The plants of some classes form cell walls largely by the secretion of cellulose; those of other classes, by the secretion of chitin. The typical reserve food manufactured by the organisms of some groups is a sugar; in other groups it is starch; in others, glycogen; in still others, a fat. An illustration of a function characteristic of a relatively small group of plants is furnished by members of the pulse family; the reserve foods which most of them store in largest amount in their seeds are proteins, whereas starch is the most abundant reserve food in the seeds of most other families of angiosperms.

The light thrown upon evolution by the development of individual organisms may be considered with that supplied by other functions, since development is itself a function of the developing organism. The history of all many-celled plants and animals is alike in that each individual begins its existence as a single cell and in that its development to maturity consists in a series of cell divisions together with an increasing differentiation of cells into what are, in the more complex species, tissues and organs. In addition to this general resemblance between all organisms, more detailed similarities appear in the development of individuals of separate divisions, classes, and orders. For instance, the seedlings of most if not all conifers bear needle-like leaves on long branches, although mature plants of different species, such as pines and arbor vitae, differ greatly in the form and arrangement of their leaves. The structure of the embryonic sporophyte of the bracken, consisting of root, leaf, foot, and stem, is characteristic of the corresponding stage in the sporophytic development of most other ferns. Other pteridophytes, such as Equisetum and the club mosses, have embryos similar to that of the bracken in general plan, although differing in important respects. The differences indicate a more remote relationship between Equisetum, club mosses, and ferns than that among the ferns themselves. As has been seen, dicotyledons and monocotyledons are distinguished in several ways which indicate that these two classes of angiosperms have long been separate.

Evidence from Geographic Distribution. The distribution of plants also furnishes much evidence as to relationships between species as well as between genera, families, and orders. In general, where a large area of land exists, sufficiently uniform as to climate and soil and not broken by barriers which interfere with the migration of plants, its native flora is likewise uniform; that is, its whole extent is inhabited by the same or by closely similar species. Instances of such large areas in North America occupied by uniform floras are to be found in the tundra, the northern evergreen forest, and other regions to be described in the following chapter. On the other hand, if an effective barrier exists, such as a high mountain range, an extensive desert, or a large body of water, the floras on opposite sides of the barrier are likely to be very different. For example, the flora of the region west of the Rocky Mountains differs greatly from that of the region to the east. Much of this difference, to be sure, is due to climatic differences; but when, as is frequently the case, two species of the same genus occur on opposite sides of the mountains, they are usually so different as to suggest that they have been separated and have undergone evolutionary changes in divergent directions during a considerable time. The flora of Madagascar and that of the neighboring coast of Africa are very distinct. Marked differences exist also between the floras of Australia and of the Asiatic mainland.

The degrees of similarity or difference between the floras of separate bodies of land, such as islands or continents, furnish indications as to whether or not such land areas were at one time connected; and conclusions upon such points, based upon the characteristics of floras, agree in general with conclusions founded upon geological study. There is sufficient likeness between the floras of eastern North America and western Europe—although the native species of these regions are as a rule distinct—to render it probable that at a not very distant geological period the two continents were connected by land that has now disappeared.

Evidence from the Fossil Record. (See also Chapter XXXII.) Necessarily, fossils, with rare exceptions, show only broken, often partly decayed, fragments of plants. The softer plants, such as algae and mosses, are less often preserved than are harder, more woody plants or those with silicified cell walls. In the time that has elapsed since fossil-bearing rocks were formed, these rocks have been subjected to great changes in consequence especially of heat and pressure; and in the course of such changes many of the fossils present were destroyed. For all these reasons, the fossil record of ancient plants is very fragmentary, with many large gaps which laborious investigation is but slowly closing.

In spite of its incompleteness, however, the fossil record supplies much information regarding the nature of plants of past times. The evidence so obtained as to the general course of evolution agrees with that furnished by the structure and functions of living plants. The distribution of fossils through rocks of different ages indicates, for example, that the earliest plants of which traces remain were simple water-inhabiting forms, including algae and bacteria. Later there appeared more complex algae, simple and then more complex pteridophytes, primitive seed plants, forms more or less like present-day conifers and cycads, and finally angiosperms. Evidences of decay-producing fungi appear in connection with fossilized remains of plants of various groups throughout most of this history.

General Course of Evolution. Six classes of evidence have now been cited as indicating that evolution has been a continuous process from the first appearance of living organisms upon the earth. All this evidence, except that belonging in the first category (the observed origin of new races) agrees in indicating that the course of evolution has been in general, though with many exceptions, from simplicity to complexity. So strongly is this conception of the course of evolution supported by the available facts that it is virtually unquestioned. The series of types described in previous chapters, leading from Chlamydomonas to angiosperms, illustrates the accepted notion as to the general course that the evolution of plants has followed.

This conception implies that from time to time heritable variations have occurred, each of which introduced a new character or a new group of characters. But it is notable that, so far as the actual origin of new races is now observed, such a race seems to arise in the great majority of cases in consequence of a recombination (by crossing) of genes already existing or as a result of a change in, or loss of, a gene. Only in rare cases is a new race observed to arise apparently because of the acquisition of a new gene. It is true, because of the complicated interrelations between genes and characters (Chapter XXXIII), that a new combination of genes, or even at times perhaps the loss of a gene, may result in the appearance of what must be considered a new character. Nevertheless, the progressive evolution of new species possessed of new possibilities would seem to have meant the acquisition from time to time of new genes. The apparent discrepancy between the general course that evolution appears to have followed in the past and the course that it is observed to be following at present is not to be overlooked. This discrepancy may perhaps be explained by the consideration that the progress of evolution has been extremely slow. Even the rare development of new genes may, in the course of the hundreds of millions of years during which organic evolution has been going on, have brought into existence the diversified forms of plants and animals that now populate the earth.

Survival and Extinction of Races. The evidence just outlined indicates that, as new forms are now coming into being, so new races and species have arisen in the past. Of the plant and animal forms that have originated by variation, some have been very short-lived; some have become well-established species which have persisted during long periods, although the great majority of species that lived in previous ages sooner or later disappeared. Evolution—the progressive change in the sum total of organisms inhabiting the earth—depends not only upon the appearance of new races as a result of variation but also upon the relative ability of new as well as of older races to perpetuate themselves.

Whether or not a race shall persist, and if it does how widely it shall become distributed, depend upon the interaction of many factors. These factors may be classed under four heads: the ability of the race to reproduce; the degree of its adjustment to the non-living environment; conflict of interests with other organisms; and coöperation with other organisms.

Power of Reproduction. Reproduction includes all means by which the number of individuals of a species may be increased; among them, cell division in one-celled organisms; in many-celled organisms, the formation of spores and other special reproductive bodies, gametic union, and varied methods of vegetative multiplication. Other things being equal, a species which multiplies rapidly is more likely to survive and spread than is one which multiplies slowly. The great success of weeds like the dandelion and Canada thistle is largely a result of their power of reproduction. Rapid multiplication is especially important to such saprophytic plants as the bread mold or to parasitic plants like the wheat rust. Both are dependent upon the more or less accidental and temporary presence of the necessary substrate or host; and both produce immense numbers of spores, so increasing the chance that some spores may reach the host or substrate.

Adjustment to the Nonliving Environment. An organism is dependent for existence upon the conditions surrounding it. If it lives in water, the substances essential to its metabolic processes must be present in solution. If, like most seed plants, it lives partly in the soil and partly in the air, its structure must enable it to secure from these two sources the necessary materials, such as carbon dioxide, oxygen, water, and inorganic salts, and must prevent the loss of water at a more rapid rate than that at which it can be obtained. If surrounding conditions are subject to periodic changes, the organism must be able to pass into stages in which its functions or structure, or both, are modified to correspond with the changes in environment. Thus, Spirogyra, which often lives in ponds that become dry in summer, forms zygotes that can endure drying and can germinate when water is again present. Any perennial seed plant of a temperate or cold region has means of preserving alive through the winter, though in a dormant condition, either its whole body (as an evergreen tree) or a part (such as a tuber or underground stem) and of resuming vegetative activity upon the return of warmer weather.

Now and then the environment changes in a way that affects all plants and animals over a large area. A low region is uplifted, becoming drier and perhaps colder; or marked climatic changes occur, such as led to the glacial period in the northern hemisphere and later to the disappearance of glaciers and the restoration of a milder climate over most of Europe and North America. Such changes on a large scale profoundly affect the course of plant and animal evolution. Among the older organisms of the region, only those survive that are adjusted to the new conditions; and among new forms that may result from variation, especial opportunities are offered, because of the disappearance of many older species, to those whose structure and functions fit them to the changed environment.

Conflict of Interests. The interests of different individuals of the same or of different species come into conflict in many ways. In general, as Darwin long ago pointed out, most species can give rise by reproduction to vastly more individuals than the available supply of foods could support. An illustration in the case of bacteria was cited on page 305. While bacteria reproduce more rapidly than do most other organisms, the general principle applies widely. Consequently, there occurs among the individuals of each species a competition for food materials; and those individuals that are best adapted by length of root, rapidity of growth, power of absorption, or in any one of many ways to succeed in obtaining nutrients are those which will survive and will in turn produce offspring. In so far as the advantages possessed by such individuals are heritable, their offspring will possess the same favorable characteristics. In this way the competition for food materials tends to *select* those strains within a species that are best fitted to secure nourishment, and so tends to improve the average of the species in this respect. Just as does a competition for food materials, so a competition for favorable conditions, such as a temperature suitable for growth, results from the presence of an increasing population. In various respects, therefore, the tendency to overpopulation brings about, through competition, an improvement in the average capacity of each species to maintain itself. Similarly, there is competition between different species for food materials and other necessities. The net result of the crowding of populations and of the consequent competition is to select those species, and those strains or races within each species, that are best fitted to maintain themselves under the conditions surrounding them.

The survival of strains, races, and species is affected by other forms of conflict which are not so obviously competitive. One is the preying of some organisms upon others; a particular form of this is parasitism. The relations between a parasitic fungus and its host plant favor, on the side of the parasite, those individuals best fitted to secure nourishment from the host, and on the side of the host, those individuals that are most effectively guarded from the attacks of the parasite or that can best survive the injuries which the parasite inflicts. Another illustration of conflict is that between the human species and weeds. Weeds conflict with man's practical interests when they interfere with the growing of crops, and with his esthetic interests when they deface lawns and parks.

Coöperation. Competition as an evolutionary factor is much discussed. Not so much is ordinarily said of the bearing upon evolution of coöperation between individuals of the same or of different species. Yet the part played by coöperation in evolutionary development has perhaps been fully as great as that played by competition. Among very primitive organisms, coöperation is illustrated by the tendency in many lines of descent for one-celled organisms to come together or to remain together in colonies. Further steps in coöperation were taken when different cells of the same colony took on different functions and became differentiated in structure, this differentiation finally leading to the development of tissues. As between more complex plants and animals of the same or of different species, there are innumerable illustrations of the tendency to coöperate. One type of coöperation is the establishment of a partnership, as between a leguminous plant and the bacteria in the nodules of its roots, between forest trees and the fungi whose mycelia become closely associated with their roots, or between the fungus and the alga in a lichen. Another type of coöperation is seen in the formation of plant associations, illustrated by the relations between forest trees and the shrubs and herbaceous plants that grow in their shade. Another is illustrated by insect pollination and the accompanying interrelations between angiosperms and insects; still another, by the cultivation by man of useful and desirable plants and animals. A very extensive piece of coöperation is involved in the nitrogen cycle (p. 315), participated in by most of the many-celled plants and animals, some of the higher fungi, and many bacteria.

Natural Selection. The facts summarized under the three preceding headings (adjustment to the nonliving environment, conflict of interests, and coöperation) may be grouped together as involving the relations between an organism and its environment, since the environment of any individual includes the other organisms, as well as the nonliving things, with which it comes in contact. The combined effect of all these environmental factors upon the course of evolution is often referred to as "natural selection," because the net result of the influences at work is to preserve or select those individuals, races, and species that are best adapted to the environment. Differences in power of reproduction between different species may tend to the perpetuation and extension of a species which is favored also by natural selection. On the other hand, it may and often does happen that these two sets of selective factors (natural selection and differential powers of reproduction) work in opposite directions, so that a species which is favored by its power of rapid reproduction is discriminated against by natural selection, or vice versa. Much the same idea as that involved in natural selection, but with emphasis upon the competitive factors, is expressed by the phrase "struggle for existence." The term "artificial selection" is sometimes applied to the conscious selection of desirable races by man. But since man is one of the species that constitute a part of the environment of other species, the distinction between natural and artificial selection is meaningless.

CHAPTER XXXV

THE MAJOR REGIONS OF VEGETATION IN NORTH AMERICA

Factors Concerned in Distribution. Under natural conditions the distribution of plants over a given area is governed by a complex of factors which are in part hereditary and in part environmental. The nature of the hereditary factors, which affect in very important ways the ability of a plant to live in a particular environment, has been discussed in Chapter XXXIII. The environmental factors fall naturally into two groups: those related to climate, such as temperature, moisture, light, and wind; and those related to the soil, including its physical make-up, its chemical composition, its slope and drainage, and the amount of available water.

FIG. 450. Relation of soil moisture to the distribution of vegetation. The portion of the hill at the right is exposed to drying summer winds. The soil of the sheltered northern slope at the left retains sufficient moisture to permit the growth of a forest.

The hereditary endowment of some plants is such that they can become adapted to a wide range of habitats. The common dandelion, for example, thrives on a great variety of soils, and ranges from lowlands to mountain tops. Most plants, however, are not adaptable to so wide a range of conditions; their distribution, therefore, is dependent upon a more definite set of factors, the absence of any one of which from the environment makes the existence of the plant in that habitat impossible. Many species of tropical or subtropical

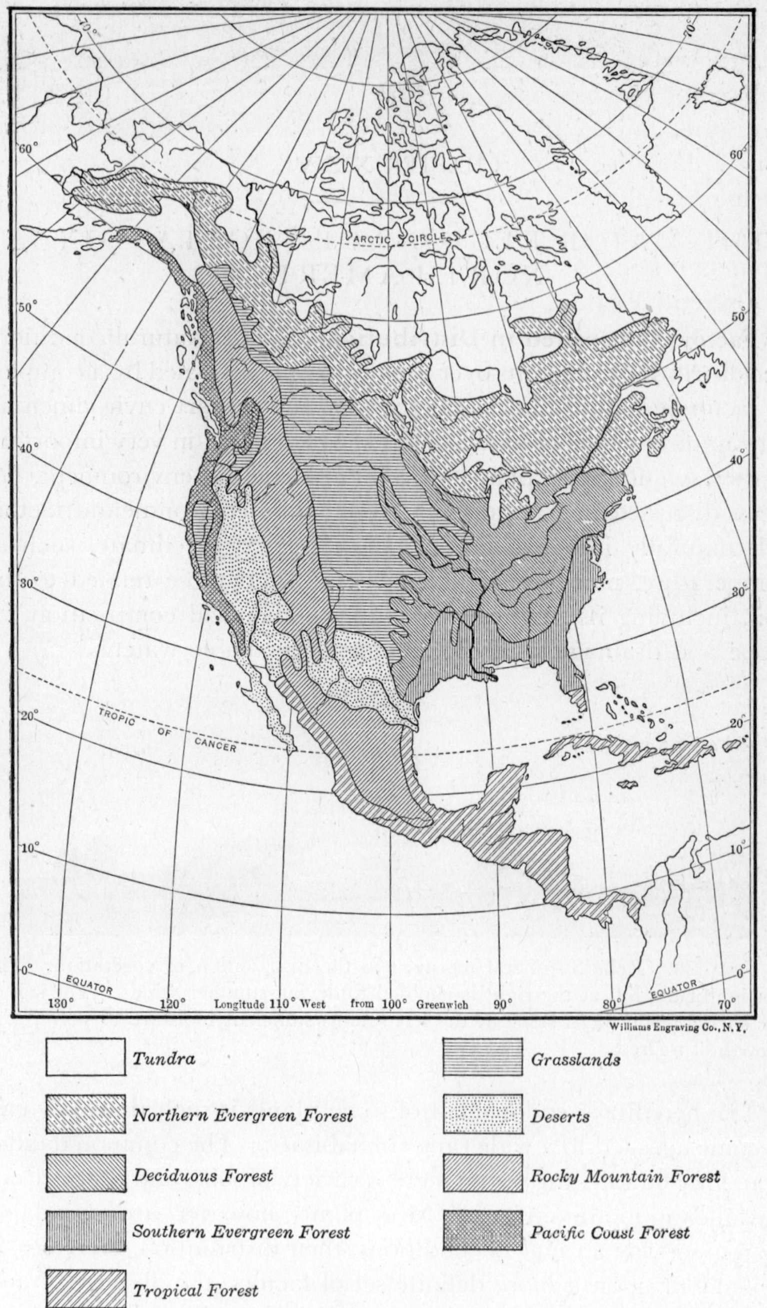

FIG. 451. The major regions of vegetation in North America.

plants, such as palms, oranges, lemons, and bananas, are badly injured or killed by freezing temperatures. Cacti, growing best on arid soils, are unable to live in wet, poorly aerated soils. Cranberries find their natural habitat in acid bogs and die quickly if transferred to neutral or slightly alkaline soil. Seedlings of hemlock grow best in dense shade, but those of some poplars require abundant light for growth and development.

General Regions of Vegetation. In consequence of the interaction of the various factors concerned in the distribution of plants, North America may be divided roughly into four regions of vegetation: tundra, forests, grasslands, and deserts. Each of these general regions is capable of further division and subdivision. In the following discussion the boundaries of the respective regions are given only in a general way, since they merge one into another, often

Fig. 452. The tundra near Nome, Alaska. Photograph courtesy of Dow V. Baxter.

with broad transitional zones; and the brief descriptions are of the vegetation as it existed before the extensive settlement of the continent. In the United States, particularly, man has destroyed or profoundly modified much of the native vegetation.

Tundra. The tundra, in general, fringes the northern limits of the continent from Alaska to Labrador. Here the winters are long and cold, with relatively light snowfall. The air in winter is very dry, and often strong winds blow. The growing season is of short duration. Only the upper portion of the soil thaws, to a depth of from a few inches to one or more feet, this depth varying chiefly with the direction of the slope; consequently the soil temperature

Fig. 453. Pines in the northern evergreen forest (Oconto County, Wisconsin). Photograph courtesy of the Wisconsin Conservation Department.

is low, and the ground water is cold. The plants that can thrive under these conditions include certain mosses, lichens, grasses, and sedges, a few other herbs, and some shrubs. Many of the herbaceous species bear relatively large and brightly colored flowers, although their stems are for the most part very short so that they form rosettes or compact cushions. The shrubs of the tundra are likewise characteristically low; there are several species of willow that grow to only a few inches in height.

Northern Evergreen Forest. In general, the northern evergreen forest stretches across the continent from the Atlantic to the Rocky Mountains. Its southern boundary extends from Vermont westward to the Great Lakes and, including the northern portions of Michigan, Wisconsin, and Minnesota, swings sharply northwest to the eastern slopes of the Rockies. Thence it extends northward to Alaska. A wide transitional belt of mixed type joins the tundra with the densely forested area. In this belt forests fringe the rivers, but over large areas trees are scattered singly or in small groups. The dense forest is composed for the most part of conifers. Among them are black spruce, white spruce, balsam fir, tamarack, arbor

FIG. 454. A deciduous forest. Photograph courtesy of E. J. Kraus.

vitae, hemlock, white pine, red ("Norway") pine, and jack pine. Deciduous trees (belonging to the angiosperms) occur intermixed with the conifers; and, especially where the original forest has been

FIG. 455. Bald cypress in the southern evergreen forest. This tree grows in standing water or in very wet soil. The projections rising above the surface of the soil are "cypress knees"—upgrowths from the roots which have been thought to give access to the oxygen required in the respiration of the roots. Photograph courtesy of Homer A. Stephens.

removed by cutting or burning, deciduous trees may form extensive pure stands. Prominent among them are the aspens, white birch, and balsam poplar.

Deciduous Forest. Merging on the north with the evergreen forest, the deciduous forest occupies an area extending approximately from central New York southwest along the Appalachians to

FIG. 456. Young pines in the southern evergreen forest. Some have been chipped for turpentining. Photograph courtesy of Ralph O. Marts; received through the Forest Products Laboratory, Madison, Wis.

Louisiana and Texas, its western boundary stretching from eastern Oklahoma to southern Minnesota. This forest reaches its most characteristic development in the mountainous area of western

North Carolina and eastern Tennessee. Among the common trees of this area are the white oak, black oak, scarlet oak, shagbark hickory, pignut, sugar maple, red maple, chestnut, birch, ash, elm, walnut, and tulip tree. Associated with some of the deciduous trees, conifers such as the shortleaf pine, white pine, and hemlock occur in the mountainous regions or on high hills. Rhododendron, mountain laurel, and various other shrubby plants often form extensive undergrowths on the mountainsides.

FIG. 457. A liana-covered tree in the tropical forest of Florida. Photograph courtesy of E. J. Kraus.

Southern Evergreen Forest. This forest area covers the coastal plains from eastern Virginia to Texas. The low, rolling, sandy land near the coast from South Carolina to Louisiana is the habitat of the longleaf pine. In and about the numerous and extensive swamps are live oaks, water oaks, bald cypress, gums, and magnolias. These trees are often heavily draped with an epiphytic seed plant, Tillandsia, commonly called "gray moss" or "Florida moss." On the higher portions of the coastal plain, and more remote from the sea, are areas of shortleaf pine which merge into the deciduous forest of the Appalachian foothills.

Tropical Forest. The tropical-forest area includes the southern quarter of the peninsula of Florida, most of the coastal margin of Mexico, all of Central America, and the islands of the West Indies. The type of tropical forest developed in southern Florida is meager; but the tropical-forest relationship is shown by various palms and other tropical trees, by lianas (climbing woody vines, Fig. 457), and by tropical epiphytes such as bromeliads and orchids. Along the coast and fringing the keys are characteristic mangrove swamps such as are usually found on muddy tropical shores.

The broad coastal plain of Mexico, except for the dry northwestern portion, contains grassy savannas, broken by jungle; but the southern portion, in consequence of its warm, moist climate, possesses a luxuriant tropical forest. Such a forest in its fullest development is remarkable for the great abundance and variety of its flora and fauna. Commonly the tall trees form so dense a canopy as to shut off much of the light from the floor of the forest, resulting in a sparse undergrowth and making the forest open and easily penetrable. The trunks and upper branches of the trees, however, are heavily populated with a great variety of epiphytes—lichens, mosses, ferns, orchids, bromeliads, and shrubs. Lianas also are numerous, twining about the trunks of trees and pushing their tangled branches into the forest canopy.

In Central America and the West Indies much of the open forest has been destroyed by centuries of nomadic agriculture; and in its place, over large districts, has grown up a dense and almost impenetrable jungle.

Grasslands. A vast area of grassland once extended between the eastern forests and the foothills of the Rocky Mountains from southern Texas to southern Saskatchewan and Alberta. The irregular eastern boundary extended across the Mississippi and included portions of Illinois, Indiana, and Wisconsin. The name "prairie" is applied to the easternmost irregular strip of this grassland, reaching from Texas to Manitoba. The prairie region was formerly covered with a rich growth of various kinds of tall grasses, forming a characteristically dense turf. Growing with the grasses were many other herbaceous plants, such as blazing star, asters, goldenrods, and sunflowers. In general, the soil of the prairie is rich in humus, beneath which lies clay or sand. The nature of the soil seems, however, to have played little part in determining the absence of trees in this region. The treelessness of the prairie has been variously accounted for, having been ascribed, for example, to frequent and extensive fires or to the grazing of vast herds of buffalo. Whatever minor part these factors may have played, it is probable that the prairie has remained treeless chiefly in consequence of an excessive evaporation in proportion to the amount of soil water available for the use of plants.

That extensive area of the grasslands which lies west of the prairie constitutes the Great Plains and is the home of grasses which are characteristically short and grow in patches or tufts. Scattered over the Great Plains also are various cacti as well as other herbs and shrubs adapted to dry habitats. The western margin of the plains passes into various types of scrub growth. Climatic conditions apparently are responsible for the typical vegetation. The light annual rainfall and the high rate of transpiration seem to make the development and growth of tree seedlings impossible under natural conditions.

Deserts. The area extending south from Eastern Oregon and western Idaho, embracing most of Nevada and Arizona, the southern portions of California and New Mexico, and including a part of southern Texas and northern Mexico adjacent to the Rio Grande, is largely made up of desert areas. Most of the peninsula of Lower California also is desert. This whole region is in general one of low rainfall and high evaporation.

The area between the Sierra Nevadas and the Rocky Mountains is often called the "Great Basin." Much of this is dominated by the sagebrush, a dusty-gray shrub with strongly scented leaves. Associated with sagebrush are a few other shrubs of similar appearance. Most of the scanty rainfall occurs during the winter, and this is followed by a sudden growth of small annual plants which flower and fruit and as quickly wither and disappear. The appearance of the desert therefore varies greatly with the time of year.

To the south and southeast the Great Basin passes into a region of intense summer heat and scanty rainfall. Here is a remarkable development of plants peculiarly adapted to an arid habitat. The creosote bush, cacti (Fig. 458) of weird shapes, yuccas (Fig. 39), and thick-leaved agaves are among the characteristic plants of this region. Bunch grasses are found in certain areas, and after the seasonal rains annual grasses and other small herbs appear.

Western Evergreen Forest. The western evergreen forest extends in general from Alaska to southern Mexico and may be divided roughly into two areas: the Rocky Mountain forest and the Pacific Coast forest. Conifers are the chief forest trees in both areas.

FIG. 458. Giant cacti (*Cereus giganteus*) in a desert region of Arizona. Photograph courtesy of Frank N. Campbell.

The Rocky Mountain forest stretches along the Rockies from northern British Columbia to southern Mexico. This great system of mountains, extending nearly the whole length of North America, presents a wide range of climates, which vary with the latitude as well as with the elevations at any given latitude. In consequence of the diverse climatic conditions, not all of this mountain area is covered with forests. Thus, within the United States, the eastern slopes of the Rockies, grading into the more or less arid plains, have a general level below which trees do not grow. This level lies roughly between 4000 and 6000 feet. There is likewise a general level (the "timber line") above which trees do not grow. The height of the timber line also varies in different localities; in the Rockies of the United States it ranges approximately from 9000 to 11,000 feet. Above this timber line a low alpine vegetation occurs, resembling that of the tundra. Farther and farther north along the mountains, both alpine and forest belts appear at increasingly lower levels; consequently, in the Canadian Rockies the forest covers the lower mountain sides and the valleys.

The dominant tree of the Rocky Mountain forest is the western yellow pine. The lodgepole pine also is widely distributed. Among other conifers are some of the true firs, the Douglas fir, the western larch, and the western hemlock.

Fig. 459. The dense growth of trees characteristic of the western evergreen forest in Oregon.

The Pacific Coast forest occupies the slopes of the coastal mountains from southern Alaska into California. The area from Alaska to southern British Columbia is dominated by the Sitka spruce. With this spruce occur other conifers, among them the western hemlock and the Douglas fir. The coastal region of southern British Columbia, Washington, and Oregon has a mild winter climate and a heavy annual rainfall. Because of these favorable conditions the conifers here reach a luxuriance unequaled in any other part of the world. Many of them grow to heights of 200 feet or more, and the bases of their trunks often exceed 10 feet in diameter. Douglas fir and western hemlock, already mentioned, dominate among the large species; associated with them are other conifers such as the western white pine, Sitka spruce, white fir, and western white cedar. As a rule, the forest can be penetrated only with difficulty on account of the dense undergrowth of ferns, shrubs, and low-growing deciduous trees, including maples, poplars, alders, and birches.

On the coastal range, and confined to a narrow belt extending from the southern edge of Oregon into central California, are the coast redwoods. Their even larger relatives, the "big trees" (Fig. 47), occur only in a few groves on the west slopes of the Sierras in central California.

INDEX

References in **bold face** are to pages containing illustrations.